Finite MATHEMATICS

Sixth Edition

Daniel P. **Maki**
Maynard **Thompson**
Stephen C. **McKinley**

2 3 4 5 6 7 8 9 0 SCI SCI 19 18 17 16

ISBN-13: 978-1-259-81976-6
ISBN-10: 1-259-81976-0

Solutions Program Manager: Mark Bodensteiner
Project Manager: Lisa Haverland
Cover Designer: SPi-Global
Cover Photo Credits: Exactostock/Exactostock/SuperStock

Contents

Preface

Probability and linear mathematics, the core of the traditional course in finite mathematics, provide some of the most basic and widely used mathematical tools in business, and the social and life sciences. These core topics and their applications are presented in Parts I and II of this text. Throughout the book there is an emphasis on ideas and techniques useful in constructing models and solving problems.

You learn to solve problems by working problems. Therefore, we include many exercises for you to use in developing and testing your problem-solving ability. Some are very easy, most are similar in difficulty to the discussions and the examples explained in the text, and a few are fairly tough. To solve problems, you must know where to start and how to proceed. We use discussions and examples to introduce and illustrate ideas and techniques to aid you in acquiring these skills. Some of the examples are straightforward computation, others show you how to solve problems by combining several ideas and techniques, and yet others illustrate the important method of breaking a problem into simpler problems, solving them one at a time, and then putting the results together to solve the original problem. Since we cannot provide examples of every type of problem and every setting you may encounter, we identify fundamental principles that should be helpful in unfamiliar situations.

Chapters 1 through 4 present basic concepts in probability, and it is common for this material to constitute about one-half of a one-semester finite mathematics course. The other half of such a course is usually devoted to linear equations, matrices, and linear programming, and these topics are covered in

Chapters 5, 6, and 7. There are many applications in Chapters 1 through 7 in a variety of settings in the discussions and in exercises. Chapter 8 is devoted to a topic, Markov chains, that combines probability and matrices and serves as a useful mathematical model in many applications.

The sixth edition of *Finite Mathematics* includes:

- revision of examples and exercises to include additional situations of contemporary significance in business and society;
- modest reorganization of the topics on probability, random variables, and expected value to consider only discrete probability;
- an expanded number of exercises, including over 250 that are new or revised
- discussions of mathematical modeling, especially as related to linear systems and linear programming;
- a balance in the emphasis on ideas and techniques.

Parts I and II are each sequentially dependent, but independent of each other. Chapter 8 requires familiarity with several topics from Parts I and II.

Each chapter is followed by a set of review exercises. These exercises are of varying degrees of difficulty (not necessarily graded from easy to difficult) and are related to the topics of the chapter, although not always to a specific section.

Appendix A contains sample examinations, Appendix B contains tables necessary to solve some of the problems in Chapter 4, and Appendix C contains the answers to odd-numbered exercises.

Previous editions of this book contained material beyond that in the sixth edition including chapters on the simplex method; two-person zero-sum games; and logic. This material is available from the publisher as individual chapters, and additional information can be obtained from McGraw-Hill.

Acknowledgments

It is a pleasure to acknowledge the support and advice we received from our colleagues and reviewers over many years. Members of the McGraw-Hill Education organization have provided consistent encouragement and help in bringing the sixth edition to fruition.

We particularly recognize and thank Virginia K Jones who provided valuable assistance in manuscript preparation for this edition.

It is a special pleasure to welcome Steve McKinley to the Maki-Thompson collaboration. Steve's experience and insights have contributed a great deal to the Sixth edition of *Finite Mathematics*.

PART

1

Probability Models

Shutterstock/Gabriel Petrescu

© Ingram Publishing/SuperStock

JGI/Jamie Grill/Blend Images LLC

CHAPTER 1

Sets, Partitions, and Tree Diagrams

1.0 THE SETTING AND OVERVIEW

We develop a common notation and terminology for sets and set operations which will be helpful in explaining and understanding probability. The discussion begins with sets, ways of combining sets, and a connection between set operations and certain logical operations. A useful technique of representing sets with diagrams is developed. We introduce a special type of set needed in our work on probability, the set of outcomes of an experiment. We develop three key methods for counting the elements in particular kinds of sets. These methods are partitions, tree diagrams, and the multiplication principle, concepts that will be applied and extended in Chapters 2, 3, and 4.

1.1 REVIEW OF SETS AND SET OPERATIONS

The students in a finite mathematics class form a set. So do the workers in an office, the books on a shelf, and the courses taken by a student this semester. A *set* is a collection whose members are specified by a list or a rule. The items in the collection are the *elements* of the set. To use a rule to specify a set, the rule must make it possible to determine precisely which things are in the set and which are not. When a set is specified by a list, the usual practice is to list the elements, each one exactly once, between a pair of braces, thus, the set S of names of states beginning with the letter A may be denoted by

$$S = \{\text{Alabama, Alaska, Arizona, Arkansas}\}$$

When a rule is used to specify a set, the usual practice is to write the rule after a symbol denoting a general element of the set followed by a colon and to include all the information in braces. For instance, to specify the set S with a rule, we can write

$$S = \{x\text{: } x \text{ is the name of a state beginning with the letter A}\}$$

In this expression the symbols "$S = \{x\text{: } \ldots\}$" are read "$S$ is the set of all x such that . . . ."

Whether a list or a rule is used to specify a set, it is important to remember that either something belongs to a set or it does not. It cannot partly belong to a set, and it cannot belong to a set several times.

Example 1.1 Consider the set $I = \{2, 3, 4, 5, 6, 7, 8, 9, 10, 11, 12\}$. Here we have specified the set by listing all elements in the set. This can also be described in more than one way by using a rule. Two such ways are the following:

$I = \{n : n$ is a positive integer that is not less than 2 or greater than 12$\}$

$I = \{s : s$ is the sum of the two numbers on top when two standard six-sided dice are rolled$\}$ ■

In some cases a list of the elements provides the simplest and most useful representation of a set. In other cases a rule is preferable. For sets with large numbers of elements, the use of a rule is often the only practical way to define the set.

To indicate that x is an element of a set X, we write $x \in X$. To indicate that x is *not* an element of X, we write $x \notin X$. Thus in Example 1.1 we have $8 \in I$, but $15 \notin I$.

A set A is a *subset* of a set B, written $A \subset B$, if every element in A is also in B. If $A \subset B$ and $B \subset A$, then A and B have exactly the same elements, and we say that A and B are *equal*. We write $A = B$.

To illustrate the notation, let $F = \{4, 8, 12\}$ and $G = \{1, 4, 6\}$, and let I be the set of Example 1.1. Then $F \subset I$ since every element of F is also an element of I. The set G is not a subset of I since not all elements of G are in I. Indeed, $4 \in I, 6 \in I$, but $1 \notin I$. In such a case it is sometimes convenient to write $G \not\subset I$.

It is often helpful to describe sets in terms of other sets. For instance, if

$$A = \{2, 4, 8, 12\}$$
$$B = \{2, 6, 10, 12, 14\}$$

and

$$C = \{2, 4, 6, 8, 10, 12, 14\}$$

then C is the set of all elements which are in A or in B or in both. Thus, we can view C as the set which results from combining A and B in a specific way. The operation which combines sets in this way is known as the *union*.

Let A and B be sets. The set $A \cup B$, called the *union* of A and B, consists of all elements which are in A or in B or in both.

$$A \cup B = \{x: x \in A \text{ or } x \in B\}$$

Note that in expressions such as "$x \in A$ or $x \in B$" the "or" is inclusive; that is, the condition is fulfilled if at least one of $x \in A$ or $x \in B$ holds. This includes the possibility that both hold.

To continue, let

$$A = \{2, 4, 8, 12\} \qquad B = \{2, 6, 10, 12, 19\} \qquad J = \{2, 12\}$$

Then J is the set of elements which are in both A and B. The operation which combines sets in this way is known as the *intersection*.

Let A and B be sets. The set $A \cap B$, called the *intersection* of A and B, consists of all elements which are in both A and B.

$$A \cap B = \{x: x \in A \text{ and } x \in B\}$$

Example 1.2 Let sets S, E, C, and M be defined as follows:

$$\begin{aligned} S &= \{\text{CT, MA, MD, CA, CO, MI, MN}\} \\ E &= \{\text{CT, MA, MD}\} \\ C &= \{\text{CA, CO, CT}\} \\ M &= \{\text{MA, MD, MI, MN}\} \end{aligned}$$

The elements of these sets are actually the standard abbreviations for names of states. The meaning is unimportant, however, and the elements can be viewed simply as symbols. Since each element of E is also an element of S, set E is a subset of S and we write $E \subset S$. Likewise, $C \subset S$ and $M \subset S$. However, since CT $\in E$ but CT $\notin M$, set E is not a subset of M, written $E \not\subset M$. Sets E and C have only the element CT in common, but sets E and M share the elements MA and MD. Therefore,

$$E \cap C = \{\text{CT}\} \qquad \text{and} \qquad E \cap M = \{\text{MA, MD}\}$$

Combining pairs of sets with the union operation, we have

$$\begin{aligned} E \cup C &= \{\text{CA, CO, CT, MA, MD}\} \\ E \cup M &= \{\text{CT, MA, MD, MI, MN}\} \\ \text{and} \qquad C \cup M &= \{\text{CT, MA, MD, CA, CO, MI, MN}\} = S \end{aligned}$$

■

Note that the element CT which appears in both E and C appears only once in $E \cup C$. As we noted earlier, when a set is specified by a list, each element in the set must appear in the list exactly once. Also, if a set is specified by a list, then the order in which the elements appear in the list does not matter. Thus {CT, MA, MD} is the same as {MA, MD, CT} or {MD, CT, MA}.

In Example 1.2 the sets $C = \{\text{CA, CO, CT}\}$ and $M = \{\text{MA, MD, MI, MN}\}$ have no elements in common. That is, the set $C \cap M$ has no elements. Likewise, the set

$$S = \{x\text{: } x \text{ is the name of a state beginning with the letter B}\}$$

has no elements.

The set which contains no elements is known as the *empty set*, and it is denoted by $\emptyset$. By convention the empty set is considered to be a subset of every set.

Since the empty set has no elements, we see that for every set A,

$$A \cap \emptyset = \emptyset \qquad \text{and} \qquad A \cup \emptyset = A$$

Two sets A and B are *disjoint* if $A \cap B = \emptyset$.

The sets $C = \{\text{CA, CO, CT}\}$ and $M = \{\text{MA, MD, MI, MN}\}$ are disjoint since $C \cap M = \emptyset$.

The definitions of union and intersection were formulated for two sets. With the use of parentheses they can be used in expressions which involve more than two sets. For instance, if we have three sets A, B, and C, then the set of all elements which are in A and in B and in C can be written as either $A \cap (B \cap C)$ or $(A \cap B) \cap C$. In this case the parentheses do not matter, and thus we can write $A \cap B \cap C$ for short. Likewise the set of all elements in A or in B or in C (or in more than one of these sets) can be unambiguously denoted by $A \cup B \cup C$. However, when an expression involves both union and intersection operations, it is generally necessary to use parentheses in writing the expression. The operations within the parentheses are to be carried out first.

Example 1.3 Let $A = \{a, b, c\}$, $B = \{a, c, e\}$, and $C = \{a, d\}$. Then

$$\begin{aligned} A \cap B \cap C &= \{a\} \\ A \cup B \cup C &= \{a, b, c, d, e\} \\ (A \cap B) \cup C &= \{a, c\} \cup \{a, d\} = \{a, c, d\} \\ A \cap (B \cup C) &= \{a, b, c\} \cap \{a, c, d, e\} = \{a, c\} \end{aligned}$$

Here we have $(A \cap B) \cup C \neq A \cap (B \cup C)$. The parentheses are clearly crucial to the meaning of the expressions. ■

We have defined the intersection of two sets A and B (the set of elements which are in A *and* B) and the union of A and B (the set of elements which are in A *or* B or both). Thus we have operations on sets which associate naturally with "and" and "or." We turn next to an operation on sets which is the natural associate of the word "not."

A set U is said to be a *universal set* for a problem if all sets being considered in the problem are subsets of U. Given a universal set U, the *complement* of a subset A of U is the set of all elements in U which are not in A. The complement of A is written A'.

$$A' = \{x, x \in U \text{ and } x \notin A\}$$

Notice that if A and B are subsets of U, then the set of elements in A which are not in B can be written as $A \cap B'$. Such sets arise frequently in applications.

Example 1.4 Let $U = \{\text{CA, CO, CT, IL, IN}\}$, $X = \{\text{CA, CT, IL}\}$, $Y = \{\text{CO, CT, IN}\}$, and $Z = \{\text{CO, IN}\}$. Then

$$X' = \{\text{CO, IN}\} = Z, \qquad Y' = \{\text{CA, IL}\} \qquad Z' = \{\text{CA, CT, IL}\} = X$$
$$Y \cap Z' = \{\text{CT}\} \qquad X \cap Z' = \{\text{CA, CT, IL}\} = X \qquad Z \cap Y' = \emptyset$$ ■

In addition to taking unions, intersections, and complements, there are other useful ways of building new sets from given ones. For example, suppose that a sociologist has enough money to conduct one survey. The survey can be conducted either by mail (M) or by phone (P) in one of three cities: Atlanta (A), Boston (B), or Cincinnati (C). Thus the choice for the sociologist can be viewed as selecting a method (M or P) and a city (A, B, or C). Each possible survey can be denoted by an *ordered pair* of elements, one from the set $\{M, P\}$ and one from the set $\{A, B, C\}$. Thus selecting a survey is clearly the same as selecting an element from the set

$$\{(M, A), (M, B), (M, C), (P, A), (P, B), (P, C)\}$$

The *cartesian product* of sets A and B, denoted by $A \times B$, is the set of all ordered pairs (a, b) where $a \in A$ and $b \in B$.

$$A \times B = \{(a, b) \colon a \in A, b \in B\}$$

Example 1.5 Let

$$A = \{a, c, e\} \quad B = \{b, d, e\} \quad C = \{b, d\}$$

Then

$$\begin{aligned} A \times C &= \{(a, b), (a, d), (c, b), (c, d), (e, b), (e, d)\} \\ B \times C &= \{(b, b), (b, d), (d, b), (d, d), (e, b), (e, d)\} \\ C \times C &= \{(b, b), (b, d), (d, b), (d, d)\} \end{aligned}$$

■

Since $A \times C$ in Example 1.5 is a set, the order of the elements within the braces is *not* important. In particular, we could also write

$$A \times C = \{(a, b), (c, b), (e, b), (a, d), (c, d), (e, d)\}$$

The order of the symbols within the parentheses *is* important: The element (x, y) is different from (y, x) for x different from y. Our next example illustrates this.

Example 1.6 A division of a soccer league consists of four teams: the Argots (A), Bots (B), Cams (C), and Drams (D). Each game can be represented as an ordered pair of teams in which the first entry denotes the home team. With this notation the set of all possible games is a subset of the cartesian product of the set $L = \{A, B, C, D\}$ with itself, $L \times L$. Note that the cartesian product $L \times L$ contains elements such as (A, A), which are not legitimate games. In fact, the set of all possible games is

$$G = \{(A, B), (A, C), (A, D), (B, A), (B, C), (B, D), (C, A), (C, B), (C, D), (D, A), (D, B), (D, C)\}$$

and the set of all games involving the Argots, Bots, and Cams is

$$H = \{(A, B), (A, C), (B, A), (B, C), (C, A), (C, B)\}$$

■

Example 1.6 illustrates the importance of order in the construction of an ordered pair. For instance, the game between A and B with A as the home team is denoted by (A, B), while (B, A) denotes the game between the same teams with B as the home team. Thus, the ordered pair (A, B) is not the same as the ordered pair (B, A). However, as we noted earlier, the order of elements in the list specifying the set is unimportant, and set H can also be represented, e.g., as

$$H = \{(A, B), (B, A), (A, C), (C, A), (B, C), (C, B)\}$$

Exercises for Section 1.1

1. Let $R = \{a, b\}$, $S = \{a, c, f\}$, and $T = \{a, b, c, d, e\}$. Decide whether each of the following assertions is correct.
   (a) $S \subset T$ (b) $R \subset S$ (c) $b \in R \cap T$
2. With R, S, and T defined as in Exercise 1, decide whether each of the following assertions is correct.
   (a) $R \subset T$ (b) $(R \cup S) \subset T$ (c) $c \in S \cap T$
3. With R, S, and T defined as in Exercise 1, find $(R \cup S) \cap T$.
4. Let $U = \{1, 2, t, u, v, x, y, z\}$, $E = \{2, t, y\}$, $F = \{1, 2, u, y, z\}$, and $G = \{1, 2, u, y\}$. Find $(E \cup F) \cap G'$.
5. Let $A = \{p, q, r\}$. Find all nonempty subsets B and C of A such that $B \cap C = \emptyset$ and $B \cup C = A$.
6. Let $U = \{1, 2, 3, 4, 5, 6, 7\}$ be a universal set with subsets $A = \{1, 3, 5\}$ and $B = \{1, 5\}$. List the elements in each of the following sets.
   (a) A' (b) $A' \cap B'$ (c) $A \cup B$ (d) $(A \cup B)'$
7. The sets M, A, B, and C are defined as follows:

$$\begin{aligned} M &= \{\text{Minnesota, Michigan, Montana, Massachusetts}\} \\ A &= \{\text{Alabama, Arkansas, Michigan}\} \\ B &= \{\text{Montana, Michigan}\} \\ C &= \{\text{Alabama, Arkansas}\} \end{aligned}$$

   Decide which of the following subset relationships are correct.
   (a) $B \subset M$ (b) $B \subset C$ (c) $C \subset A$
   (d) $C \subset B$ (e) $C \subset M$ (f) $A \subset (B \cup C)$
8. The sets R, S, and T are subsets of a universal set U. Which of the following always holds?
   (a) $R \cap S \subset R$ (b) $T \subset T \cap \emptyset$
   (c) $R \cup (S \cap T) \subset R \cap (S \cup T)$ (d) $R' \cup S' = (R \cup S)'$
9. Let $U = \{u, v, w, x, y, z, 1, 2, 3\}$, $E = \{2, y, w, z\}$, $F = \{2, 3, u, y, z\}$, and $G = \{1, 2, 3, w, y\}$. List the elements in each of the following sets.
   (a) E' (b) $F \cup G'$ (c) $(E \cup F) \cap G'$
10. Let $U = \{x, y, z, 1, 2, 3\}$, $A = \{y, z, 2\}$, $B = \{y, 1, 2\}$, and $C = \{x, 3\}$. List the elements in each of the following sets.
   (a) $A \cup B$ (b) $B \cap C$ (c) A'
   (d) $(A \cup B) \cap (B \cup C)$ (e) $(B \cap A') \cap C'$
11. Let U, A, B, and C be defined by

$$U = \{a, b, c, 1, 2, 3\}$$
$$A = \{a, b, c\} \qquad B = \{a, 2, 3\} \qquad C = \{1, 2, 3\}$$

   List the elements in each of the following sets.
   (a) $A \cup B$ (b) $B \cap C$ (c) $(A \cup B) \cap (B \cup C)$
   (d) A' (e) $A \cap B'$ (f) $A \cup C'$
12. Let $X = \{b, p, 4, 7\}$ and $Y = \{a, p, 4\}$ be subsets of a universal set $U = \{a, b, p, 1, 4, 7\}$. Which of the following are not true statements?
   (a) $b \in X \cup Y$ (b) $\{p, 4\} = X \cap Y$ (c) $7 \in X \cap Y'$
   (d) $1 \in X' \cap Y$ (e) $1 \in X' \cup Y$

13. Let sets A, B, C, and D be defined by

$$\begin{aligned} A &= \{x : x \text{ owns a GM car}\} \\ B &= \{x : x \text{ works for GM}\} \\ C &= \{x : x \text{ is the president of GM}\} \\ D &= \{x : x \text{ owns stock in GM}\} \end{aligned}$$

Describe in words each of the following sets.
(*a*) $A \cap B$ (*b*) $B \cap A'$ (*c*) $(A \cup B) \cap D$ (*d*) $C \cap A$

14. Let X and Y be sets with $a \in X$ and $b \in Y$. Is it *always* true (yes or no) that $\{a, b\} \subset X \cup Y$? That $\{a, b\} \subset X \cap Y$?

15. Let A and B be subsets of a universal set U. It is *always* true that
(*a*) $B \cap A' \subset A$ (*b*) $A \cap B \subset A \cup B$
(*c*) $A' \cap B' \subset (A \cap B)'$ (*d*) $A' \cup B' \subset (A \cup B)'$

16. Let A, B, C, and D be subsets of U with $A \subset B$ and $C \subset D$. Is it *always* true that
(*a*) $A \cap C \subset B \cap D$ (*b*) $A' \cap C' \subset B' \cap C'$

17. Let $U = \{2, 4, 8, 16, 32, 64\}$. Which of the following pairs of subsets A, B, of the universal set U, satisfy the condition: $A \cap B' = \{2, 16\}$
(*a*) $A = \{2, 8, 16\}$, $B = \{4, 8, 64\}$
(*b*) $A = \{2, 16, 32\}$, $B = \{4, 8, 64\}$
(*c*) $A = \{2, 16\}$, $B = \{4, 64\}$

18. Let $U = \{w, x, y, z\}$. Find examples of subsets A and B of U which satisfy the stated condition.
(*a*) $A \cup B = A$ (*b*) $A \cap B = A$
(*c*) $A \cap B' = A$ (*d*) $A \cap B' = B \cap A'$

19. Let $U = \{1, 2, 3, 4, x, y\}$ be a universal set with subsets $X = \{1, 2, 3, x, y\}$, $Y = \{2, 4, y\}$, and $Z = \{2, x\}$. Use intersections, unions, and complements to express each of the following sets in terms of X, Y, and Z.

$$A = \{2, y\} \qquad B = \{1, 3, y\} \qquad C = \{2, 4, x, y\}$$

20. With X, Y, Z, and U as in Exercise 19, use intersections, unions, and complements to express the set $\{2, x, y\}$ in terms of X, Y, and Z.

21. List all subsets of the following sets.
(*a*) $\{x\}$ (*b*) $\{x, y\}$ (*c*) $\{x, y, z\}$

22. Counting the empty set and the set itself, how many subsets does each of the following sets contain?
(*a*) $\{x\}$ (*b*) $\{x, y\}$ (*c*) $\{x, y, z\}$ (*d*) $\{w, x, y, z\}$
Is there a pattern? If so, what is the pattern? How many subsets does a set with seven elements contain?

23. Let $U = \{a, b, c, 2, 4, 6\}$ be a universal set with subsets X, Y, and Z. Suppose that $X \cup Y = \{b, c, 2, 4, 6\}$, $X \cap Y = \{b, 2, 4\}$, $Y' \cap Z' = \{a, c\}$, and $Z' = \{a, c, 2\}$. Find sets X, Y, and Z which satisfy these conditions.

24. If $A = \{r, s, t\}$ and $B = \{s, t, u\}$: list the elements in $A \times A$, $A \times B$, $B \times A$, and $B \times B$.

25. Let $A = \{a, b, c\}$ and $B = \{a, b, d\}$.
(*a*) List the elements in $A \times B$.
(*b*) List the elements in $(A \times B) \cap (B \times A)$.

26. Let $U = \{1, 2, 3, 4, 5, 6\}$ be a universal set with subsets X, Y, and Z. Suppose that $X \cup Y = \{1, 2, 4\}$, $Y \cap Z = \{4\}$, $(Y \cup Z)' = \{1, 3, 5\}$, $X \cap Y = \{4\}$, and $Z' = \{1, 2, 3, 5\}$. Find subsets X, Y, and Z.
27. Suppose $A \times B = \{(a, 1), (b, 1), (a, 2), (b, 2), (a, 3), (b, 3)\}$. Find A and B.
28. Let $A = \{1, 2, 3\}$ and $B = \{1, 2, 4\}$. Decide which of the following are correct.
    (*a*) $(A \times B) \cap (B \times A) = (A \times A) \cap (B \times B)$
    (*b*) $(A \times B) = \{(2,1), (1, 4), (1, 2), (3, 4), (3, 2), (1,1), (2, 2), (2, 4), (3,1)\}$
    (*c*) $(A \times A) \subset ((A \times B) \cap (B \times A))$
    (*d*) $(A \times A) \subset ((A \times B) \cup (B \times A))$
29. Let $U = \{-2, -1, 0, 1, 2\}$ and $S = \{-1, 0, 1\}$. Also, let $A = \{(x, y) : x \in S, y = x^2\}$ and $B = \{(x, y) : x \in U, y = x^2\}$. Is it true that
    (*a*) $A \subset B$ (*b*) $A \subset S \times S$ (*c*) $B \subset S \times S$ (*d*) $B \subset U \times U$
30. Let A, B, S, and U be the sets given in Exercise 29. Find $A \times A$ and $B \times B$. Show that $A \times A \subset B \times B$. Is it always true that if $A \subset B$, then $A \times A \subset B \times B$? Why or why not?
31. Suppose $A \times B = \{(1, a), (1, b), (1, c), (2, a), (2, b), (2, c)\}$. If $C = \{d, e\}$, then $C \times A = ?$
32. Let $A = \{1, 2, 3, 4, 6, 8\}$ and $B = \{5, 6, 7, 8, 9\}$. A set W is defined to be the elements (pairs) of $B \times A$ for which at least one of the numbers is even. How many elements are there in W? How many elements are in $A \times W$?
33. Let $A = \{x, y, z, 1\}$ and $B = \{1, 2, 4\}$. If a set $U = (A \times B) \cup (B \times A)$, how many elements are there in U?
34. The set $F = \{1, 2, 3, 5, 8, 13, 21, 34\}$. Describe the set F by two different rules.
35. A set S has 6 elements, two of them being a and b. How many subsets of S do not include a or b? How many include a, but not b?

1.2 VENN DIAGRAMS AND PARTITIONS

In working with sets and the relations between sets, it is often helpful to represent them with diagrams or pictures. A *Venn diagram* serves this purpose. In a Venn diagram, a universal set U and its subsets are pictured by using geometric shapes. By convention the set U is usually represented by a rectangle, and the subsets of U are usually circles inside the rectangle. For example, subset A of U is shown as the shaded region in Figure 1.1*a*, subset B is shown in Figure 1.1*b*, and subset A' is shown in Figure 1.1*c*.

FIGURE 1.1

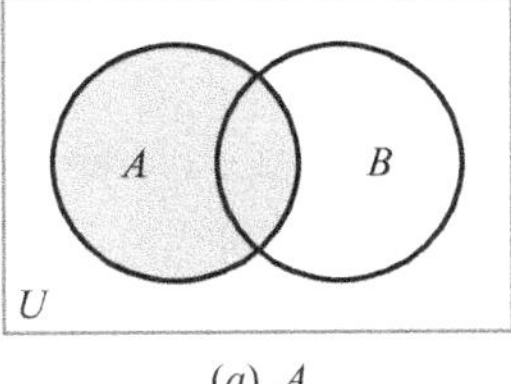

(*a*) A

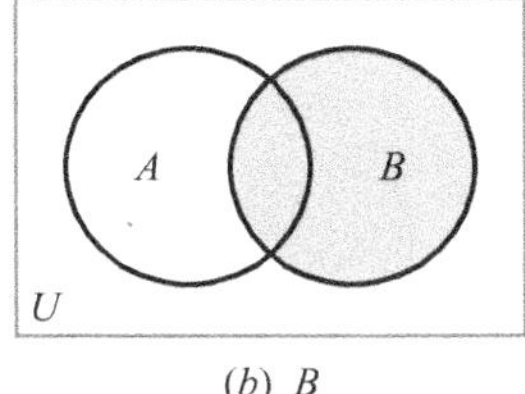

(*b*) B

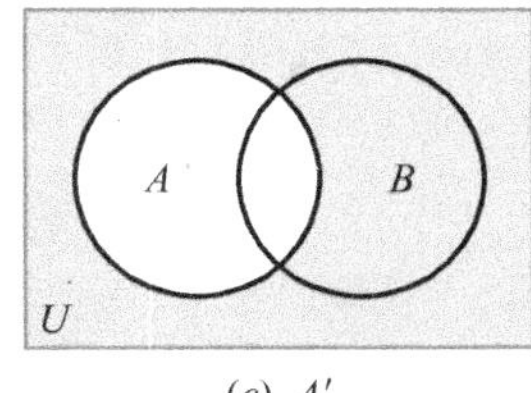

(*c*) A'

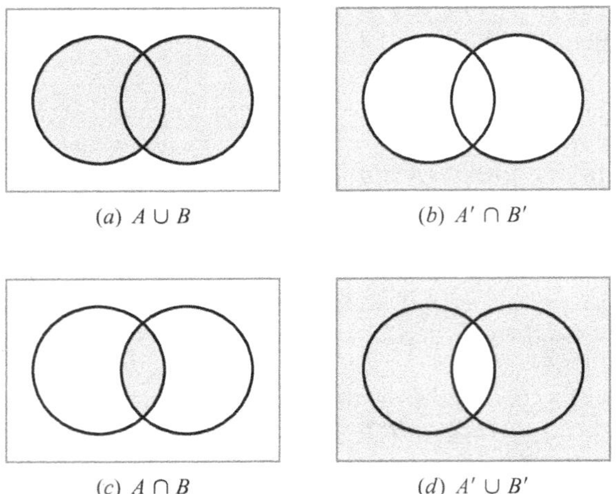

FIGURE 1.2

Subsets of U obtained by taking unions, intersections, and complements of A or B or both can also be represented by Venn diagrams. For instance, $A \cup B$ is illustrated in Figure 1.2*a*, and $A \cap B$ is illustrated in Figure 1.2*c*.

Two useful set equalities are known as *deMorgan's laws*.

For any subsets A and B of a universal set U

$$(A \cup B)' = A' \cap B'$$
$$(A \cap B)' = A' \cup B'$$

These equalities are illustrated in Figure 1.2. First, Figure 1.2*a* and *b* illustrate that $(A \cup B)' = A' \cap B'$. This relation can be read "The complement of a union is the intersection of the complements," and it follows from the definitions of union, intersection, and complement. Likewise, Figure 1.2*c* and *d* illustrate that $(A \cap B)' = A' \cup B'$, which can be read "The complement of an intersection is the union of the complements."

Other useful relations can be illustrated with Venn diagrams and verified by using the definitions. Among these relations are the following distributive laws:

$$A \cap (B \cup C) = (A \cap B) \cup (A \cap C)$$
$$A \cup (B \cap C) = (A \cup B) \cap (A \cup C)$$

These relations hold for any three sets A, B, and C. As we mentioned earlier, the parentheses are essential, and the expressions would be ambiguous without them.

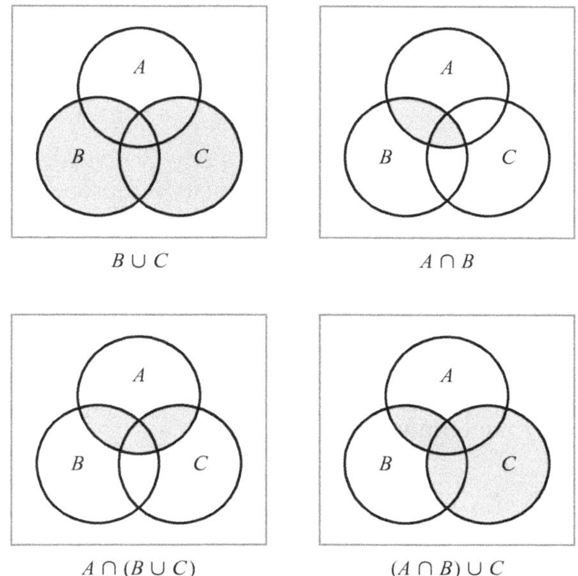

FIGURE 1.3

Example 1.7 Figure 1.3 illustrates that in general the sets $A \cap (B \cup C)$ and $(A \cap B) \cup C$ are different. ■

FIGURE 1.4

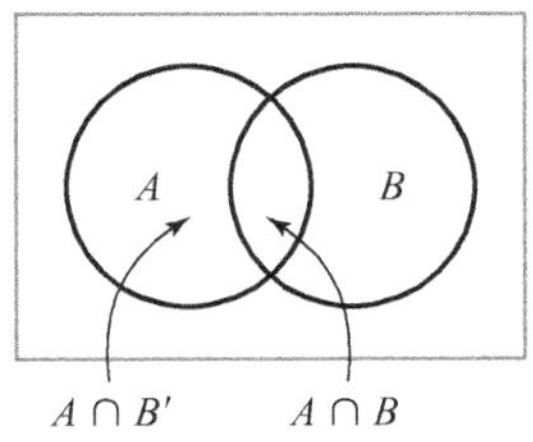

Venn diagrams provide us with a geometric way to represent the decomposition of a set into subsets. For example, in Figure 1.4 we illustrate how the set A can be decomposed into subsets $A \cap B$ (the football-shaped region) and $A \cap B'$ (the crescent-shaped region). The notion of decomposition of a set into subsets is extremely useful in the study of probability, and we consider the situation in greater detail.

Example 1.8 Let $X = \{2, 4, 6, 8, 10, 11, 12, 13, 14, 16, 18\}$.

Problem Find subsets X_1, X_2, and X_3 such that X_1 contains all even numbers in X less than 10, X_2 contains all odd numbers in X, and X_3 contains all even numbers in X at least as large as 10.

Solution

$$X_1 = \{2, 4, 6, 8\}, \qquad X_2 = \{11, 13\}, \qquad X_3 = \{10, 12, 14, 16, 18\}$$ ■

Note that $X = X_1 \cup X_2 \cup X_3$ and $X_1 \cap X_2 = \emptyset, X_1 \cap X_3 = \emptyset, X_2 \cap X_3 = \emptyset$.

Example 1.9 Let $U = \{\text{Cairo, Copenhagen, Lima, Paris, Rio de Janeiro, Vienna}\}$.

Problem Find subsets A, E, and S of U such that

$$\begin{aligned} A &= \{x : \ x \text{ is a city in Africa}\} \\ E &= \{x : \ x \text{ is a city in Europe}\} \\ S &= \{x : \ x \text{ is a city in South America}\} \end{aligned}$$

and find the union of these three sets and the intersection of each pair of them.

Solution The sets A, E, and S are the following: $A = \{\text{Cairo}\}$, $E = \{\text{Copenhagen, Paris, Vienna}\}$, and $S = \{\text{Lima, Rio de Janeiro}\}$. Then A, E, and S satisfy the following:

$$A \cup E \cup S = U \qquad A \cap E = \emptyset \qquad A \cap S = \emptyset \qquad E \cap S = \emptyset \tag{1.1}$$

■

In Example 1.9 sets A and E are disjoint. Likewise sets A and S are disjoint, and sets E and S are disjoint. Relationships like this occur frequently enough for us to use a special expression to describe them.

The sets in a collection are said to be *pairwise disjoint* if every pair of sets in the collection is disjoint.

Also in Example 1.9, the result of each classification assigns a city to A, E, or S; the union $A \cup E \cup S$ is the set of all cities to be considered: $A \cup E \cup S = U$. Subsets A, E, and S of U which satisfy condition (1.1) form a *partition* of U. In general, a partition is the result of cutting up a set into subsets; each subset contains some elements of the set, and no two subsets can overlap. Formally,

A *partition* of a set U is a collection of nonempty subsets of U which are pairwise disjoint and whose union is the entire set U.

In the use of sets in finite mathematics, one of our main concerns is to count the number of elements in certain sets. This is the primary topic of the next section, and it will recur frequently in our work on probability. Partitions are especially useful in helping us count the number of elements in a set. To show how, we need some notation.

Let A be a set with a finite number of elements. The number of elements in A is denoted by $n(A)$.

For instance, if X, A, E, and S are the sets of Example 1.9, then $n(X) = 6$, $n(A) = 1$, $n(E) = 3$, and $n(S) = 2$. In this case we have

$$6 = n(X) = n(A) + n(E) + n(S) = 1 + 3 + 2$$

In fact, the definitions of a partition and the number of elements in a set lead to the following useful principle:

Partition Principle
If a set X is partitioned into subsets $X_1, X_2, \ldots, X_k$, then

$$n(X) = n(X_1) + n(X_2) + \cdots + n(X_k) \tag{1.2}$$

If each of the subsets $X_1, X_2, \ldots, X_k$ has the same number of elements, then Equation (1.2) can be simplified to

$$n(X) = kn(X_1) \tag{1.3}$$

This version of (1.2) will be useful when X is a cartesian product.

Example 1.10 A student is to plan a schedule which consists of one science course and one humanities course. The student can choose a science course in astronomy (A), biology (B), or chemistry (C) and a humanities course in history (H), philosophy (P), religion (R), or theater (T).

Problem Determine the number of possible schedules.

Solution A schedule is a science course (A, B, or C) *and* a humanities course (H, P, R, or T). Thus, a class schedule can be represented as an ordered pair in which the first entry is a science course and the second entry is a humanities course. The set of class schedules S is a cartesian product of the set of science courses $X = \{A, B, C\}$ and the set of humanities courses $Y = \{H, P, R, T\}$. This cartesian product can be arranged in the array

$$\begin{array}{cccc} (A, H) & (A, P) & (A, R) & (A, T) \\ (B, H) & (B, P) & (B, R) & (B, T) \\ (C, H) & (C, P) & (C, R) & (C, T) \end{array}$$

There are three rows in the array, one corresponding to each element in the set $\{A, B, C\}$; and there are four columns in the array, one corresponding to each element in the set $\{H, P, R, T\}$. We can view the set S as partitioned into three subsets, one corresponding to each row of the array. Each row of the array contains four elements, and we conclude from (1.3) that

$$n(S) = n(\{A, B, C\}) \cdot n(\{H, P, R, T\}) = 3 \cdot 4 = 12$$ ■

The technique used in Example 1.10 for counting the number of elements in a set which can be represented as the cartesian product of two sets is perfectly general. We have the following rule.

If A and B are sets, then

$$n(A \times B) = n(A) \cdot n(B) \tag{1.4}$$

As we shall see in our next example, it is often necessary to consider cartesian products of more than two sets. The definition is similar to the definition of the cartesian product of two sets. For instance, the cartesian product $E \times F \times G$ of three sets is the set of all ordered triples (e, f, g), with $e \in E, f \in F$, and $g \in G$.

Example 1.11 Suppose that the student of Example 1.10 also plans to take one language course, either French (F) or German (G). Then the possible class schedules can be represented by ordered triples (x, y, z) where $x \in \{A, B, C\}$, $y \in \{H, P, R, T\}$, and $z \in \{F, G\}$. That is,

$$S = \{A, B, C\} \times \{H, P, R, T\} \times \{F, G\}$$

The number of class schedules available to the student is $n(S)$. Hence, as in Example 1.10, $n(S)$ can be obtained by taking the product of the numbers of elements in each of the sets in the cartesian product:

$$n(S) = n(\{A, B, C\}) \cdot n(\{H, P, R, T\}) \cdot n(\{F, G\}) = 3 \cdot 4 \cdot 2 = 24$$ ■

The result illustrated in Example 1.11 for three sets can be extended to an arbitrary number of sets. The corresponding general result is as follows:

If $X_1, X_2, \ldots, X_k$ are sets, then

$$n(X_1 \times X_2 \times \cdots \times X_k) = n(X_1) \cdot n(X_2) \cdots n(X_k)$$

Example 1.12 Suppose X_1 and X_2 form a partition of X, and Y_1, Y_2 form a partition of Y.

Problem If $n(X_1) = 4$, $n(X_2) = 5$, $n(Y_1) = 3$, and $n(Y_2) = 6$, find $n(X_1 \times X_2 \times Y)$.

Solution Since $n(Y) = n(Y_1 \cup Y_2) = 9$, we have $n(X_1 \times X_2 \times Y) = 4 \cdot 5 \cdot 9 = 180$. ■

Exercises for Section 1.2

1. Let A, B, and C be subsets of a set U. Draw a Venn diagram to illustrate each of the following sets. In each case, shade the area corresponding to the designated set.
   (a) $A' \cap B$ (b) $A \cup B'$
   (c) $A \cup B \cup C$ (d) $(A \cup B) \cap C'$
2. In each case determine which of points v, w, x, y, and z in Figure 1.5 are contained in the specified set.
   (a) $A \cap C'$ (b) $A \cup C'$
   (c) $A \cup (B \cap C)$ (d) $(B \cap C)'$
3. In each case determine which of points v, w, x, y, and z in Figure 1.5 are contained in the specified set.
   (a) $A \cup C$ (b) $A \cap B$
   (c) $A \cup B$ (d) $B \cap C$
4. Using Figure 1.5, decide which of the following statements are true and which are false.
   (a) $z \in A \cup C'$ (b) $y \in B \cup (A \cap C')$
   (c) $y \in (B \cup C) \cap A'$ (d) $v \in (B \cup C) \cap (A \cup C)$
5. Using Figure 1.5, decide which of the following statements are true and which are false.
   (a) $\{x, y\} \subset A \cap B \cap C$ (b) $\{v, y, z\} \subset (A \cap C) \cup B$
   (c) $\{w, x, y\} \subset (A \cup B) \cap C$ (d) $\{y, z, v\} \subset (A \cup B) \cap C$
6. Describe the shaded areas in each Venn diagram of Figure 1.6, by using the set operations of union, intersection, and complement and the sets A, B, and C.

FIGURE 1.5

FIGURE 1.6

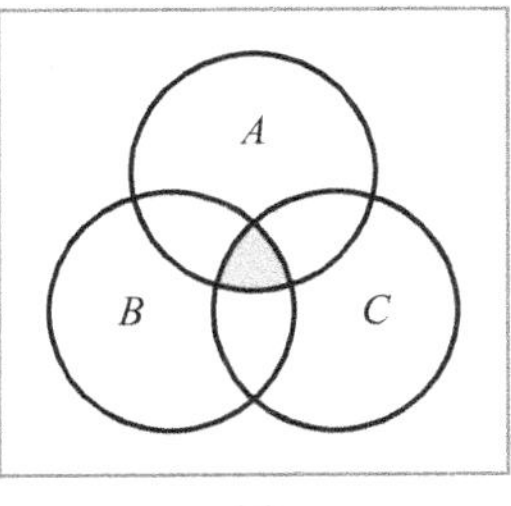

(a)

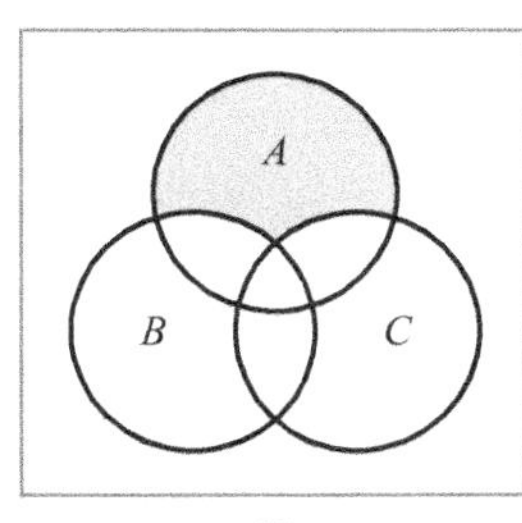

(b)

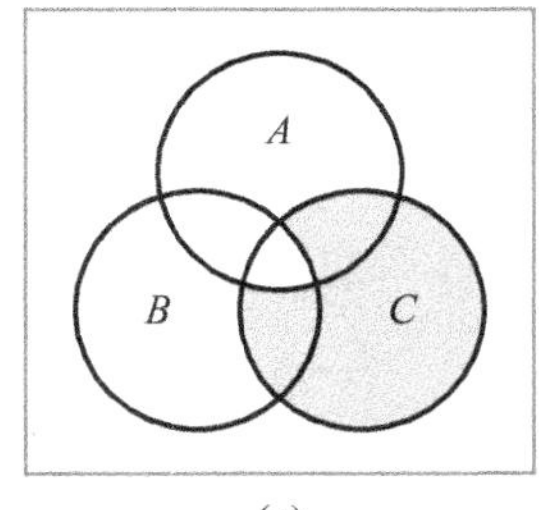

(c)

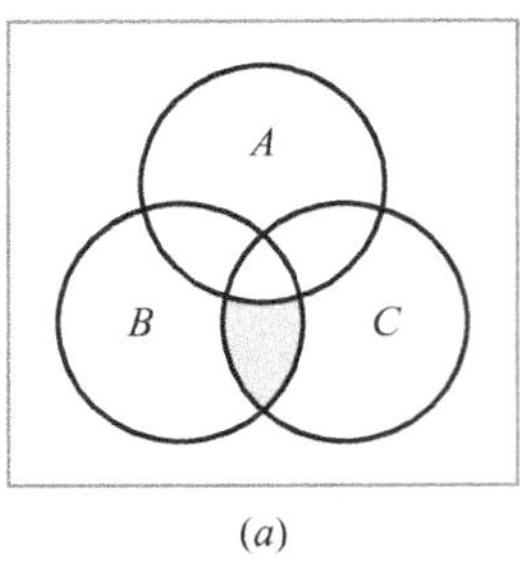

(a)

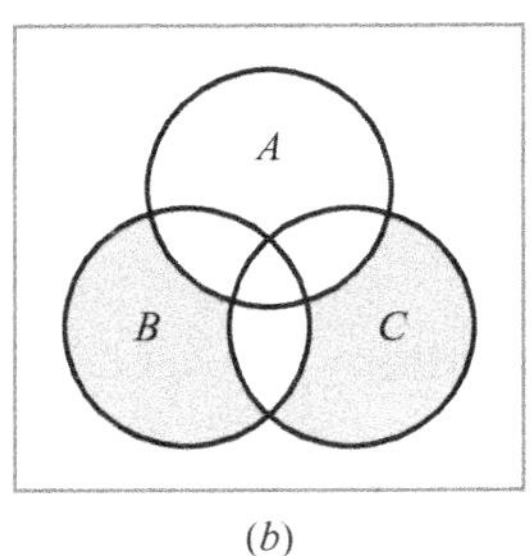

(b)

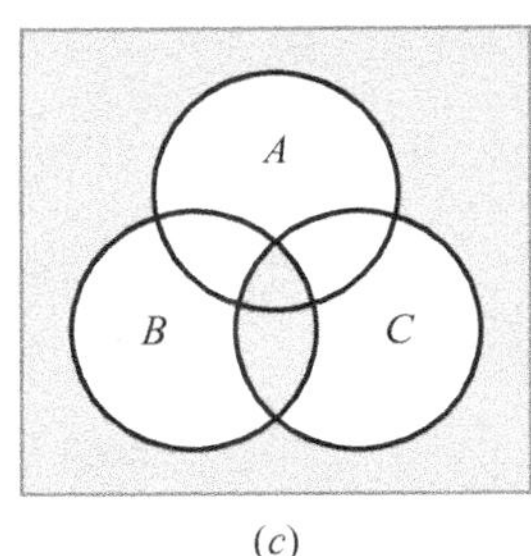

(c)

FIGURE 1.7

7. Repeat Exercise 6, using Figure 1.7.
   (a) $x \in A \cap C$ (b) $z \in (A \cap B)' \cup C$ (c) $y \in B'$
   (d) $x \in C'$ (e) $y \in A' \cup C$
8. Decide which of the following are "always true", "sometimes true", or "never true".
   (a) $A \cap (B \cup C) = (A \cap B) \cup (A \cap C)$
   (b) $A \cup (B \cap C) = (A \cup B) \cap (A \cup C)$
   (c) $(A \cup B') \cap C' = (A \cup C') \cap B'$
9. Determine which (if any) of the following set relations are true for *all* sets A, B, and C. (*Hint*: Use Venn diagrams.)
   (a) $A' \cap B' = (A \cap B)'$ (b) $(A \cap B') \subset A'$
   (c) $A' \cap B' \subset (A \cup B)'$ (d) $(A \cap B)' \subset A'$
   (e) $(A \cup B)' \cap C = (A' \cap B') \cup C$ (f) $(A \cap B)' \cup C' = (A' \cup B') \cup C'$

FIGURE 1.8

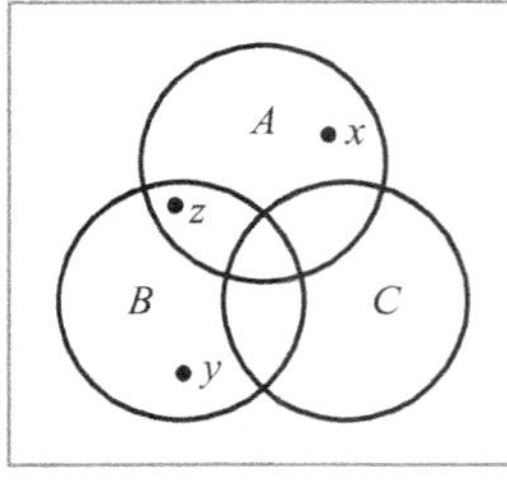

10. Which of the following is a true statement about the Venn diagram shown in Figure 1.8?
    (a) $x \in A \cap C$ (b) $z \in (A \cap B)' \cup C$ (c) $y \in B'$
    (d) $x \in C'$ (e) $y \in A' \cup C$
11. Let U be a universal set with disjoint subsets A and B; $n(U) = 60$, $n(A) = 25$, and $n(B) = 30$. Find $n((A \cup B)')$.
12. Let A and B be disjoint subsets in a Universal set U with $n(U) = 50$, $n(A \cup B) = 35$, and $n(B') = 25$. Find $n(A)$.
13. Let U be a universal set with disjoint subsets A and B; $n(A) = 25$, $n(A') = 40$, and $n(B') = 30$. Find $n(A \cup B)$.
14. Let $n(X \times Y) = 24$, $n(X \times Z) = 15$, and $n(Y \times Z) = 40$. Find $n(X \times Y \times Z)$.
15. Let X, A, B, and C be defined by

$$X = \{a, b, c, 1, 2, 3\}$$
$$A = \{a, b, c\} \qquad B = \{a, 2, 3\} \qquad C = \{1, 2, 3\}$$

    Which of the following pairs of subsets form a partition of X?
    (a) A and B (b) A and C
    (c) B and C (d) $(A \cup B)$ and $(C \cap B')$

FIGURE 1.9

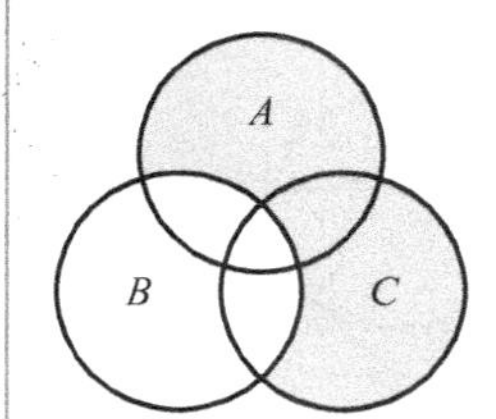

16. The shaded region in Figure 1.9 is properly described by which two of the following:
    (a) $(A \cup C) \cap B'$ (b) $(A \cup C) \cap (B' \cup C)$
    (c) $(B' \cap C) \cup (B' \cap A)$ (d) $(A \cup B' \cup C)$

17. Let $A = \{1, 2, 3\}$ and $B = \{v, w\}$. By listing the elements in each of the three sets, show that $A \times \{v\}$ and $A \times \{w\}$ provide a partition of $A \times B$.

18. A set P is partitioned into subsets P_1, P_2, P_3. The number of elements in P_2 is 5 times the number in P_1 and the number of elements in P_3 is twice the number in P_1. If $n(P) = 40$, find $n(P_2)$.

19. Let $A = \{1, 7, 3, a, b\}$ and $B = \{3, c\}$. Determine
(*a*) $n(A \times B)$ (*b*) $n(B \times B \times B)$

20. A set U with $n(U) = 8$ is partitioned into 4 nonempty subsets A, B, C, and D. If all four sets are pairwise disjoint, then which of the following statements *must* be true?
(*a*) $n(A) + n(B) = n(C) + n(D)$ (*b*) $n(A) + n(B) \neq n(C) + n(D)$
(*c*) $n(A) + n(B) \geq 2$ (*d*) $n(A) + n(B) + n(C) + n(D) \neq 8$

21. A sociologist has a project which involves the collection of data. She is interested in data which can be obtained by mail, by phone, or in person in any of the cities of Atlanta, Boston, Chicago, Denver, or Elmira. She has funds for one project, that is, to collect data in one way from one city. Determine the number of possible ways to carry out the project.

22. Let A, B, and C be subsets of a universal set U with A and B disjoint, $n(U) = 110$, $n(A) = 35$, $n(B) = 44$, $n(A \cup B \cup C) = 96$, and $n((A \cup B) \cap C) = 28$. Find $n(C)$.

23. Let A, B, and C be distinct subsets of a universal set U with $A \subset B \subset C$. Also suppose $n(A) = 3$ and $n(C) = 7$. In how many different ways can you select B such that $n(B) = 4$? Repeat this exercise with $n(B) = 5$.

24. Suppose $n(A) = 5$, $n(B) = 10$, and $n(C) = 20$. Which of the following sets has more elements, $A \times B \times C$ or $B \times B \times B$?

25. A bag contains 6 green balls, 1 yellow ball, and 2 red balls. An experiment consists of selecting three balls, one after another without replacement, and noting the color of each ball selected. Suppose the set X of outcomes is partitioned into X_1, X_2, and X_3 where X_1 is the set of outcomes containing no red balls, X_2 is the set of outcomes containing 1 red ball, and X_3 is the set of outcomes containing 2 red balls. Find $n(X_1)$, $n(X_2)$, and $n(X_3)$.

26. Let A, B, and C be subsets of a universal set U with A and B disjoint, $n(U) = 120$, $n(A) = 35$, $n(B) = 44$, $n(A \cup B \cup C) = 100$, and $n((A \cup B) \cap C) = 28$.
(*a*) Find $n(C')$. (*b*) Find $n(C \cap A' \cap B')$.

27. A set X is partitioned into subsets X_1, X_2, and X_3. The number of elements in X_1 is twice the number in X_2, and the number in X_3 is 5 times the number in X_2. If $n(X) = 40$, find $n(X_1)$, $n(X_2)$, and $n(X_3)$.

28. A set X with $n(X) = 45$ is partitioned into three subsets X_1, X_2, and X_3. If $n(X_2) = 2n(X_1)$ and $n(X_3) = 3n(X_2)$, find the number of elements in subset X_1.

29. A set X with $n(X) = 60$ is partitioned into subsets $X_1, \ldots, X_6$. If $n(X_1) = n(X_2) = n(X_3)$, $n(X_4) = n(X_5) = n(X_6)$ and $n(X_1) = 4n(X_4)$, find $n(X_1)$.

30. Let A_1 and A_2 be a partition of A, and let B_1 and B_2 be a partition of B. Is it true that $A_1 \times B_1$, $A_1 \times B_2$, $A_2 \times B_1$, and $A_2 \times B_2$ form a partition of $A \times B$? Why or why not?

31. A set X with $n(X) = 100$ is partitioned into subsets A, B, C, D, and E. Suppose $n(B) = 3n(A)$, $n(C) = 4n(A)$, $n(E) = n(B) + n(C)$, and $n(D) = n(E) - 10$. Find the number of elements in subset D.
32. A set X with $n(X) = 120$ is partitioned into five subsets X_1, X_2, X_3, X_4, and X_5. If $n(X_5) = 5n(X_1)$, $n(X_4) = 2n(X_2)$, $n(X_2) = 2n(X_1)$, and $n(X_3) = n(X_2) + 8$, find $n(X_5)$.
33. A universal set U has subsets A, B, C, and D. It is known that $n(U) = 100$, $n(A) = n(B) = 30$, $n(C) = n(D) = 80$ and $n(A \cup B \cup C \cup D) = 80$. Find $n((A \cup B \cup C) \cap D)$.

1.3 SIZES OF SETS

We have seen that "the whole is equal to the sum of the parts" when we are dealing with subsets which form a partition of a set. This is summarized in the partition principle, formula (1.2). What if the sets of interest do not form a partition of another set? For instance, what if they are not disjoint? In such cases Venn diagrams and the partition principle are still useful when applied appropriately. We begin by analyzing a specific example in some detail. Our goal is both a technique and a very useful formula.

Example 1.13 A set U with nondisjoint subsets A and B has the following:

$$n(U) = 10 \qquad n(A) = 7 \qquad n(B) = 6 \qquad n(A \cap B) = 4$$

Problem Find $n(A \cup B)$.

Solution We use a Venn diagram with universal set U and subsets A and B. Inside subset $A \cap B$ we insert the number 4 to indicate that $n(A \cap B) = 4$. At this stage we have the diagram shown in Figure 1.10*a*. Next, since A has 7 elements and since 4 of them are in $A \cap B$, the portion of A not in $A \cap B$, that is, $A \cap B'$, must contain $7 - 4 = 3$ elements. We insert a 3 in the set $A \cap B'$ to indicate this. Likewise, since $n(B) = 6$, there must be 2 elements in $A' \cap B$. The information $n(A \cap B) = 4$, $n(A \cap B') = 3$, and $n(A' \cap B) = 2$ is shown

FIGURE 1.10

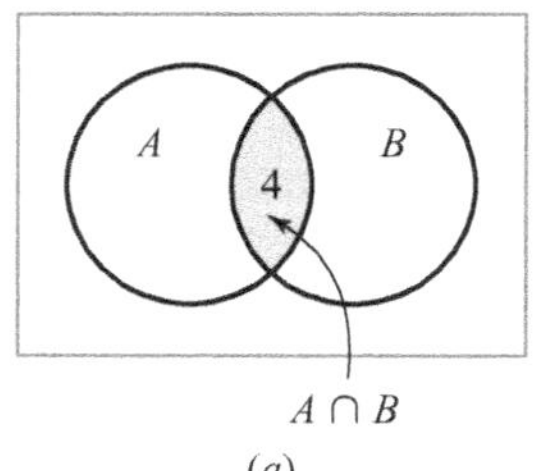

(*a*)

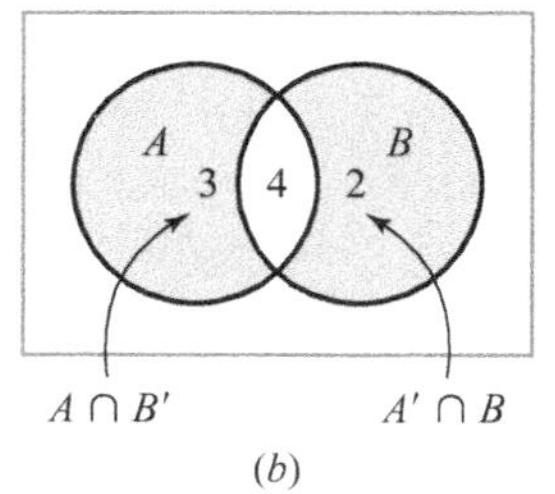

(*b*)

in Figure 1.10b. Using this information, we see from the partition principle [formula (1.2)] that $n(A \cup B) = 3 + 4 + 2 = 9$. ■

It is helpful to examine this example more closely. Since $n(A \cup B) = 9$ while $n(A) + n(B) = 6 + 7 = 13$, it is clear that in general we cannot obtain $n(A \cup B)$ simply by adding $n(A)$ and $n(B)$. In fact, by examining Figure 1.10 we see that adding $n(A)$ and $n(B)$ actually counts the elements in $A \cap B$ twice. It follows that to find $n(A \cup B)$, we must subtract $n(A \cap B)$ from $n(A) + n(B)$. In this way each element in $A \cup B$ will be counted exactly once. In Example 1.13 we have

$$n(A \cup B) = (3 + 4) + (4 + 2) - 4 = 9 = n(A) + n(B) - n(A \cap B)$$

Our argument holds for any two sets A and B. We have the useful formula

$$n(A \cup B) = n(A) + n(B) - n(A \cap B) \tag{1.5}$$

Example 1.14 The webmaster for a new web site asked 100 recent visitors to the site about their impressions of the appearance and functionality of the home page for the site. In particular, she asked the following two questions:

(a) Do you prefer the simple appearance now used or would you prefer to have more information and options on the home page?

(b) Do you prefer a home page with no product ads or would you like to see ads for special sales?

The results of the survey are that 60 prefer the current simple home page, 45 prefer not to have ads for sales on the home page, and 25 prefer both a simple home page and not to have ads for sales.

Problem How many of the 100 responders to the survey prefer both a more informative home page and ads for sale items?

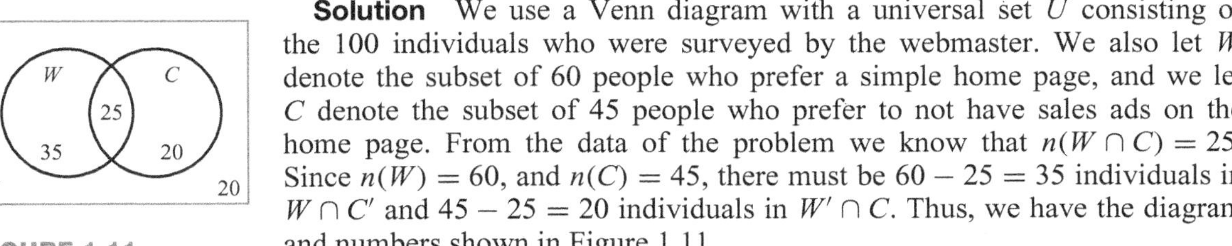

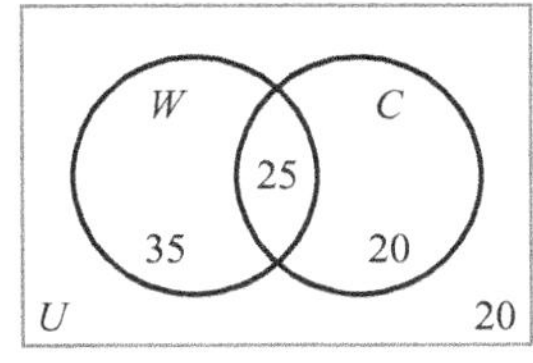

FIGURE 1.11

Solution We use a Venn diagram with a universal set U consisting of the 100 individuals who were surveyed by the webmaster. We also let W denote the subset of 60 people who prefer a simple home page, and we let C denote the subset of 45 people who prefer to not have sales ads on the home page. From the data of the problem we know that $n(W \cap C) = 25$. Since $n(W) = 60$, and $n(C) = 45$, there must be $60 - 25 = 35$ individuals in $W \cap C'$ and $45 - 25 = 20$ individuals in $W' \cap C$. Thus, we have the diagram and numbers shown in Figure 1.11.

From Figure 1.11 we see that $n(W \cup C) = 35 + 25 + 20 = 80$ and $n((W \cup C)') = 100 - 80 = 20$. We are interested in the individuals who are in W' (prefer more information on home page) and who are also in C'

(prefer sales ads on the home page), and therefore are in $W' \cap C'$. Since $W' \cap C' = (W \cup C)'$, the answer to the problem is

$$n(W' \cap C') = n((W \cup C)') = 20$$ ■

In Example 1.14 we used the fact that the number of elements in $(W \cup C)'$ is the difference between the number of elements in $W \cup C$ and the number of elements in the universal set U. This result holds for any subset A of U, and we have the formula

$$n(A') = n(U) - n(A) \tag{1.6}$$

The question raised in Example 1.14 can also be answered directly (without using a Venn diagram) by applying formulas (1.5) and (1.6). Proceeding in this way, we have

$$\begin{aligned} n(W \cup C) &= n(W) + n(C) - n(W \cap C) \\ &= 60 + 45 - 25 \\ &= 80 \end{aligned}$$

and therefore,

$$\begin{aligned} n[(W \cup C)'] &= n(U) - n(W \cup C) \\ &= 100 - 80 \\ &= 20 \end{aligned}$$

Nevertheless, *in general, it is best to draw the Venn diagram.* The diagram is a useful aid in organizing the information of the problem, and it helps us to spot mistakes which may result from using the formulas incorrectly. Also, the logic followed in using a Venn diagram is the same when there are three or more subsets of interest as when there are only two. This is illustrated in the following example.

Example 1.15 The GetFitFast Company requires each of its employees to pass a yearly physical examination. The results of the most recent examination of 50 employees were that 30 employees were overweight, 25 had high blood pressure, and 20 had a high cholesterol count. Moreover, 15 of the overweight employees also had high blood pressure, and 10 of those with a high cholesterol count were also overweight. Of the 25 with high blood pressure, there were 12 who also had a high cholesterol count. Finally, there were 5 employees who had all three of these undesirable conditions. When the reports reached the desk of the president, Jox Chinup, he asked, "Don't we have any completely healthy employees around here?"

Problem Answer his question and find the exact number of employees free of all these symptoms.

Solution Let U be the set of all employees, with O, B, and C the sets of employees who are overweight, who have high blood pressure, and who have a high cholesterol count, respectively. The information gathered in the tests can then be summarized as follows:

$$n(U) = 50 \qquad n(O) = 30 \qquad n(B) = 25 \qquad n(C) = 20$$
$$n(O \cap B) = 15 \qquad n(O \cap C) = 10 \qquad n(B \cap C) = 12$$
$$n(O \cap B \cap C) = 5$$

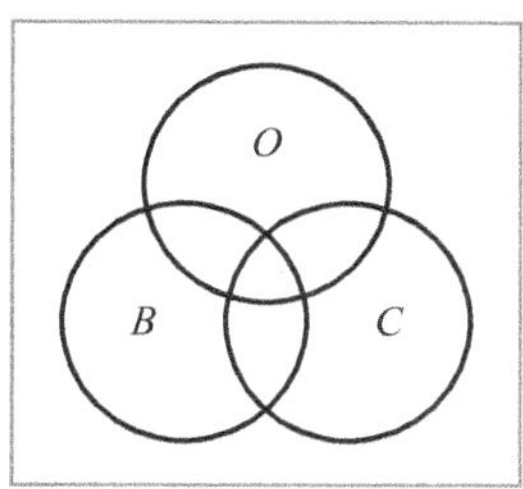

FIGURE 1.12

This problem is concerned with three subsets of U, and an appropriate Venn diagram is shown in Figure 1.12. Let us begin with the intersection $O \cap B \cap C$, which is known to have 5 elements, and place a 5 in that portion of the diagram, as in Figure 1.13a. Since $O \cap B$ has 15 elements, it follows that the portion of $O \cap B$ which is not in $O \cap B \cap C$ contains 10 elements. Likewise, since $O \cap C$ contains 10 elements, the part of $O \cap C$ not in $O \cap B \cap C$ contains 5 elements, and since $B \cap C$ contains 12 elements, the part of $B \cap C$ not in $O \cap B \cap C$ contains 7 elements. This information is shown on Figure 1.13a.

Next, since the numbers of elements in O, B, and C are known, we can use the information determined thus far to compute the number of elements in O but not in B or C, and so forth. This information is shown on Figure 1.13b. Note that each number on the Venn diagram gives the number of employees in the set corresponding to that particular portion of the Venn diagram in which the number is printed. Thus there are 25 employees in set B but only 3 in the part of B not in $O \cup C$, and consequently there is a 3 printed in the portion of the Venn diagram corresponding to $B \cap (O \cup C)'$. The seven regions bounded by arcs in Figure 1.13b represent a partition of $O \cup B \cup C$, and the number of elements in each of them is known. Using Equation (1.2), we have

$$n(O \cup B \cup C) = 3 + 10 + 5 + 7 + 10 + 5 + 3 = 43$$

Therefore, since there are 50 elements in U, there are $50 - 43 = 7$ elements in $(O \cup B \cup C)'$. That is, 7 employees do not have high blood pressure or high cholesterol, nor are they overweight. ■

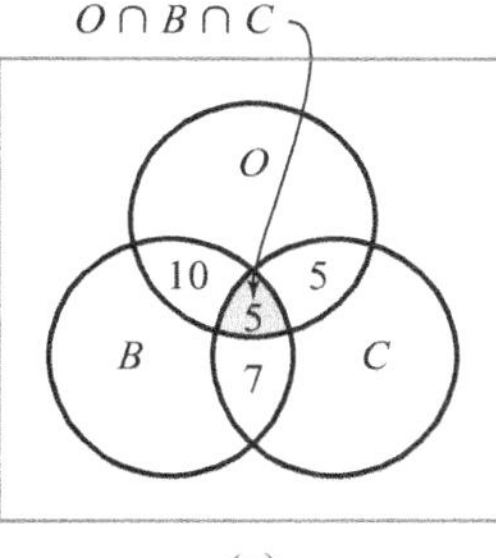

(a)

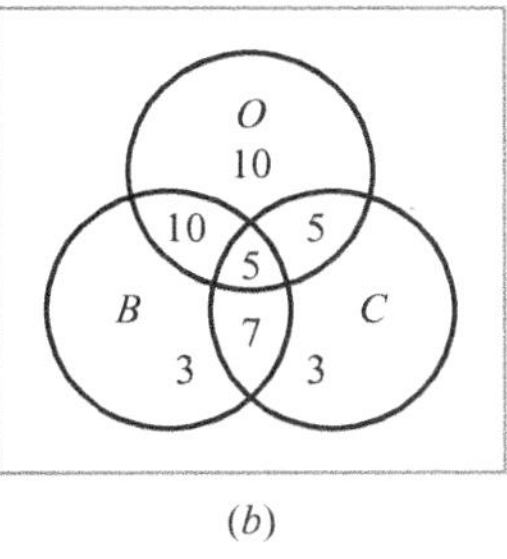

(b)

FIGURE 1.13

In some situations similar to that of Example 1.15, it initially appears that we do not have enough information to solve the problem. However, by introducing unknowns, or variables, to represent quantities we do not know, we can sometimes achieve our goal.

Example 1.16

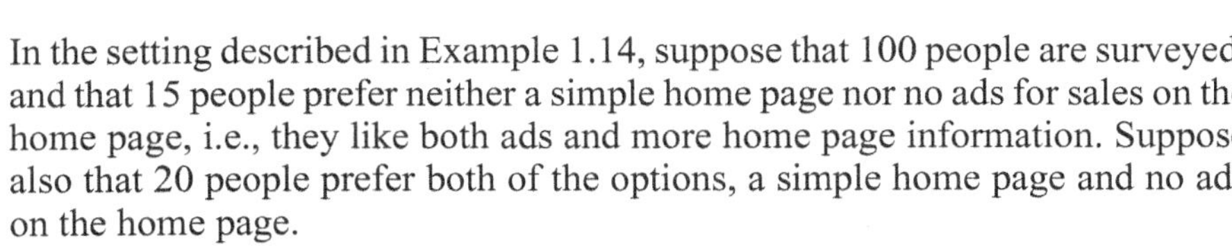

In the setting described in Example 1.14, suppose that 100 people are surveyed, and that 15 people prefer neither a simple home page nor no ads for sales on the home page, i.e., they like both ads and more home page information. Suppose also that 20 people prefer both of the options, a simple home page and no ads on the home page.

Problem How many people prefer exactly one of the two, either a simple home page or no ads, but not both.

Solution Let E denote the set of people who prefer exactly one of the two: a simple home page or no sale ads on the home page. Our goal is to determine the unknown quantity $x = n(E)$. We use the notation of Example 1.14, namely, W denotes the subset of people who prefer a simple home page and C denotes the subset of people who prefer to not have sale ads on the home page. We can write the given information as $n((W \cup C)') = 15$ and $n(W \cap C) = 20$. The sets $(W \cup C)'$, E, and $W \cap C$ form a partition of the set of people sampled. Therefore, from (1.2) we have

$$n((W \cup C)') + n(E) + n(W \cap C) = 100$$

Since $n((W \cup C)') = 15$ and $n(W \cap C) = 20$, it follows that

$$x = n(E) = 100 - 15 - 20 = 65$$ ■

In Example 1.16, it is impossible to determine the number of people who prefer a simple home page and ads on the home page. Likewise, it is impossible to determine the number of people who prefer more information on the home page and no sale ads on the home page.

Example 1.17 We are given sets A, B, and C with

$$n(A \cup B \cup C) = 85 \quad n(A) = 50 \quad n(B) = 40 \quad n(C) = 35$$
$$n(A \cap B) = 18 \quad n(B \cap C) = 12 \quad n(A \cap B \cap C) = 5$$

Problem Find $n(A \cap C)$.

Solution We begin, as usual, "to work from the inside out," and we enter 5 in the set $A \cap B \cap C$, as shown in Figure 1.14a. Since $n(A \cap B) = 18$ and there are 5 elements in $A \cap B \cap C$, there must be 13 elements in $A \cap B \cap C'$.

FIGURE 1.14

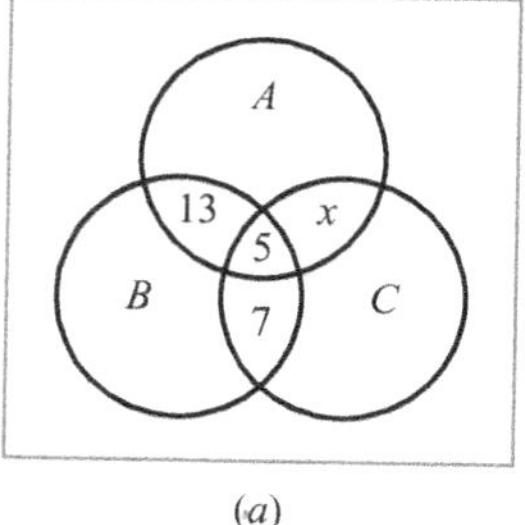

(a)

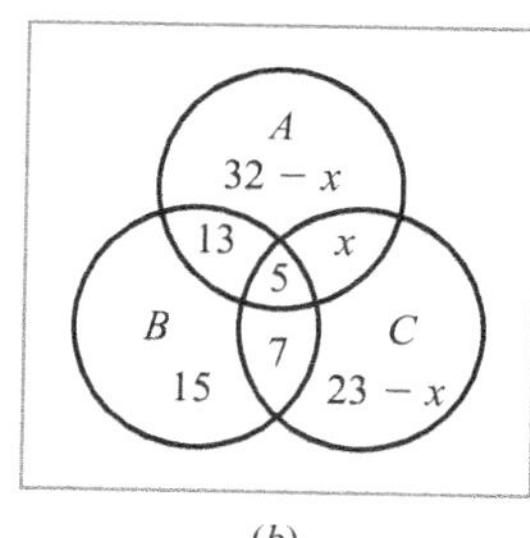

(b)

Likewise, there must be 7 elements in $A' \cap B \cap C$. However, from the given information, there is no direct way to calculate the number of elements in $A \cap B' \cap C$, and we denote this number by x. This information is also shown in Figure 1.14*a*. Next, using the partition of B shown in the figure and the numbers of elements in three of the four subsets (which we know), we conclude from the partition principle that there are 15 elements in $B \cap (A \cup C)'$. A similar argument can be used with set A. Indeed, there is a partition of the set A into four sets, and we have the numbers of elements in three of these sets as 13, 5, and x. Since $n(A) = 50$, we must have $n(A \cap (B \cup C)') = 50 - 13 - 5 - x = 32 - x$. Using a similar argument and set C, we find $n(C \cap (A \cup B)') = 23 - x$. These results are shown in Figure 1.14*b*. Finally, all the sets shown in Figure 1.14*b* give a partition of $A \cup B \cup C$, and consequently

$$\begin{aligned} n(A \cup B \cup C) = 85 &= 5 + 7 + 13 + x + 15 + (23 - x) + (32 - x) \\ &= 95 - x. \end{aligned}$$

Thus $85 = 95 - x$, and consequently, $x = n(A \cap B' \cap C) = 10$. Finally, since $n(A \cap B \cap C) = 5$, we have $n(A \cap C) = 10 + 5 = 15$. ■

Exercises for Section 1.3

1. Suppose A and B are subsets of U with $n(U) = 38$, $n(A) = 17$, $n(B) = 22$, and $n(A \cap B) = 8$.
   (*a*) Find $n(A')$ (*b*) Find $n(A \cup B)$ (*c*) Find $n((A \cup B)')$
2. Suppose A and B are subsets of U with $n(U) = 60$, $n(A) = 40$, $n(B') = 25$, and $n(A \cap B) = 22$.
   (*a*) Find $n(B)$ (*b*) Find $n(A \cup B)$ (*c*) Find $n((A \cap B)')$
3. Let A and B be subsets of U with $n(U) = 100$, $n(A) = 60$, $n(B') = 30$, and $n(A \cup B) = 75$. Find $n(A \cap B)$.
4. Suppose E and F are subsets in a universal set U with $n(U) = 70$, $n(E) = 32$, $n(E \cap F) = 8$, and $n(E' \cap F) = 18$. Find $n(F)$.
5. Let A and B be subsets of U with $n(U) = 150$, $n(B') = 70$, $n(A \cap B') = 30$, and $n(A \cap B) = 75$. Find $n(A \cup B)$.
6. Let A and B be disjoint subsets of U with $n(U) = 45$, $n(A) = 12$, and $n(B') = 22$. Find $n(A' \cap B)$.
7. A state legislature is considering increases in the gas tax and additional spending for highways, and 50 likely voters are asked their views. Of these voters, 25 favor additional spending for highways, 10 favor a gas tax increase, and 8 favor both. How many of these voters favor neither a gas tax increase nor additional spending for highways?
8. An item is said to be defective if it has a major defect or minor defect or both. In a batch of 25 defective items, 20 have major defects and 14 have minor defects. How many items in the batch have both major and minor defects?
9. Fifty students are asked about their plans for the weekend. Thirty-five plan to go to a football game, twenty plan to attend a concert, and fifteen plan to do both. How many plan to do neither?

10. Let A and B be subsets of a universal set U: $n(U) = 60$, $n(B) = 25$, and $n(A \cup B') = 45$. Find $n(A \cap B)$ and $n(A' \cap B)$.
11. At the local high school, 34 students take a course in mathematics, 26 take a course in psychology, and 12 take both. How many students take exactly one of these two courses?
12. A survey of 150 college students results in the following data:

    100 read the student paper published by their school.
    20 read the local city paper.
    85 who read the student paper *do not* read the city paper.

    (*a*) How many of the students surveyed read the city paper but not the student paper?
    (*b*) How many read *at least* one of the papers?
13. A quality control analyst for Very Smart-Phone Company is reviewing the performance of 15 difference types of phones. He finds that in comparison with the previous year, 12 have improved reliability and 8 have improved durability. Only 2 types have improved neither reliability nor durability. How many types of phones have improved both reliability and durability?
14. A hybrid automobile tested by a consumer testing company was found to have 20 production defects. Of these, 11 were classified as major defects and 8 were design defects; 4 were neither major defects nor design defects. How many of the design defects were major?
15. There were 100 premedical students who were not admitted to medical school. Asked whether they would be interested in careers as medical technicians or registered nurses, 54 of these students expressed an interest in medical technology, 32 in nursing, and 23 in both. How many students were interested in neither of these careers?
16. A sports enthusiasts' club has 123 members. Of the members, 102 like basketball, 69 like football, 17 like baseball, 7 like basketball and baseball, 9 like football and baseball, 52 like basketball and football, and only 2 like all three sports. How many members of the sports enthusiasts' club like none of these three sports?
17. Let A and B be subsets of U, with $n(U) = 50$. If $n(A) = 24$, $n(B') = 30$, and there are 8 elements of U in A which are not in B, find the number in B which are not in A.
18. Let A and B be subsets of U with $n(U) = 50$, $n(A' \cap B') = 20$, and $n(A \cap B) = 6$. Find the number of elements which are in A or in B but not in both.
19. Let A and B be subsets of a universal set U: $n(U) = 60$, $n(B) = 25$, and $n(A \cup B') = 45$. Find $n(A \cap B)$.
20. In a mathematics class with 250 students, 100 are also taking accounting, 150 are taking economics, and 200 are in an English composition class. Of those students in the mathematics class who are also taking economics, 25 are *not* taking either accounting or English, 75 are taking both accounting and English, and 25 are taking English but not accounting.
    (*a*) How many of the mathematics students are taking accounting and economics but not English?
    (*b*) How many are taking mathematics and accounting but neither English nor economics?

21. The local pet store surveyed 50 people about pets. Eleven of these people owned dogs, 13 owned cats, and 6 owned fish. One person owned all three types of pets, 2 people owned only fish and dogs, 3 people owned only fish and cats, and 5 people owned only cats and dogs. How many people owned none of these pets?
22. A survey of 50 college men gave the following results:

    20 regularly watch ESPN
    15 regularly watch Fox Sports
    10 regularly watch CBS Sports Network
    5 regularly watch both ESPN and Fox Sports
    7 regularly watch both ESPN and CBS Sports Network
    3 regularly watch all three networks
    18 regularly watch none of the three networks

    How many students regularly watch Fox Sports and CBS Sports Network but not ESPN?
23. An accounting firm has partners who are specialists in specific areas. The areas of specialization and the number of partners with each specialty are shown in Table 1.1. If every partner is a specialist in at least one area, how many partners are there?

TABLE 1.1

Specialization	Number
Auditing	11
Consulting	9
Tax	12
Auditing and consulting	5
Auditing and tax	8
Consulting and tax	7
All three	3

24. There are 288 university bookstores which offer at least one of the following: early bird discounts, buyback plans, and a pizza coupon for purchases over \$20. Of these schools, 129 offer discounts, 242 offer buyback plans, 103 offer a pizza coupon, 36 offer both a pizza coupon and buyback plan, and 51 offer discounts and pizza coupons. How many stores offer buyback plans and discounts but not pizza coupons?
25. A market analyst at Healthful Drug Corporation is analyzing the results of a market survey on a new product, Acheaway pain reliever. Each individual surveyed was asked to respond (positively, neutral, or negatively) to the effectiveness of the drug, the side effects (if any), and its cost. There are 150 completed surveys. Of those surveyed, 60 responded positively to effectiveness, 50 responded positively to side effects, and 40 responded positively to cost. Also, 20 responded positively to both effectiveness and side effects, 15 to side effects and cost, 10 to cost and effectiveness, and 37 to none of the items. Find the number that responded positively to all three.

26. Eighty-two individuals have complained to the Consumer Protection Agency about the 2016 Self Driving Starcar. The information contained in the letters of complaint is summarized below.

    25 complained about steering.
    23 complained about comfort.
    22 complained about visibility.
    11 complained about steering and comfort.
    7 complained about steering and visibility.
    5 complained about all three.
    33 complained about none of the three.

    (*a*) How many people complained about comfort and visibility but not about steering?
    (*b*) How many complained about *exactly* one of the three items: steering, comfort, and visibility?
27. Sets A, B, and C are subsets of a universal set U. Suppose $n(U) = 80$, $n(A) = 15$, $n(A \cap B) = 2$, $n(C) = 30$, $n((A \cup B)') = 35$, and $(A \cup B) \cap C = \emptyset$. Find:
    (*a*) $n(C')$ (*b*) $n(A \cap C)$ (*c*) $n(A' \cap B)$
28. Suppose A, B, and C are subsets of a universal set U. Also suppose $n(A) = 15$, $n(B) = 25$, $n(C) = 35$, $n(A' \cap B' \cap C') = 55$, and $n(A \cap B) = n(A \cap C) = n(B \cap C) = n(A \cap B \cap C) = 10$. Find $n(U)$.
29. Each of the students in the Outdoor Club at Gigantic State University likes at least one of the activities of hiking, camping, and canoeing. Of these students, 90 like either hiking or camping or both, 60 like canoeing, and 30 like all three. What can be said about the number of students who like canoeing and exactly one of hiking or camping?
30. A corporation employs 95 people in the areas of sales, research, and administration. Some of the employees can function in more than one area; indeed, 10 can function in any of the three areas, 30 can function in sales and administration, 20 can function in sales and research, and 15 can function in administration and research. There are twice as many people in sales as in research and the same number in sales and in administration.
    (*a*) How many can function in exactly one area?
    (*b*) How many of these employees can function in sales?
    (*c*) How many can function only in sales?
    (There really is enough information to answer these questions.)
31. Data, including geographic location, city size, and marital status, on 200 recent graduates of Gigantic State University are collected by the Alumni Association. The results are as follows:

    108 live in the west.
    86 live in a large city.
    68 are married.
    41 live in the west in a large city.
    23 are married and live in a large city.
    19 are married and live in the west.
    12 are married and live in a large city in the west.

    How many are unmarried, do not live in a large city, and do not live in the west?

32. The Transportation and Parking Committee at Gigantic State University collects data from 100 students on how they commute to campus. The following data are obtained:

    8 drive a car at least part of the time.
    20 use the bus at least part of the time.
    48 ride a bicycle at least part of the time.
    38 do none of these.
    No student who ever drives a car also uses the bus.

    How many students who ride a bicycle also drive a car or use the bus?
33. The 2500 students at My Online Mathematics (MOM) may take at most two mathematics courses. Available courses are Algebra, Big Numbers, and Common Fractions. Recent enrollment numbers show that 400 students opted to take no math classes, 600 chose Algebra, 1100 chose Big Numbers, 200 chose Algebra and Big Numbers, 300 chose Algebra and Common Fractions, and 500 chose Big Numbers and Common Fractions. What is the maximum possible number who chose to take Common Fractions?
34. A recent survey of 30 college students found 18 had not declared their major and 19 were living off campus. If 5 students in the survey had declared their major and lived on campus, how many had declared their major and lived off campus?
35. A recent study of 20 mall shoppers found 14 owned a smartphone, 11 owned a tablet, and 9 owned a laptop. Interestingly, none of those surveyed owned only a tablet and a laptop and all of those surveyed owned at least one of the three types of device. If two people of those surveyed owned only a tablet, how many owned only a laptop?

1.4 SETS OF OUTCOMES AND TREES

Certain types of sets are of special interest in the study of probability. The elements of these sets represent outcomes of experiments. The term "experiment" is used here in a much more general sense than in the physical sciences. We refer to activities such as flipping coins, rolling dice, drawing cards, interviewing people, and testing things as examples of experiments. Outcomes describe the consequences of an experiment. For instance, in an experiment consisting of flipping an ordinary coin once and noting which side lands on top, the outcome is either a head or a tail; the set of outcomes is $S = \{\text{head, tail}\}$. It is helpful to introduce the terminology here but to defer a more detailed discussion of the concepts to Chapter 2.

A *sample space* is a set consisting of all possible outcomes of an experiment.

Example 1.18 An experiment consists of making two telephone calls, one after the other, and noting in order whether each is completed, i.e., whether someone answers the phone.

Problem Describe the set of outcomes of this experiment, and form a sample space.

Solution Either each call is completed, or it is not. We use C to denote the result of a call which is connected and N to denote the result that it is not connected. The result of making two calls in succession is a pair of letters, the results of the two calls in order. For instance, CN denotes the outcome that the first call is completed and the second is not. With this notation the possible outcomes of the two calls are the pairs CC, CN, NC, and NN. It is important to note that the outcome CN (the first call is completed but the second is not) is different from the outcome NC (the first call is not completed but the second is). The set of outcomes of the experiment can be represented by S:

$$S = \{CC, CN, NC, NN\}$$

■

Notice that each outcome of the experiment of Example 1.18 is an ordered pair, and we could have described the sample space as a cartesian product. However, in many cases it is not possible to describe the set of outcomes of an experiment as a cartesian product, and it is useful to have an approach which is applicable to all experiments.

Since the sample space is a set of outcomes of an experiment, the nature of the elements in the sample space depends on exactly how the experiment is conducted and how the outcomes are described. For instance, when we made the telephone calls of Example 1.18, suppose that we were interested only in the number of completed calls. In this case the sample space could be represented by the set

$$T = \{0, 1, 2\}$$

Here the outcome corresponding to both calls being completed is denoted by 2, the outcome of exactly one call being completed is denoted by 1, and the outcome of neither call being completed is denoted by 0. Not only are the sets S and T different, but even $n(S) \neq n(T)$. That is, the two sample spaces do not even have the same number of elements.

Example 1.19 An experiment consists of flipping a coin 3 times and recording the result of each flip (head or tail) in order.

Problem Describe the outcomes of this experiment, and form a sample space.

Solution Each time the coin is flipped, it comes up either heads (denoted H) or tails (denoted T). The experiment consists of *three* flips of the coin, so an outcome must tell what happened on each flip. If all three flips result in heads, it is natural to denote the outcome by HHH. Similarly, if the first two flips

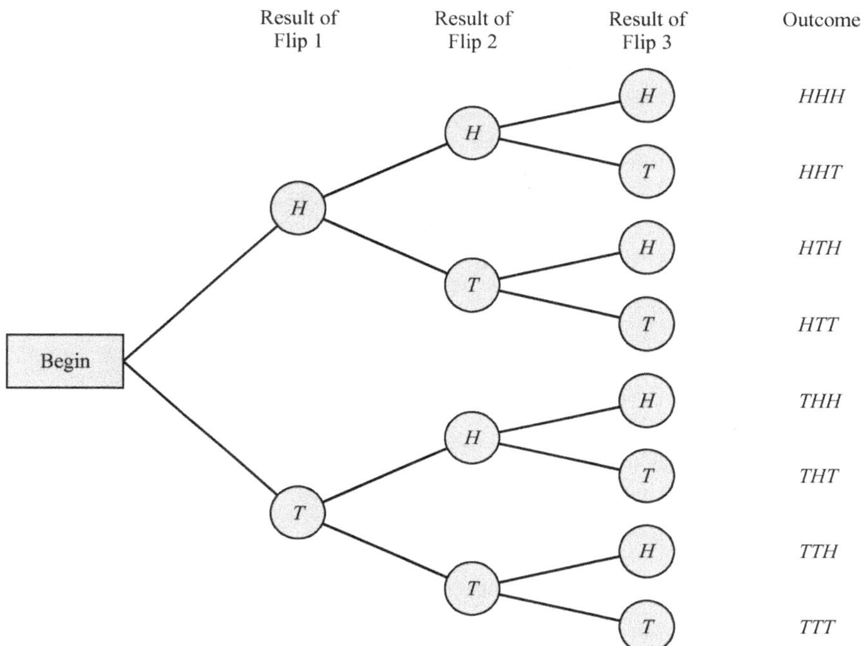

FIGURE 1.15

result in heads and the third flip results in a tail, then we denote the outcome by *HHT*. In this way we can represent any outcome as a sequence of three letters, each letter an H or a T. We must take care, however, that in listing the outcomes we do not omit any of them or include any one outcome more than once. One way to construct a list which includes each outcome exactly once is to use a diagram to represent the result of each flip as it occurs. The diagram shown in Figure 1.15 provides a systematic way of identifying all the possible outcomes of the experiment. We see that the sample space is

$$S = \{HHH, HHT, HTH, HTT, THH, THT, TTH, TTT\}$$ ■

Diagrams such as the one in Figure 1.15 are called *tree diagrams*. They are very useful in representing the outcomes of experiments which take place in steps or stages. In a tree diagram, the results of each stage are represented by using the forks and branches of the tree. Each path through the tree (from left to right in our diagrams) represents the results of all stages of the experiment and therefore is one outcome of the experiment. For example, the diagram in Figure 1.16 represents an experiment with two stages. At the first stage there are two possible results, marked a and b. If result a occurs, then there are three possible results for the second stage, marked R, W, and G. If b occurs at the first stage, then there are two possible results for the second stage, marked R

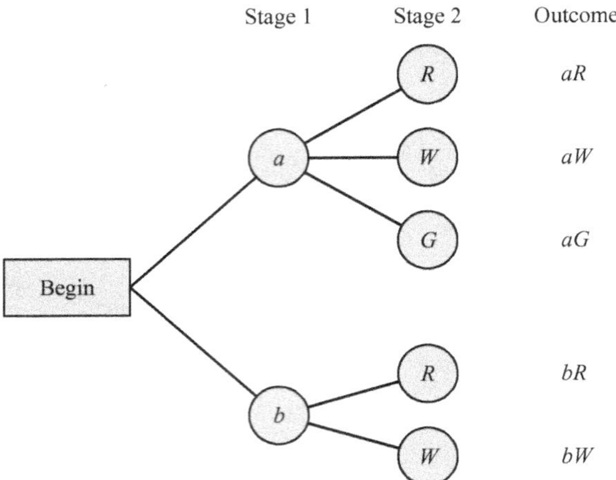

FIGURE 1.16

and W. It is clear from Figure 1.16 that the experiment has five outcomes. The sample space for the experiment is

$$S = \{aR, aW, aG, bR, bW\}$$

In the experiment with the tree diagram in Figure 1.16, a typical outcome such as aR could have been denoted by (a, R) or by a-R or in any of a number of other ways. Thus the sample space for the experiment could have been denoted by

$$S = \{(a, R), (a, W), (a, G), (b, R), (b, W)\}$$

This representation of S and the one given just above differ only in notation. This will always be the case for us. That is, experiments will be defined in such a way that the outcomes are specified and therefore the sample space is determined except possibly for notation. This is the justification of our use of the phrase ''the sample space'' rather than ''a sample space.''

Example 1.20 A two-stage experiment consists of first selecting a bowl from the two shown in Figure 1.17 and noting its label (a or b) and then selecting a ball from that bowl and noting its color (R is red, W is white, and G is green).

Problem Describe the outcomes of this experiment, and find the sample space.

Solution The experiment has two stages: Select a bowl; then select a ball. Consequently, each outcome must include the result of stage 1 (the bowl)

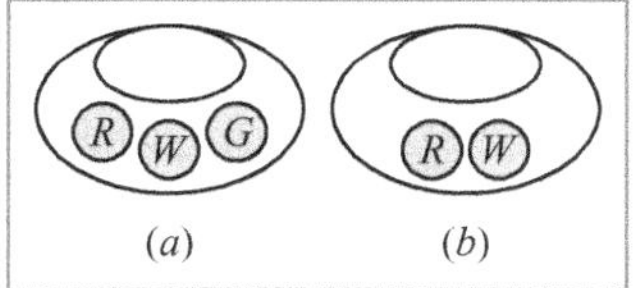

FIGURE 1.17

and the result of stage 2 (the color of the ball). Clearly, the tree diagram of Figure 1.16 depicts the experiment, and therefore the sample space is

$$S = \{aR, aW, aG, bR, bW\}$$

■

Example 1.21 A manufacturer produces smartphones, and each phone can be classified as either acceptable or defective. An experiment consists of checking phones one after another until either a defective phone has been found or three phones have been checked. Once a phone has been checked, it is set aside and not checked again.

Problem Draw a tree diagram to represent the experiment, and find the sample space.

Solution The first phone checked is either acceptable or defective. If it is defective, the testing process ends. If it is acceptable, then a second phone is checked and the process is repeated. Since at most three phones are to be checked, the tree diagram is as shown in Figure 1.18. Given the notation that A represents the result that an acceptable phone is selected and D represents the selection of a defective phone, the sample space for the experiment is

$$S = \{D, AD, AAD, AAA\}$$

■

Many of the problems which we shall meet in our study of probability do not require us to obtain the sample space S of an experiment. Instead they require only the *number* of outcomes $n(S)$. Of course, one way of determining the number of outcomes is to specify the sample space by a list and then count the elements in the list. However, for certain experiments there is a simple formula which can be used to obtain $n(S)$ without obtaining S. These experiments have a symmetric tree diagram. The next three examples illustrate that type of experiment and the formula.

Example 1.22 The local delicatessen has three types of meat—beef (B), ham (H), and turkey (T)—and two types of bread—light (L) and dark (D). An experiment consists of selecting a type of meat and then a type of bread.

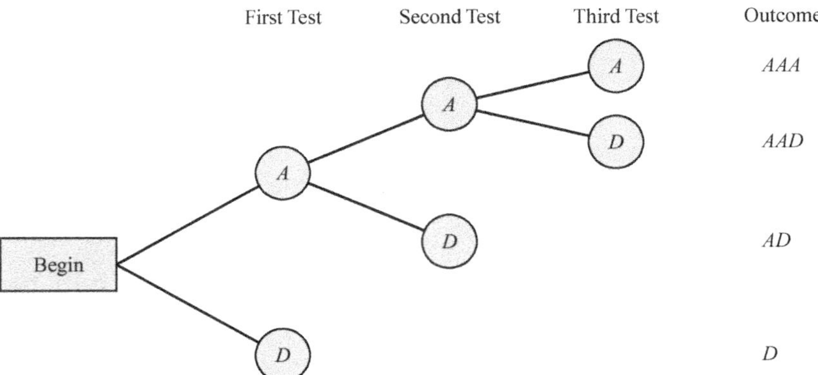

FIGURE 1.18

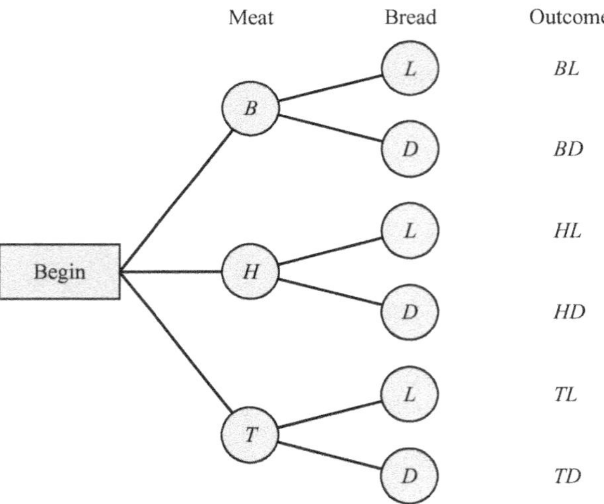

FIGURE 1.19

Problem Draw a tree diagram for this experiment, and find the sample space.

Solution The tree diagram is shown in Figure 1.19. The sample space is

$$S = \{BL, BD, HL, HD, TL, TD\}$$

■

It is useful to analyze this example in greater detail. Note that the tree diagram has the property that at the second stage (selecting bread) the number of results (2) is independent of the result at the first stage. That is, if the meat selected is beef, then there are 2 possible results for the second stage, and the same result holds if the meat is ham or turkey. Since there are 3 possible results at the first stage (B, H, T), and since for each of the results at the first stage there are 2 possible results at the second stage (L and D), it follows that there are $3 \times 2 = 6$ possible outcomes for the experiment: $n(S) = 6$.

Example 1.22 is a simple one in that the tree is easy to draw and it is clear that there are 6 possible outcomes for the experiment. The example could be made more complicated by increasing the number of possible results at each stage. However, if the structure of the experiment remains the same, it is still a simple matter to determine the number of possible outcomes of the experiment without drawing the tree diagram. For instance, suppose that at the first stage of a two-stage experiment any of 6 possible results can occur. Also, suppose that at the second stage there are 4 possible results for each of the results of the first stage. Then the associated tree diagram would have 6 branches at the first stage and each of these 6 branches would split into 4 branches at the second stage (see Figure 1.20). The complete tree diagram represents $6 \times 4 = 24$ outcomes for the experiment.

In the general case of a two-stage experiment like that of Example 1.22, suppose that the first stage has n_1 results and the second stage has n_2 results (for each of the results at the first stage). Then the experiment has $n_1 \times n_2$ possible outcomes, which is the number of elements in the cartesian product of the sets of results for the first and second stages. Indeed, an outcome of a multistage experiment of this type is an ordered set of results of the component stages, i.e., an element of the cartesian product of the sets of results of the individual stages. Counting the number of outcomes is the same as counting the number of elements in a cartesian product. The general result can be formulated as the following principle.

FIGURE 1.20

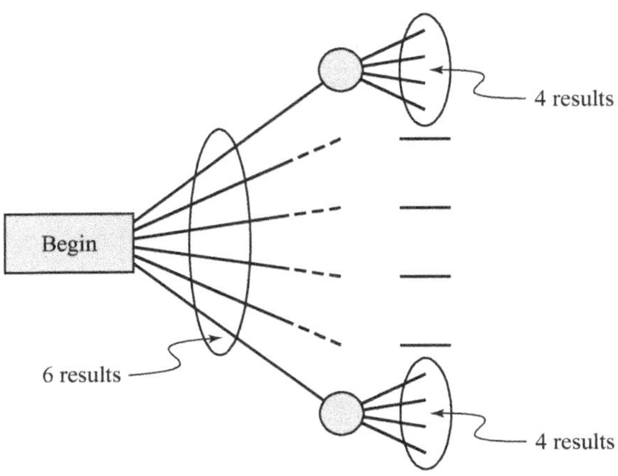

Multiplication Principle

Consider a multistage experiment consisting of k stages. Suppose that the first stage has n_1 possible results, the second stage has n_2 possible results regardless of the result of stage 1, the third stage has n_3 results regardless of the results of the first two stages, ..., and the kth stage has n_k results regardless of the results of the earlier stages. Then there are

$$n_1 \times n_2 \times n_3 \times \cdots \times n_k$$

elements in the sample space of the experiment.

Example 1.23 An experiment consists of flipping a coin twice, noting which face comes up each time, and then drawing a card from an ordinary deck and noting its suit.

Problem Find the number of elements in the sample space of this experiment.

Solution This experiment has three stages: flip a coin, flip a coin again, draw a card. The first stage has two results, so $n_1 = 2$. Likewise, $n_2 = 2$. There are four suits in an ordinary deck (spades, hearts, diamonds, and clubs), so $n_3 = 4$. It follows from the multiplication principle that there are $2 \times 2 \times 4 = 16$ elements in the sample space. ■

Example 1.24 A doctor and a pharmaceutical manufacturer plan to test a new pain-relieving drug. The tests can be performed on either men or women, on people in any of four age groups, and in any of five geographical areas.

Problem Find the number of plans for the test from which the doctor must choose.

Solution A plan for the test, i.e., a choice of women or men, an age group, and a geographical location, is equivalent to a path in the tree diagram of the experiment. The multiplication principle can be applied in this case, and we conclude that there are $2 \times 4 \times 5 = 40$ outcomes and, consequently, 40 paths in the tree diagram. The doctor must choose among 40 plans. ■

Example 1.25 A state has used all the license plate numbers available under the current plate design, and alternatives are being considered. One of the proposed designs consists of a number from 1 through 99 followed by three letters selected from the standard alphabet with I and O removed (to avoid confusion with the integers 1 and 0). Thus, there are 24 choices for each letter.

Problem (*a*) How many different plates are available with the proposed design?

(*b*) How many plates do not include the letter Q?

(*c*) How many plates are there in which the first of the 3 letters is not a Q?

Solution (*a*) The proposed design is a number followed by 3 letters. The number is to be selected from the integers 1 through 99, for 99 choices. Each letter is to be selected from among the 26 letters with I and O removed, for 24 choices. Thus, by the multiplication principle, there are $99 \times 24 \times 24 \times 24 = 1{,}368{,}576$ different plates available under the proposed design.

(*b*) If the plate does not contain the letter Q, then there are only 23 possible choices for each of the letters, and there are $99 \times 23 \times 23 \times 23 = 1{,}204{,}533$ different plates available.

(*c*) If the first of the three letters is not a Q, then there are 23 choices for that letter. There are 24 choices for each of the other two letters. Therefore, there are $99 \times 23 \times 24 \times 24 = 1{,}311{,}552$ different plates available in which the first letter is not a Q. ■

Exercises for Section 1.4

Note: The result of rolling a die is the number of dots on the side which lands facing up.

1. An experiment consists of flipping a coin three times and noting the result, head (H) or tail (T), after each flip. Find the sample space of this experiment.
2. A multiple-choice test has 10 questions, and there are 5 choices for the answer to each question. An answer sheet has 1 answer for each question.
   (*a*) How many different answer sheets are possible?
   (*b*) How many different answer sheets are possible if the same answer is not used for every question?
3. There are 8 different wall paper patterns for your computer screen, 5 different colors for each pattern, and 3 choices of cursor symbol. An experiment consists of a choice of wallpaper pattern, color, and cursor symbol. How many outcomes for this experiment?
4. A cooler contains 2 cans of diet cola and 4 cans of regular cola. An experiment consists of selecting cans one after another without replacement, and noting the type at each selection, until two consecutive cans of the same type of cola or a total of four cans are selected. Find the number of elements in the sample space.
5. An experiment consists of flipping a coin four times and noting the number of times a head occurs. Find the sample space of this experiment.
6. An experiment consists of rolling a die twice and noting the sum of the results.
   (*a*) Find the sample space of the experiment.
   (*b*) How many elements in this sample space are odd numbers?
7. An experiment consists of rolling a die twice, each time recording a 0 if the result is an odd number and the number if the result is an even number. Describe the outcomes of this experiment, and find the sample space.

8. Let $X = \{A, B, C\}$ and $Y = \{1, 2, 3, 4, 5\}$. A product code consists of 2 different symbols selected from set X followed by 2 not necessarily distinct symbols selected from the set Y. How many different product codes are there?
9. A wildlife biologist plans an experiment to determine the effect of a growth inhibitor on freshwater algae. There are 3 different ways in which the tests can be performed; the biologist can choose any one of 4 different lakes, and the tests can be performed during any single month from March through September, inclusive. Find the number of plans for the experiment from which the biologist must choose.
10. A box contains 1 red, 2 green, and 3 black balls. An experiment consists of selecting balls, one after another without replacement, and noting the color of each ball selected, until *either* a red ball *or* both green and black balls have been selected. How many outcomes in the sample space of this experiment?
11. A shipper has 3 routes from New York to Chicago, 4 routes from Chicago to Denver, and 3 routes from Denver to Los Angeles. In how many ways can merchandise be shipped from New York to Los Angeles by using these routes?
12. Consider the following experiment. A coin is tossed repeatedly, and the result (H or T) of each toss is recorded. The experiment stops if there are two consecutive tosses with the same result (examples: TT, THH) or if the coin is tossed three times (example: THT). How many possible outcomes are there for this experiment?
13. A sales representative makes 5 calls to potential customers. Each call has 3 possible results: She reaches the customer in person, the phone is answered by someone other than the customer and she leaves a message, and the phone is unanswered. A phone record is a list of the results of each call. How many possible phone records are there?
14. An experiment consists of flipping a coin and noting whether the result is a head or a tail. If it is heads, then the coin is flipped three more times and the number of heads in these three flips is noted. If the result of the first flip is a tail, then the coin is flipped one more time and the result is noted.
    (*a*) How many outcomes in the sample space of this experiment?
    (*b*) How many elements in the sample space include at least one toss which resulted in a head?
15. Of 4 rats in a cage in a psychology laboratory, 3 are untrained and 1 is trained. A rat is removed form the cage, and it is noted whether or not it is trained, and then it is put into another cage. Two more rats are removed and treated in the same way. Draw a tree diagram for this experiment, and find the sample space.
16. An experiment consists of flipping a coin and noting whether the result is a head or a tail. If it is heads, then the coin is flipped three more times and the number of heads in these three flips is noted. If the result of the first flip is tails, then the coin is flipped once more and the result (H or T) is noted. How many outcomes in the sample space of this experiment?
17. A product code is formed from the symbols Q, R, T, V, and Z. The code consists of four symbols arranged one after another, for example, QQRT.
    (*a*) How many different product codes are there?
    (*b*) How many different product codes do not contain Z?
    (*c*) How many different product codes contain exactly one T?

18. There are direct flights from Indianapolis to Denver, flights which stop at St. Louis, and flights with a stop at Kansas City. Each of these 3 types of flights can be taken either during the day or at night.
    (*a*) An experiment consists of selecting a type of flight and then a time. Draw the tree diagram for this experiment.
    (*b*) Another experiment consists of selecting a time and then the type of flight. Draw the tree diagram for this experiment.
19. In the situation describe in Exercise 18, suppose that the only flights which stop at St. Louis are night flights. Repeat parts (*a*) and (*b*) of Exercise 18 in this situation.
20. There are two boxes marked A and B on a shelf. Box A contains 2 red balls and 1 green ball. Box B contains 1 green ball and one blue ball. A ball is randomly selected from Box A, its color is noted, and it is placed in Box B. Then a ball is randomly selected from Box B and its color is noted. How many outcomes are in the sample space for this experiment?
21. Let $X = \{1, 2, 5, 6, 9\}$ and $Y = \{A, B, C, D, E\}$. A product code is formed in the following manner: First, two distinct numbers are selected from X at random, in order, and they are used to form a two-digit number. For example, if 2 is selected first and then 9, the two-digit number is 29. If the number is larger than 30, then three not necessarily distinct letters are chosen from Y. If the number is smaller than 30, then four distinct letters are chosen from Y. How many codes are possible?
22. A game is such that the player involved can either win (W), lose (L), or draw (D). An experiment consists of a player continuing to play the game repeatedly and recording the result (W, L, D) of each play. The game ends when he wins, when he loses 2 consecutive plays, when 2 consecutive plays result in draws, or when there has been a total of 4 plays. How many outcomes are possible for this experiment?
23. Suppose you are considering the purchase of a new car, and you are interested in 2 models each of which has 3 different option packages available. For each model, you can purchase none, any, or all of the option packages. How many alternatives are there for you to consider?
24. A student is planning a ski trip. He can go to Colorado or New England. There are 3 possible ski areas for Colorado and 2 times that he can go to each ski area. There are 4 ski areas in New England and 2 times for 2 of the areas but only 1 time for the other 2 areas. A plan involves a location, a ski area, and a time. How many possible plans are there?
25. A box contains three white balls and three blue balls. An experiment consists of selecting a ball at random, noting its color and replacing it. If it is white, then two additional balls are selected, one after another without replacement, and the color of each is noted. If the first ball is blue, then two additional balls are selected simultaneously and the number of white balls is noted. Find the number of outcomes in the sample space of this experiment.
26. A box contains 1 red, 1 white, and 2 green balls. An experiment consists of drawing balls in succession without replacement and noting the color of each until a red ball is drawn.
    (*a*) Draw a tree diagram for this experiment.
    (*b*) How many outcomes in the sample space?

27. A telephone sales representative makes a sale, gets a tentative commitment, or fails to make a sale on each call. Today she plans to make telephone calls, one after another, until she makes 3 sales, gets 2 tentative commitments, or fails to make a sale. Her log for the day consists of a list of the calls, with sale, tentative commitment, or no sale noted for each. How many possible logs are there?
28. Suppose that you have \$50 to spend on meals and that a meal in an expensive restaurant costs \$20 and a meal at a moderately priced restaurant costs \$10. An experiment consists of deciding on a sequence of meals (expensive or moderate) whose total cost is exactly \$50. Draw a tree diagram for this experiment, and find the sample space.
29. An experiment consists of flipping a coin and noting whether the result is a head or a tail. If it is a head, then the coin is flipped three more times and the number of heads is noted. If the result of the first flip is a tail, then the coin is flipped once more and the result, head or tail, is noted. How many outcomes are there in the sample space of this experiment?
30. A sociologist can conduct a study in a rural area or in a suburb. If it is conducted in a rural area, it can be done by mail or by telephone, and either a short or a long questionnaire can be used. If it is conducted in a suburb, then it can be done by mail, telephone, or personal interview, and either a short or a long questionnaire can be used. How many different plans for a study are there?
31. A security entry lock consists of a keyboard with the numbers 1 through 9. An "entry code" consists of three single numbers to be punched in order, or two single numbers followed by one pair of numbers (a pair is two different numbers), the pair to be pushed simultaneously. How many different entry codes are there?
32. A box contains 3 green balls, 1 white ball, and 2 blue balls. An experiment consists of selecting three balls, one after another without replacement, and noting the color of each ball selected.
    (*a*) Find the number of outcomes in the sample space of this experiment.
    (*b*) How many outcomes exist if the balls are placed back in the box after being selected?
33. An experiment consists of flipping an unfair coin four times and noting the number of heads that come up. If at least 3 heads come up, the experiment ends. If at most 2 heads come up, the coin is flipped another 2 times, and after each flip, the resulting heads or tails is noted. How many outcomes are possible for this experiment?
34. An experiment consists of rolling a fair die 5 times and noting how many times an even number is rolled. If there are at least 2 even numbers, a fair coin is flipped once, and the resulting heads or tails is noted. If there are less than 2 even numbers, the coin is flipped 5 times, and the number of tails that come up is noted. How many outcomes are possible for this experiment?
35. Two grandparents take their three grandchildren to ride on a Ferris wheel. The ride operator tells them that for safety purposes he must record the arrangement of the people on the ride (each bench seat on the ride has room for exactly 5 people). How many ways can they be arranged if a grandparent sits on one end of the bench and a grandchild sits on the other end?

IMPORTANT TERMS AND CONCEPTS

You should be able to describe, define, or give examples and use each of the following:

Set
Element
Subset
Set equality
Intersection
Union
Empty set
Disjoint sets
Partition
Partition principle
Universal set
Complement
Cartesian product
Venn diagram
Number of elements in a set
Experiment
Sample space
Tree diagram
Multiplication principle

REVIEW EXERCISES

1. Let $A = \{1, 2, 3, u, v, x, z\}$, $B = \{2, 4, x, y\}$, and $C = \{2, 3, x, z\}$.
   (*a*) Find $A \cap B$ (*b*) Find $A \cup B$ (*c*) Find $(A \cap B) \cup C$
2. The sets A and B are subsets of a universal set U. Which of the following relations is always true?
   (*a*) $A' \cap B' \subset (A \cap B)'$ (*b*) $B \cap A \subset B$
   (*c*) $(A \cup B) \subset A' \cap B'$ (*d*) $A \cup B \subset A \cap B$
3. Let $A = \{k, m, p, s, y\}$, $B = \{j, n, p, r, s\}$, and $C = \{g, m, r, w\}$.
   (*a*) Find $A \cap (B \cup C)$. (*b*) Find $A \cup (B \cap C)$.
4. Let $U = \{a, b, c, d, e, f\}$, $A = \{a, d, e\}$, $B = \{b, d\}$.
   (*a*) Find $n(A \cup B')$.
   (*b*) Find $n((A \cup B') \times B)$.
5. Let $A = \{1, x, y\}$ and $B = \{1, y, z\}$. Find $(A \times B) \cap (B \times A)$.
6. Let A, B, and C be subsets of U. Use Venn diagrams to illustrate the following sets.
   (*a*) $A' \cup B$ (*b*) $B' \cap C$ (*c*) $(A \cup B') \cap C$
7. Let F, G, and H be sets, and suppose $n(F \times G) = 60$, $n(G \times H) = 20$, and $n(F \times H) = 48$. Find $n(F \times G \times H)$.
8. Suppose A and B are subsets of U, $n(U) = 60$, $n(A' \cap B') = 12$, and $n(A' \cap B) = n(A \cap B') = 17$.
   (*a*) Find $n(A \cap B)$. (*b*) Find $n(A \cup B)$. (*c*) Find $n(A' \cup B')$.
9. In a group of 75 students, 43 said they enjoyed tennis and 24 said they enjoyed swimming but not tennis. Which of the following can be determined:
   (*a*) The number of students who enjoy both sports
   (*b*) The number of students who enjoy neither sport

10. Let A, B, and C be subsets of a universal set U with A and B disjoint, $n(U) = 100$, $n(A) = 30$, $n(B) = 44$, $n(A \cup B \cup C) = 86$. Find the number of elements in $(A \cup B)' \cap C$.
11. The staff at the Metroburg Zoo asked visitors to complete a survey concerning visits to the Primate House and the Elephant House. The results were 246 of the visitors went to the Primate House, 271 visited the Elephant House, and 185 went to both. How many of those people visited only one of the two?
12. Suppose A and B are subsets of U with $n(A') = 23$, $n(B') = 16$, $n(A \cup B) = 18$, and $n((A \cap B) \cup (A \cup B)') = 24$.
    (*a*) Find $n(A \cap B)$. (*b*) Find $n(A' \cap B')$.
13. One hundred first-year students are asked about their music preferences. Their preferences are as follows: 65 like rock, 35 like country, and 10 like both rock and country. How many like rock but not country music?
14. Consider the following data concerning 160 English majors:

    76 take French.
    85 take German.
    33 take French and German.
    35 take German and Farsi.
    32 take French as their only foreign language.
    15 take French, Farsi, and German.

    Every student takes at least one foreign language.
    (*a*) How many take Farsi?
    (*b*) How many take French and Farsi but not German?
15. Each of 300 students was asked to identify exactly 2 of the following 3 areas as concerns about the campus computer system: email, printing, and reliability. Student responses were:

    176 identified email, 161 identified printing, and 263 identified reliability

    How many of the students identified both email and reliability?
16. A set X is partitioned into 3 subsets X_1, X_2, and X_3. Suppose that $n(X) = 80$, $n(X_2) = 3n(X_1)$, and $n(X_3) = 4n(X_2)$. Find $n(X_1)$.
17. A box contains 3 red, 1 white, and 2 green balls. An experiment consists of drawing balls in succession without replacement and noting the color of each ball selected until either a red ball or 2 green balls are drawn. Draw a tree diagram for this experiment, and list the elements in the sample space.
18. A box contains 1 red, 1 white, and 2 green balls. An experiment consists of drawing balls in succession without replacement and noting the color of each ball selected until both a red and a white ball have been selected.
    (*a*) Draw a tree diagram for this experiment, and list the elements in the sample space.
    (*b*) How many elements of the sample space do not include drawing a green ball?
19. A box contains 1 red, 1 white, and 2 green balls. An experiment consists of drawing a ball and noting its color. If it is red, it is set aside: otherwise, it is replaced. A second ball is drawn, and its color is noted. Draw a tree diagram for this experiment, and list the elements in the sample space.

20. The menu at a restaurant includes 5 appetizers, 4 salads, 6 main courses—one of which is steak, and 3 deserts.
    (*a*) If a meal consists of an appetizer, a salad, a main course, and a desert, how many different meals are there?
    (*b*) How many of the meals defined in a (*a*) include steak as the main course?
    (*c*) If a meal consists of an appetizer or a salad but not both, a main course, and a desert, how many different meals are there?
21. A product code is to be formed with three distinct letters from the set $\{B, H, K, Q, T, V, Z\}$. How many different product codes are there? (*Note*: BHK is a different product code than KBH.)
22. A product code consists of a string of 4 different letters selected from the set $\{A, H, Q, T, Z\}$. How many such codes contain the letter H?
23. Tina, Debbie, and Harriet decide to order a pizza. Tina is to select the crust—thin, thick, or deep dish; Debbie picks the size—small, medium, large, or jumbo; and Harriet picks one topping—sausage, pepperoni, green pepper, mushrooms, or black olives. How many different pizzas could be ordered?
24. How many different numbers between 10 and 900 can be formed with the digits in the set $\{1, 2, 3, 4, 6, 8, 9\}$ if no digit is repeated in any number? How many such numbers can be formed if digits can be repeated?
25. A utility company must lay lines from the point labeled A to the point labeled B on the map shown in Figure 1.21. The company is constrained to lay lines only in streets (shown by line segments), and it is interested in keeping its lines as short as possible. How many paths must be considered if all blocks are the same length? (*Hint*: Label all vertices and use a tree diagram.)

FIGURE 1.21

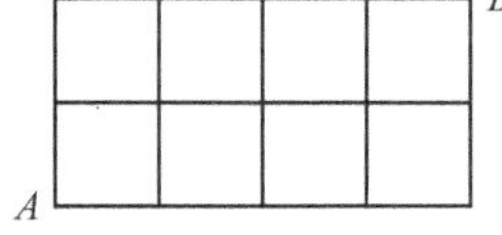

26. Alice's Restaurant is well known for its menu variety. She has 10 types of salad, 24 types of entrée, and 16 types of drink. With every entrée ordered, you receive (free of charge) either one of her 8 desserts or one of her 12 specialty cocktails. A well-rounded meal consists of a salad, entrée, drink, and choice of either a dessert or specialty cocktail. How many well-rounded meals are possible at Alice's?
27. A chair manufacturer has 4 types of upholstery, 2 types of wood, and 4 designs to choose from. If 2 of the designs allow any choice of upholstery and wood and the other 2 designs allow only a choice of upholstery, how many different chairs can he make? (*Hint*: Use a tree diagram in which the first choice is the design.)
28. Sarah is planning a Spring break at the beach, and she is considering possibilities in Florida and Mexico. She is interested in 4 locations in Florida and there are 4 airlines that provide service to each of them. She is interested in 2 locations in Mexico, and there are 3 airlines serving each. A plan for Spring break is a location and an airline. How many plans are there?
29. A part-time secretary works 20 hours each week typing reports and market surveys. A report requires 5 hours of typing; a market survey requires 10 hours. Use a tree diagram to find the ways in which the work for a week can be organized so that exactly 20 hours are used and there is no partly completed job at the end of the week.
30. A publisher produces oversized, normal-size, and pocket-size books that are in hardcover and/or paperback form. Oversized books are produced only in hardcover, pocket books are produced only in paperback, and normal-size books are produced in both hardcover and paperback. Hardcover books come in both

standard and deluxe editions. An experiment consists of noting the size of a book, the type of cover, and (if applicable) whether it is a standard or deluxe edition. Draw a tree diagram for this experiment.

31. Let A, B, and C be subsets of a universal set U with $A \cup B \cup C = U$, $A \subset C'$, $B \subset C'$, $n(U) = 85$, $n(C) = 55$, $n(A) = 21$, and $n(B) = 15$. Find $n(A \cap B)$.
32. A product carries an identification number which consists of a letter, a single-digit number, and a four-digit number, for example, B-3-1018. The letter corresponds to the inspector, the single-digit number to the place of manufacture, and the four-digit number to the date (month and day) of manufacture. If there are 8 plants with 15 inspectors for each plant and if each month has 20 working days, how many possible identification numbers are there?
33. Suppose that you have \$50 to spend on meals and that a meal in an expensive restaurant costs \$15 and a meal at a moderately priced restaurant costs \$10. An experiment consists of deciding on a sequence of meals (expensive or moderate) whose total cost is exactly \$50. Draw a tree diagram for this experiment, and find the sample space.
34. An engine inspector at an auto plant must inspect engines each hour in the following way: Each engine produced after the start of the hour is checked until either 5 good engines are found or 2 bad engines are found, whichever occurs first. View this inspection process as an experiment in which each outcome is a list (in order) of the engines tested with each engine labeled good or bad. How many elements are there in this sample space?
35. Let U be the set of integers 1 through 20. Find the largest subset X of U for which the sets X_1 and X_2 form a partition of X where

$$X_1 = \{n : n \in U \text{ and } n \text{ is a multiple of } 2\}$$
$$X_2 = \{n : n \in U \text{ and } n \text{ is a multiple of } 3\}$$

36. A market analyst for Cleanup Inc. is planning the next market survey. Products which have been recommended by management for survey are laundry soap, bleach, shampoo, and toothpaste. A survey can be conducted in New England, the Gulf states, or the west coast. Each survey can be conducted by mail or in the supermarkets, and either a short or a long form can be used. Suppose that a survey consists of a set of products (one or more), an area, a method, and a form. Determine the number of possible surveys.
37. One quarter, two dimes, one nickel and one penny are in a change purse. Coins are drawn one after another without replacement and both the value of the coin and the order in which it is selected are noted. Coins are selected until the sum of the selected coins is at least 10 cents.
    (*a*) How many outcomes are in the sample space for this experiment?
    (*b*) If the coins are drawn until the sum exceeds 20 cents, how many outcomes are in the sample space?

CHAPTER 2

Probabilities, Counting, and Equally Likely Outcomes

2.0 THE SETTING AND OVERVIEW

Each of us encounters situations involving uncertainty in our classes, in the workplace, and in everyday life. In this chapter we begin a study of probability—a mathematical tool which helps us understand and deal with uncertainty. Our study uses concepts from set theory and develops the idea of the probability of an event (a set of outcomes). To compute probabilities (numbers assigned to events), it is frequently necessary to count the number of elements in a set. Accordingly, we develop tools (counting principles) to help us count in situations where straightforward enumeration is inefficient. In some cases, we will be able to count the elements in a set by directly applying one of our tools; in other cases, two or more tools must be used together. We conclude the chapter by using these counting tools to compute probabilities in some special situations.

2.1 PROBABILITIES, EVENTS, AND EQUALLY LIKELY OUTCOMES

Probabilities are numbers assigned to sets of outcomes of an experiment; the probability of a set of outcomes represents the likelihood that one of the outcomes in the set will occur on a performance of the experiment. Probabilities arise in various ways. In some situations an experiment can be repeated any number of times under essentially identical conditions. In such circumstances an estimate of the probability (the likelihood) of the occurrence of a specific outcome of the experiment is given by the ratio of the number of times that outcome occurs to the number of times the experiment is repeated. That is, if a specific outcome occurs 62 times in 100 repetitions of an experiment, then the ratio 62/100 provides an estimate of the probability of that outcome. We call this method of assigning probabilities to outcomes the *relative frequency method.* Of course, a different number of repetitions or even the same number of repetitions another time may yield a different estimate of the probability. Assessing the relationship between different estimates and the number assigned as the probability of an outcome requires a deeper study of statistics than is possible in this book. Accordingly, if probabilities are assigned according to the relative frequency method, only one estimate will be given.

In many situations it is not practical to repeat an experiment hundreds of times, and the relative frequency method cannot be used. For some of these situations we will be able to use a method which is based on properties of the experiment. For instance, an ordinary coin has two faces which have different designs but are otherwise identical. It is reasonable to assume that if the coin is flipped hundreds (or thousands) of times, each face will come up about the same number of times. Likewise, it is reasonable to assume that if the coin is flipped only once, then it is just as likely to come up heads as to come up tails. Therefore, if we wish to assign probabilities to reflect these likelihoods, then we must assign the same probability to heads as to tails. Since there are two possible outcomes and we expect each to occur one-half of the time, we assign probability $\frac{1}{2}$ to each outcome. Similarly, if we have three balls colored blue, green, and red and otherwise identical and if a blindfolded person selects one ball arbitrarily, then it is reasonable to assume that each ball will be selected one-third of the time. We assign probability $\frac{1}{3}$ to the selection of the blue ball, $\frac{1}{3}$ to the selection of the green ball, and $\frac{1}{3}$ to the selection of the red ball to reflect this assumption. The method in which we assign probabilities by making assumptions and reasoning about the situation is called the *deductive method.*[1]

Using the deductive method, we can assign probabilities in situations not involving repeated experiments. For instance, even though a particular coin may not have been flipped repeatedly, we can assign probabilities by analyzing the situation and making assumptions. Such assumptions correspond to idealizations of real coins and may be used independently of any actual experiment. Thus in an example, we might consider a biased coin (as contrasted with a fair coin) for which the probability of a tail is $\frac{2}{3}$. This coin is an idealization of an actual coin which is somehow weighted so that if it were

[1]There is a third method of assigning probabilities to outcomes known as the *subjective*, or *measure of belief*, method. This method corresponds to the use of the term "probability" in the sentence: The probability of a flight to Mars with astronauts by the year 2030 is $\frac{1}{100}$. In this case the assigned probability is neither a sample frequency nor a probability deduced in the sense described above. Instead it is a subjective evaluation by the speaker of the likelihood that an event will take place. This is a common use of the term "probability," but we shall not pursue it in this book.

flipped many times, then tails would come up two-thirds of the time and heads one-third of the time.

The term "experiment" has been used in this book several times (see also Section 1.4), and it is time for us to make it somewhat more precise. For us, activities such as testing smartphones for defects, flipping coins and noting heads or tails, and drawing balls and noting their colors are examples of experiments. An important part of the definition of an experiment is a clear specification of the outcomes of the experiment. For example, flipping a coin 3 times in succession and noting the result (heads or tails) of each flip define a different experiment than flipping a coin 3 times and noting the number of heads. In the first, a typical outcome might be recorded as *HTH*, and in the second as 2. A *performance* of an experiment is the carrying out of the activity which defines the experiment once. Note that in the experiment of flipping a coin 3 times, a single flip of the coin is not a performance of the experiment. Each performance of an experiment gives an outcome, and the set of all possible outcomes of an experiment is the sample space of the experiment (Section 1.4).

In addition to sample spaces, we are frequently interested in subsets of sample spaces. For instance, if we flip a coin 3 times, we might be interested in outcomes which include both heads and tails.

An *event* is a subset of a sample space of an experiment.

Example 2.1 A coin is flipped 3 times in succession, and the result is noted after each flip. The sample space (determined in Example 1.19) is

$$S = \{HHH, HHT, HTH, HTT, THH, THT, TTH, TTT\}$$

Problem Find the events (*a*) all heads, (*b*) exactly 2 heads, and (*c*) at least 2 heads.

Solution (*a*) $\{HHH\}$
(*b*) $\{HHT, HTH, THH\}$
(*c*) $\{HHT, HTH, THH, HHH\}$ ■

Note that the event "at least 2 heads" can be partitioned into the subevents "exactly 2 heads" and "exactly 3 heads." Thus

$$\{HHT, HTH, THH, HHH\} = \{HHT, HTH, THH\} \cup \{HHH\}$$

Partitioning events in this way is often a useful technique for solving certain types of counting and probability problems.

Example 2.2 A Security Check for an online bank account requires the user to answer four security questions correctly to gain access to their account. The questions are asked sequentially, and if at any point in the process the user answers a total of two questions incorrectly, then the questioning process stops and the user is denied access to their account. Each time the user answers a question, their response is noted as either satisfactory (S) or not satisfactory (N).

Problem Make a tree to find the sample space of this experiment, and find the event E that exactly one question is satisfactory, as well as the event F that exactly one question is not satisfactory.

Solution A tree diagram for the situation is shown in Figure 2.1. The set listed under the column labeled "outcome" is the sample space for the

FIGURE 2.1

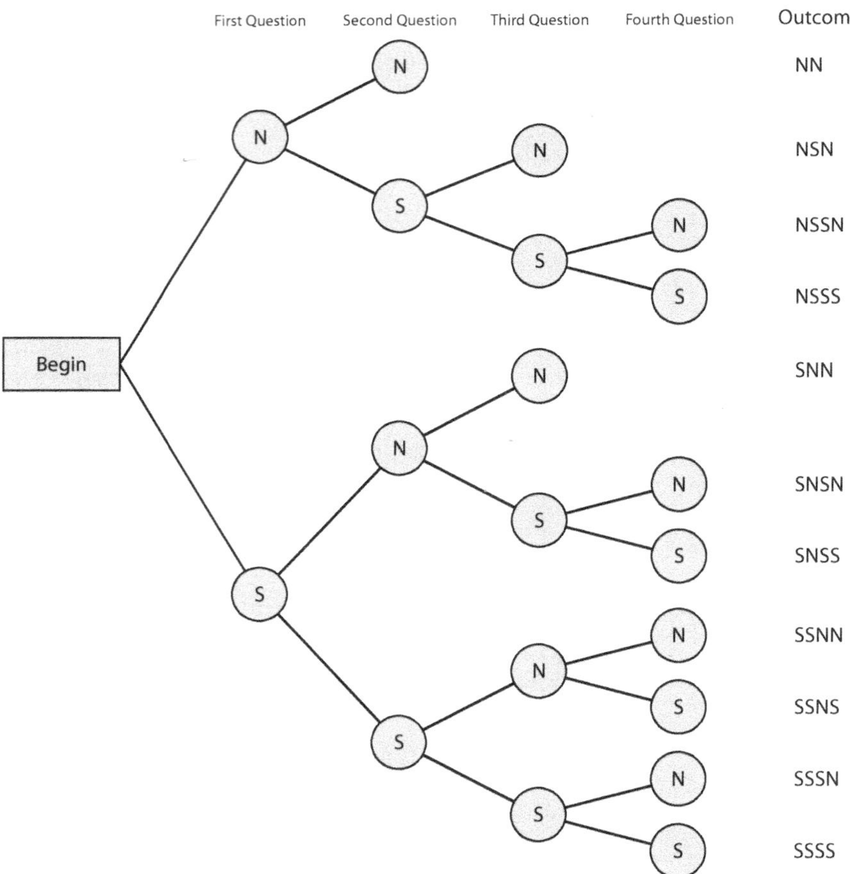

problem. Inspection of the sample space shows that events E and F are

$$E = \{NSN, SNN\}$$
$$F = \{NSSS, SNSS, SSNS, SSSN\}$$

■

Example 2.3 An experiment consists of rolling a red die and a green die and noting the result of each roll.

Problem Find the sample space of the experiment, and identify the outcomes in events E and F, where

$$E = \{\text{the red die shows a 3}\}$$
$$F = \{\text{the sum of the results for the two dice is 5}\}$$

Solution We represent an outcome by an ordered pair (m, n), where m is the number of dots on the red die and n is the number of dots on the green die. With this notation the sample space can be represented as in the array in Table 2.1. Events E and F are

$$E = \{(3, 1), (3, 2), (3, 3), (3, 4), (3, 5), (3, 6)\}$$
$$F = \{(1, 4), (2, 3), (3, 2), (4, 1)\}$$

■

TABLE 2.1

Number on Red Die	Number on Green Die					
	1	2	3	4	5	6
1	(1, 1)	(1, 2)	(1, 3)	(1, 4)	(1, 5)	(1, 6)
2	(2, 1)	(2, 2)	(2, 3)	(2, 4)	(2, 5)	(2, 6)
3	(3, 1)	(3, 2)	(3, 3)	(3, 4)	(3, 5)	(3, 6)
4	(4, 1)	(4, 2)	(4, 3)	(4, 4)	(4, 5)	(4, 6)
5	(5, 1)	(5, 2)	(5, 3)	(5, 4)	(5, 5)	(5, 6)
6	(6, 1)	(6, 2)	(6, 3)	(6, 4)	(6, 5)	(6, 6)

Our goal is to develop methods of assigning numbers to events, numbers which represent the likelihoods of the events occurring. An outcome is an event with only one element—that outcome. We begin by considering the assignment of numbers to these special events. Later, in Chapter 3, we study methods of assigning numbers to certain events in settings where we do not have numbers assigned to all outcomes.

Suppose we have an experiment with three outcomes denoted 1, 2, and 3; and in n repetitions of the experiment outcome 1 occurs n_1 times, outcome 2 occurs n_2 times, and outcome 3 occurs n_3 times. Then $n_1 + n_2 + n_3 = n$. The relative frequency of outcome 1 is n_1/n, the relative frequency of outcome 2 is n_2/n, and the relative frequency of outcome 3 is n_3/n. If we use these frequencies as measures of likelihood, then we see that each is between 0 and 1 and that the sum of the likelihoods of all outcomes is 1.

Suppose that an experiment has a sample space S with n outcomes $\mathcal{O}_1, \mathcal{O}_2, \ldots, \mathcal{O}_n$. We have an *assignment of probabilities* to these outcomes if with each outcome $\mathcal{O}_i \in S$ there is associated a number w_i such that

$$0 \le w_i \le 1 \quad \text{for } i = 1, 2, \ldots, n \tag{2.1}$$

$$w_1 + w_2 + \cdots + w_n = 1 \tag{2.2}$$

The probability of an outcome is also called the *weight* of that outcome. It is the probability associated with an outcome that we use as a measure of the likelihood of the event consisting of that outcome.

Different probability problems contain different information and ask different questions. In some cases the information provided enables us to determine the probabilities of all outcomes. This is the primary situation considered in this chapter.

Example 2.4 The equipment on a customer telephone service line records the length of incoming calls and classifies the calls according to length: a call of length less than 1 minute, 1 minute or more but less than 3 minutes, 3 minutes or more but less than 5 minutes, and 5 minutes or more. Denote the outcomes by $\mathcal{O}_1, \mathcal{O}_2, \mathcal{O}_3$, and $\mathcal{O}_4$, respectively. The choice $w_1 = \frac{1}{4}$, $w_2 = \frac{1}{4}$, $w_3 = \frac{1}{4}$, and $w_4 = \frac{1}{4}$ gives an assignment of probabilities. Another option is $w_1 = .15$, $w_2 = .25$, $w_3 = .40$, and $w_4 = .20$, and this choice also gives an assignment of probabilities. Although both choices are acceptable as assignments of probabilities, we need more information about the situation to know which choice is more appropriate. ■

Example 2.5 A naturalist is studying the wildlife population on an island that supports only three species of bird—gulls, parrots, and eagles. Using digital videography and photography, the naturalist determines that gulls outnumber eagles by 4 to 1, and parrots outnumber eagles by 5 to 1.

Problem View the experiment of locating and photographing one bird as an experiment with the outcomes "gull", "parrot", and "eagle". Find an assignment of probabilities that reflects the data.

Solution Let $\mathcal{O}_1$, $\mathcal{O}_2$, and $\mathcal{O}_3$ denote the outcomes "Gull," "Parrot," and "Eagle," respectively, and let w_1, w_2, and w_3 be the associated probabilities.

Since we know that gulls outnumber eagles by 4 to 1, we have $w_1 = 4w_3$; and since parrots outnumber eagles by 5 to 1, we have $w_2 = 5w_3$. Using these relations and Equation (2.2), we have

$$w_1 + w_2 + w_3 = 4w_3 + 5w_3 + w_3 = 10w_3 = 1$$

We conclude that

$$w_3 = .1 \qquad w_1 = 4w_3 = .4 \qquad w_2 = 5w_3 = .5$$ ■

Up to this point we have assigned probabilities to outcomes only. We are also interested in the likelihoods of events, and we extend our use of the term "probability" from outcomes to events, i.e., sets of outcomes.

Suppose that we are given an experiment with a sample space S and an assignment of probabilities to outcomes. For any event $E \subset S$, the probability of E, denoted $\Pr[E]$, is defined to be the sum of the probabilities of the outcomes in E.

There are, of course, events consisting of a single outcome. By our definition, the probability of such an event is the same as the probability assigned to the outcome. Thus, for any outcome $\mathcal{O}$, the probability w associated with this outcome is equal to the probability of the event $\{\mathcal{O}\}$: $w = \Pr[\{\mathcal{O}\}]$. For notational convenience we use $\Pr[\mathcal{O}]$ to denote this probability.

Example 2.6 In the situation described in Example 2.4, suppose that the following assignment of weights is used:

$$w_1 = .15 \qquad w_2 = .25 \qquad w_3 = .40 \qquad w_4 = .20$$

Let E be the event that a call of length *at least* 1 minute is received.

Problem Find $\Pr[E]$.

Solution The event E is $\{\mathcal{O}_2, \mathcal{O}_3, \mathcal{O}_4\}$, and using the definition of the probability of an event,

$$\Pr[E] = w_2 + w_3 + w_4 = .25 + .40 + .20 = .85$$ ■

One of the conditions for an assignment of weights is that the sum of the weights of all outcomes in the sample space S be 1. Let E be an event in S, and let E' be the complement of E with respect to S as a universal set. Clearly those outcomes which are not in E must be in E', and consequently

$$\Pr[E] + \Pr[E'] = w_1 + w_2 + \cdots + w_n = 1$$

This relation, summarized below, is a useful tool in solving problems. We shall use it extensively in our future work on probability.

If E is any event in a sample space S and E' is the complementary event, then

$$\Pr[E] + \Pr[E'] = 1 \tag{2.3}$$

There are many situations in which *one* of $\Pr[E]$ or $\Pr[E']$ is easy to compute while the other is extremely difficult. The use of Equation (2.3) sometimes provides the only workable method of obtaining a certain probability.

Equally Likely Outcomes

In many situations in which the deductive method is used to assign probabilities, it can be argued that the probabilities of all outcomes should be the same. In such a case, since the sum of the probabilities of all outcomes is 1, it follows that the probability assigned to each outcome should be $1/n$, where n is the number of possible outcomes. For instance, rolling a die once and noting the result is an experiment with 6 outcomes, and if the die is fair, then each outcome should be assigned probability $\frac{1}{6}$. Also, flipping a coin and noting which face comes up is an experiment with 2 outcomes, and if the coin is fair, then each outcome should be assigned probability $\frac{1}{2}$. Experiments like this are said to be experiments with *equally likely outcomes*.

In experiments with equally likely outcomes, the probability assigned to each outcome is the same number, and this number is determined by finding the total number of outcomes n and taking $1/n$. Our first step is to find the total number of outcomes $n = n(S)$, the number of elements in the sample space.

Example 2.7 A bowl contains 3 balls: 1 blue, 1 white, and 1 green. An experiment consists of selecting a ball, noting its color, and then flipping a coin and noting the result, heads or tails.

Problem Find the number of outcomes. If the outcomes are equally likely, what weight should be assigned to each?

Solution There are 3 results for the color of the ball selected, and there are 2 results for the flip of the coin. Therefore, by the multiplication principle there are $3 \times 2 = 6$ outcomes for the experiment. Each outcome should be assigned probability $\frac{1}{6}$. ■

Example 2.8 An experiment consists of rolling a red die and a green die and noting the result of each roll.

Problem Assuming that the dice are fair and that all outcomes are equally likely, find the probability that should be assigned to each outcome.

Solution There are 6 numbers which can come up on the red die and 6 numbers which can come up on the green die. Therefore, $n(S) = 6 \times 6 = 36$; the 36 outcomes are shown in Table 2.1. Each outcome should be assigned probability $\frac{1}{36}$. ■

We have defined the probability of an event to be the sum of the probabilities of the outcomes in that event. If all outcomes are equally likely, then the probability of each outcome is $1/n(S)$. Since event E contains $n(E)$ outcomes, we have the following fundamental formula:

> If an experiment with sample space S has equally likely outcomes, then for any event E the probability of E is given by
>
> $$\Pr[E] = \frac{n(E)}{n(S)} \tag{2.4}$$
>
> where $n(E)$ and $n(S)$ denote the number of elements in E and S, respectively.

It is important to remember that *Equation (2.4) is to be used only for experiments with equally likely outcomes.* For instance, it cannot be used to determine the probability of event E of Example 2.6 (a call of length at least 1 minute is received).

Example 2.9 An experiment consists of rolling a red die and a green die and noting the result of each roll.

Problem Find the probability that the sum is 8.

Solution Let S be the sample space, and let E be the event that the sum is 8. Then $n(S) = 36$ by Example 2.8. Using the notation of Example 2.3 [i.e., an outcome is denoted by (m, n) where m is the number of dots on the red die and n is the number of dots on the green die], we have

$$E = \{(6, 2), (5, 3), (4, 4), (3, 5), (2, 6)\}$$

and consequently $n(E) = 5$. Applying Equation (2.4), we have

$$\Pr[E] = \frac{n(E)}{n(S)} = \frac{5}{36}$$ ■

The assignment of probabilities based on an assumption of equally likely outcomes provides an example of a *probability measure.* It is known as the *equiprobable measure.* Probability measures in general will be defined and studied in Chapters 3 and 4. The equiprobable measure is frequently adopted in applications, and it gives an assignment of probabilities which corresponds closely to an intuitive idea of randomness. Indeed, when we use a phrase like "a card selected at random from an ordinary deck" without further comment regarding the likelihood of outcomes, it is understood that we assume all outcomes, i.e., all selections, to be equally likely. That is, for us the phrase "selected at random" indicates that an equiprobable measure is to be used. Also, we often use the term "fair" to refer to a die in which each face is equally likely to land up when the die is rolled or to a coin in which heads and tails are equally likely when the coin is flipped.

In Examples 2.8 and 2.9, the solution of the problem involves counting the number of elements in certain sets. Many sets S are too large or too complicated for us to list and count the elements. For these sets we need to use special counting techniques and formulas (such as the partition principle and the multiplication principle) to obtain $n(S)$. More of these techniques and formulas are developed in the next two sections. We then conclude the chapter by using these counting techniques and the formula $\Pr[E] = n(E)/n(S)$ to solve a variety of probability problems.

In some of the exercises for this section (Exercise 29, for instance) and elsewhere in the book, the phrase "without replacement" is used to describe experiments in which the item selected at one stage or step is not available to be selected again. If an item can be selected repeatedly, we use the phrase "with replacement."

Exercises for Section 2.1

1. A telephone sales representative makes successive calls to potential customers, and the result of each call is recorded as sale (S) or no sale (N). Calls are continued until either two successive sales are made, two successive calls result in no sale, or a total of 3 calls is made. Find the sample space for this situation.
2. In the situation described in Exercise 1, suppose calls are continued until either 3 sales are made, 3 calls result in no sale, or a total of 5 calls is made. Find the sample space for this situation.
3. An experiment with outcomes O_1, O_2, O_3, O_4, O_5 has an assignment of probabilities w_1, w_2, w_3, w_4, and w_5. Suppose O_2 is three times as likely as O_4, $w_1 = .40$, and $w_3 = w_4 = w_5$. Find w_2.
4. An experiment with 6 outcomes has $w_1 = 0.18$, $w_2 = 0.27$, $w_3 = 2w_4$, $w_5 = 0.15$, and $w_6 = 0.10$. Find w_3.

5. In Example 2.3, find the events

$$\begin{aligned} E &= \{\text{exactly 1 die has a result of 3}\} \\ F &= \{\text{at least 1 die has a result of 3}\} \\ G &= \{\text{the sum of the results is an odd number}\} \\ H &= \{\text{the sum of the results is at most 7}\} \end{aligned}$$

6. Let $S = \{O_1, O_2, O_3, O_4\}$ be a sample space. Suppose $Pr[\{O_1, O_3\}] = 0.55$, and $Pr[\{O_1, O_2, O_4\}] = 0.75$
   (*a*) Find $Pr[\{O_2, O_4\}]$. (*b*) Find $Pr[\{O_2, O_3, O_4\}]$.
7. A purse contains 3 nickels, 3 dimes, and 2 quarters. Coins are withdrawn, one at a time, without replacement, and the value of each selected coin is noted. Selections stop when 1 nickel has been selected or the total value of the coins is at least 35 cents. Find the sample space of the experiment.
8. Students in an English class are given two separate grades for their work—a grade reflecting grammatical accuracy (Satisfactory or Unsatisfactory), and a grade reflecting overall organizational efficiency (Poor, Average, or Good).
   (*a*) Find the sample space for the experiment of assigning both grades to one student's paper. Assume that the grammatical accuracy grade is assigned first, followed by the organizational efficiency grade.
   (*b*) Find the event that the organizational efficiency grade is Average.
9. Suppose an experiment has 4 outcomes and the frequencies of the outcomes are $\frac{3}{n}$, $\frac{11}{n}$, $\frac{5}{n}$, $\frac{7}{n}$. What does n have to be, for these frequencies to reflect probabilities?
10. Suppose a die is weighted so that outcome 1 is twice as likely as 2, which is twice as likely as 3, which is twice as likely as 4, which is twice as likely as 5, which is twice as likely as 6. What probabilities (weights) should be assigned to the outcomes to reflect this information?
11. An experiment has outcomes $\mathcal{O}_1$, $\mathcal{O}_2$, and $\mathcal{O}_3$, with $\Pr[\{\mathcal{O}_1, \mathcal{O}_2\}] = .9$, $\Pr[\{\mathcal{O}_1, \mathcal{O}_3\}] = .85$. What is $\Pr[\mathcal{O}_2]$?
12. An experiment has 5 possible outcomes with weights: $w_1 = 0.09$, $w_2 = 0.08$, $w_3 = 0.27$, and $w_4 = 3w_5$. If the event E contains outcomes 1, 3, and 4, and the event F contains outcomes 2, 4, and 5, then find the following:
    (*a*) $Pr[E]$ (*b*) $Pr[F']$ (*c*) $Pr[E \cap F]$
13. An experiment with five outcomes has $w_1 = .2$, $w_2 = w_3$, $w_4 = .35$, and $w_5 = w_1 + w_2$. Find w_2.
14. A sample space consists of three outcomes a, b, c. We know that $\Pr[a] = \frac{1}{3}$ and b is three times as likely as c. Find $\Pr[b]$.
15. A die is weighted so that outcomes 1 and 2 are equally likely; outcome 1 is three times as likely as each of outcomes 3, 4, 5, and 6; and these outcomes are equally likely. What probabilities (weights) should be assigned to the outcomes to reflect this information?
16. A die is weighted so that the odd numbers are 3 times as likely to come up as the even numbers. All the even numbers are equally likely, and all the odd numbers are equally likely. What probabilities $w_1, w_2, w_3, w_4, w_5, w_6$ should be assigned to the outcomes 1, 2, 3, 4, 5, 6, respectively?
17. Suppose an experiment has three possible outcomes $\mathcal{O}_1$, $\mathcal{O}_2$, and $\mathcal{O}_3$. Also suppose that $\mathcal{O}_1$ occurs with frequency $1/a$, outcome $\mathcal{O}_2$ with frequency $2/a$, and $\mathcal{O}_3$ with

frequency $3/a$. What probabilities should be assigned to the outcomes to reflect this?

18. Consider a die constructed so that outcomes of 1, 2, 3, or 4 dots are equally likely, 5 is twice as likely as 1, and 6 is twice as likely as 5. What probabilities should be assigned to the outcomes to reflect this?
19. An unfair die has the property that when rolled each of the odd numbers is equally likely to land uppermost, each of the even numbers is equally likely to land uppermost, and each odd number is twice as likely to land up as an even number. The die is rolled and the result is noted. Find the probability that the result is in the event $\{1, 3, 6\}$.
20. A die is weighted so that the odd numbers are equally likely, the even numbers are equally likely, and the odd numbers are k times as likely as the even numbers. If $\Pr[2] = \frac{1}{12}$, what is k?
21. Suppose an experiment has sample space $S = \{\mathcal{O}_1, \mathcal{O}_2, \mathcal{O}_3, \mathcal{O}_4, \mathcal{O}_5\}$. Also, let outcome $\mathcal{O}_i$ be assigned probability w_i, where $w_1 = w_2 = \frac{1}{5}$, $w_3 = \frac{2}{5}$, and $w_4 = w_5 = \frac{1}{10}$. Find $\Pr[E]$ and $\Pr[F']$, where $E = \{\mathcal{O}_2, \mathcal{O}_4\}$ and $F = \{\mathcal{O}_1, \mathcal{O}_4\}$.
22. Consider a 10-sided die (5 different odd-numbered sides and 5 different even-numbered sides). This die is weighted so that:
    (*a*) The probabilities for all the odd sides are the same.
    (*b*) The probabilities for all the even sides are the same.
    (*c*) The probability of obtaining a given odd side is twice that of a given even side.

    What is the probability of obtaining a given odd side?
23. A calculus-based physics course has 300 students enrolled. Of these, 30 will withdraw, 45 will receive a grade of A, 60 will receive B, 105 will get C, 45 will get D, and 15 will receive F. Consider the experiment of randomly selecting one student from the class. Assign probabilities to the events "pass the course" (grade of D or better) as well as the event "withdraw or fail the course".
24. Two hundred duck hatchlings are weighed, and it is found that 38 are underweight, 12 are extremely underweight, and the remainder are normal weight. Consider an experiment which consists of weighing a single hatchling.
    (*a*) What are the possible outcomes of this experiment?
    (*b*) What probabilities should be assigned to these outcomes on the basis of the data?
25. A lottery is designed so that on average it pays \$10 on 1 play out of 100, \$1,000 on 1 play out of 5,000, and \$10,000 on 1 play out of 100,000. All other plays have no return. Assign probabilities to the four possible outcomes of buying a lottery ticket.
26. Of the 300 students in a Finite Math class, 140 are Freshmen, 85 are Sophomores, 45 are Juniors, and the remaining students are Seniors. An experiment consists of randomly selecting one student from the class and noting whether or not the student is a Freshman. What probabilities should be assigned to the outcomes of this experiment on the basis of the data?
27. A product code consist of one number selected from $\{1, 2, 3, 5\}$ followed by two letters, not necessarily distinct, selected from the set {Q, T, Z}. For example, 3QT is such a code. An experiment consists of selecting a code at random.
    (*a*) How many codes are possible?

(*b*) What probability should be assigned to each code?
(*c*) Find the probability of the event that the code contains the number 3.

28. For the experiment described in Exercise 27:
    (*a*) Find the probability of the event that the code contains exactly one Q.
    (*b*) Find the probability of the event that the code contains at least one Q.
29. There are balls numbered 1 through 5 in a box. Two balls are selected at random in succession without replacement, and the number on each ball is noted.
    (*a*) How many outcomes does this experiment have?
    (*b*) What probability should be assigned to each?
    (*c*) What probability should be assigned to the event that at least one ball has an odd number?
30. In the experiment described in Exercise 29, find the probability of the event that the sum of the numbers is less than 7.
31. A fair coin is flipped 3 times, and the result (heads or tails) is noted after each toss. How many outcomes does this experiment have? What probability should be assigned to each?
32. In the experiment of Exercise 31, find the probability of the event that there are at least two heads.
33. In a large law school class, the professor decides to call on students by using their initials. Thus, Dirty Harry is called *DH* and Mary Contrary is called *MC*. A colleague from the math faculty notes that at least two students will have the same initials. How many students are in the class?
34. Suppose the faculty member in Exercise 33 decides to assign distinct codes to each student, and the code consists of two letters followed by a one-digit number (from 1 to 9). For example, *AB*3 and *EE*9 are such codes. If this assignment is initially done randomly, what is the probability that Mary receives a code that includes the letter *M* and the number 1?
35. A box contains 3 balls: 1 red, 1 blue, and 1 yellow. The balls are drawn at random one after the other until all have been removed from the box. The color of each ball is noted as it is drawn. How many outcomes are there for this experiment?
36. The outcomes of the experiment described in Exercise 35 are equally likely.
    (*a*) Find the probability that the red ball is selected first.
    (*b*) Find the probability that the red ball is selected before the blue ball.
37. An experiment similar to that of Exercise 29 is conducted, except the first ball selected is replaced before the second ball is selected. Repeat Exercise 29 for this situation.
38. An economist reviews historical data on economic recoveries after recessions. On the basis of the data, she classifies each recovery as weak (*W*), strong (*S*), or exceptionally strong (*E*). Also she measures the increase in inflation during each recovery and classifies each recovery as having low (*L*), moderate (*M*), or high (*H*) inflation.
    (*a*) Find the sample space for the experiment of reviewing one recovery and noting its strength and inflation level.
    (*b*) Find the event that the recovery is strong.
    (*c*) Find the event that the recovery is strong or has low inflation.
    (*d*) Find the event that the recovery is strong and has low inflation.

39. A psychology experiment consists of presenting a stimulus to a subject and noting the response. At each presentation of the stimulus, the subject is evaluated as making a strong association (S), a weak association (W), or no association (N). If the subject makes a strong association on the first presentation, the experiment ends. Otherwise it continues and a second stimulus is presented. The experiment ends after the second stimulus if the subject makes a strong association; otherwise it continues and a third stimulus is presented. The experiment ends after the response to the third stimulus (if one is presented) is recorded. An outcome is a sequence of responses to stimuli.
(*a*) Find the event that there is a strong association.
(*b*) Find the event that there is at least one weak association.
(*c*) Find the event that there is exactly one weak association.

2.2 COUNTING ARRANGEMENTS: PERMUTATIONS

Many experiments which take place in steps or stages have outcomes, each of which can be viewed as a list of the results of successive steps in the experiment: an ordered list or arrangement. The number of elements in the set of outcomes of such an experiment can often be determined by using the multiplication principle. In fact, a special case of the multiplication principle, the *permutation principle*, is especially useful. Before stating the latter principle, we illustrate the type of situation to which it applies with two examples. Notice that in both examples, to apply the multiplication principle, we *create* the setting of an experiment; the experiment is not explicitly given in the statement of the problem.

Example 2.10 A Student Music Board consists of 5 members: Audra (A), Bill (B), Connie (C), David (D), and Emita (E). The Board is planning the next campus concert, and one member is to handle hiring the band, and a different member is to handle reserving a suitable auditorium for the concert.

Problem Find the number of different ways of assigning pairs of board members to the two tasks of hiring the band and reserving an auditorium for the concert. Two assignments are different if either task is handled by a different person; in particular, if two people switch tasks, the result is a new assignment.

Solution Think of assigning people to the tasks as a two-stage experiment: the assignment of a person to hire the band followed by the assignment of a different person to reserve a suitable auditorium. The first stage, assigning someone to hire the band, has 5 possible results. After the person hiring the band has been identified, and regardless of who has been given that assignment, there remain 4 people from which to select someone to reserve an auditorium. Thus, by the multiplication principle, the number of outcomes of the experiment—the number of different ways to assign 2 people selected from the 5 available to 2 tasks—is $5 \times 4 = 20$. ■

Let us examine Example 2.10 more closely. We can think of assigning 2 people to 2 tasks as making a list of 2 names: The first person is to hire the band, and the second is to reserve an auditorium. If we use letters instead of names, then each list can be represented as an ordered pair of letters, (A, B), (D, E), etc.. The list (A, B) means that Audra hires the band, and Bill reserves an auditorium. Clearly the list (A, B) is different from the list (B, A); in the latter, B handles hiring a band and A reserves an auditorium. The multiplication principle can be applied to the formation of lists in exactly the way it was used in Example 2.10. We use the term ''permutation'' to denote an ordered list.

A *permutation* is an ordered list of elements selected from a set. Two permutations are *different* unless they consist of exactly the same elements in exactly the same order.

Recall that either an element occurs in a set or it does not. An element cannot belong to a set ''several times.'' Consequently, the elements in a permutation are necessarily distinct—they have been selected from a set without replacement.

Example 2.11 How many permutations of 3 letters can be formed with letters selected from a set of 6 distinct letters?

Solution The first letter (first in the list) can be selected in 6 ways. After the first has been selected, the second can be selected in 5 ways. After the first 2 letters have been selected, there are 4 letters remaining and, consequently, the third letter can be selected in 4 ways. Using the multiplication principle, we conclude that the number of arrangements of 3 letters selected from 6 is

$$6 \times 5 \times 4 = 120$$

■

As a variation of Example 2.10, suppose that the number of tasks in that example were expanded to include a third task, say, arranging for the concert to be advertised. Approaching this new problem in the same way as in Example 2.10, we ask for the number of different ways of making a list of 3 names: the first person hires the band, the second person reserves an auditorium, and the third arranges for the concert to be advertised. By the multiplication principle, the number of different ways to assign 3 people selected from 5 people to do 3 tasks is $5 \times 4 \times 3 = 60$.

Another variation of Example 2.10 is illustrated by supposing that the board consists of 6 members rather than 5. In this case 2 people selected from the 6 available can be assigned to the 2 tasks of Example 2.10 in $6 \times 5 = 30$ different ways.

Example 2.10, and its variations, and Example 2.11 illustrate a very common application of the multiplication principle. In such applications there is a set of objects (board members in Example 2.10, letters in Example 2.11), and the goal is to count the number of ways a subset of objects can be selected from the entire set and arranged in order. When used in this way, the multiplication principle has a special name.

Permutation Principle
The number of permutations (ordered lists) of r objects selected from a set of n distinct objects is

$$n \times (n-1) \times \cdots \times (n-r+1)$$

Example 2.12 A city is divided into 3 districts which are to be surveyed for opinions on municipal services. There are 5 experienced survey takers available to do the job.

Problem How many different ways can surveyors be assigned to districts, exactly one surveyor to each district?

Solution There are 5 people available, and we must assign a person to each of 3 districts. Using the permutation principle with $n = 5$ and $r = 3$, we conclude that the assignment can be made in

$$5 \times 4 \times 3 = 60$$

ways. (Note that since $n - r + 1 = 5 - 3 + 1 = 3$, the smallest number which appears in the product is 3.) ■

Example 2.13 A map showing the 4 states of Arizona, Colorado, New Mexico, and Utah is to be colored so that each state is a different color. There are 8 colors available.

Problem In how many different ways can the map be colored? We consider two colorings to be different unless they have identical colors in each of the 4 states.

Solution We apply the permutation principle to conclude that the map can be colored in

$$8 \times 7 \times 6 \times 5 = 1680 \text{ different ways}$$ ■

It is convenient to introduce the notation $n!$ (read "n factorial") to denote $n \times (n-1) \times \cdots \times 2 \times 1$. Thus $5! = 5 \times 4 \times 3 \times 2 \times 1 = 120$, and $10! = 10 \times 9 \times 8 \times \cdots \times 2 \times 1 = 3{,}628{,}800$. When this notation is used, the expression

$n \times (n-1) \times \cdots \times (n-r+1)$, which occurs in the permutation principle, can be written

$$\begin{aligned} n \times (n-1) \times \cdots \times (n-r+1) \\ &= \frac{n \times (n-1) \times \cdots \times (n-r+1) \times (n-r) \times \cdots \times 2 \times 1}{(n-r) \times \cdots \times 2 \times 1} \\ &= \frac{n!}{(n-r)!} \end{aligned}$$

We also define 0! to be 1. Therefore, when $r = n$, $(n-r)! = 0! = 1$.

Finally, it will be helpful to have a symbol for the expression $n!/(n-r)!$ which occurs frequently in applications. We introduce the symbol $P(n, r)$ by setting

$$P(n, r) = \frac{n!}{(n-r)!} \tag{2.5}$$

We refer to $P(n, r)$ as the *number of permutations of n objects taken r at a time.* With this notation the permutation principle can be restated as follows:

The number of permutations of n distinct objects taken r at a time is

$$P(n, r) = \frac{n!}{(n-r)!}$$

Remember that in permutations *order is important.* Thus $ABCD$ and $ACBD$ are different permutations of the 4 letters A, B, C, D. In fact, the total number of permutations of the 4 letters is

$$\begin{aligned} P(4, 4) &= \frac{4!}{(4-4)!} \\ &= \frac{4!}{0!} = \frac{4!}{1} = 4 \times 3 \times 2 \times 1 = 24 \end{aligned}$$

Example 2.14 A financial services company has regional offices in Atlanta, Baltimore, Chicago, Denver, Rochester, Seattle, and Tampa. A consultant is to visit 4 different offices.

Problem (*a*) A schedule is a set of 4 different offices to visit and an order in which to visit them. How many schedules are there? (*b*) How many schedules include visits to Chicago or Denver or both?

Solution (*a*) There are 7 cities, and by the permutation principle there are $P(7, 4) = 7 \times 6 \times 5 \times 4 = 840$ schedules.

(*b*) We answer this question by finding the number of schedules which *do not* include visits to either Chicago or Denver, and we subtract this number from the answer to part *a*. Excluding Chicago and Denver, there are 5 cities. Therefore, there are $P(5, 4)$ schedules which do not include visits to either Chicago or Denver. We conclude that there are

$$P(7, 4) - P(5, 4) = (7 \times 6 \times 5 \times 4) - (5 \times 4 \times 3 \times 2) = 840 - 120 = 720$$

schedules which include either Chicago or Denver or both. ■

Our solution of Example 2.14*b* (there are other ways to solve this problem as well) illustrates a method based on solving two or more subproblems and then combining the solutions of the subproblems to solve the original problem. In this example we used the permutation principle twice, each time to solve a subproblem. First we used it to count all schedules, and then we used it to count the schedules which included neither Chicago nor Denver. Finally, the answer to (*b*) is the difference of these two numbers. This is a typical example of a multistep problem.

Example 2.15 A product code consists of 3 different symbols. There are 5 different symbols available. We assume that the order in which the symbols appear in a product code is important and that two product codes are different unless they have exactly the same symbols in the same order.

Problem Find the number of distinct product codes which can be formed from 5 symbols.

Solution It is useful to think of a product code as a permutation of 3 symbols selected from 5 symbols. Adopting this point of view, we conclude from the permutation principle that the number of product codes is

$$P(5, 3) = \frac{5!}{(5-3)!} = \frac{5!}{2!} = 5 \times 4 \times 3 = 60$$ ■

Example 2.16 A director of a community theater is conducting auditions for a play which has 6 distinct roles: 4 for females and 2 for males. There are 7 females trying out for the female roles and 8 males trying out for the male roles.

Problem How many possible casts are there? A cast is an assignment of people to roles, and two casts are different unless exactly the same people are assigned to the same roles.

Solution This problem cannot be solved by direct application of the permutation principle. Instead we must use both the permutation principle and the multiplication principle. Since we assume that all roles are distinguishable, there are $7 \times 6 \times 5 \times 4 = 840$ ways of selecting 4 females to play the female roles and $8 \times 7 = 56$ ways of selecting 2 males to play the male roles.

Consider the task of selecting a cast as a two-stage experiment: Select the female players, and then select the male players. The first stage has 840 results. For each of these results, there are 56 possible results of the second stage. Consequently, there are $840 \times 56 = 47,040$ outcomes of the experiment. That is, there are 47,040 possible casts (probably a good deal more than the director even cares to contemplate, let alone try out). ■

In the counting problems studied so far, we have considered only distinct objects. However, the techniques can be used in settings where not all the objects are distinct. We illustrate the method in a simple setting.

Example 2.17 How many different 4-letter "words" can be formed with the 4 letters in the word "book"?

Solution To use the techniques of this section, we begin by assuming that the two o letters are tagged in some way, with subscripts, for instance, to distinguish them. In such a case there are 4 distinct letters, and the number of permutations is

$$P(4, 4) = 24$$

If we imagine a list of these permutations, then each of the following appears: bo_1ko_2 and bo_2ko_1. Now suppose the subscripts are erased. Then the word "boko" appears *twice* in the list. Indeed, each permutation appears twice, and consequently there are $24 \div 2 = 12$ different words which can be formed with the letters of the word "book." ■

Example 2.18 How many different 8-letter words can be formed by using the 8 letters in the word "notebook"?

Solution As in Example 2.17, we begin by assuming the three o letters are tagged in some way (for example, $\text{no}_1\text{tebo}_2\text{o}_3\text{k}$). In such a case there would be 8 different "letters" and there would be $P(8, 8) = 8! = 40{,}320$ different words. However, a list of these words would include items such as $\text{no}_1\text{tebo}_2\text{ko}_3$, $\text{no}_2\text{tebo}_3\text{ko}_1$, and $\text{no}_3\text{tebo}_1\text{ko}_2$; and after the subscripts are removed, these will all be the same word. In fact, since the three o letters can be permuted in $P(3, 3) = 3! = 6$ ways, the list of 40,320 words can be divided into groups of 6 words, all of which are the same after the subscripts are removed. Thus the answer to the problem is the number of these groups. That is,

$$\frac{P(8, 8)}{P(3, 3)} = \frac{40{,}320}{6} = 6720$$

■

The ideas introduced in Examples 2.17 and 2.18 can be extended and used in situations where there is more than one repeated letter. For instance, suppose we consider the situation described in Example 2.17 with the word "college". That is, how many different 7-letter words can be formed with the letters in the word "college"? Here we have a situation in which each of two letters, the letters e and l, appears twice. If, as in Example 2.17, we imagine that each of the two letters e is distinguished by a subscript, and each of the two letters l is distinguished similarly, then there are 7 distinct letters. These 7 distinct letters can be arranged in $P(7, 7)$ ways. Now, when we remove the subscripts on the letters e, then each of the resulting words appears twice [since $P(2, 2) = 2! = 2$], and after doing so we see there are $\frac{P(7,7)}{2}$ distinct words. Finally, when we remove the subscripts on the letters l, then each of the resulting words appears twice, and consequently after doing so we see there are $\frac{P(7,7)}{2 \cdot 2}$ distinct words. We now have the answer to the original question: there are $\frac{P(7,7)}{2 \cdot 2}$ distinct words formed from the letters in the word "college." This technique can be used in more complex situations, some of which are the topics of exercises (Exercises 31 to 34).

Exercises for Section 2.2

1. Evaluate the following numbers expressed in terms of the factorial symbol.
   (*a*) $7!$ (*b*) $\dfrac{8!}{5!3!}$ (*c*) $\dfrac{9!}{6!}$ (*d*) $\dfrac{52!}{47!5!}$
2. Evaluate the following numbers expressed in terms of the factorial symbol.
   (*a*) $(6 - 2)!$ (*b*) $6! - 2!$ (*c*) $(5 + 3)!$ (*d*) $5! + 3!$
3. A traveller plans to visit four of the cities Athens, Berlin, Cairo, Düsseldorf, Edinburgh, and Florence. An itinerary is a list of the four cities to be visited, in order. How many different itineraries are there?
4. A committee has 7 members. One member is to be selected as chairperson, and another member is to be selected as secretary. In how many ways can these selections be made?
5. A conductor has 5 songs to conduct during a concert, and he can conduct them in any order. In how many ways can he organize the concert?
6. A group of 7 students is to make a presentation on 3 issues: parking fees, campus safety, and recreational sports facilities. One student is to be assigned primary responsibility for each issue. In how many ways can this assignment be made?
7. A football team has 44 players, 22 on offense and 22 on defense. How many ways can 2 team captains be selected if 1 must be from the offense and 1 from the defense?
8. Suppose that in Example 2.12 there are 4 districts in the city and 6 individuals available to carry out the surveys. How many different assignments of survey takers to districts can be made, assuming no one surveys more than one district?
9. How many 3-digit numbers can be formed with the digits 2, 4, 6, 8, and 9 if each digit is used at most once? How many of these numbers are smaller than 500?

10. An olympic race has 9 competitors. In how many ways can the 3 medals, gold, silver, and bronze be awarded? (assume no ties occur).
11. How many 2-letter words can be formed from the letters of the word ''consider''?
12. How many 4 letter words can be formed from the letters in ''formula''? How many of them contain the letter *m*?
13. A product code is formed by arranging 5 different letters from the collection $\{B, H, Q, T, W, Z\}$ one after another. How many different such product codes are there? How many of them contain the letter *H*?
14. Each player on a 25 player college baseball team is assigned a locker at the start of the season. If there are 100 lockers from which to choose, how many ways can the assignments be made so that each player gets a different locker?
15. A committee has 9 members, and 3 different members are to be given special tasks: one is to serve as a delegate to a convention, one is to seek new members, and one is to seek donations. In how many different ways can the tasks be assigned?
16. In the situation described in Exercise 15, suppose the committee consists of 5 men and 4 women. In how many ways can the tasks be assigned so that both men and women are given assignments?
17. A city has 7 fire stations and each one is to get a new chief. If there are 11 qualified candidates, how many ways can the chiefs be selected so that each station has a different chief?
18. In Example 2.16, suppose that only 6 females and 5 males are trying out for the 4 female roles and 2 male roles, respectively. How many possible casts are there?
19. A group of 6 students including Vania has been working on a research project for a course. The project has been completed, and a report is to be written. The report consists of an introduction, 2 chapters, and a conclusion, a total of 4 sections.
    (*a*) In how many ways can the students divide up the task of writing the report if each section is to be written by a different student?
    (*b*) In how many ways can the student divide up the report writing if each section is to be written by a different student and Vania writes the conclusion?
20. Six students including Joe are planning a trip to attend a concert in Chicago. Three of these students are assigned the tasks of arranging for a hotel, getting a new Chicago map, and purchasing concert tickets, one task per student. In how many different ways can three students be assigned these tasks if Joe is NOT assigned the task of getting the map?
21. A traveler can visit 3 of these cities: Amsterdam, Barcelona, Copenhagen, Rome, and Zurich. An itinerary for a trip is a list of the 3 cities in the order to be visited. How many different itineraries are there for the trip?
22. You are given the situation described in Exercise 21.
    (*a*) How many of the itineraries include Copenhagen?
    (*b*) In how many of these is Copenhagen the first city to be visited?
    (*c*) How many of the itineraries include both Copenhagen and Rome?
23. A committee has 10 members including Alice. Three offices (chairperson, secretary, treasurer) must be filled.
    (*a*) If each person can fill at most one office, in how many different ways can the offices be filled?
    (*b*) In how many ways can the offices be filled so that Alice is one of the officers?
    (*c*) In how many ways can the offices be filled so that Alice is chairperson?

24. There are 12 students trying out for a talent show. Four of the 12 students will be chosen to perform during the talent show. The program for the show contains a list of the four students chosen in the order in which they will perform during the show. How many different programs are possible?
25. A product code consists of a string of 4 different letters from the set $\{A, B, H, Q, T, Z\}$. How many such codes contain the letters H or Q, or both?
26. There are 3 unfilled roles in a play at the community theater, 2 for females and 1 for a male. Auditioning for the female roles are 4 females including Susan; 3 males audition for the male role. A cast consists of an assignment of specific people to specific roles.
    (*a*) How many different casts are there?
    (*b*) How many casts include Susan?
    (*c*) How many casts do not include Susan?
27. Let $S = \{1, 2, 4, 5, 6, 7, 9\}$, and suppose a 4-digit number is formed by selecting digits, without replacement, from S.
    (*a*) How many different such numbers can be formed?
    (*b*) How many different such numbers can be formed if both even and odd digits must be used?
28. A small service organization consisting of 8 females and 2 males meets to elect a president, secretary, and treasurer (assume one person per office). In how many ways can the offices be filled if both sexes must be represented?
29. During their morning show, a new satellite radio channel utilizes its airtime as indicated below, where C denotes a commercial, and S denotes a song.

$$\underline{}\ \underline{}\ \underline{}\ \underline{}\ \underline{}\ \underline{}\ \underline{}$$
$$C \quad S \quad S \quad C \quad S \quad S \quad C$$

    If there are 5 songs and 3 commercials available, how many different morning shows can be produced? We assume that a song is never repeated, but (unfortunately) commercials can be repeated any number of times.
30. Forty students take an examination and 4 of them turn in their paper without putting their name on it. Each of these 4 exams receives a different score. In how many ways can these exams be returned if at least one of these 4 students receives the wrong paper?
31. How many 5-digit numbers can be formed from the digits of the number 12321?
32. How many 6-letter words can be formed from the letters in the word "bottom"?
33. How many 6-letter words can be formed from the letters in the word "feeder"?
34. How many 7-letter words can be formed from the letters in the word "breeder"?
35. A basketball coach needs to field a starting lineup of 5 players, where each player is assigned to one of the following positions: point guard, shooting guard, small forward, power forward, and center. The coach has 12 players on the team. Seven of these players can only play a guard position. The other five can only play either forward position or center. How many starting lineups are possible?
36. For which values of the integer n is it true that $P(n + 2, 3)$ and $P(n, 5)$ are both defined and $2n \cdot P(n + 2, 3) \geq P(n, 5)$?
37. How many different four letter "words" can be formed from the letters in the word FEEDER?
38. How many different four-digit numbers can be formed from the digits 111234?

2.3 COUNTING SUBSETS: COMBINATIONS

In the preceding section we developed a method for determining the number of ways that r objects can be selected from a set of n objects and arranged in order. Suppose now that we are interested simply in selecting r objects from n but *not* in arranging these r objects in a particular order. Each such selection is called a *combination* of r objects selected from n. To study this new operation, it is convenient to view the process discussed in Section 2.2 as a two-step process consisting of *selecting* and *arranging*. That is, by the *multiplication principle*,

Number of ways r objects can be selected from n objects and arranged in order	=	number of ways r objects can be selected from n objects	×	number of ways r objects can be arranged in order

The permutation principle can be used to evaluate the numbers represented by the quantities on the extreme right and left. We have

$$P(n, r) = \frac{n!}{(n-r)!} \qquad \text{and} \qquad P(r, r) = r!$$

and consequently

$$\frac{n!}{(n-r)!} = \boxed{\text{number of ways } r \text{ objects can be selected from } n \text{ objects}} \times r!$$

This expression leads immediately to a formula for the number of ways r objects can be selected from n objects. If we divide both sides of the equality by $r!$, the result is our next counting principle.

Combination Principle

A subset of r objects can be selected from a set of n distinct objects in $\dfrac{n!}{(n-r)!r!}$ different ways.

As an illustration of the ideas involved in the combination principle, consider the situation in which a retail merchant selects colored tags for sale merchandise. Suppose the merchant decides to discount some merchandise 10 percent, some 20 percent, and some 50 percent. Also suppose that he has tags colored blue (B), green (G), orange (O), red (R), and yellow (Y). He decides to color code the sale so that all items discounted 10 percent are tagged one color, those discounted 20 percent are tagged another color, and those discounted 50 percent are tagged a third color. Thus, a color code for the sale may be represented by an ordered list of 3 letters, the colors of the tags for items discounted 10 percent, 20 percent, and 50 percent, in that order. The merchant must first select the 3 colors to be used from the 5 colors available and then decide how to use them. For instance, if the colors selected are blue, green, and red, then there are 6 different color codes which can be formed with these colors—the 6 permutations of B, G, and R: BGR, BRG, GBR, GRB, RBG, RGB. In fact, using the permutation principle, we know that there are $P(3, 3) = 3! = 6$ color codes for *each* choice of 3 colors. We also know that the total number of color codes is the number of permutations of 5 things taken 3 at a time, or $P(5, 3)$. Since there are $P(5, 3) = 5!/2! = 60$ color codes and 6 color codes for each choice of 3 colors, there must be $60/6 = 10$ ways to choose 3 colors from 5 colors. In the terminology of the combination principle:

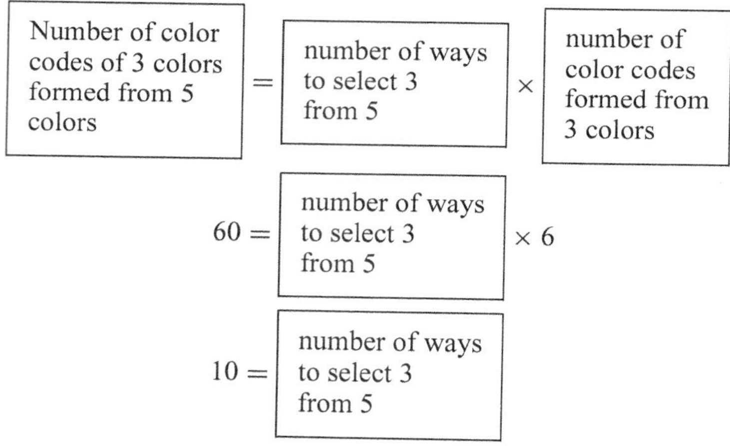

Example 2.19 An apartment complex has 12 smoke alarms, and 3 are to be selected for testing.

Problem In how many ways can the selection be made? Notice that the question involves only *selection*, not selection and order.

Solution To emphasize the underlying ideas, we shall once again solve the problem in a way which illustrates the derivation of the combination principle, instead of simply applying the result. In later examples, after the underlying ideas are familiar, we apply the result directly.

The number of ways that 3 alarms can be selected from a set of 12 and arranged in order is $12 \times 11 \times 10$. Moreover, for each choice of 3 alarms, these 3 can be arranged (permuted) in $3 \times 2 \times 1$ different ways. Therefore, viewing the total process as selection and arrangement, we have

$$12 \times 11 \times 10 = \boxed{\begin{array}{l}\text{number of ways}\\ \text{3 alarms can be}\\ \text{selected from 12}\end{array}} \times (3 \times 2 \times 1)$$

Consequently, there are

$$\frac{12 \times 11 \times 10}{3 \times 2 \times 1} = 220$$

ways of selecting 3 alarms from the 12 available. ■

If we want to select 4 alarms for testing from the set of 12, then we can use the method of Example 2.19 except that we select 4 rather than 3. In particular, we can select 4 alarms and arrange them in order in $12 \times 11 \times 10 \times 9$ different ways. Next, for each choice of the 4 alarms, they can be arranged in $4 \times 3 \times 2 \times 1$ different ways. Consequently, there are

$$\frac{12 \times 11 \times 10 \times 9}{4 \times 3 \times 2 \times 1} = 495$$

ways of selecting 4 alarms for testing from the 12 alarms available.

Example 2.20 There are 8 computer programmers who are qualified to serve on the design team for a new video game. If the team will consist of 5 programmers, how many different teams can be created?

Solution This is a problem of selecting subsets of 5 elements each from a set of 8 elements. An application of the combination principle yields

$$\frac{8!}{(8-5)!5!} = \frac{8 \times 7 \times 6}{3 \times 2 \times 1} = 56$$

as the number of possible teams (note that $8! = 8 \times 7 \times 6 \times 5!$). ■

The expression $\frac{n!}{(n-r)!r!}$ will occur frequently in our study of probability, and it is useful to introduce a shorter notation for it.

The number of combinations of n things taken r at a time is

$$C(n, r) = \frac{n!}{(n-r)!r!} \tag{2.6}$$

The numbers $C(n, r)$ are also known as binomial coefficients, and they have many interesting and important properties. We list here several of these properties.

1. Each selection of r elements from a set of n elements identifies a subset of r elements (those selected). Thus, $C(n, r)$ denotes the number of different subsets of size r in a set of size n.
2. $C(n, r) = C(n, n - r)$. This fact, which is often useful in working problems, follows from the observation that to each r-element subset which is selected from a set of n elements, there is associated an $(n - r)$-element subset consisting of elements which are not selected. This can be directly verified by replacing r by $n - r$ in Equation (2.6).
3. $P(n, r) = r!C(n, r)$. This fact follows from the definitions of $P(n, r)$ and $C(n, r)$.
4. For computational purposes it is convenient to divide both the numerator and denominator of $C(n, r)$ by $(n - r)!$. The result is

$$C(n, r) = \frac{n(n-1)(n-2)\cdots(n-r+1)}{r(r-1)(r-2)\cdots 2 \cdot 1}$$

Note that there are r factors in both the numerator and the denominator. This together with the fact that the first factor in the numerator is n and the first factor in the denominator is r makes the formula easy to remember. For example,

$$C(10, 4) = \frac{10 \times 9 \times 8 \times 7}{4 \times 3 \times 2 \times 1} = 210$$

An alternative notation for the binomial coefficient $C(n, r)$ is $\binom{n}{r}$, and many books use this symbol in place of $C(n, r)$.

In many of the problems which we solve by using counting techniques, it is necessary to combine counting principles in ways that vary from problem to problem. Problems which require combining counting techniques are often multistep problems, problems in which the eventual goal—solving the original problem—is achieved by first solving a series of (two or more) subproblems and then using the solutions of the subproblems to solve the original problem. Each subproblem may require its own counting technique, and the results may be combined by yet another technique. The following examples illustrate the use of the combination principle and the multiplication principle.

Example 2.21 The core curriculum at Gigantic State University (GSU) requires that each student take 2 humanities courses from an approved set of 5 courses and 2 science courses from an approved set of 4 courses.

Problem Find the number of different course selections available to each student, assuming no schedule conflicts.

Solution We apply the combination principle to conclude that it is possible to select the 2 humanities courses in $C(5, 2)$ ways and the 2 science courses in $C(4, 2)$ ways. The process of pairing 2 humanities courses with 2 science courses to form a complete course selection can be treated as a two-stage experiment. The first stage consists of selecting 2 different humanities courses. There are $C(5, 2)$ results at the first stage. The second stage consists of selecting 2 different science courses. For each result at the first stage, there are $C(4, 2)$ results at the second stage. Thus, using the multiplication principle, we conclude that there are

$$C(5, 2) \times C(4, 2) = \frac{5 \times 4}{2 \times 1} \times \frac{4 \times 3}{2 \times 1} = 10 \times 6 = 60$$

ways of selecting 2 humanities courses and 2 science courses. That is, there are 60 different course selections available to each student. ■

Example 2.22 A student at GSU (see Example 2.21) plans to take 2 of her 4 required courses during the same term, and she prefers to take both either in humanities or in science.

Problem Find the number of course selections available to her.

Solution A direct application of the combination principle shows that there are $C(5, 2)$ selections consisting of 2 humanities courses and $C(4, 2)$ selections of 2 science courses. Since no selection is to contain both science and humanities courses, we can think of the set of course selections as partitioned into two sets: one set consisting of 2 humanities courses and one set consisting of 2 science courses. Consequently, we can use the result from Chapter 1 which gives a method for counting the number of elements in a partition [Equation (1.2)]. We conclude that there are $C(5, 2) + C(4, 2) = 10 + 6 = 16$ different course selections available to her. ■

Example 2.23 A student has 7 coins; 5 are dimes and 2 are quarters.

Problem (*a*) In how many ways can 3 coins be selected from 7?
(*b*) In how many ways can 3 coins be selected if both dimes and quarters must be included?

Solution (*a*) This part of the problem can be solved with a direct application of the combination principle: The number of ways to select 3 objects from a set of 7 is $C(7, 3) = 35$.

(*b*) Since there are only 2 quarters, every selection of 3 coins must include at least one dime. However, an arbitrary selection of 3 coins could include only dimes; we seek to count the number of selections containing at least one quarter. If we compute the number of selections which include only dimes and subtract this number from the answer to part a, then we will have the answer to part b. The number of ways we can select 3 coins from 5 dimes is $C(5, 3) = 10$. Thus, the number of ways to select 3 coins including both dimes and quarters is $C(7, 3) - C(5, 3) = 35 - 10 = 25$. ■

Example 2.24 A total quality management team consisting of 3 people from engineering, 2 people from marketing, and 1 person from finance is to be formed. There are 6 people from engineering, 5 from marketing, and 3 from finance qualified for the team.

Problem Find the number of different total quality management teams which can be formed.

Solution It is helpful to view the selection of a team as a three-stage experiment:

Stage 1: Select 3 from 6 people in engineering; $C(6, 3)$ results.
Stage 2: Select 2 from 5 people in marketing; $C(5, 2)$ results.
Stage 3: Select 1 from 3 people in finance; $C(3, 1)$ results.

We apply the multiplication principle to conclude that the number of different teams which can be formed is:

$$C(6, 3) \times C(5, 2) \times C(3, 1) = 20 \times 10 \times 3 = 600$$ ■

Example 2.25 A psychologist plans an experiment in group dynamics which can be conducted with either 3, 4, or 5 subjects. There are 7 subjects available for the experiment.

Problem With how many different groups can the experiment be conducted?

Solution We begin this problem by first noting that the entire set of groups can be partitioned into three subsets: subsets consisting of those groups with 3, 4, and 5 members, respectively. We proceed by counting the number of groups in each subset. Finally, we use Equation (1.2) and determine the total number by adding the numbers for each subset.

$$\boxed{\begin{array}{l}\text{Number}\\ \text{of groups}\\ \text{with 3}\\ \text{members}\end{array}} + \boxed{\begin{array}{l}\text{number}\\ \text{of groups}\\ \text{with 4}\\ \text{members}\end{array}} + \boxed{\begin{array}{l}\text{number}\\ \text{of groups}\\ \text{with 5}\\ \text{members}\end{array}} = C(7, 3) + C(7, 4) + C(7, 5)$$

$$= 35 + 35 + 21$$
$$= 91$$

The experiment can be conducted with 91 different groups. ■

Examples 2.21 through 2.25 give an indication of the diversity of ways in which the basic counting principles can be applied to a problem divided into subproblems. This approach frequently leads to questions which are, in one form or another, about combining the answers to the subproblems and, more particularly, when the answers should be added and when they should be multiplied. This is the standard question: *When do I multiply and when do I add?*

It is difficult to give criteria which are easy to apply and which are always applicable. However, the following guidelines will help in essentially all cases. If the problem is subdivided so that each outcome of a subproblem is an outcome of the original problem, i.e., if the sample space of the original problem has been partitioned in some way, then the results of the subproblems should be added to give the answer to the original problem. This is illustrated in Examples 2.22 and 2.25. Alternatively, if the results of the subproblems are parts of the outcomes of the original problem, but not entire outcomes, then the multiplication principle should be applied. In this case the experiment is viewed as consisting of stages, the tree diagram is split into pieces, and the subtrees are considered separately. This is illustrated in Examples 2.21 and 2.24. The following summarizes these comments.

If the sample space is partitioned, then the numbers of outcomes of the subproblems are *added*; and if the experiment consists of stages, then the numbers of results at each stage are *multiplied*.

Finally, we repeat for emphasis the comment that an important part of many problems is distinguishing between situations in which there is selection only—and therefore the Combination Principle should be used—and situations in which there is both selection and arranging in order—and therefore the Permutation Principle should be used. The actual problem may be described in terms where the selection is not explicit, and a part of the solution is to determine which of these descriptions—selection only or selecting and arranging in order—fits the problem.

Pascal's Triangle

There are a well-known and very useful algorithm and diagram which provide a convenient method of obtaining the binomial coefficients $C(n, r)$ for different values of n and r. The algorithm is based on the fact (easily verified by substitution) that $C(n+1, r) = C(n, r) + C(n, r-1)$, for $r = 1, 2, \ldots, n$. The associated diagram is shown in Figure 2.2. In this figure, each row of the triangle represents one value of n in $C(n, r)$, and the entries in the row are the numbers $C(n, r)$, in order, for $r = 0, 1, 2, \ldots, n$. In each row the first and last entries are 1s [because $C(n, 0) = C(n, n) = 1$]; each remaining entry is the sum of the two

$n = 0$								1								
$n = 1$							1		1							
$n = 2$						1		2		1						
$n = 3$					1		3		3		1					
$n = 4$				1		(4)		(6)		4		1				
$n = 5$			1		5		(10)		10		5		1			
$n = 6$		1		6		15		20		15		6		1		
$n = 7$	1		7		21		35		35		21		7		1	
⋮	⋮		⋮		⋮		⋮		⋮		⋮		⋮		⋮	

FIGURE 2.2

nearest entries in the row just above. For example, the third entry in the row for $n = 5$ is $C(5, 2) = 10$; and this is the sum of $C(4, 1) = 4$ and $C(4, 2) = 6$, the entries just above the 10. The same relationship holds for the entries in each row, and the triangle continues for all positive integers $n = 0, 1, 2, 3 \dots$.

Exercises for Section 2.3

1. Compute the values of $C(5, 3)$, $C(7, 4)$, $C(8, 5)$, and $C(9, 2) \cdot C(9, 7)$.
2. Compute the values of $C(9, 2)$, $C(9, 3)$, and, $C(9, 4)$.
3. A smartphone user would like to purchase 5 new Apps for her phone. If there are 10 Apps in which she is interested, in how many different ways can she select a set of 5 Apps to purchase?
4. Which number is larger in each of the following pairs?
   (*a*) $C(9, 3)$, $C(10, 2)$ (*b*) $C(12, 4)$, $C(18, 3)$
   (*c*) $C(9, 3)$, $6!$ (*d*) 3^5, $5!$
5. A set S has 6 elements. How many subsets of S have *exactly* 3 elements? How many subsets have either 2 or 4 elements?
6. A set S has 9 elements. How many subsets of S have *at most* 3 elements?
7. A student has 4 pencils, 3 ballpoint pens, and 1 felt-tip pen in a cup.
   (*a*) In how many different ways can 2 of the 8 be selected?
   (*b*) In how many ways can 2 items be selected so that not both are ballpoint pens?
8. In how many different ways can the chairperson of a 10-person committee select a subcommittee of 3 from the other 9 members of the committee?
9. Two coins are selected from 5 coins: 3 dimes and 2 quarters.
   (*a*) In how many ways can the selection be made?
   (*b*) In how many ways can the selection be made so that both are dimes?
   (*c*) In how many ways can the selection be made so that 1 dime and 1 quarter are selected?
   (d) In how many ways can the selection be made so that at least 1 coin is a dime?
10. Three cards are drawn from a standard deck of cards.
   (*a*) In how many ways can they all be the same suit?
   (*b*) In how many ways can they all be the same rank?
   (*c*) In how many ways can they all be face cards?

11. Three coins are selected from 6 coins: 3 dimes, 2 nickels, and 1 quarter. In how many ways can the selection be made so that the value of the coins chosen is at least 25 cents?
12. A camper has 4 jackets, 3 sleeping bags, and 10 different packages of freeze-dried food. An outfit for a camping trip consists of 1 jacket, 1 sleeping bag, and 3 packages of freeze-dried food.
    (*a*) How many different outfits are possible?
    (*b*) If she decides to bring 2 jackets instead of just 1 jacket, then how many outfits are possible (she is still bringing 1 sleeping bag and 3 packages of freeze-dried food)?
13. A box in a high school gym contains nine balls: 4 footballs, 3 basketballs, and 2 baseballs. A gym teacher must select 3 of the 9 balls to be used in a gym class.
    (*a*) In how many ways can the 3 balls be selected?
    (*b*) In how many ways can the selections be made if at least two different types of balls are to be selected?
14. How many different ways can a grocery shopper select one item each from a selection of 6 frozen dinners, 5 desserts, and 4 beverages?
15. You have 3 types of vegetables and 5 types of fruits. A vegetable salad consists of a mixture of any 2 kinds of vegetables, and a fruit salad consists of a mixture of any 2 kinds of fruits.
    (*a*) In how many different ways can you prepare a vegetable salad and a fruit salad?
    (*b*) In how many ways can you prepare a vegetable salad or a fruit salad?
    (*c*) You are to take 2 different kinds of salads on a picnic. In how many ways can you do this?
16. A student is to take 1 mathematics course, 1 history course, 1 business course, and 2 electives. There are 3 courses in mathematics, 3 in history, and 5 in business for which she is prepared. Also, she is interested in 5 elective courses. How many course selections are available to her if there are no time conflicts?
17. A candle manufacturer produces 5 types of round candles and 4 types of square candles. Gift packages contain 2 round candles and 2 square candles, all of different types. How many different gift packages are there?
18. A flag designer is to construct a new flag by first choosing 3 of the seven available colors for three stripes on the flag, and then choosing 2 of 5 available symbols to be placed on the flag. How many different flags are possible, each using 3 colors and 2 symbols?
19. A senate committee consists of 6 Democrats and 4 Republicans. How many different subcommittees can be formed in the following situations?
    (*a*) Each subcommittee must consist of exactly 3 Democrats and 2 Republicans.
    (*b*) Each subcommittee must consist of either 3 Democrats and 2 Republicans or 4 Democrats and 1 Republican.
20. A group of 9 students includes 6 students who live in the dorms and 3 who do not. In how many ways can you select a subgroup of 4 students consisting of 2 students who live in the dorms and 2 who do not?
21. A pizza can be ordered with any of 3 different crusts (thin, regular, and deep-dish) and 4 toppings selected from the 6 available (sausage, pepperoni, olives, green peppers, mushrooms, and onions). How many different pizzas are there?

22. A security entry lock consists of a keyboard with the numbers 1 through 9. An "entry code" consists of three single numbers to be punched in order, or two single numbers followed by one pair of numbers (a pair is two different numbers), the pair to be pushed simultaneously. How many different entry codes are there?
23. A neighborhood club has 8 girls and 6 boys. A basketball team of 5 members is to be selected.
    (*a*) In how many ways can the selection be made?
    (*b*) In how many ways can the selection be made so that the team contains both boys and girls?
24. A student has invitations for job interviews in Atlanta, Boston, Chicago, Detroit, and Seattle.
    (*a*) In how many ways can he select 3 cities to visit?
    (*b*) In how many ways can he select 3 cities to visit if both Atlanta and Seattle are included?
    (*c*) In how many ways can he select 3 cities to visit if not both Atlanta and Seattle are included?
25. A bowl contains 6 red balls and 4 blue balls. In how many ways can 2 balls be selected so that both red and blue balls are obtained?
26. There are 6 defective smart phones and 4 non-defective smart phones in a lost-and-found. Five of the 10 smart phones are randomly selected. In how many ways can at most 3 defective smart phones be selected?
27. A "hand" consists of a set of 5 cards selected from an ordinary deck of 52 cards.
    (*a*) How many different hands contain exactly 3 spades?
    (*b*) How many different hands contain exactly 3 cards of some suit (any of the 4 suits)?
    (*c*) How many different hands contain cards of all 4 suits?
28. Refer to Exercise 27.
    (*a*) How many different hands of cards contain exactly 4 aces?
    (*b*) How many different hands contain cards of only 1 suit?
29. The Tiny State College Student Advisory Board has rules to the effect that the officers of the board (i.e., Chairperson, Vice-Chairperson, and Treasurer) must always include at least one in-state student and at least one senior. The TSC Student Council consists of 6 members: 1 in-state senior, two in-state students who are not seniors, 1 out-of-state senior, and two out-of-state students who are not seniors. In how many ways can the officers of the Student Advisory Board be selected from these 6 Student Council members if they must obey the rules? Note that if individual members switch offices, this produces a different Board.
30. A committee consists of 4 males and 5 females. Three different members are to be selected to serve as delegates to three different national delegations, one to each delegation. How many ways can the selection of 3 be made so that both males and females are selected?
31. The faculty at GSU is divided into four schools: Humanities, Science, Music, and Athletics. The faculty council has 8 members, and it must contain at least 1 faculty member from each school. In how many different ways (in terms of school representatives) can the council be constituted? (For example, one possible way is to have 2 members from each of the 4 schools.)
32. For what values of the natural number n are both $C(2n, 4)$ and $C(n, 2)$ defined and equal?

33. Show that for $n = 3, 4, 5, \ldots$

$$C(n, 2) + C(n, 3) = C(n + 1, 3)$$

34. Show that for $n = 2, 3, 4, \ldots$ and $r = 1, 2, 3, \ldots, n$

$$C(n, r) + C(n, r - 1) = C(n + 1, r)$$

35. For what values of n is it true that $C(100, 2n) > C(1000, n)$?
36. A Science Fair team will consist of one male, one female, and one 'alternate', who can be of either gender. There are 4 males and 3 females trying out for the team. A team roster is a list of the 3 members of the team, *without mention of which one of the three team members is the alternate.* How many different team rosters are possible?

2.4 COMPUTING PROBABILITIES BY USING EQUALLY LIKELY OUTCOMES

We have used counting techniques to determine the number of outcomes of an experiment, where the term "experiment" has a fairly general meaning. We continue by using the same techniques to determine probabilities. If a sample space S contains n outcomes and if these outcomes are equally likely, then each should be assigned the same probability (weight), namely $1/n(S)$. In this special case of equally likely outcomes, to determine the probability of an event E (a subset of S), we need only count the number of elements in each of sets E and S and use the fact that the probability of any event is the sum of the probabilities of the outcomes in that event. Thus, if each outcome in event E has probability $1/n(S)$, then the probability of E, denoted $\Pr[E]$, is $\Pr[E] = n(E)/n(S)$. We repeat for emphasis that this technique should be used *only when the outcomes are equally likely.* In this section we illustrate the use of the four counting principles (partition, multiplication, permutation, and combination) to compute $n(E)$ and $n(S)$ and consequently $\Pr[E]$.

Example 2.26 A student has 5 coins—2 dimes and 3 quarters—and 2 coins are selected simultaneously and at random.

Problem Find the probability that both are quarters.

Solution Recall that the phrase "selected at random" means that equally likely outcomes are to be used. Since there are 5 coins, there are $C(5, 2) = 10$ ways of selecting 2 coins. Since there are 3 quarters, there are $C(3, 2) = 3$ ways of selecting 2 quarters. Therefore, if S is the sample space for the experiment of selecting 2 coins, then $n(S) = 10$; and if E is the event that 2 quarters are selected, then $n(E) = 3$. Consequently, $\Pr[E] = \frac{3}{10}$; the probability of selecting 2 quarters is $\frac{3}{10}$. ■

Example 2.27 During a finite math exam, four students have their smartphones taken away from them by their teacher. After the exam is over, the four phones are returned to the four students in a random order.

Problem What is the probability that all 4 students receive their own phone?

Solution Each assignment of phones to students corresponds to an arrangement of the names of the four students. Thus there are $P(4, 4) = 4!/0! = 24$ possible assignments. Only one of these assignments will be such that each student receives their own phone, hence Pr[all four students receive their own phone] $= \frac{1}{24}$. ■

Example 2.28 A runner enters two races, both to be run on an 8-lane track. The runner is assigned a lane for each race.

Problem Assuming that the lane assignments are made at random, what is the probability that the runner has lane 1 (the inside lane) for at least one race?

Solution The runner could be assigned any one of 8 lanes for the first race and any one of 8 lanes for the second race. By the multiplication principle, there are $8 \times 8 = 64$ possible pairs of lane assignments for the two races. Let E be the event that the runner has lane 1 for at least one race, F the event that she has lane 1 for the first race, and G the event that she has lane 1 for the second race. Then $E = F \cup G$. Clearly $n(F) = 8$ since she could have lane 1 in the first race and any of the 8 lanes for the second race. Likewise, $n(G) = 8$ and $n(F \cap G) = 1$. Using Equation (1.6), we have

$$n(E) = n(F \cup G) = n(F) + n(G) - n(F \cap G)$$

and

$$n(E) = 8 + 8 - 1 = 15$$

Since $n(S) = 64$, it follows from Equation (2.4) that $\Pr[E] = \frac{15}{64}$. ■

Example 2.29 A 12-unit apartment building has 9 smoke alarms which pass inspection and 3 which do not. If 3 smoke alarms are selected at random and tested, what is the probability that all pass inspection?

Solution In Example 2.19 it was shown that there are $C(12, 3) = 220$ ways of selecting 3 smoke alarms from 12. Thus, $n(S) = 220$. Since 9 of the alarms pass inspection, there are $C(9, 3) = 84$ ways of selecting 3 alarms which pass. Therefore, $n(E) = 84$. Finally, the probability of selecting 3 alarms which pass inspection is $\Pr[E] = \frac{84}{220} = \frac{21}{55}$. ■

Example 2.30 A total quality management team contains 8 people: 5 from customer service and 3 from data processing. Two team members are selected at random to present the results of the team's work.

Problem What is the probability of event E that 1 of the people selected is from customer service and 1 is from data processing?

Solution The two team members can be selected in $(8 \times 7)/2 = 28$ ways, so $n(S) = 28$. Event E is the complement of the event that both come from the same department. Since both can come from customer service in $(5 \times 4)/2 = 10$ ways, and since both can come from data processing in $(3 \times 2)/2 = 3$ ways, we see by the partition principle that $n(E') = 10 + 3 = 13$. Finally, $n(E) = n(S) - n(E') = 28 - 13 = 15$, and $\Pr[E] = \frac{15}{28}$. ■

Example 2.31 A student must select 3 courses from a list of 7. The list includes 4 humanities courses and 3 science courses.

Problem If the selection is made at random, what is the probability that 3 humanities courses will be chosen?

Solution The number of ways to choose 3 courses from a list of 7 is

$$C(7, 3) = \frac{7 \times 6 \times 5}{3 \times 2 \times 1} = 35$$

The number of ways to choose 3 courses from a list of 4 humanities courses is

$$C(4, 3) = \frac{4 \times 3 \times 2}{3 \times 2 \times 1} = 4$$

Thus the probability of selecting all 3 courses from the humanities is $\frac{4}{35}$. ■

Example 2.32 Sam and Sally are members of a committee studying the effects of government regulation on business. The committee consists of 4 men and 3 women, and a subcommittee of 3 is to be chosen to study "paperwork." The subcommittee must include at least 1 woman, but it cannot consist entirely of women.

Problem If the subcommittee is selected at random from the set of all subcommittees which meet these conditions, what is the probability that the subcommittee selected will include Sam? What is the probability that it will include Sally?

Solution The subcommittee may consist of 1 man and 2 women or 2 men and 1 woman. The number of subcommittees with 1 man and 2 women is

$$C(4, 1) \times C(3, 2) = 4 \times 3 = 12$$

The number of subcommittees with 2 men and 1 woman is

$$C(4, 2) \times C(3, 1) = 6 \times 3 = 18$$

Thus there are $18 + 12 = 30$ possible subcommittees.

To answer the questions about Sally and Sam, we need to know the number of possible subcommittees which include them. If Sam is on a subcommittee, the remaining 2 members could be 2 women or 1 woman and 1 man. The number of ways 2 women could be chosen is $C(3, 2)$, and the number of ways 1 woman and 1 man could be chosen is $C(3, 1) \times C(3, 1)$. Therefore the number of such subcommittees is

$$C(3, 2) + C(3, 1) \times C(3, 1) = 3 + 3 \times 3 = 12$$

Thus the probability that the subcommittee selected will include Sam is

$$\frac{12}{30} = \frac{2}{5}$$

The analysis is similar for Sally. If she is on the subcommittee, then the other 2 members could be 2 men or 1 woman and 1 man. The number of such subcommittees is

$$C(4, 2) + C(4, 1) \times C(2, 1) = 6 + 4 \times 2 = 14$$

and the probability that the subcommittee selected will include Sally is

$$\frac{14}{30} = \frac{7}{15}$$

■

Exercises for Section 2.4

1. Two coins are selected at random from 5 coins: 3 dimes and 2 quarters. What is the probability that both are dimes?
2. A group of 6 students—4 males and 2 females—selects 2 students at random to make a report. Find the probability that 2 females are selected.
3. Three cards are selected at random from a deck of 52 cards. What is the probability that all 3 are spades?
4. Four cards are randomly selected from a standard deck of 52 cards.
   (*a*) What is the probability that all four cards are Aces?
   (*b*) What is the probability that all four cards are red?

5. A cooler contains 7 cans of cola: 4 regular colas and 3 diet colas. If 3 cans of cola are selected at random, what is the probability that all 3 are regular colas?
6. Howard has 6 tan socks and 4 blue socks in a drawer. If he selects 2 socks at random, find the probability that he selects 2 socks of the same color.
7. An experiment consists of rolling 1 red die, 1 white die, and 1 blue die and noting the result of each roll. If the dice are fair, and all outcomes are equally likely, find the probability that should be assigned to each outcome.
8. Using the experiment of Exercise 7, what is the probability that the sum of the results on the three dice is 7? What is the probability that the sum is an odd number?
9. Five qualified individuals including a wife and husband apply for 3 vacant sales positions. If people are hired at random, what is the probability that both the husband and wife are hired? What is the probability that one is hired and one is not?
10. A fair coin is flipped 4 times.
    (*a*) What is the probability that all four tosses result in heads landing up?
    (*b*) What is the probability that both heads and tails occur during the 4 tosses?
11. Your friend has 8 tickets to a concert: 2 in the front row and 6 in the tenth row. She selects 2 tickets at random and gives them to you. Find the probability that both are in the front row.
12. Suppose that 3 digits are selected at random from the set $S = \{1, 2, 4, 5, 6\}$ and are arranged in random order. Find the probability that the resulting 3-digit number is less than 300.
13. A bucket contains 5 orange tennis balls and 5 yellow tennis balls. Five balls are selected simultaneously and at random. What is the probability that *at least* one is orange *and at least one* is yellow?
14. In the setting of Exercise 13, what is the probability that *at least* two balls are yellow *and at least* two are orange?
15. There are 5 black and 5 white mice available for an experiment which requires 4 mice. If a random selection of 4 mice is made from the set of 10, what is the probability that 2 black and 2 white mice are selected?
16. Suppose you have seven cards numbered 1 through 7. You select 4 cards at random, one after another, noting the number of each card selected, then setting it aside. What is the probability that the first card selected is 1 and the third card is 3?
17. Seven friends, including Dexter and Darwin, have put their names in a lottery for free bagels. If 3 different names are drawn at random, what is the probability that both Dexter and Darwin will have their names drawn?
18. For the first day of school an elementary school teacher randomly assigns desks to students. She has 4 tall desks in the room, 7 medium sized desks in the room, and 7 small desks in the room. If she has the same number of desks as students, what is the probability the tallest student in the class gets a tall desk?
19. A student selects 5 frozen dinners from 9 alternatives. The alternatives include 4 different pasta dinners, 3 different chicken dinners, and 2 different seafood dinners. If the selection is made at random, find the probability that *at least* 2 pasta dinners will be selected.

20. There are nine balls numbered 1 through 9 in a box. An experiment consists of randomly selecting five balls, one after another and without replacement, and noting the number on each selected ball.
    (*a*) Find the probability that the first three balls selected are 1, 2, and 3, in that order.
    (*b*) Find the probability that all five balls are odd-numbered.
21. The Student Union Board has 10 members: 7 females and 3 males including Steve. Three tasks are to be assigned, including that of reserving a room for meetings. The tasks are assigned at random, at most one task per person.
    (*a*) Find the probability that Steve is asked to reserve a room.
    (*b*) Find the probability that Steve is given a task.
22. You are given the situation in Exercise 21.
    (*a*) Find the probability that both males and females are given tasks.
    (*b*) Find the probability that Steve and at least 1 female are given tasks.
23. A congressional committee contains 5 Democrats and 4 Republicans. A subcommittee of 3 is to be randomly selected from all subcommittees of 3 which contain at least 1 Democrat. What is the probability that this new subcommittee will contain at least 2 Democrats?
24. A cast consists of 4 roles. One of the roles is reserved for a woman and the other three roles can be played by either men or women. There are 5 men and 9 women auditioning for these roles. What is the probability that a randomly selected cast contains exactly 2 women?
25. A pair of fair dice is tossed. What is the probability that the sum or the product or both the sum and the product of the numbers that land uppermost are exactiy 8?
26. A box contains 6 red, 5 white and 5 blue marbles. An experiment consists of randomly selecting nine marbles from the box without replacement.
    (*a*) What is the probability that at most two of the selected marbles are red?
    (*b*) What is the probability that marbles of only two different colors are selected?
27. Suppose a basketball team is equally likely to win or lose each game. After 5 games the team has a "record", i.e., a sequence of wins and losses. What is the probability that there is a string of at least 3 consecutive wins in the team's record?
28. A student has 4 pencils, 3 ballpoint pens, and 1 felt-tip pen in a cup. An experiment consists of randomly selecting two of the 8 items in the cup.
    (*a*) What is the probability that a ballpoint pen is NOT selected?
    (*b*) What is the probability that both items selected are pencils?
    (*c*) What is the probability that one of the selected items is the felt-tip pen?
29. A student plans to purchase three new video games. He is interested in 3 Action games (including *World of Woodcraft*), 4 Role-playing games, and 2 Strategy games. The student randomly selects 3 games from the 9 in which he is interested. Find the probability of each of the following.
    (*a*) Exactly one is a role-playing game.
    (*b*) One of the games is *World of Woodcraft.*
30. In the situation described in Exercise 29, find the probability that
    (*a*) One is an Action game and two are Strategy games.
    (*b*) At least one is a Strategy game.

31. The coach of the Gigantic State University football team must form a game plan by selecting 7 plays from his list of 14 plays. The list includes 8 pass plays and 6 running plays. If the selection is made at random, what is the probability that the game plan will include at least 2 running plays *and* at least 2 pass plays?
32. A legislative committee consists of 4 conservatives and 2 liberals. A subcommittee of 3 is to be selected. If such a subcommittee is formed at random, what is the probability that it contains at least one liberal and at least one conservative?
33. There are 5 unique positions available within a Fortune 500 company. Two of these positions must be filled with women, and the others could be filled with either men or women. Six men, including Shawn, have applied, and 7 women have applied.
    (*a*) In how many ways can the positions be filled?
    (*b*) If the positions are filled at random, what is the probability that Shawn is appointed?
34. A group of 6 men enters a restaurant and check their coats. The checker puts all 6 coats on the same hook and gives one of the men a tag. When the men leave the restaurant, the checker hands each of the men a coat. If the checker hands out the coats at random, what is the probability that each man receives the correct coat?
35. There are n cans of regular cola and 3 cans of diet cola in a cooler. Three cans are selected at random, and the type of cola, regular or diet, is noted. For what values of n is the probability of having all diet cola less than .01?
36. In the situation described in Exercise 35, for what values of n is the probability of having 1 regular and 2 diet colas more than .5? Less than .1? Less than .01?
37. There are n red balls and $2n$ blue balls in a box. Three balls are selected at random, and their colors are noted. For what values of n is the probability of having all blue balls less than .28?
38. A three-player game uses 10 colored chips: 5 white chips, 3 red chips, and 2 blue chips. Each player randomly selects chips from the table as follows: Player 1 selects 2 chips from the 10 available, then Player 2 selects 5 of the remaining 8 chips, and finally Player 3 takes the 3 remaining chips. What is the probability that Player 1 selects the 2 blue chips, Player 2 selects the 5 white chips, and Player 3 is left with the 3 red chips?

IMPORTANT TERMS AND CONCEPTS

You should be able to describe, define, or give examples and use each of the following:

Relative frequency method of assigning probabilities
Equally likely outcomes
Experiment
Event
Assignment of probabilities
Probability of an event
Deductive method of assigning probabilities
Selected at random
Permutation principle
Combination principle
Binomial coefficients
Pascal's triangle

REVIEW EXERCISES

1. A bowl contains 3 red balls and 2 blue balls. An experiment consists of drawing 3 balls, in succession and without replacement, and noting the color of each ball drawn. Describe the sample space of this experiment. What is the event that *at least* 1 blue ball is drawn?
2. In the experiment described in Exercise 1, what is the event that *at most* 1 blue ball is drawn? What is the event that *exactly* 1 blue ball is drawn?
3. A student in an automotive repair class decides to paint his car three different colors—one color for the front of the car, a different color for the middle of the car, and a third color for the back of the car. There are 5 different colors to choose from, and the student decides to choose the 3 colors randomly from the 5 available. (Note that if the same 3 colors are chosen, but arranged in a different order on the car, the result is a different outcome.)
   (*a*) How many different ways can the car be painted?
   (*b*) If instead of painting each part of the car with a different color, the student decides to take the 3 selected colors and mix them together before painting the entire car with the mixture, then how many different ways can the car be painted?
4. An experiment has 5 outcomes, with $w_1 = 2w_2$, $w_2 = \frac{1}{3}w_3$, $w_3 = \frac{3}{2}w_4$, $w_4 = w_5$. Find w_1.
5. A die is weighted so that outcomes 3, 4, and 6 are equally likely, and they are 3 times as likely as outcomes 1, 2, and 5, which are all equally likely. What probabilities should be assigned to the outcomes to reflect these facts?
6. A product code consists of a string of 4 different letters from the set $\{A, H, Q, T, Z\}$. How many such codes contain the letters H and Q?
7. A choir contains 4 tenors, 3 altos, and 2 sopranos. The director of the choir needs all 9 choir members to form a line so that they can have their picture taken. However, the choir director is very picky and wants all 4 tenors to be next to each other, all 3 altos to be next to each other and both sopranos to be next to each other. In how many different ways can the 9 singers be arranged for the picture?
8. There are 5 conservatives and 3 liberals on a congressional committee.
   (*a*) In how many ways can you select a subcommittee of 4 that consists of 2 liberals and 2 conservatives?
   (*b*) In how many ways can you select a subcommittee of 4 that consists of no more than one liberal?
9. Gwen & Harry's Ice Cream Shoppe has 3 types of cones and 14 flavors of ice cream.
   (*a*) In how many different ways can you order 1 cone and 2 scoops of ice cream? Of course, vanilla on top of chocolate is different from chocolate on top of vanilla.
   (*b*) In how many different ways can you order 1 cone and 2 scoops of ice cream which are not the same flavor?
10. A motor pool contains 5 subcompact sedans, 4 compact sedans, and 3 midsize sedans. In how many ways can 3 cars be selected so that not all are the same size?
11. There are 4 jugglers, 3 singers, and 2 dancers auditioning for the 2 remaining spots in a talent competition. If all are equally talented, and the 2 performers are selected randomly, then what is the probability that neither of those selected is a singer?

12. In the context of Exercise 11, find the probability that at least one performer is a singer.
13. There are 4 adjacent seats in a row in a theater. In how many different ways can 4 people be seated?
14. First, second and third prizes are to be awarded at a science fair in which 16 exhibits have been entered. In how many different ways can the prizes be awarded?
15. There is one winning number for the Pick-4 daily lottery. The set of possible numbers consists of all sequences of 4 digits, each digit between and including 0 and 9. If you randomly select one such number, what is the probability that you select the winning number?
16. Two fair dice are rolled. What is the probability of each of the following?
    (*a*) A sum of 4, 6, or 8 is obtained.
    (*b*) A sum of at least 10 is obtained.
17. Two fair dice are rolled, and the number on each is noted. Find the probability that one of the numbers is a 6 or the sum of the numbers is at least 9.
18. There are 2 nickels and 3 quarters in a box. Two coins are selected simultaneously and at random, and the value of each coin is noted.
    (*a*) Find the probability that both coins selected are nickels.
    (*b*) Find the probability that the total value of the selected coins is at least 30 cents.
19. There are 5 ham sandwiches and 3 turkey sandwiches in a cooler. If you select 2 sandwiches at random, what is the probability that at least 1 is a ham sandwich?
20. An economics exam has two parts. The first part consists of 10 true-false questions, and the second part consists of 5 multiple-choice questions where 1 answer in 4 possible is correct. How many different answer sheets can be submitted, assuming 1 answer is given for each question?
21. A committee of 6 students is selected from a group of 12 students. A meeting of the committee is called, and each member will either attend the meeting or miss it. How many different subsets of the group could attend the meeting?
22. For the first day of school a teacher randomly assigns desks to students. She has 4 tall desks in the room, 7 medium sized desks in the room, and 7 small desks in the room. If she has the same number of desks as students, what is the probability that the tallest person in the class gets a tall desk and the shortest person gets a short desk?
23. You are given a pair of fair dice, one with 4 sides, numbered 1, 2, 3, 4, and one with 5 sides numbered 1, 2, 3, 4, 5. What is the probability that a roll of these two dice will yield a sum of 6?
24. A softball team has 6 aluminum bats and 9 magnesium bats. Three bats are selected at random from the bat rack.
    (*a*) What is the probability that all 3 are aluminum?
    (*b*) What is the probability that at least 1 bat is aluminum?
25. There are 24 cans of cola in a cooler; 6 are regular, and the remainder are diet. In how many ways can you select each of the following?
    (*a*) 3 cans from the cooler
    (*b*) 3 regular colas
    (*c*) 3 diet colas
    (*d*) 3 colas of which at least 2 are diet

26. In the setting of Exercise 25, find the probability of selecting 3 colas from the cooler such that
    (*a*) all are regular;
    (*b*) all are diet;
    (*c*) at least 2 are diet;
    (*d*) there are both regular and diet colas.
27. A poker hand consists of 5 cards selected at random from an ordinary deck. Find the probability that a poker hand contains
    (*a*) 4 aces;
    (*b*) 4 of a kind (4 cards of the same rank);
    (*c*) 5 consecutive cards of the same suit (each ace can be used either as the first card, A2345, or as the last card, 10JQKA).
28. Find the probability that a poker hand contains
    (*a*) Exactly 3 of a kind;
    (*b*) Exactly 2 pairs;
    (*c*) Exactly 1 pair.
29. A student is making out her schedule for next year. Her advisor has given her a list of courses she could take consisting of 9 required courses and 12 elective courses. She must take at least 4 courses but cannot take more than 6 courses. In how many ways can she select courses such that she takes at least one elective course?
30. Suppose that a bag containing 10 basketballs has 4 with defective valves. If 2 balls are selected at random from the bag, what is the probability that *at least* 1 will have a defective valve?
31. A coach has 6 stopwatches: 3 are accurate, 1 is fast, and 2 are equally slow. The coach makes a random selection of 2 watches to be used to time the first-place finisher in a race.
    (*a*) What is the probability that the first-place finisher is timed accurately by both watches?
    (*b*) What is the probability that the first-place finisher is timed accurately by at least 1 watch?
    (*c*) What is the probability that the watches used to time the first-place finisher both show the same time?
32. A five-card poker hand is chosen at random. A ''full house'' consists of two of one type of card and three of a second type of card. In how many ways can a ''full house'' be chosen?
33. Four people at a magic show are asked to place their Driver's Licenses face down on a table. The four licenses are then mixed up. The magician claims that she can, without looking at the licenses, give each license to its rightful owner. If the magician is not telling the truth, and her selections can be considered random, then what is the probability that each person receives their own Driver's License?
34. A green die and a red die are rolled, and the numbers on each are noted. Assume both dice are fair.
    (*a*) Find the probability that the numbers are the same on both dice.
    (*b*) Find the probability that the sum of the numbers is even.
    (*c*) Find the probability that the product of the numbers is less than 19.

35. A casting director is casting for a play with roles for 1 female, 1 child, and 2 males. There are 6 males, including Sam, 3 females, and 2 children, including Heidi, auditioning for the roles.
    (*a*) In how many different ways can the roles be filled from those auditioning?
    (*b*) In how many different ways can they be filled if exactly 1 of Sam and Heidi is given a role?
    (*c*) If the roles are filled at random, what is the probability that both Heidi and Sam are given roles?
36. A box of 50 flash drives contains 5 defective ones. Three flash drives are selected at random from the box and tested. What is the most likely number of defective flash drives in the sample?
37. For what values of n does the number of ways of selecting n items from a set of 50 exceed the number of ways of selecting 10 items from a set of 100?
38. There are n defective items in a box of 50. Three items are selected and tested, and 1 is found to be defective.
    (*a*) Determine the probability of finding exactly 1 defective item in a random selection of 3 items. This probability will depend on n.
    (*b*) For what value of n is the probability determined in (a) as large as possible?
39. At the start of an experiment, Box A contains 1 red card and 2 black cards, and Box B contains 1 red card and 1 black card. An experiment consists of randomly selecting one card from Box A, placing the selected card in Box B, and then randomly selecting one card from Box B. What is the probability that a red card is selected from Box B?
40. A grocery store shelf contains 5 cans of beans, 3 cans of soup, and 4 cans of corn. A shopper randomly selects four cans from the shelf. What is the probability that the shopper selects at least one can of each type of item?

CHAPTER

3

Probability

3.0 THE SETTING AND OVERVIEW

The outcomes of an experiment do not always occur with the same frequency. As a result, when using the concepts and methods of probability to study experiments, we cannot always assume that the outcomes are equally likely. In this chapter we shall see how the properties of probabilities which hold in general settings are related to those which hold when outcomes are equally likely. We shall use these properties to study the results of experiments and to compute the probabilities of various events. Also we shall study experiments for which we have partial advance information about the outcomes. In these cases we develop methods to determine probabilities in light of this information. We further develop the concept of a tree diagram as a way of representing certain types of experiments and as an aid in solving problems.

3.1 PROBABILITY MEASURES: AXIOMS AND PROPERTIES

Probability theory is a method of assigning numbers to events, i.e., to subsets of a sample space. In Chapter 2, we considered events which were subsets of a sample space of equally likely outcomes. However, many very interesting and important events do not consist of equally likely outcomes. For example, consider the experiment of checking computer memory chips one after another until either a defective chip is found or three chips have been checked. If we let G represent a good chip and D represent a defective chip, then a natural sample space for this experiment is the set $S = \{D, GD, GGD, \text{and } GGG\}$. The outcomes in set S do not usually occur equally often, and hence they should not be assigned the same probability. This means that we need a more general method of assigning probabilities to events than the one used in Chapter 2, $\Pr[E] = n(E)/n(S)$, because in that method it was assumed that all outcomes had the same probability. Our more general method should include the situation of equally likely outcomes as a special case, and we begin with a brief review of this special case. First, however, it is useful to introduce some additional terminology.

Assigning probabilities to outcomes attaches a number to each outcome of an experiment. This probability is a measure of the likelihood of that outcome and is frequently referred to simply as the *weight* of that outcome. The result of all these assignments is a *probability measure*. In the special case in which all outcomes are equally likely, this is called the *equiprobable measure*.

If we use the equiprobable measure in a sample space S containing n outcomes, then we assign probability $1/n$ to each outcome, and we assign probability m/n to an event (subset of the sample space) which contains m outcomes. Several facts about this assignment are clear. First, the probability of each event is a nonnegative number. Second, since the sample space contains all outcomes, the probability assigned to the sample space is $n/n = 1$. Third, if we have two *disjoint* events E_1 and E_2 containing m_1 and m_2 outcomes, respectively, then there are $m_1 + m_2$ outcomes in the event $E_1 \cup E_2$, and

$$\Pr[E_1 \cup E_2] = \frac{m_1 + m_2}{n} = \frac{m_1}{n} + \frac{m_2}{n} = \Pr[E_1] + \Pr[E_2]$$

We require that any assignment of probabilities satisfy these three conditions. To use the terminology which is common in mathematics in such circumstances, we take these conditions as *axioms* for an assignment of probabilities.

Axioms for a Probability Measure

A *probability measure* assigns to each event E of a sample space S a number denoted by $\Pr[E]$ and called the *probability* of E: This assignment must satisfy

i. $0 \leq \Pr[E] \leq 1$ for each event E in S
ii. $\Pr[S] = 1$
iii. If E_1 and E_2 are disjoint events in S, then

$$\Pr[E_1 \cup E_2] = \Pr[E_1] + \Pr[E_2]$$

We note that a probability measure is an example of a function, a function defined on the subsets of a sample space S. To each subset E of S, this function assigns a number $\Pr[E]$. It is natural to refer to this function as Pr.

In Chapter 2 we defined the probability of an event by using the probabilities of outcomes. In particular:

For any event E, $E \neq \emptyset$,

$$\Pr[E] = \text{sum of probabilities of outcomes in } E$$

and

$$\Pr[\emptyset] = 0$$

Given any assignment of probabilities to outcomes, this definition can be used to define the probability of any event. To confirm that it defines a probability measure, it is necessary to verify that axioms i to iii are fulfilled. This is a straightforward application of the properties (2.1) and (2.2). We omit the details.

Example 3.1 The point of sale terminals in the Super Deals electronics store record information about the time of each sale and the goods sold. The manager is interested in when high value sales (sales over $500) occur. Suppose the manager has data on the size of each sale (high value or not) and the time of sale. For simplicity, sales are aggregated as before 6:00 PM or after 6:00 PM. Recovering the record of a sale (value and time) during a day can be thought of as an experiment with four possible outcomes, the outcomes shown in Table 3.1. Suppose the manager uses data collected to determine the relative frequencies of the four outcomes and obtains the probabilities shown in the table. Note that the four outcomes shown are mutually exclusive and make up the entire sample space so the probabilities add to 1.

TABLE 3.1

Outcome		Probability
Sale before 6:00 PM and high value	(BH)	.05
Sale before 6:00 PM and not high value	(BN)	.26
Sale after 6:00 PM and high value	(AH)	.17
Sale after 6:00 PM and not high value	(AN)	.52

Problem Using the data from Table 3.1, determine each of the following probabilities:

(a) Probability[sale before 6:00 PM],

(b) Probability[sale after 6:00 PM],

(c) Probability[sale after 6:00 PM or high value].

Solution We use the following notation for events:

B: a sale before 6:00 PM
A: a sale after 6:00 PM
H: a high-value sale
N: not a high-value sale

(*a*) It follows that $B = \{BH, BN\}$ and $A = \{AH, AN\}$. Using the fact that the probability of an event is the sum of the probabilities of the outcomes in the event, we have

$$\Pr[B] = \Pr[BH] + \Pr[BN] = .05 + .26 = .31$$

(*b*) Also events B and A form a partition of the sample space of all sales (every sale is either B or A, and no sale is in $B \cap A$), so $\Pr[B] + \Pr[A] = 1$, and therefore

$$\Pr[A] = 1 - \Pr[B] = 1 - .31 = .69$$

(*c*) Finally, since every sale in $A \cup H$ is either after 6:00 PM or high value (or both), we have

$$\begin{aligned}\text{Probability[sale after 6:00 PM or high value]} &= \Pr[A \cup H] \\ &= \Pr[\{AH, AN, BH\}] \\ &= .17 + .52 + .05 \\ &= .74\end{aligned}$$

■

There are a number of useful properties of probability measures which can be deduced from the axioms.

Properties of a Probability Measure

1. For any event E, $\Pr[E'] = 1 - \Pr[E]$.
2. For any collection of pairwise disjoint events $E_1, E_2, \ldots, E_k$,

$$\Pr[E_1 \cup E_2 \cup \cdots \cup E_k] = \Pr[E_1] + \Pr[E_2] + \cdots + \Pr[E_k] \tag{3.1}$$

3. For any events E and F,

$$\Pr[E \cup F] = \Pr[E] + \Pr[F] - \Pr[E \cap F] \tag{3.2}$$

Equation (3.2), which holds for any probability measure, can be deduced from Equation (1.6) in the special case of equally likely outcomes. Indeed, Equation (1.6) for events E and F is

$$n(E \cup F) = n(E) + n(F) - n(E \cap F)$$

Dividing both sides of this equality by $n(S)$ and using the definition of probabilities for equally likely outcomes [Equation (2.4)], we have Equation (3.2).

Other properties can be deduced easily from these three. For instance, since the empty set $\emptyset$ is a subset of S, $\Pr[\emptyset]$ is defined. Also $S' = \emptyset$. It follows from axiom ii and property 1 that

$$\Pr[\emptyset] = \Pr[S'] = 1 - \Pr[S] = 1 - 1 = 0$$

The solution of many of the problems in applied probability considered in this book rests on properties 1 to 3 of a probability measure. In particular, we note that in Example 3.1 we used both properties 1 and 2.

Example 3.2 Let E and F be events in a sample space S with $\Pr[E] = .65$, $\Pr[F] = .4$, and $\Pr[E \cap F] = .3$.

Problem (*a*) Find $\Pr[E \cup F]$.

(*b*) Find the probability of event G, where G is the set of all outcomes which are in exactly one of events E or F.

Solution (*a*) We can apply property 3 directly. We have

$$\begin{aligned}\Pr[E \cup F] &= \Pr[E] + \Pr[F] - \Pr[E \cap F] \\ &= .65 + .4 - .3 = .75\end{aligned}$$

(*b*) We recall from Chapter 1 that the set of all elements which are in exactly one of sets E or F can be written as the union of two sets: the set of elements which are in E but not in F and the set of elements which are in F but not in E. Therefore,

$$G = (E \cap F') \cup (E' \cap F)$$

Since $E \cap F'$ and $E' \cap F$ are disjoint, it follows from axiom 3 that

$$\begin{aligned}\Pr[G] &= \Pr[(E \cap F') \cup (E' \cap F)] \\ &= \Pr[E \cap F'] + \Pr[E' \cap F]\end{aligned}$$

FIGURE 3.1

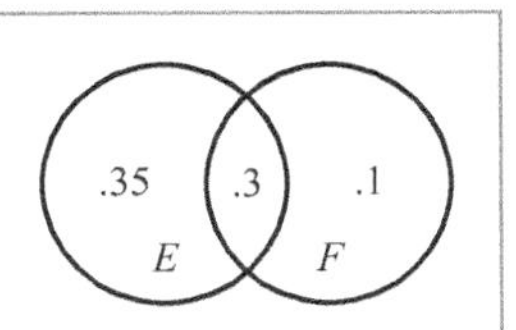

Consequently, our goal is to determine $\Pr[E \cap F']$ and $\Pr[E' \cap F]$. To do so, it is useful to draw a Venn diagram and include the probabilities of appropriate subsets. Figure 3.1 shows sets E and F. We insert probabilities in Figure 3.1 in the same way that we inserted the numbers of elements in subsets of Venn diagrams in Section 1.3. Thus, in the set $E \cap F$, we write the probability .3. Since set E is partitioned into $E \cap F$ and $E \cap F'$, $\Pr[E] = \Pr[E \cap F] + \Pr[E \cap F']$ and $.65 = .3 + \Pr[E \cap F']$, so that $\Pr[E \cap F'] = .35$. The number .35 has been inserted in Figure 3.1 in set $E \cap F'$. Likewise, we find $\Pr[E' \cap F]$ to be .1, and the number .1 has been inserted in Figure 3.1 in set $E' \cap F$. Using the information in Figure 3.1, we have

$$\Pr[G] = .35 + .1 = .45$$

■

Example 3.3 Let A, B, and C be events in a sample space S, with $A \cup B \cup C = S$, $A \cap (B \cup C) = \emptyset$, $\Pr[A] = .2$, $\Pr[B] = .5$, and $\Pr[C] = .7$.

Problem Find $\Pr[A']$, $\Pr[B \cup C]$, and $\Pr[B \cap C]$.

Solution Using property 1 and the information $\Pr[A] = .2$, we find

$$\Pr[A'] = 1 - \Pr[A] = .8$$

Next we are given that events A and $B \cup C$ are disjoint since $A \cap (B \cup C) = \emptyset$. Therefore, by property 2 and the fact that $\Pr[S] = 1$, we have $1 = \Pr[S] = \Pr[A \cup (B \cup C)] = \Pr[A] + \Pr[B \cup C] = .2 + \Pr[B \cup C]$. It follows that

$$\Pr[B \cup C] = .8$$

Finally, using property 3, we have

$$\begin{aligned} \Pr[B \cup C] &= \Pr[B] + \Pr[C] - \Pr[B \cap C] \\ .8 &= .5 + .7 - \Pr[B \cap C] \end{aligned}$$

from which we conclude that $\Pr[B \cap C] = .4$. ■

FIGURE 3.2

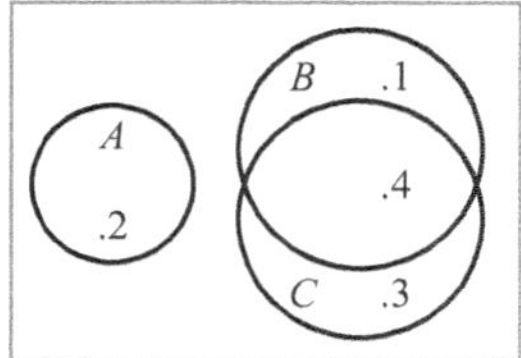

Note: The Venn diagram for Example 3.3 is shown in Figure 3.2. Although we did not need the diagram to answer the questions posed in the example, it is very useful to indicate the relationships between sets A, B, and C. Since $A \cap (B \cup C)$ is empty, sets A and $B \cup C$ do not overlap on the diagram. Also since $A \cup (B \cup C)$ is the entire sample space S, there is zero probability outside these sets. With this diagram it is clear that $\Pr[B \cup C] = .8$.

In Examples 3.2 and 3.3 the problems were solved by directly using the properties of a probability measure. Problems containing information given in descriptive form normally require an additional step. The events needed to answer the question must be identified, and the problem must be translated from words into symbols.

Example 3.4 Each week the host of a daily radio jazz program chooses a specific era in jazz music and selects songs representing that era from the station library. The host selects songs which satisfy conditions on length and artistic merit. The latter means that the song must be a good representative of the era and be a good recording. A song selected at random can be of appropriate length,

TABLE 3.2

Event		Probability
Appropriate in length and artistic merit	(F)	.72
Too short	(G_1)	.12
Too long	(G_2)	.08
Poor representative of era	(H_1)	.15
Good representative of era but poor recording	(H_2)	.02

too long, or too short. With regard to artistic merit, it can be a good or poor representative of the era, and even if it is a good representative of the era, it can be a poor recording. If a song is selected at random from all songs of the chosen era in the library and its attributes noted, then probabilities based on past data are assigned (by the frequency method) as shown in Table 3.2. Note that since some of the songs may fail both criteria, the sum of the probabilities in Table 3.2 is more than 1.

Problem Find the probability of each of the following events.

(*a*) A randomly selected song is not of appropriate length.

(*b*) A randomly selected song is of appropriate length.

(*c*) A randomly selected song is unacceptable on the artistic merit criteria.

Solution We begin by labeling the events with the symbols F, G_1, G_2, H_1, and H_2 as shown in Table 3.2.

(*a*) The event that a randomly selected song is not of appropriate length is $G_1 \cup G_2$. Since $G_1 \cap G_2 = \emptyset$, we have

$$\Pr[G_1 \cup G_2] = \Pr[G_1] + \Pr[G_2] = .12 + .08 = .20$$

(*b*) The event that a song is of appropriate length is $(G_1 \cup G_2)'$, and

$$\Pr[(G_1 \cup G_2)'] = 1 - \Pr[G_1 \cup G_2] = 1 - .20 = .80$$

(*c*) The event that a song fails the artistic criteria is $H_1 \cup H_2$. Again, since $H_1 \cap H_2 = \emptyset$, we have

$$\Pr[H_1 \cup H_2] = \Pr[H_1] + \Pr[H_2] = .15 + .02 = .17$$

■

In assigning probabilities to events, we assign probability 1 to any event which always occurs and probability 0 to any event which never occurs. Thus in Example 3.4 we assign probability 1 to the event that a randomly selected song is either appropriate (in length and artistic merit) or not, and we assign probability 0 to the event that a randomly selected song is appropriate and not appropriate.

The computation of the desired probabilities in Example 3.4 is relatively direct. The solution of other probability problems may require several steps and the use of more than one of the properties. This is illustrated in our next example.

Example 3.5 In the situation described in Example 3.4, find the probabilities of the following events:

(*a*) A randomly selected song is either inappropriate on the length criteria or the artistic merit criteria (or both).

(*b*) A randomly selected song fails on both the length and the artistic merit criteria.

Solution (*a*) Let $E_1 = G_1 \cup G_2$ denote the event that a randomly selected song is either too long or too short, and let $E_2 = H_1 \cup H_2$ denote the event that a randomly selected song fails the artistic merit criteria. In Example 3.4 we determined $\Pr[E_1]$ and $\Pr[E_2]$. We have $E_1 \cup E_2 \cup F = S$, and clearly the event F (a song which is appropriate in length and artistic merit is selected) is disjoint from $E_1 \cup E_2$. We conclude that $E_1 \cup E_2 = F'$, and therefore

$$\Pr[E_1 \cup E_2] = \Pr[F'] = 1 - \Pr[F] = 1 - .72 = .28$$

(*b*) The event that a randomly selected song fails both criteria is $E_1 \cap E_2$, and we determine $\Pr[E_1 \cap E_2]$ by using property 3, the results of Example 3.4, and part (*a*) of this example. Indeed, property 3 applied to events E_1 and E_2 gives

$$\Pr[E_1 \cup E_2] = \Pr[E_1] + \Pr[E_2] - \Pr[E_1 \cap E_2]$$

From Example 3.4, $\Pr[E_1] = .20$ and $\Pr[E_2] = .17$. Combining this with the result of part (*a*), we have

$$\Pr[E_1 \cap E_2] = \Pr[E_1] + \Pr[E_2] - \Pr[E_1 \cup E_2] = .37 - .28 = .09$$

Notice that the solution of part (*b*) uses the results of part (*a*) and the results of Example 3.4. If the problem of part (*b*) were posed as the only task, it would still be necessary to determine several other probabilities to solve it. It is a problem whose solution requires several steps.

Exercises for Section 3.1

1. Let A and B be events in the sample space S, and let $\Pr[A] = .45$, $\Pr[B] = .75$, and $\Pr[A \cap B] = .25$. Find the probability of each of the following events.
   (*a*) $B' \cap A$ (*b*) $A' \cap B$ (*c*) $A' \cap B'$
2. Let A and B be events in the sample space S, and let $\Pr[A] = .45$, $\Pr[B] = .75$, and $\Pr[A' \cap B] = .35$. Find the probability of each of the following events.
   (*a*) $B' \cap A$ (*b*) $A \cap B$ (*c*) $A' \cap B'$

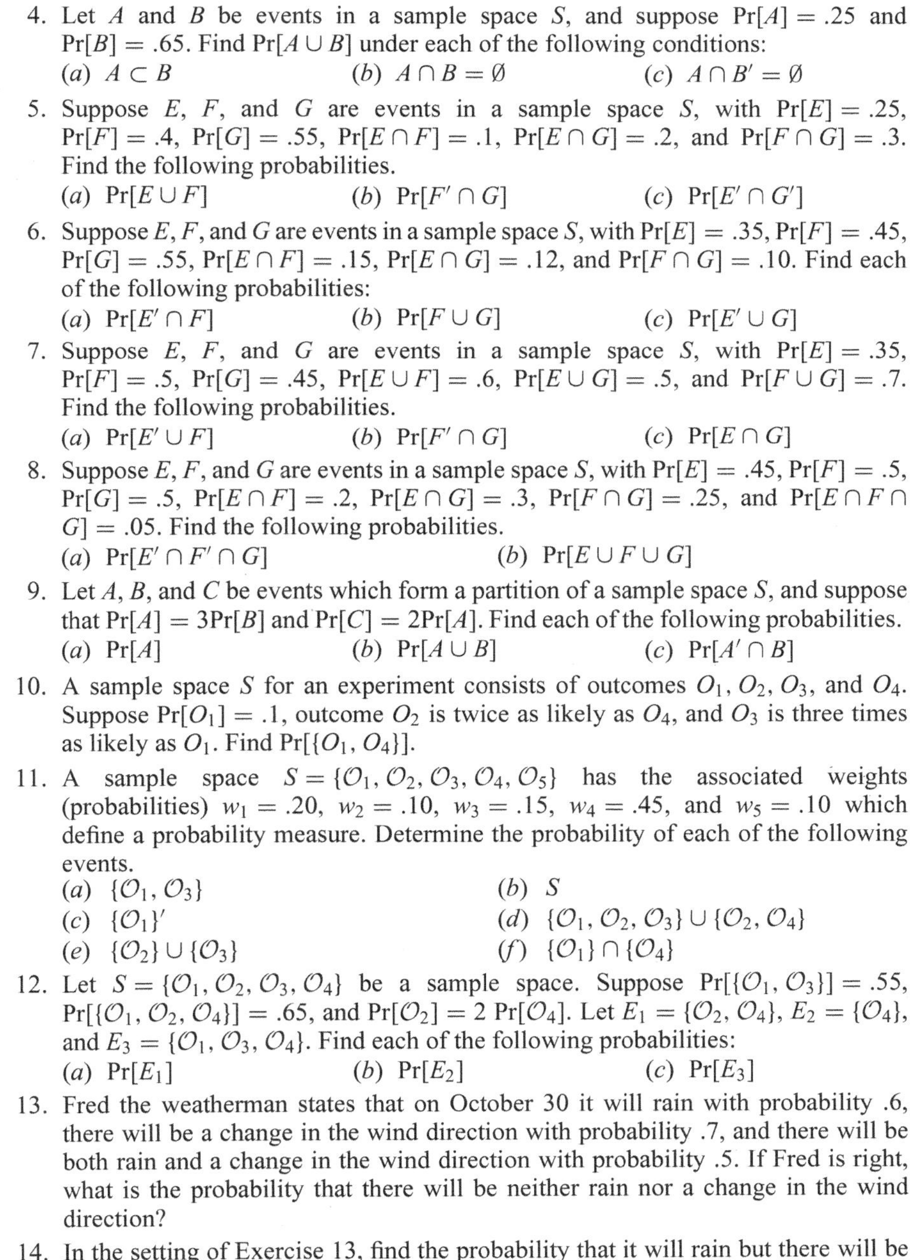

3. Let A and B be events in a sample space S, and suppose $\Pr[A'] = .65$, $\Pr[B] = .50$, and $\Pr[A' \cap B] = .15$. Find the probability of each of the following events.
   (*a*) $\Pr[A \cap B]$ (*b*) $\Pr[A \cup B]$ (*c*) $\Pr[A' \cup B]$
4. Let A and B be events in a sample space S, and suppose $\Pr[A] = .25$ and $\Pr[B] = .65$. Find $\Pr[A \cup B]$ under each of the following conditions:
   (*a*) $A \subset B$ (*b*) $A \cap B = \emptyset$ (*c*) $A \cap B' = \emptyset$
5. Suppose E, F, and G are events in a sample space S, with $\Pr[E] = .25$, $\Pr[F] = .4$, $\Pr[G] = .55$, $\Pr[E \cap F] = .1$, $\Pr[E \cap G] = .2$, and $\Pr[F \cap G] = .3$. Find the following probabilities.
   (*a*) $\Pr[E \cup F]$ (*b*) $\Pr[F' \cap G]$ (*c*) $\Pr[E' \cap G']$
6. Suppose E, F, and G are events in a sample space S, with $\Pr[E] = .35$, $\Pr[F] = .45$, $\Pr[G] = .55$, $\Pr[E \cap F] = .15$, $\Pr[E \cap G] = .12$, and $\Pr[F \cap G] = .10$. Find each of the following probabilities:
   (*a*) $\Pr[E' \cap F]$ (*b*) $\Pr[F \cup G]$ (*c*) $\Pr[E' \cup G]$
7. Suppose E, F, and G are events in a sample space S, with $\Pr[E] = .35$, $\Pr[F] = .5$, $\Pr[G] = .45$, $\Pr[E \cup F] = .6$, $\Pr[E \cup G] = .5$, and $\Pr[F \cup G] = .7$. Find the following probabilities.
   (*a*) $\Pr[E' \cup F]$ (*b*) $\Pr[F' \cap G]$ (*c*) $\Pr[E \cap G]$
8. Suppose E, F, and G are events in a sample space S, with $\Pr[E] = .45$, $\Pr[F] = .5$, $\Pr[G] = .5$, $\Pr[E \cap F] = .2$, $\Pr[E \cap G] = .3$, $\Pr[F \cap G] = .25$, and $\Pr[E \cap F \cap G] = .05$. Find the following probabilities.
   (*a*) $\Pr[E' \cap F' \cap G]$ (*b*) $\Pr[E \cup F \cup G]$
9. Let A, B, and C be events which form a partition of a sample space S, and suppose that $\Pr[A] = 3\Pr[B]$ and $\Pr[C] = 2\Pr[A]$. Find each of the following probabilities.
   (*a*) $\Pr[A]$ (*b*) $\Pr[A \cup B]$ (*c*) $\Pr[A' \cap B]$
10. A sample space S for an experiment consists of outcomes O_1, O_2, O_3, and O_4. Suppose $\Pr[O_1] = .1$, outcome O_2 is twice as likely as O_4, and O_3 is three times as likely as O_1. Find $\Pr[\{O_1, O_4\}]$.
11. A sample space $S = \{O_1, O_2, O_3, O_4, O_5\}$ has the associated weights (probabilities) $w_1 = .20$, $w_2 = .10$, $w_3 = .15$, $w_4 = .45$, and $w_5 = .10$ which define a probability measure. Determine the probability of each of the following events.
    (*a*) $\{O_1, O_3\}$ (*b*) S
    (*c*) $\{O_1\}'$ (*d*) $\{O_1, O_2, O_3\} \cup \{O_2, O_4\}$
    (*e*) $\{O_2\} \cup \{O_3\}$ (*f*) $\{O_1\} \cap \{O_4\}$
12. Let $S = \{O_1, O_2, O_3, O_4\}$ be a sample space. Suppose $\Pr[\{O_1, O_3\}] = .55$, $\Pr[\{O_1, O_2, O_4\}] = .65$, and $\Pr[O_2] = 2\Pr[O_4]$. Let $E_1 = \{O_2, O_4\}$, $E_2 = \{O_4\}$, and $E_3 = \{O_1, O_3, O_4\}$. Find each of the following probabilities:
    (*a*) $\Pr[E_1]$ (*b*) $\Pr[E_2]$ (*c*) $\Pr[E_3]$
13. Fred the weatherman states that on October 30 it will rain with probability .6, there will be a change in the wind direction with probability .7, and there will be both rain and a change in the wind direction with probability .5. If Fred is right, what is the probability that there will be neither rain nor a change in the wind direction?
14. In the setting of Exercise 13, find the probability that it will rain but there will be no change in the wind direction.

15. For the members of a small community the events ''express enthusiasm for expanded municipal services'' and ''agree to pay higher taxes'' are disjoint events with

    Pr[member expresses enthusiasm for expanded municipal services] = .6
    Pr[member agrees to pay higher taxes]= .3.

    For a randomly selected member of the community, find the probability that the person expresses enthusiasm for expanded municipal services but does NOT agree to pay higher taxes.
16. Let A, B, and C be events in a sample space S and suppose the events A and $B \cup C$ form a partition of S. If $\Pr[A] = .35$, $\Pr[B] = .25$, and $\Pr[C] = .5$, find each of the following probabilities:
    (*a*) $\Pr[A \cup B]$ (*b*) $\Pr[B \cup C]$ (*c*) $\Pr[B \cap C]$
17. An unfair die has the property that when it is rolled each of the odd numbers is equally likely to land uppermost, each of the even numbers is equally likely to land uppermost, and each odd number is twice as likely to land up as an even number. The die is rolled and the result is noted. Find the probability that the result is in the event $\{1, 3, 6\}$.
18. A sample space has 5 outcomes with weights w_1, w_2, w_3, w_4, and w_5. If $w_1 = 2w_2$, $w_2 = w_3 = w_4$, and $w_5 = 3w_2$, find w_4.
19. The sound system at a musical events center has the property that when sound testing for a concert a microphone malfunctions with probability .1, a speaker malfunctions with probability .05, and both malfunction with probability .01. Find the probability that neither a microphone nor a speaker malfunctions.
20. In the setting of Exercise 19, find the probability that either a microphone or a speaker malfunctions, but not both.
21. Each Monday a student attends mathematics class with probability .6, skips accounting class with probability .3, and attends both with probability .5. Find the probability that she attends at least one class on Monday.
22. In the setting of Exercise 21, find the probability that she attends exactly one class.
23. At the end of the year a movie critic tabulates her reviews for the year. She finds that 45 percent of the movies reviewed were given positive comments about the plot and 65 percent were given positive comments about the acting. Fifteen percent were not given positive comments on either plot or acting. If a film is selected at random from among those reviewed by the critic, find the probability that it was given positive comments on both plot and acting.
24. An experiment has a sample space $S = \{O_1, O_2, O_3, O_4\}$ with $\Pr[\{O_1, O_2\}] = .49$, $\Pr[\{O_1, O_3\}] = .51$, and $\Pr[\{O_1, O_2, O_3\}] = .69$. Find the probabilities w_1, w_2, w_3, w_4.
25. In a class with 120 students, there are 80 freshmen and 40 sophomores. Of the freshmen, 50 are residents of Indiana and of the sophomores 22 are Indiana residents. A student is selected at random from among the members of the class. Find the probability that
    (*a*) The student is a resident of Indiana
    (*b*) The student is NOT a resident of Indiana

26. A marketing firm surveyed consumers about their electronics purchases in the last year. The following data were obtained:
    46 percent had purchased electronics in a specialty store
    38 percent had purchased electronics in a discount store
    44 percent had purchased electronics over the internet
    15 percent had purchased electronics in both specialty and discount stores
    20 percent had purchased electronics in a specialty store and over the internet
    18 percent had purchased electronics in a discount store and over the internet
    12 percent had purchased electronics in specialty and discount stores and over the internet

    A consumer response is selected at random. Find the probability that:
    (*a*) The consumer had purchased electronics at exactly one of these outlets.
    (*b*) The consumer had purchased electronics at none of these outlets.
27. A television set which sometimes malfunctions has
    A clear picture with probability .7
    Good sound with probability .5
    Good color with probability .6
    Both a clear picture and good sound with probability .4
    Both a clear picture and good color with probability .5
    Both good sound and good color with probability .4
    A clear picture, good sound, and good color with probability .3

    Find the probability that the television set has exactly one of these three characteristics (clear picture, good sound, good color).
28. An inspector on an assembly line of a refrigerator plant classifies each refrigerator according to the properties of its enamel. Based on his data, the inspector assigns the probabilities listed in Table 3.3. Assume that no refrigerator has both too much and too little enamel and that the defects associated with E_1, E_2, E_3 are the only ones of concern to the inspector. What is the probability that a randomly selected refrigerator has each of the following?
    (*a*) A paint defect
    (*b*) A paint defect which includes an improper amount of paint
    (*c*) A paint defect which results from an improper amount of paint and uneven application
    (*d*) A paint defect which results from the proper amount of paint but uneven application

TABLE 3.3

	Event	Observed Probability
E_1	Too much enamel	.04
E_2	Too little enamel	.12
E_3	Uneven application	.09
E_4	No defects noted	.82

29. Suppose that events A and $B \cup C$ form a partition of a sample space S, $\Pr[B \cup C] = .68$, $\Pr[B] = .45$, and $\Pr[C] = .35$. Let E be the event consisting of all outcomes in exactly one of the sets A, B, and C. Find $\Pr[E]$.
30. A pet store owner has a database with information on the pets each customer has purchased. The data show that 50 percent of her customers have purchased a dog, 40 percent a cat, and 30 percent a gerbil. No customer has purchased all three, but 25 percent have purchased exactly 2 of these animals. A customer is selected at random. Find the probability that the customer has purchased none of these animals.
31. Suppose the sample space S contains 100 disjoint events $E_1, E_2, \ldots, E_{100}$ and event E_n has probability K/n, where K is a constant, $n = 1, \ldots, 100$. Does there exist a value of K so that the events E_n form a partition of S? If such a K exists, find its value.
32. In the setting of Exercise 31, suppose that event E_n has probability K/n^2, $n = 1, \ldots, 100$. Answer the questions posed in Exercise 31.
33. Computer passwords are to be created by using the letters N, K, Y, F, R, and H. Each password must consist of either 4 or 5 letters, all different. Find the probability that if a password is created at random in this way, it contains the letters K and R.
34. In the situation described in Exercise 33, find the probability that if a password is created at random in this way, it contains the letters K, F and R.

3.2 CONDITIONAL PROBABILITY AND INDEPENDENCE

The probability of an event is a number which indicates the likelihood that the event will occur. In certain situations we are naturally led to consider two events which are very similar, but which are distinguished in that for one we have more information on the outcomes than for the other. This additional information may mean that the two events have different probabilities.

Example 3.6 Suppose that we have a bag[1] containing 3 red balls, 2 blue balls, and 4 white balls, and a ball is selected at random and its color is noted. Assuming that each ball is equally likely to be selected, i.e., each ball has probability $\frac{1}{9}$ of being selected, we conclude that

$$\begin{aligned} \Pr[\text{red ball}] &= \tfrac{3}{9} \\ \Pr[\text{blue ball}] &= \tfrac{2}{9} \\ \Pr[\text{white ball}] &= \tfrac{4}{9} \end{aligned}$$

[1] It has been customary for textbook discussions of probability to use the term ''urn'' when referring to a container from which items (balls, cards, coins, etc.) are selected. The image of reaching into a tall container with a fairly narrow opening at the top for an object which cannot be seen is a useful one for many discussions. However, the term urn is not a familiar one for most readers, and it is currently used most frequently in connection with coffee or cremation. As a result, when we describe experiments in which objects are selected from a container, we will use boxes, bags, bowls, etc., rather than urns.

Now suppose that we are given the additional information that the ball selected is *not white.* Since only 5 of the 9 balls are not white, we may think of the sample space as being limited to those 5 outcomes. With this information the probabilities become

$$\Pr[\text{red ball selected, given that the ball selected is not white}] = \tfrac{3}{5}$$

$$\Pr[\text{blue ball selected, given that the ball selected is not white}] = \tfrac{2}{5}$$

$$\Pr[\text{white ball selected, given that the ball selected is not white}] = \tfrac{0}{5} = 0$$

Indeed, in the latter case there are only 5 balls—3 red and 2 blue—which satisfy the condition of being not white, and the probabilities assigned to the outcomes are those determined by the equiprobable measure with 5 possible outcomes. ■

Example 3.6 illustrates the concept of *conditional probability*, i.e., the probability assigned to an event which is described in terms of two other events: the drawing of a red ball and the drawing of a ball which is not white. A precise definition is as follows.

Let A and B be events in the sample space of an experiment with $\Pr[B] \neq 0$. The *conditional probability of event A given B*, written $\Pr[A|B]$, is

$$\Pr[A|B] = \frac{\Pr[A \cap B]}{\Pr[B]}$$

In Example 3.6 we see that the conditional probability of an event is just the probability of that event in the smaller sample space specified by the condition. If A is the event "a red ball is selected" and B is the event "a white ball is not selected," then

$$\Pr[A|B] = \frac{\frac{3}{9}}{\frac{5}{9}} = \frac{3}{5}$$

This final ratio $\frac{3}{5}$ is simply the result of using the equiprobable measure in the sample space consisting of those outcomes in which the ball selected is not white.

In the general case we can illustrate the concept of conditional probability by using Venn diagrams. A sample space S and events A and B are shown in the Venn diagram of Figure 3.3*a*. The probability of A is the sum of the weights of all outcomes in A. Equivalently, since the weight of all outcomes in S is 1, this sum is the fraction of the total weight due to outcomes in A. The conditional probability of A given B corresponds to the situation in which B represents the sample space and $\Pr[A|B]$ is the weight of the outcomes in $A \cap B$ compared to the total weight of B. This is shown in Figure 3.3*b*.

FIGURE 3.3

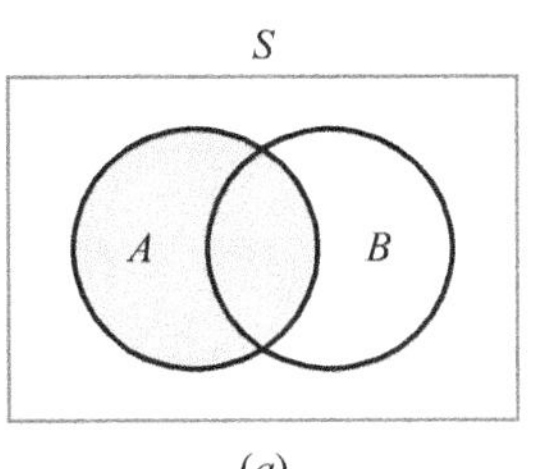

(*a*)

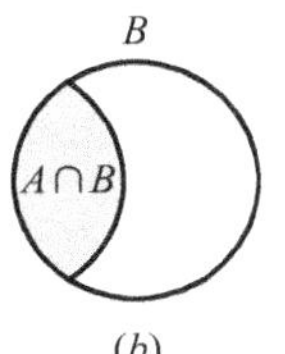

(*b*)

Example 3.7 Let A and B be events in a sample space S with $\Pr[A] = .4$, $\Pr[B'] = .4$, and $\Pr[A \cap B] = .2$.

Problem Find $\Pr[A|B]$ and $\Pr[B|A]$.

Solution In order to apply the formula in the definition of $\Pr[A|B]$ we need to know $\Pr[B]$, and we can obtain it from the relation $\Pr[B] = 1 - \Pr[B'] = 1 - .4 = .6$. Therefore

$$\Pr[A|B] = \frac{\Pr[A \cap B]}{\Pr[B]} = \frac{.2}{.6} = \frac{1}{3}$$

Also,

$$\Pr[B|A] = \frac{\Pr[B \cap A]}{\Pr[A]} = \frac{.2}{.4} = \frac{1}{2}$$

■

Remark Note that, in general, $\Pr[A|B] \neq \Pr[B|A]$, and in fact $\Pr[A|B]$ may be greater than, less than, or equal to $\Pr[B|A]$.

Example 3.8 People who requested information from a state tourism office over the internet were asked to complete a short survey about their travel plans. The data collected yield the probabilities shown in Table 3.4. For instance, the probability that a randomly selected survey indicated plans to visit the state by commercial transportation during the next summer is .18.

TABLE 3.4

Event		Probability
Traveler plans to visit the state next summer and travel by personal car	(*P*)	0.12
Traveler plans to visit the state next summer and use commercial transportation	(*C*)	0.18
Traveler has no plans to visit the state next summer	(*N*)	0.70

Problem Suppose that a survey is selected at random, and it shows that the traveler does plan to visit the state the next summer. What is the probability that the traveler plans to use commercial transportation.

Solution Let the events P, C, and N be as shown in Table 3.4. The condition given in the problem, that the responder plans to visit the state, means that the selected survey is in the set N'. The problem is to find the probability that the tourist plans to use commercial transportation (C), given N'. Using the notation of the problem, we seek $\Pr[C|N']$. Since $\Pr[N] = .70$, we have $\Pr[N'] = 1 - \Pr[N] = .30$. Also, $C \cap N' = C$ (a tourist who plans to use commercial transportation during a visit does plan to visit the state), and we have

$$\Pr[C|N'] = \frac{Pr[C \cap N']}{Pr[N']} = \frac{Pr[C]}{Pr[N']} = \frac{.18}{.30} = .60$$

That is, if a randomly selected survey indicates that the tourist plans to visit the state, then the probability that commercial transportation will be used is .60. ■

Note: The situation which occurs in Example 3.8 is a common one: In determining the conditional probability $\Pr[A|B]$ we have a situation where the event A is a subset of the event B, and $A \cap B = A$. In Example 3.8, the event C is a subset of the event N', so $C \cap N' = C$, and $\Pr[C|N'] = \Pr[C]/\Pr[N']$.

Example 3.9 Suppose that a bag contains red balls marked 1, 2, 3; a blue ball marked 4; and white balls marked 5, 6, 7, 8. A ball is selected at random, and its color and number are noted.

Problem What is the probability that it is red? If the ball is known to have an even number, what is the probability that it is red?

Solution Let A be the event that the ball is red, and let B be the event that the ball has an even number. Then, since $n(A) = 3$ and $n(S) = 8$, we have $\Pr[A] = \frac{3}{8}$. This gives an answer to the first question. Next, $n(B) = 4$ and $n(A \cap B) = 1$. Therefore

$$\Pr[A|B] = \frac{\Pr[A \cap B]}{\Pr[B]} = \frac{n(A \cap B)/n(S)}{n(B)/n(S)} = \frac{\frac{1}{8}}{\frac{4}{8}} = \frac{1}{4}$$

and the answer to the second question is $\frac{1}{4}$. Clearly, *in this case*, $\Pr[A] \neq \Pr[A|B]$. Thus the knowledge that B has occurred can affect the probability assigned to A. ■

It can also happen that the knowledge that event B occurs does not affect the probability that A occurs. Events for which this is the case are said to be *independent*. It is convenient to define the concept in slightly different terms and then to connect the definition with this interpretation.

Events A and B are said to be *independent* if

$$\Pr[A \cap B] = \Pr[A]\Pr[B] \qquad (3.3)$$

The connection between this definition and the intuitive interpretation of the word "independent" is provided by the following observation: If A and B are independent events and $\Pr[B] \neq 0$, then

$$\Pr[A|B] = \frac{\Pr[A \cap B]}{\Pr[B]} = \frac{\Pr[A]\Pr[B]}{\Pr[B]} = \Pr[A]$$

Thus for some events A and B, in particular for independent events, we have $\Pr[A|B] = \Pr[A]$. In such cases we may say that knowing that B has occurred does not affect the probability that A occurs. Likewise, if A and B are independent and $\Pr[A] \neq 0$, then

$$\Pr[B|A] = \frac{\Pr[B \cap A]}{\Pr[A]} = \frac{\Pr[B]\Pr[A]}{\Pr[A]} = \Pr[B]$$

Thus, a knowledge of the occurrence of A does not affect the probability that B occurs.

It is important to recognize that independence (as we have defined the concept) has a precise *mathematical meaning*, and it may not be clear from the description of an experiment whether certain events are or are not independent. The only way to determine if events A and B are independent is to compute $\Pr[A]$, $\Pr[B]$, and $\Pr[A \cap B]$ and then check whether $\Pr[A \cap B] = \Pr[A]\Pr[B]$.

Example 3.10 Consider again the bag of Example 3.9 which contains red balls marked 1, 2, 3; a blue ball marked 4; and white balls marked 5, 6, 7, 8. Let A, B, and C be the following events:

A: A red ball is drawn.
B: A ball with an even number is drawn.
C: A white ball is drawn.

As before, the experiment consists of drawing a ball and noting its color and number.

Problem Decide whether A and B are independent and whether B and C are independent.

Solution We have (using equally likely outcomes)

$$\Pr[A] = \tfrac{3}{8} \qquad \Pr[B] = \tfrac{4}{8} \qquad \Pr[C] = \tfrac{4}{8}$$
$$\Pr[A \cap B] = \tfrac{1}{8} \qquad \Pr[B \cap C] = \tfrac{2}{8}$$

Thus

$$\Pr[A]\Pr[B] = \tfrac{3}{8} \cdot \tfrac{4}{8}$$

and

$$\Pr[A \cap B] \neq \Pr[A]\Pr[B]$$

Therefore the events A and B are *not* independent. However, since

$$\tfrac{1}{4} = \tfrac{2}{8} = \Pr[B \cap C] = \Pr[B]\Pr[C] = \tfrac{4}{8} \cdot \tfrac{4}{8} = \tfrac{1}{4}$$

events B and C are independent. ■

The question of whether two events are independent and the question of whether two events are disjoint are two quite different questions, even though both involve pairs of events. If A and B are disjoint, then $A \cap B = \emptyset$ and $\Pr[A \cap B] = 0$; if A and B are independent, then $\Pr[A \cap B] = \Pr[A]\Pr[B]$.

In general, two events which are independent are *not* disjoint. In fact, independent events which are also disjoint are very special: If two events A and B are both independent and disjoint, then $\Pr[A] = 0$ or $\Pr[B] = 0$ or both.

Example 3.11 A university IT Service Group obtains its printers from one manufacturer and the printer cables from another manufacturer. Based on recent experience, it is estimated that about 2 percent of the printers will have a manufacturing defect, and .5 percent of the printer cables have such a defect.

Problem If manufacturing defects in printers and cables are independent,

(a) find the probability that a random installation of printer and cable has both parts defective

(b) find the probability that a random installation of printer and cable has a defective printer but a non-defective cable.

Solution The probability that a randomly selected printer is defective is .02 and the probability that a randomly selected cable is defective is .005.

(a) Since these events are assumed to be independent, we have

$$\Pr[\text{defective printer and defective cable}] = .02 \times .005 = .0001.$$

(b) The two events

defective printer and defective cable are selected, and
defective printer and non-defective cable are selected

form a partition of the event

defective printer is selected

It follows from Property 2 of a probability measure that

$$\begin{aligned}&\Pr[\text{defective printer is selected}]\\ &= \Pr[\text{defective printer and defective cable are selected}]\\ &+ \Pr[\text{defective printer and non-defective cable are selected}]\end{aligned}$$

And finally we have

Pr[defective printer & non-defective cable are selected] $= .02 - .0001 = .0199$.

Exercises for Section 3.2

1. Suppose A and B are events in a sample space S with $\Pr[A] = .4$, $\Pr[B] = .5$, and $\Pr[A \cap B] = .2$. Find $\Pr[A|B]$ and $\Pr[B|A]$.
2. Suppose E and F are events in a sample space S with $\Pr[E] = .48$, $\Pr[F] = .75$, and $\Pr[E \cap F] = .32$. Find $\Pr[E|F]$ and $\Pr[F|E]$.
3. Let E and F be events in a sample space S. Suppose $\Pr[E] = \frac{5}{8}$, $\Pr[F] = \frac{3}{8}$, and $\Pr[(E \cup F)'] = 0$. Find $\Pr[E|F]$ and $\Pr[F|E]$.
4. Let E and F be events in a sample space S. Suppose $\Pr[E] = \frac{3}{8}$, $\Pr[F] = \frac{1}{2}$, and $\Pr[E \cap F'] = \frac{1}{8}$. Find $\Pr[E|F]$ and $\Pr[F|E]$.
5. Suppose A and B are events in a sample space S with $\Pr[A|B] = \frac{3}{4}$, $\Pr[A] = \frac{1}{2}$, and $\Pr[B'] = \frac{3}{4}$. Find $\Pr[B|A]$ and $\Pr[B|A']$.
6. Suppose E and F are events in a sample space S with $\Pr[E] = .36$, $\Pr[F] = .72$, and $\Pr[E' \cap F] = .45$. Find $\Pr[E|F]$ and $\Pr[F|E]$.
7. Suppose E and F are independent events in a sample space S with $\Pr[E] = .32$ and $\Pr[F] = .48$. Find $\Pr[E|F]$ and $\Pr[E'|F]$.
8. Suppose E and F are independent events in a sample space S with $\Pr[E] = .4$ and $\Pr[F] = .8$. Find $\Pr[E'|F]$ and $\Pr[E|F']$.
9. Let A and B be events such that $\Pr[A \cup B] = .8$ and $\Pr[A] = .6$. What is $\Pr[B]$ in the following cases:
   (*a*) A and B are independent.
   (*b*) A and B are disjoint events.
10. Let A and B be events such that $\Pr[A \cup B] = .9$ and $\Pr[A] = .5$. What is $\Pr[B]$ in the following cases:
    (*a*) A and B are independent.
    (*b*) A and B are disjoint events.
11. Let A and B be events such that $\Pr[A|B] = \frac{1}{2}$, $\Pr[B|A] = \frac{1}{3}$, and $\Pr[A \cap B] = \frac{1}{5}$. Are A and B independent?
12. There are 3 red balls and 4 blue balls in a box, and 2 balls are selected simultaneously and at random. Find the probability that exactly 1 is red given that at least 1 is red.
13. In Example 3.9, are the following two events independent?
    F: A blue ball is drawn.
    B: An even-numbered ball is drawn.
14. A company has ten laptop computers for the sales staff to take on calls. Six are Dell, and 4 are Lenovo. Two of the Dell laptops have a custom graphics program installed and 4 do not; three of the Lenovo laptops have the program installed and one does not. A sales representative selects a laptop at random and notes that the custom program is installed. Find the probability that the laptop is a Dell.
15. An automobile manufacturer collects data on the options chosen by potential purchasers when pricing a car on its website. The data show that 50 percent of potential purchasers chose a navigation system, 30 percent chose a remote engine

starter, and 20 percent chose both. Find the probability that a randomly selected data record shows a choice of a navigation system given that exactly one of the two options is chosen.

16. Suppose for Joe the events "late for class" and "prepared for class" are independent events with Pr[late for class] = .2 and Pr[prepared for class] = .6. Find the probability that Joe is late for class and is not prepared for class.
17. Two fair dice are rolled, and the numbers on the uppermost faces are noted.
    (*a*) What is the probability that exactly one die shows a 4 given that the sum of the numbers is 6?
    (*b*) What is the probability that the sum of the numbers is 6 given that exactly one die shows a 4?
    (*c*) What is the probability that the sum of the numbers is 6 given that at least one die shows a 4?
18. A group of 6 students consists of 4 freshmen and 2 sophomores. Two students are selected simultaneously and at random. Find the probability that both are freshmen given that at least one is a freshman.
19. A veterinarian has 4 dogs, 3 cats, and 2 gerbils. Two animals are selected at random. Find the probability that both are dogs given that both are the same type of animal.
20. There are 7 sandwiches in a cooler: 3 are beef, 2 are ham, and 2 are turkey. Suppose you select two sandwiches at random, and you see that one is *not* beef.
    (*a*) Find the probability that both are turkey.
    (*b*) Find the probability that both are the same; that is, both ham or both turkey.
21. There are 3 Chevrolets and 4 Hondas in the company motor pool. Two cars are selected at random and assigned to sales representatives. If they are both of the same make, find the probability that both are Hondas?
22. There are 2 white balls, 2 red balls, and 3 blue balls in a box. Two balls are selected at random, and their colors are noted. Find the probability that neither is white given that neither is blue.
23. Twelve students have phone plans through Verizon and 8 through ATT. Three students are selected at random. Find the probability that exactly one student uses ATT given that not all students use the same carrier.
24. A subcommittee of 3 people is selected at random from a committee consisting of 6 women and 4 men. Find the probability that the committee consists of 2 men and 1 woman given that it contains both women and men.
25. Three students are selected at random from a class consisting of 5 freshmen, 3 sophomores, and 2 juniors. Find the probability that 2 freshmen and 1 junior are selected given that at least 1 freshman is selected.
26. There are 8 sophomores, 7 juniors, and 5 seniors on an athletic team, and two players are selected at random. Find the probability that one is a junior and one a senior given that they are not both in the same class.
27. A biologist has 12 mice in a cage: 2 gray females, 3 gray males, 3 white females, and 4 white males. Two mice are selected simultaneously and at random, and their color and sex are noted.
    (*a*) Find the probability that both are females given that both are gray.
    (*b*) Find the probability that 1 mouse is male and 1 mouse is female given that both are gray.

28. In the situation described in Exercise 27:
    (*a*) Find the probability that at least 1 mouse is male given that 2 are white.
    (*b*) Find the probability that 1 mouse is female and 1 is male given that 1 is gray and 1 is white.
29. There are 3 male roles in a play and there are 5 males auditioning for these roles, including Alex. Also, there are 2 female roles in the same play and there are 4 females auditioning, including Zelda. Suppose that each person is equally likely to be assigned a role. Find the probability that Alex is selected given that exactly one of Alex and Zelda is assigned a role in the play.
30. An experiment consists of drawing a ball from a bag containing 2 red balls, 3 white balls, and 1 blue ball, noting the color, and then (without replacement) drawing a second ball and noting the color. Draw a tree diagram to represent this experiment, and assign conditional probabilities to the branches to reflect the likelihood of each selection.
31. Using the setting of Exercise 30, suppose that the first ball drawn is returned to the bag before the second ball is drawn. Again, draw the tree to represent this experiment, and assign conditional probabilities to the branches to reflect the likelihood of each selection.
32. A veterinarian has 5 dogs and 4 cats available for adoption. Four of the dogs are brown and 1 is gray. Three of the cats are brown and 1 is gray. Jena selects two of the animals at random. Find the probability that at least 1 is a cat given that at least 1 is gray.
33. Amy, Bob, Carlos, Debra, and Erin have tickets numbered A101–A105, and A101 is an aisle seat. If they select seats at random, find the probability that Amy has seat A103 given that her seat has a lower number than Bob's seat. Work the same problem for seat A102.
34. Suppose 5 cards are randomly drawn from a standard deck. If it is known that 2 of them are aces, what is the probability that the other 3 cards are face cards?
35. In the setting of Exercise 34 (i.e., it is known that 2 of the cards are aces), which of the following is most likely to be the other 3 cards: 3 cards of the same kind (such as kings) or 3 cards in a run (such as 5, 6, 7)?
36. Suppose 5 cards are randomly drawn from a standard deck. If it is known that at least 2 of them are aces, what is the probability that the remaining card(s) are face cards, that is, jacks, queens, or kings?

3.3 STOCHASTIC PROCESSES AND TREES

Many experiments are naturally carried out in steps or stages, or they can be represented as being carried out in steps or stages. For these experiments, it is very useful to represent the steps and the outcomes by using a tree diagram with probabilities on the branches. We think of the main experiment as a sequence of subexperiments, one for each step or stage of the main experiment. Each of the subexperiments has a set of outcomes, and these outcomes have probabilities associated with them. Each outcome of the main experiment is determined by the results of the subexperiments, and the probabilities of these outcomes are determined in a simple way by the probabilities of the outcomes of the subexperiments. A natural method of representing the possible outcomes of both the subexperiments and the main experiment is to use a tree diagram.

An experiment which consists of a sequence of subexperiments is called a *stochastic process*.

Flipping a coin three times and noting the result of each flip is a simple example of a stochastic process. Most stochastic processes are more complicated than this, and it is useful to develop special techniques to use in studying them. The tree diagrams introduced in Chapter 1 are helpful, and our goal in this section is to refine and extend their use.

Example 3.12 Consider an experiment which consists of two steps. First a box is selected at random from a set of two boxes labeled a and b (see Figure 3.4), and then a bowl is selected at random from the chosen box. Box a contains 3 bowls, labeled A, B, and C, and box b contains 2 bowls, labeled D and E.

Problem Draw a tree diagram to represent the outcomes of this experiment, and assign conditional probabilities to the tree to reflect the probabilities of the possible results at each stage.

Solution At the first stage of the experiment there are 2 possible results (a or b). Hence the tree diagram should begin with a fork with 2 branches, one ending at a and the other at b. Since the boxes are selected at random (i.e., each choice is equally likely), we assign weights $\frac{1}{2}$ to each of these branches. After the first stage of the experiment is completed (and we have either box a or box b), the number of possible results for the second stage depends on the result at the first stage. This is represented in the tree diagram by having a fork with 3 branches at a and a fork with 2 branches at b. Again we use the fact that selections are made at random, and we assign conditional probabilities of $\frac{1}{3}$ to each of the 3 branches at a and $\frac{1}{2}$ to each of the 2 branches at b. The resulting

FIGURE 3.4

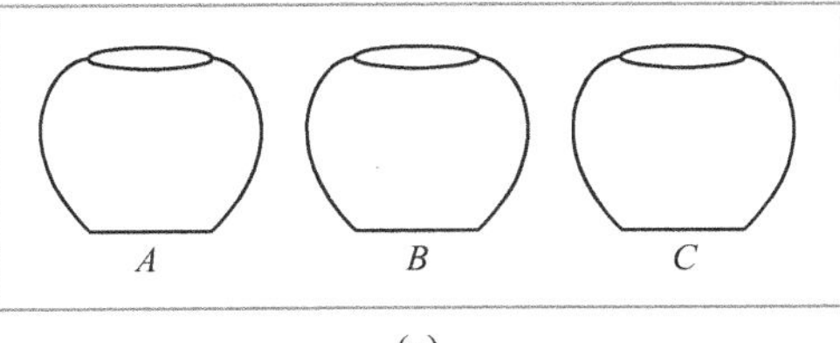

(a)

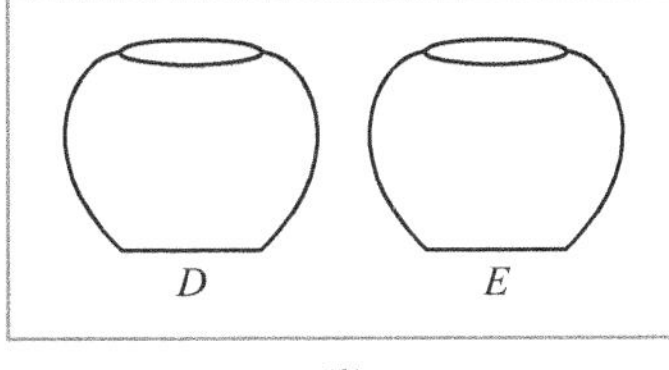

(b)

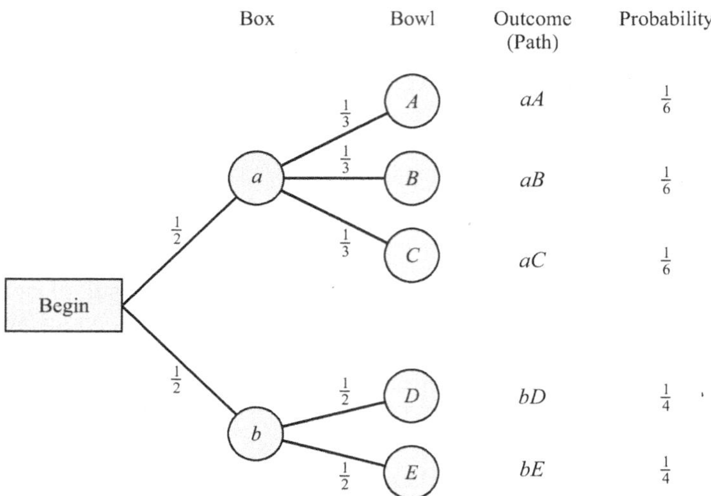

FIGURE 3.5

tree with weights is shown in Figure 3.5. We have noted the outcomes of the experiment to the right of the tree, each outcome corresponding to a path which connects the left side of the tree ("Begin") to a result at each stage of the experiment. ■

The method used to obtain the tree diagram in Example 3.12 is typical of the method used to construct tree diagrams for any experiment which consists of a sequence of subexperiments. Each possible result of each subexperiment is represented by a branch of the tree. Each outcome of the complete experiment is represented pictorially by a path which connects the left of the tree (marked "Begin") to the successive results of the subexperiments in the order they occur. Each branch of the tree is assigned a number, the conditional probability associated with the result of the subexperiment represented by that branch. Thus the probability $\frac{1}{3}$ on the branch from a to A in Figure 3.5 is $\Pr[A \mid a]$; the $\frac{1}{2}$ on the branch from b to D is $\Pr[D \mid b]$.

Before we continue our discussion of tree diagrams, it is necessary for us to look more carefully at our notation for the outcome of a sequential experiment. For example, in Figure 3.5 outcome aA means that a occurs at the first stage and A at the second stage. This outcome can be viewed as the intersection of two events. The first is the set of all outcomes in which a occurs at the first stage. Our shorthand notation for this event is simply a. The second event is the set of all outcomes in which A occurs at the second stage. Our shorthand notation for this is A. With this shorthand, the outcome aA can also be written $a \cap A$.

We use tree diagrams in studying stochastic processes to provide a simple method of finding an appropriate assignment of probabilities to the outcomes of the experiment. For example, in Figure 3.5 the outcome aA (which can also be written as $a \cap A$) is assigned probability $\frac{1}{6}$. This probability is the product $\frac{1}{2} \times \frac{1}{3}$ of the probability on the branch from "Begin" to a (that is, $\frac{1}{2}$) and the probability on the branch from a to A (that is, $\frac{1}{3}$). The reason this is the appropriate probability is that $\Pr[aA] = \Pr[a]\Pr[A \mid a]$. (This fact follows immediately from the definition of conditional probability: $\Pr[A \mid a] = \Pr[A \cap a]/\Pr[a]$.) This method of assigning a probability to an outcome, i.e., multiplying together the conditional probabilities on the branches of the path corresponding to the outcome, can be used for all tree diagrams. This method defines a probability measure.

Suppose we have a multistage experiment in which conditional probabilities can be assigned to each branch of the associated tree diagram. The *probability measure* of that experiment can be obtained by defining the probability of each outcome to be the product of the conditional probabilities assigned to the branches of the path in the tree diagram corresponding to that outcome.

Example 3.13 Consider the three-stage experiment which uses the boxes, bowls, and colored balls of Figure 3.6 and which proceeds as follows: Select a box, then select a bowl, then select a ball from that bowl, and note the color of the ball. Suppose that all selections are random.

Problem Form a tree diagram for this experiment, and compute the probabilities for all outcomes.

Solution The first two stages of this experiment are identical to the two stages of the experiment in Example 3.12. Consequently, the first two stages of the tree diagram are identical to Figure 3.5. The third stage is formed by considering each of the bowls in Figure 3.6 and placing one branch for each color which can be drawn from that bowl at the fork of the tree representing that

FIGURE 3.6

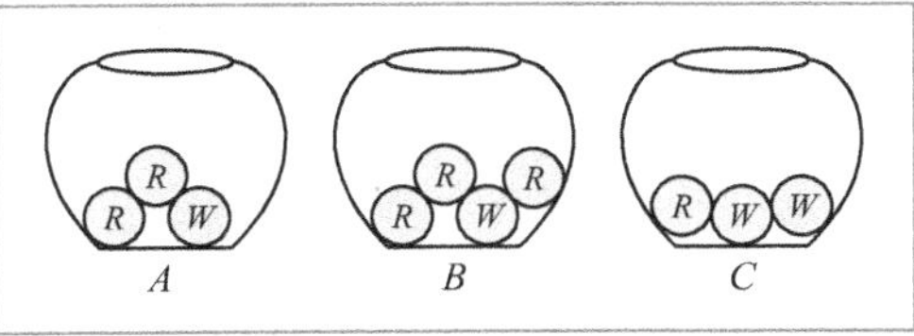

(a)

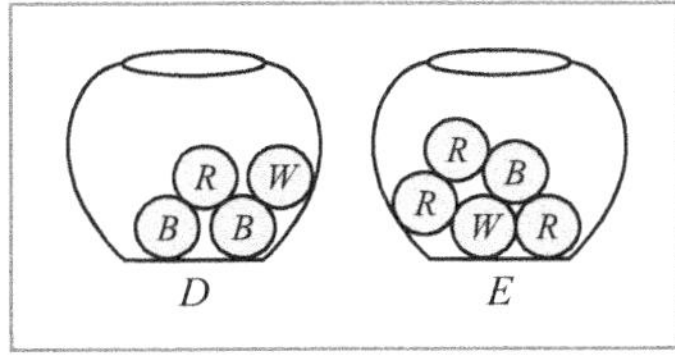

(b)

bowl. For example, the fork for bowl A has a branch for white and a branch for red since there are both red and white balls in bowl A. There is only one branch for red even though there are 2 red balls. The branches at a fork correspond to distinct results. Since there are 2 red balls and only 1 white ball, the probability of drawing a red ball from bowl A is $\frac{2}{3}$ and the probability of a white ball is $\frac{1}{3}$. These conditional probabilities are assigned to the branches from A to R and from A to W, respectively. In the same way we compute the other conditional probabilities, and the resulting tree is shown in Figure 3.7. The probability of any outcome is simply the product of the conditional probabilities for the branches in the path corresponding to that outcome. ■

FIGURE 3.7

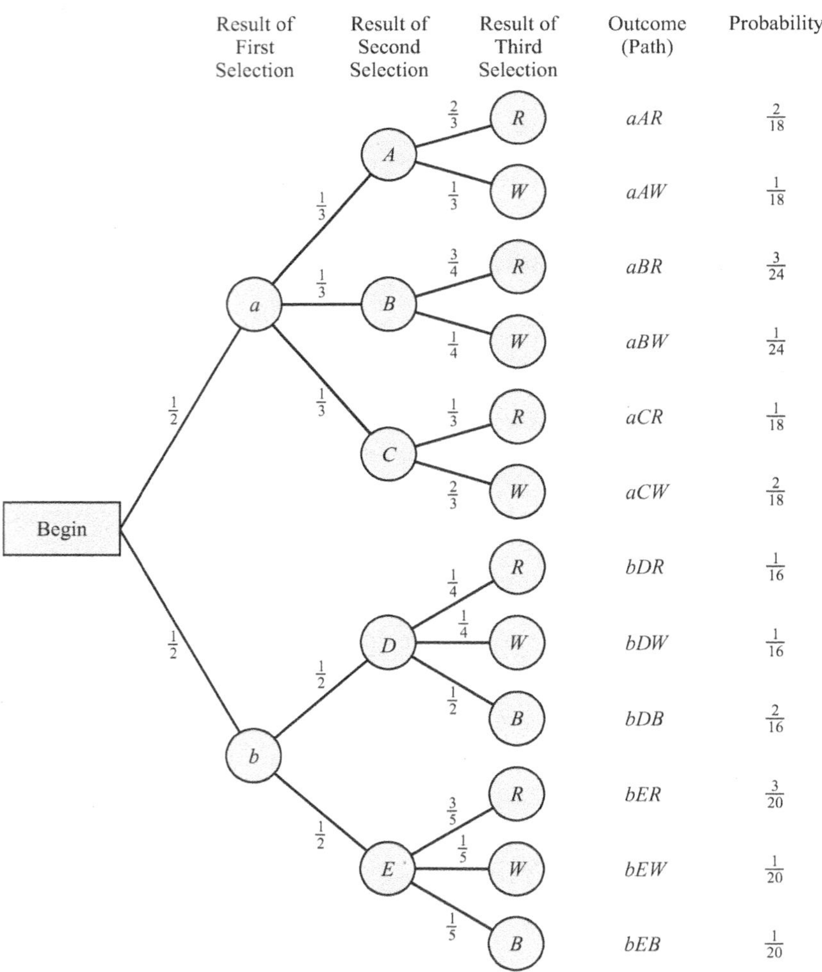

Example 3.14 In the experiment described in Example 3.13, find the probabilities of these events:

$$F = \{\text{a red ball is drawn}\}$$
$$G = \{\text{a white ball is drawn}\}$$
$$H = \{\text{a blue ball is drawn}\}$$

Solution The complete tree for this experiment is shown in Figure 3.7. The probabilities shown at the right of this Figure can be used to compute the probabilities of events F, G, and H.

Event F is the set of outcomes

$$F = \{aAR, aBR, aCR, bDR, bER\}$$

Using the definition of the probability assigned to an event, we have

$$\Pr[F] = \tfrac{2}{18} + \tfrac{3}{24} + \tfrac{1}{18} + \tfrac{1}{16} + \tfrac{3}{20} = \tfrac{121}{240}$$

Similarly,

$$\Pr[G] = \tfrac{1}{18} + \tfrac{1}{24} + \tfrac{2}{18} + \tfrac{1}{16} + \tfrac{1}{20} = \tfrac{77}{240}$$

and

$$\Pr[H] = \tfrac{2}{16} + \tfrac{1}{20} = \tfrac{42}{240}$$

Note that since events F, G, and H form a partition of the sample space for this experiment, we have

$$\Pr[F] + \Pr[G] + \Pr[H] = \tfrac{121}{240} + \tfrac{77}{240} + \tfrac{42}{240} = \tfrac{240}{240} = 1$$

■

Example 3.15 Two friends are planning an evening of entertainment and a late snack. If they go uptown they have access to entertainment choices of a play, 2 different movies or 3 different music groups. If they go downtown, they have access to one movie and 2 different music groups. Snacks can be obtained at a coffee house or at a bistro. Uptown, each of the movies or music groups is convenient to both a coffee house and a bistro for snacks, but the play is convenient only to a coffee house. Downtown, the movie is convenient only to a coffee house, but each of the music groups is convenient to both a coffee house and a bistro. The friends decide to make a plan for the evening by selecting a destination—uptown or downtown—at random, then selecting an entertainment by a random choice of the options available (6 different options for uptown and 3 for downtown), and finally, selecting a source of a snack by a random choice among the options available (one option for the uptown play and the downtown movie and 2 options for the other entertainments).

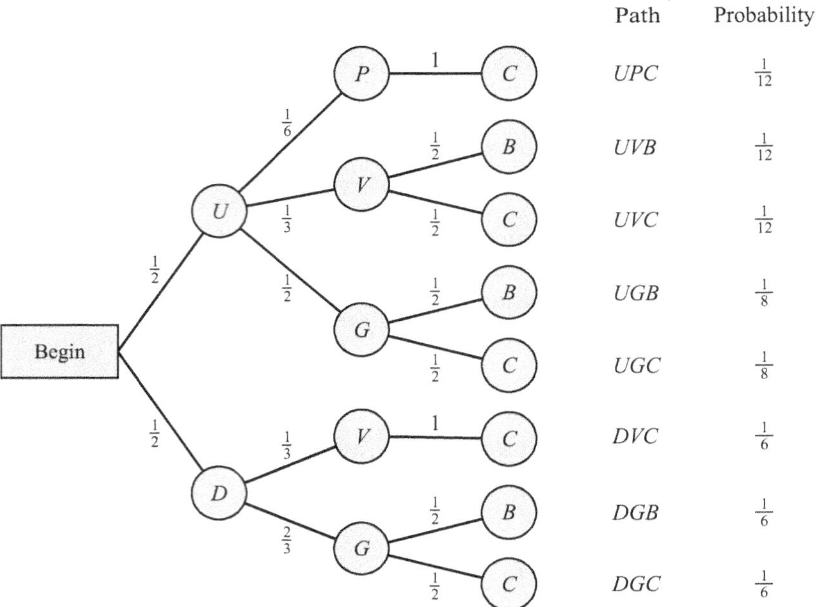

FIGURE 3.8

Problem Find the probability that the friends:

(*a*) watch one of the music groups
(*b*) have a snack in a coffee house
(*c*) watch one of the music groups and have a snack in a bistro

Solution The complete tree diagram for this situation is shown in Figure 3.8. The following abbreviations are used:

U: destination is uptown
D: destination is downtown
V: entertainment is a movie
G: entertainment is a musical group
P: entertainment is a play
B: snack is at a bistro
C: snack is at a coffee shop

Using the probabilities of the outcomes shown at the right of the tree we have:

(*a*) $\Pr[G] = \frac{1}{8} + \frac{1}{8} + \frac{1}{6} + \frac{1}{6} = \frac{7}{12}$
(*b*) $\Pr[C] = \frac{1}{12} + \frac{1}{12} + \frac{1}{8} + \frac{1}{6} + \frac{1}{6} = \frac{5}{8}$
(*c*) $\Pr[G \cap C] = \frac{1}{8} + \frac{1}{6} = \frac{7}{24}$

Note that in Example 3.15, the events ''watch a musical group'' and ''have a snack in a bistro'' are not independent, because $\left(\frac{7}{12}\right) \cdot \left(\frac{5}{8}\right) = \frac{35}{96} \neq \frac{7}{24}$. ■

Example 3.16 A part of the training routine for a high jumper is to attempt to clear the bar multiple times at a fixed height. One routine consists of repeated attempts until she has 2 consecutive successes, or 2 consecutive misses, or a total of 4 attempts, and a coach records the result of each attempt. Suppose that the probability of success on the first attempt is .5, and if any attempt is successful, then success on the next attempt is .7, and if any attempt is unsuccessful, then the probability of success on the next attempt is .4.

Problem View the results of one sequence of attempts as an outcome of an experiment, and let E be the event that she clears the bar exactly twice. Find $\Pr[E]$.

Solution A tree diagram for this experiment is shown in Figure 3.9, where S denotes a successful attempt and U denotes an unsuccessful attempt. On the

FIGURE 3.9

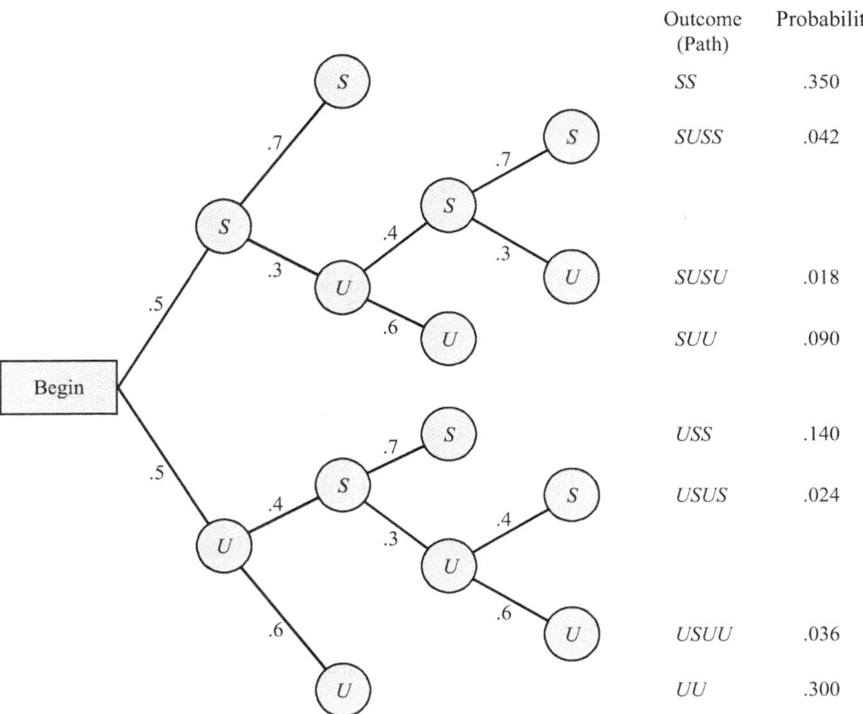

initial attempt the probability that she succeeds is .5, and if she does succeed, then on the next attempt the probability of success is .7 and the probability of not succeeding is .3. Likewise, if she is unsuccessful on the first attempt, then on the next attempt she succeeds with probability .4 and does not succeed with probability .6. Probabilities for the remaining attempts are determined in a similar manner; the probability of success depends on the result of the most recent attempt. Note: Think of moving through the tree diagram from left to right. The branch weights from "Begin" to S and U are each .5. Each branch from a result S has branch weights of .7 (to S) and .3 (to U) and the branches from U have probabilities .4 (to S) and .6 (to U).

The event E is $\{SS, SUSU, USS, USUS\}$, and using the tree diagram we have

$$\Pr[E] = .350 + .018 + .140 + .024 = .532$$

■

Exercises for Section 3.3

1. An experiment consists of flipping an unfair coin twice and noting the outcome (H or T) each time. Assume that $\Pr[H] = .2$, and draw a tree diagram for this experiment. Show all conditional probabilities on the branches of the tree, and compute the probabilities of the four outcomes of the experiment.
2. Repeat the experiment of Exercise 1. However, use a coin for which $\Pr[H] = .3$, and flip the coin 3 times.
3. Suppose you have an unfair coin $\Pr[H] = .2$, and a box containing 5 red balls, 3 blue balls and 2 green balls. An experiment consists of flipping the coin and noting the outcome, then selecting a ball at random from the box and noting its color.
   (*a*) Draw a tree diagram to represent this experiment, show the appropriate probability on each branch, and determine the probability of each outcome. Denote each outcome by the result of the coin flip (H or T) and the color of the ball drawn (R, B, or G).
   (*b*) Let E denote the event that either the coin landed with heads up or a blue ball was selected (or both). Find $\Pr[E]$.
4. Box 1 contains 2 dimes and 3 nickels, and box 2 contains 1 dime and 4 nickels. A box is selected at random, then a coin is selected at random from that box, and its value is noted. Find the probability that a dime is selected.
5. Suppose you have a bag containing one red ball, one blue ball, and three green balls. An experiment consists of selecting a ball at random and noting whether it is green or not, then replacing it. Then select another ball at random and note whether it is red or not. Draw a tree diagram to represent this experiment, show the conditional probabilities, and find the probabilities of the four outcomes.
6. A fair coin is flipped until either at least 1 head and 1 tail lands uppermost or there is a total of 4 flips. The event E consists of the outcomes with exactly 2 tails. Find $\Pr[E]$.
7. There are 9 apples in a bag; 5 are red and 4 are yellow. Two apples are selected at random, one after another without replacement, and the color of each is noted.
   (*a*) Find the probability that the second is red.
   (*b*) Find the probability that at least 1 is red.

8. A box contains 2 red balls and 3 green balls. A ball is selected at random and its color is noted. If it is red, it is not replaced in the box and a second ball is drawn and its color is noted. If the first ball is green, then it is replaced in the box, a second ball is drawn at random and its color is noted. Find the probability that the second ball is red.
9. There are 5 history courses of interest to Howard, including 3 in the afternoon, and there are 6 psychology courses which interest him, including 4 in the afternoon. Howard picks a course by selecting a department at random, then selecting a course at random. Find the probability that the course he selects is in the afternoon.
10. A multistage experiment has outcomes X and Y at the first stage and outcomes a, b, and c at the second stage. Suppose $\Pr[X] = .4$, $\Pr[Y] = .6$, $\Pr[a|X] = \Pr[b|X] = \Pr[c|Y] = .4$, and $\Pr[a|Y] = .2$. Find the probability that the outcome of the second stage is a.
11. At the local Rent-A-Reck car rental company the fleet consists of Audi, BMW, and Mercedes cars: 20 percent Audi, 45 percent BMW, 35 percent Mercedes. Half of the Mercedes, 70 percent of the BMW, and 90 percent of the Audi cars have over 100,000 miles on the odometer. A car is selected at random from the fleet.
    (*a*) Find the probability that it has over 100,000 miles on the odometer.
    (*b*) Find the probability that it is either a Mercedes or has over 100,000 miles on the odometer (or both).
12. Each morning Joe makes a decision about how he gets from his apartment to the university for class. He chooses at random, and half the time he takes the bus, forty percent of the time he walks, and ten percent of the time he takes his bike. If he takes a bus, then he is on time for class with probability .7, and with probability .3 he is late. If he walks, then he is on time for class with probability .6, and with probability .4 he is late. Finally, if he takes his bike, then he is on time for class with probability .5, and with probability .5 he is late. On a random day find the probability that Joe is late for class.
13. There are 4 red balls and 3 blue balls in a box. Two balls are selected at random, one after another without replacement, and the color of each ball is noted.
    (*a*) Find the probability that exactly 1 ball is blue.
    (*b*) Find the probability that the second ball is blue given that at least 1 of the balls is blue.
14. A Finite Mathematics class at GSU consists of 40 percent freshmen and 60 percent sophomores. Seventy percent of the freshmen and 55 percent of the sophomores are state residents, and the remainder are not state residents. Find the probability that a randomly selected student is not a state resident.
15. Half of the direct flights from Indianapolis to Metroburg are on Urban Airlines, 20 percent are on Bi-Coastal Airways, and 30 percent are on DVD Air. Eighty percent of the flights on Urban Airways, 60 percent of the flights on Bi-Coastal, and 40 percent of the flights on DVD Air are on time. A direct flight from Indianapolis to Metroburg is selected at random. What is the probability that it is on time?
16. There are four \$1 bills, one \$5 bill, and three \$10 bills in a drawer. An experiment consists of selecting bills, one at a time without replacement and noting the value of each bill selected. The experiment ends when a \$10 bill is selected or when 3 bills have been selected. Find the probability that a \$10 bill is not selected.
17. Find all missing probabilities on the tree diagram shown in Figure 3.10.

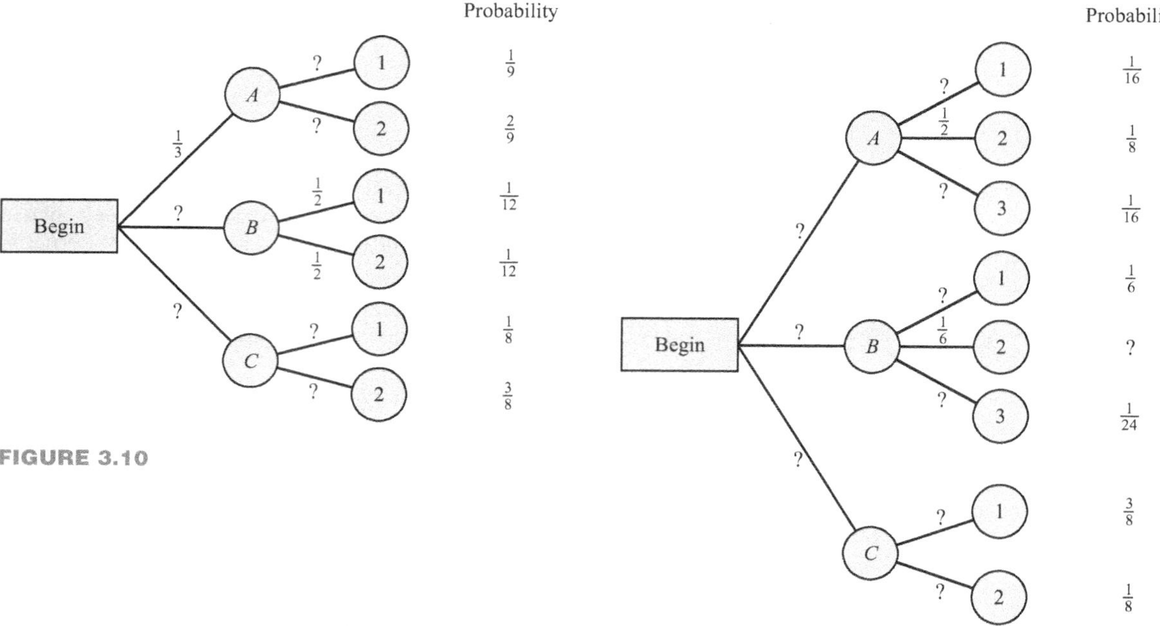

FIGURE 3.10

FIGURE 3.11

18. Find all missing probabilities on the tree diagram shown in Figure 3.11.
19. An unfair coin with $\Pr[H] = .2$ is flipped until either there is a total of 2 heads or a total of 5 flips. The result of each flip is noted. Let E be the event consisting of all outcomes with exactly one head. Find $\Pr[E]$.
20. Students at GSU are being tested for infection with the North Amazon virus. If a student is infected, the test is positive 90 percent of the time, and if a student is not infected, then the test is negative 90 percent of the time. Suppose that 2 percent of the students are infected with the virus. If a student is chosen for testing at random, find the probability that the test is positive.
21. Consider 2 bags, each of which contains 3 colored balls. Bag a contains 2 red balls and 1 white ball, and bag b contains 1 red, 1 white, and 1 blue ball. An experiment consists of randomly drawing a ball from bag a, noting its color, placing the ball in bag b, and then randomly drawing a ball from bag b and noting its color. Draw a tree diagram to represent the outcomes of this experiment, i.e., the ordered pairs of colors obtained, and show all probabilities on the tree. What is the probability of obtaining 2 red balls? Also find $\Pr[2 \text{ red balls} | \text{first ball red}]$.
22. A group of people who had recently purchased new cars was surveyed about the purchases. Each person was asked to select the single most important factor in determining his or her choice and to indicate whether the purchase had proved satisfactory. Of this group, 35 percent cited price as the most important factor, 50 percent cited fuel economy, and the remainder cited styling. Fifty percent of those who cited price as the most important factor expressed satisfaction with their purchase, 80 percent of those who cited fuel economy were satisfied, and

30 percent of those who cited styling were satisfied. View this as an experiment whose outcomes are a reason for purchase (price, fuel economy, styling) and an evaluation of satisfaction (satisfied, not satisfied).

(*a*) Draw a tree diagram for this experiment, and find the probabilities for all outcomes.

(*b*) Let E be the event consisting of all outcomes in which the purchaser was satisfied. Find $\Pr[E]$.

23. There are 5 quarters, 1 dime, and 3 nickels in a drawer. An experiment consists of selecting a coin at random, noting its value and setting it aside. If it is a dime, the experiment ends. If it is not a dime, then another coin is selected at random, and its value is noted. Find the probability that at least one nickel is selected.

24. A box labeled H contains 1 red ball and 3 yellow balls, and a box labeled T contains 2 red balls, 1 yellow ball, and 1 green ball. A fair coin is flipped and if a head comes up, a ball is selected at random from the box labeled H and its color is noted. If a tail comes up, a ball is selected at random from the box labeled T and its color is noted.

    (*a*) Draw a tree diagram for this experiment.

    (*b*) Find the probability that a red ball is drawn.

25. A new small business makes a profit the first year with probability .2. After the first year it makes a profit with probability .6 if it made a profit in the preceding year, and it makes a profit with probability .4 if it did not make a profit in the preceding year. Find the probability that it makes a profit for exactly 2 of the first 3 years.

26. An unfair coin with $\Pr[H] = .4$ is flipped 4 times and the result of each flip is noted. Find the probability that the outcome contains exactly 2 consecutive heads, that is, 2 consecutive heads but not 3 consecutive heads.

27. A basketball player is equally likely to make or miss her first shot each game. If she makes a shot, then she makes the next shot with probability .7, and if she misses a shot, then she misses the next with probability .6. Find the probability that she makes exactly 2 of her first three shots.

28. A box contains 2 red, 3 blue, and 2 yellow balls. A ball is selected at random, and its color is noted. If it is yellow, it is replaced; otherwise, it is not. A second ball is selected and its color is noted.

    (*a*) Find the probability that the second ball is yellow.

    (*b*) Find the probability that the second ball is red.

29. There are balls numbered 1 through 7 in a box. A ball is drawn at random and its number is noted. If it is odd, the ball is set aside, and if it is even, it is replaced in the box. A second ball is drawn at random and its number is noted. Find the probability that the ball numbered 5 is one of the two balls drawn.

30. Let E and F be events in a sample space S with $\Pr[F] \neq 0$, and $\Pr[F] \neq 1$. Show that

$$\Pr[E] = \Pr[E|F]\Pr[F] + \Pr[E|F']\Pr[F'].$$

31. A reduced deck of 36 cards consists of all numbered cards, that is, four cards numbered 2, four cards numbered 3, ..., four cards numbered 10. Five cards are dealt, one after another without replacement, and the number on each card is noted.

Find the probability that the numbers of the cards dealt are strictly increasing. That is, each card dealt has a larger number than the preceding card.

32. A special deck of cards consists of 10 groups of 10 cards, each labelled 1 through 10. These cards are mixed, and then random draws are made until the cards drawn include 5 consecutive numbers. What is the probability that only 5 cards will need to be drawn?
33. Suppose you have cards numbered 1, 2, 3, and 4. An experiment consists of selecting a card at random, noting its number, and setting it aside. Next, another card is randomly selected from the remaining cards with higher numbers, its number is noted and it is set aside. Continue until the card numbered 4 is selected. Find the probability that the card numbered 2 is selected at some stage of the experiment.
34. In the setting of Exercise 33, find the probability that at least one of the cards numbered 2 or 3 is selected.

3.4 BAYES PROBABILITIES

Questions which involve conditional probabilities are very common in applications of probability theory, and one type of conditional probability problem is so common that it has a special name. In this type of problem, called a *Bayes probability* problem, it is easy to compute $\Pr[A|B]$, but the goal is to determine $\Pr[B|A]$. Our approach to these problems is to use both tree diagrams and the basic formula for computing conditional probabilities. We also give a general formula which can be used to compute Bayes probabilities.

Example 3.17 The manager at Robert's Restorations of Rochester, Minnesota, orders 80 percent of the specialized hardware used in restoring cabinets from a distributor in Baltimore and the remainder from a distributor in Seattle. Shipments by air are always requested, but occasionally they come by ground transportation. Shipments from Baltimore come by ground 5 percent of the time, and shipments from Seattle come by ground 10 percent of the time.

Problem A shipment selected at random is noted to have come by air. Find the probability that it came from Seattle.

Solution Construct a tree diagram to represent the two-stage experiment of first noting the source of the shipment (B or S) and then noting whether it came by air or by ground (A or G). Using the data provided, we obtain the tree and the probabilities shown in Figure 3.12. We use the notation $B \cap A$ to indicate a path through B and A (a shipment from Baltimore by air). The probabilities of the paths are determined as shown in Section 3.3. (Since the probability that an order is shipped from Baltimore is .8 and the conditional probability that an order shipped from Baltimore by air is .95 (equal to 1 minus the probability it comes by ground), the probability of the outcome $B \cap A$ is .76.)

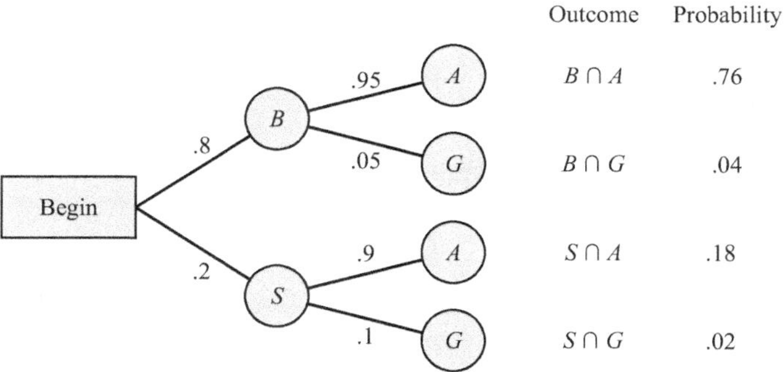

FIGURE 3.12

The event "a shipment comes by air" consists of outcomes $B \cap A$ and $S \cap A$, and consequently $\Pr[A] = \Pr[B \cap A] + \Pr[S \cap A] = .76 + .18 = .94$. We can now solve the problem posed. Using the definition of conditional probability, we have

$$\Pr[S|A] = \frac{\Pr[S \cap A]}{\Pr[A]} = \frac{.76}{.94}$$ ■

Example 3.18 Clyde has a rather casual attitude toward his courses, and he studies for one-third of his examinations selected at random. In the past he has passed three-fourths of the examinations for which he has studied and one-fourth of those for which he has not studied.

Problem Clyde passed his mathematics examination. Find the probability that he studied for it.

Solution Let S and N denote study and not study, respectively, and let P and F denote pass and fail, respectively. The problem is to determine the conditional probability $\Pr[S|P]$. By definition this is equal to $\Pr[S \cap P]/\Pr[P]$ provided $\Pr[P] \neq 0$. To evaluate this ratio, we need $\Pr[S \cap P]$ and $\Pr[P]$. There is another expression for $\Pr[S \cap P]$ which involves only known quantities, namely, $\Pr[S \cap P] = \Pr[P|S]\Pr[S]$. It remains to determine $\Pr[P]$.

Since Clyde either studies or does not study for each examination, the set of examinations which he passes can be partitioned into $P \cap S$ and $P \cap N$. It follows from axiom iii of a probability measure that

$$\Pr[P] = \Pr[P \cap S] + \Pr[P \cap N]$$

Again using the definition of conditional probability, we have

$$\Pr[P \cap S] = \Pr[P|S]\Pr[S] \qquad \text{and} \qquad \Pr[P \cap N] = \Pr[P|N]Pr[N]$$

Combining these relations, we have

$$\Pr[P] = \Pr[P|S]\Pr[S] + \Pr[P|N]\Pr[N]$$

We now have expressions for both $\Pr[S \cap P]$ and $\Pr[P]$ which involve only known quantities. Using these expressions, we have

$$\Pr[S|P] = \frac{\Pr[P|S]\Pr[S]}{\Pr[P|S]\Pr[S] + \Pr[P|N]\Pr[N]}$$

Using the data of this problem,

$$\Pr[S|P] = \frac{\frac{3}{4} \cdot \frac{1}{3}}{\frac{3}{4} \cdot \frac{1}{3} + \frac{1}{4} \cdot \frac{2}{3}} = \frac{\frac{1}{4}}{\frac{1}{4} + \frac{1}{6}} = \frac{3}{5}$$ ■

In both Example 3.17 and Example 3.18, we computed conditional probabilities for which the condition was an event at the right of the tree (the shipment was by air or Clyde passed his examination) and the probability to be determined concerned an event at the left of the tree (the shipment came from Seattle or Clyde studied for the examination). Conditional probabilities such as these are known as *Bayes probabilities.* The formula derived in the solution of Example 3.18 is a general one, and it is an instance of Bayes' formula.

Bayes' Formula

Let S be the sample space of an experiment, and suppose that S is partitioned into subsets $S_1, S_2, \ldots, S_k$ such that $\Pr[S_i] > 0$ for $i = 1, 2, \ldots, k$. If A is any event such that $\Pr[A] > 0$, then

$$\Pr[S_i\,|A] = \frac{\Pr[A\,|S_i]\Pr[S_i]}{\Pr[A\,|S_1]\Pr[S_1] + \cdots + \Pr[A\,|S_k]\Pr[S_k]} \tag{3.4}$$

for $i = 1, 2, \ldots, k$.

In Example 3.18 the sample space (set of all examinations) was partitioned into two sets: those for which Clyde studied and those for which he did not study. Using the notation of Bayes' formula, formula (3.4), we have $k = 2$, and $S_1 = S$ (the set of examinations for which Clyde studied) and $S_2 = N$ (the set of examinations for which Clyde did not study).

There are situations in which the formula is simpler to use than a tree diagram, but most problems in this book can be solved more directly by using a tree diagram.

Example 3.19 A Faculty member at Gigantic State University regularly teaches an evening class in a neighboring community. Each time she makes the trip, she is randomly assigned a car from the university motor pool. The motor pool consists of 50 percent Chevrolets, 30 percent Toyotas, and 20 percent Volkswagens. Some of the cars have satellite radio and some do not: 60 percent of the Chevrolets, 50 percent of the Toyotas, and 30 percent of the Volkswagens have satellite radio.

Problem One afternoon the faculty member is assigned a car with satellite radio. Find the probability that it is a Chevrolet.

Solution We illustrate two methods of solving the problem: the use of a tree diagram and the use of Bayes' formula. Of course, the methods are not actually different; the formula simply expresses in a concise way the operations which are being carried out on a tree diagram. The tree diagram method is somewhat longer, but it provides a convenient means of organizing information.

(*a*) *Tree diagram*: A tree diagram constructed using the information given in the problem is shown in Figure 3.13. The three branches from the Begin box designate the make of automobiles and the second branches (two in each case) designate whether it has satellite radio (Y) or not (N). The event Y that the faculty member receives a car with satellite radio can be partitioned into the disjoint events "Chevrolet with satellite radio," "Toyota with satellite radio," and "Volkswagen with satellite radio." Using the data on the tree diagram,

FIGURE 3.13

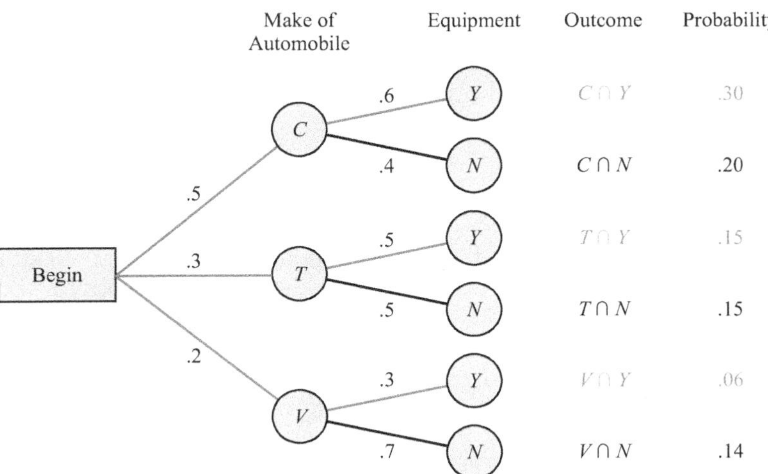

we have

$$\Pr[Y] = \Pr[C \cap Y] + \Pr[T \cap Y] + \Pr[V \cap Y] = .30 + .15 + .06 = .51$$

We can now solve the problem. We have

$$\Pr[C|Y] = \frac{\Pr[C \cap Y]}{\Pr[Y]} = \frac{.30}{.51} = \frac{30}{51}$$

(*b*) *Bayes' formula:* The sample space can be partitioned into disjoint events C, T, and V (the faculty member is assigned a Chevrolet, Toyota, or Volkswagen, respectively). Letting these events play the roles of S_1, S_2 and S_3 in formula (3.4), and letting Y (the faculty member is assigned a car with satellite radio) play the role of the event A in formula (3.4), we have

$$\begin{aligned}\Pr[C \mid Y] &= \frac{\Pr[Y \mid C]\Pr[C]}{\Pr[Y \mid C]\Pr[C] + \Pr[Y \mid T]\Pr[T] + \Pr[Y \mid V]\Pr[V]} \\ &= \frac{.6 \times .5}{.6 \times .5 + .5 \times .3 + .3 \times .2} = \frac{30}{51}\end{aligned}$$

■

Example 3.20 A bucket labeled H contains 3 yellow and 2 white balls, and a bucket labeled T contains 2 yellow balls and 1 white ball. An experiment consists of flipping a fair coin once, and according to the side which comes up, selecting two balls in succession and without replacement from the bucket labeled H (if a head) or T (if a tail). The color of each ball is noted as it is drawn: W is white and Y is yellow.

Problem (*a*) If exactly one white ball is drawn, what is the probability that the coin landed with a head up?
(*b*) If the second ball drawn is white, what is the probability that the coin landed with a head up?

Solution The tree diagram for this experiment is shown in Figure 3.14.
(*a*) We are interested in $\Pr[H|\text{ exactly one } W]$. Here we are again using a shorthand notation to represent sets. Thus the expression "exactly one W" stands for the event consisting of all outcomes for which exactly one white ball is drawn. The outcomes in the event "exactly one W" are identified by a ✓ in the tree diagram. From the tree it is clear that

$$\begin{aligned}\Pr[H \cap \text{ exactly one } W] &= \tfrac{3}{20} + \tfrac{3}{20} = \tfrac{3}{10} \\ \Pr[\text{exactly one } W] &= \tfrac{3}{20} + \tfrac{3}{20} + \tfrac{1}{6} + \tfrac{1}{6} = \tfrac{19}{30}\end{aligned}$$

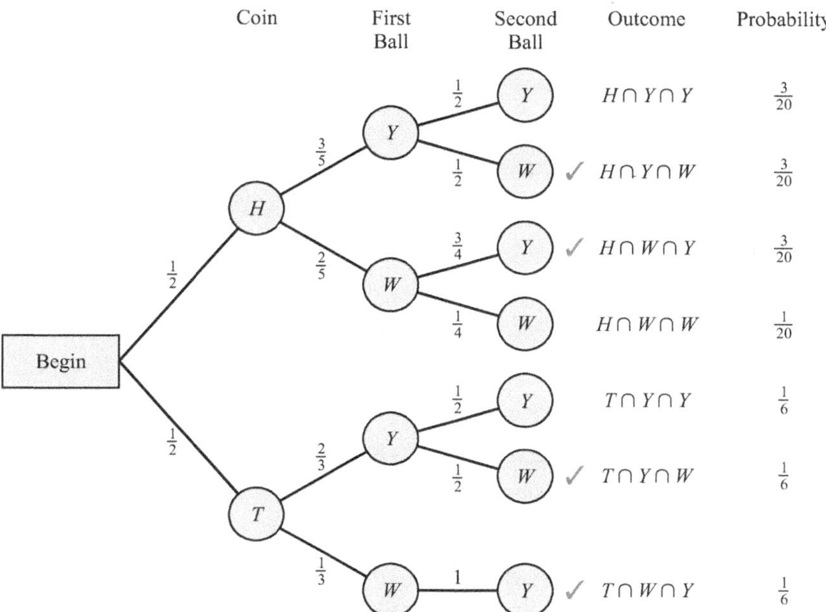

FIGURE 3.14

Using the definition of conditional probability, we find

$$\Pr[H|\text{ exactly one } W] = \frac{\Pr[H \cap \text{ exactly one } W]}{\Pr[\text{exactly one } W]} = \frac{\frac{3}{10}}{\frac{19}{30}} = \frac{9}{19}$$

(*b*) Our goal is to determine $\Pr[H \mid \text{second ball } W]$. Again using the tree diagram, we have

$$\Pr[H \cap \text{ second ball } W] = \tfrac{3}{20} + \tfrac{1}{20} = \tfrac{1}{5}$$
$$\Pr[\text{second ball } W] = \tfrac{3}{20} + \tfrac{1}{20} + \tfrac{1}{6} = \tfrac{11}{30}$$

Combining these, we find

$$\Pr[H|\text{second ball } W] = \frac{\frac{1}{5}}{\frac{11}{30}} = \frac{6}{11}$$ ■

Exercises for Section 3.4

1. The tree diagram for an experiment is shown in Figure 3.15. Compute the following probabilities.
   (*a*) $\Pr[B]$ (*b*) $\Pr[b]$ (*c*) $\Pr[b|B]$ (*d*) $\Pr[B|b]$

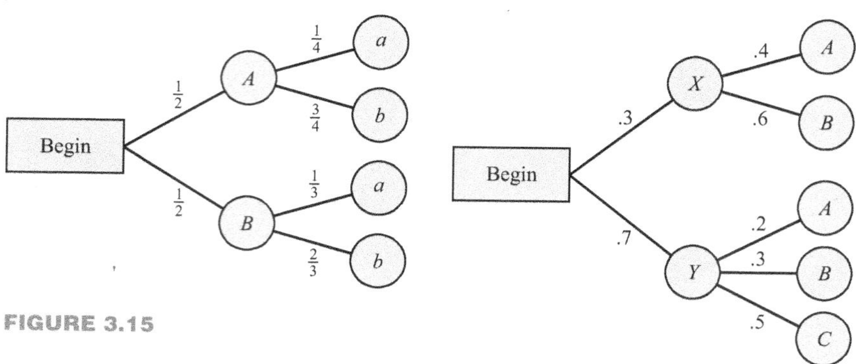

FIGURE 3.15

FIGURE 3.16

2. The tree diagram for an experiment is shown in Figure 3.16. Compute the following probabilities.
   (*a*) $\Pr[A]$ (*b*) $\Pr[X|A]$ (*c*) $\Pr[Y|B]$ (*d*) $\Pr[B|Y]$
3. A box contains 3 red balls and 2 blue balls. A ball is selected at random, its color noted and it is set aside. A second ball is selected and its color is noted. Find the probability that the first was red given that the second was blue.
4. An experiment has the three diagram shown in Figure 3.17. Find the following probabilities.
   (*a*) $\Pr[B|Y]$ (*b*) $\Pr[Y|B]$ (*c*) $\Pr[(X \text{ or } Y)|B]$
5. The tree diagram for an experiment is shown in Figure 3.18. Compute these probabilities:
   (*a*) $\Pr[(b \text{ and } B)|Y]$ (*b*) $\Pr[Y|(b \text{ and } B)]$
6. A box contains 3 red balls and 2 blue balls. A ball is selected at random and its color is noted. If it is red, it is set aside, and if it is blue it is replaced in the box. A second ball is selected and its color is noted.
   (*a*) Find the probability that the second ball is blue.
   (*b*) Find the probability that the second ball is blue given that the first ball was blue.
   (*c*) Find the probability that the first ball was blue given that the second is blue.
7. An experiment consists of making a random selection of one of the 3 bowls shown in Figure 3.19 and then drawing a single ball and noting its color. If the ball is blue (B), what is the probability that bowl X was selected? If the ball is either blue or white (W), what is the probability that bowl Y was selected?
8. There are 3 coins, 2 are fair and 1 is unfair with $\Pr[H] = .6$. A coin is selected at random, flipped twice, and the result of each flip is noted. If the results of the flips are a head followed by a tail, find the probability that a fair coin was selected.
9. Two balls are selected one after another and without replacement from a box which contains 2 red, 1 green, and 3 blue balls. Find the probability that the first ball was blue, given that the second was red. Assume random selections.
10. The host of a radio music show has selected 8 jazz tracks for today's show, and each track features a soloist: 5 are trumpet solos and 3 are saxophone solos. To begin the show, two tracks are selected at random and played one after the other.

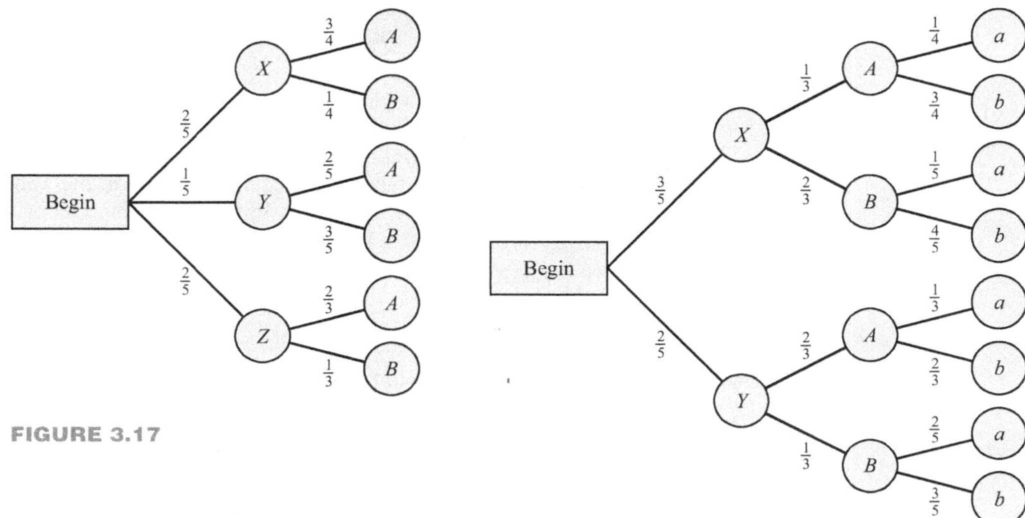

FIGURE 3.17

FIGURE 3.18

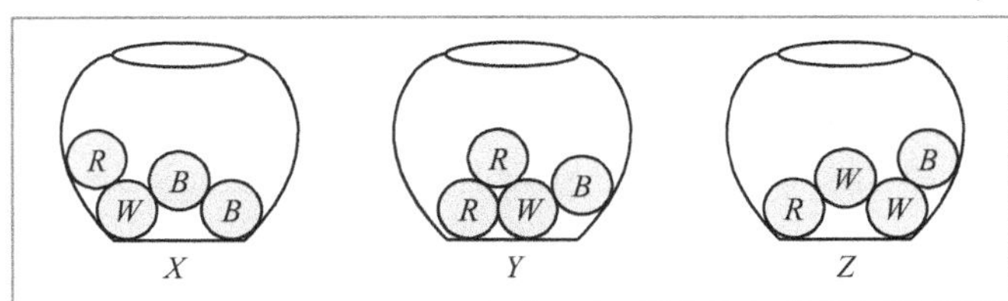

FIGURE 3.19

Find the probability that the first was a trumpet solo given that at least one was a trumpet solo.

11. Steve has two coins, one is fair and the other is weighted so that the probability of a head is .6. A coin is selected at random and flipped twice. The result of each flip is noted. Find the conditional probability that the fair coin was selected, given that there were two heads.
12. There are 4 quarters dated 2010 and 2 quarters dated 2015 in your car to use for parking meters. You select a quarter at random and put it in the meter. You then select another coin at random and note that it is dated 2010. Find the probability that the first coin was also dated 2010.
13. In the setting of Exercise 9, find the probability that the first was blue, given that the second was not blue.
14. A part of the training routine for a high jumper is to attempt to clear the bar multiple times at a fixed height. One routine consists of repeated jumps until she has 2 consecutive successes, 2 consecutive misses, or a total of 4 attempts, and a

coach records the result of each attempt. Suppose that the probability of success on any attempt is .6. Find the probability that if the routine goes on for 4 attempts, then the first was a success.

15. A manufacturer of running shoes has plants in Korea, Australia, and Venezuela. Korea produces 60 percent of the shoes, Australia 20 percent, and Venezuela 20 percent. They make 2 types of shoes at each plant, a racing shoe and a training flat. The production at each plant is allocated as shown in the Table 3.5. Suppose that these shoes are randomly distributed in stores in the United States and that you go into a store and buy a training flat. What is the probability that it came from Korea?

TABLE 3.5

Plant	Racing	Training
Korea	.50	.50
Australia	.25	.75
Venezuela	.40	.60

16. At Gigantic State University 60 percent of the students have taken 4 years of high school mathematics. Of those who have taken 4 years of high school mathematics, 20 percent plan to major in science. Of those who have not taken 4 years of high school mathematics, 5 percent plan to major in science. If a randomly selected student plans to major in science, what is the probability that she or he took 4 years of high school mathematics?

17. The World-Wide Sandal Company produces sandals at plants in Brazil, China, and Italy. Half the production comes from Brazil with the remainder split evenly between China and Italy. Each plant produces the same 3 different types of sandals, called the Peak, Racu, and Tova. Sandal production at each plant is allocated as shown in Table 3.6. Suppose that sandals are shipped from the production plants to a distribution center and then randomly to retail stores. If someone buys a pair of Peak sandals, what is the probability they were produced in Italy?

TABLE 3.6

Plant	% Peak	% Racu	% Tova
Brazil	30	40	30
China	20	10	70
Italy	40	30	30

18. Students at GSU are being tested for infection with the East Thames virus, and it is estimated that .5 percent of the students are infected. If a student is infected, the test is positive 99 percent of the time, and if a student is not infected, then the test is negative 98 percent of the time. If the test is applied to a student whose infection status is unknown, and if the test results are negative, find the probability that the student actually has the East Thames virus.

19. A used car lot contains 35 percent Honda, 45 percent Toyota, and 20 percent Hyundai automobiles. Fifty percent of the Hondas, 30 percent of the Toyotas, and 80 percent of the Hyundai have navigation systems. If a car selected at random from the lot has a navigation system, find the probability it is not a Toyota.
20. In the used car lot of Exercise 19, all of the Toyotas are silver, half of the Hyundai are silver, and 20 percent of the Hondas are silver. Also it is known that the color of the car is independent of whether it has a navigation system. In this setting, if a randomly selected car is silver and has a navigation system, find the probability that it is a Toyota.
21. Amy has three cell phones: brands K, M, and N. She uses the K brand 20 percent of the time, and M and N brands equally often. She notices that she loses the signal 10 percent of the time when using brands K and N, and 5 percent of the time when using brand M. On a random use of her cell phone she loses the signal. Find the probability she was using brand N.
22. A business supply store stocks replacement printer cartridges as follows: 50 percent are brand A, 20 percent are brand B, and the reminder are brand X. The manager knows from experience that 20 percent of brand A cartridges will not provide the number of pages advertised; also 5 percent of brand B and 20 percent of brand X will fail to provide the pages advertised. A customer returns a cartridge because it failed to provide the pages advertised. Find the probability that it is a brand X cartridge.
23. Box A contains 2 red and 1 green ball, and Box B contains 3 red and 2 green balls. A box is selected at random, and then 2 balls are selected simultaneously and at random, and their colors are noted. If both are the same color, what is the probability that Box B was selected?
24. Julie attends GSU and her home is in Los Angeles. When going home, she must change planes in either Dallas, Denver, or St. Louis. If she changes in Dallas, her flight will be late 20 percent of the time, if she changes in Denver, she will be late 30 percent of the time, and if she changes in St. Louis, she will be late 60 percent of the time. She chooses airlines at random, and she is equally likely to choose one that requires a change in Dallas as one that requires a change in Denver, and she is twice as likely to choose one that requires a change in Dallas as one that requires a change in St. Louis. On a random flight she is late arriving in Los Angeles. Find the probability that she changed planes in Denver.
25. Pine tree seeds of types A, B, and C are randomly scattered in a field. The seeds are 60 percent type A, 30 percent type B, and 10 percent type C. It is known that 30 percent of type A seeds will germinate, 40 percent of type B seeds will germinate, and 70 percent of type C will germinate. If a randomly selected seed has germinated, what is the probability that it is type A?
26. A random selection is made between two coins, and the selected coin is flipped twice. One of the coins is fair, and the other is unfair with $\Pr[H] = \frac{2}{3}$. If the result of the experiment is one head and one tail, what is the probability that the unf coin was selected?
27. There are three balls colored red, blue, and green in a box. An experiment of drawing a ball at random and noting its color.
    (*a*) If it is red the experiment ends.
    (*b*) If it is blue, then it is replaced and another ball is drawn and it

(*c*) If it is green, then it is set aside, and another ball is drawn and its color is noted.

Find the probability that the first ball is blue given that the second is blue.

28. A box contains 2 red, 3 blue, and 2 yellow balls. A ball is drawn at random, and its color is noted. If it is yellow, it is replaced; otherwise, it is not. A second ball is drawn and its color is noted. Find the probability that the first ball is yellow, given that the second ball is red.

29. A basketball player is equally likely to make and to miss his first shot in each game. If he makes his first shot, then he is twice as likely to make future shots as to miss them. If he misses the first shot, then he is twice as likely to miss as to make future shots.
    (*a*) In a game in which the player makes his third shot, find the probability that he made his first shot as well.
    (*b*) In a game in which the player makes his third shot, find the probability that he made all 3 shots.

30. In the setting of Exercise 29, let $E(n)$ denote the event that he made shot n, $n = 2, 3, 4$.
    (*a*) Find $\Pr[E(n)]$ for $n = 2, 3, 4$.
    (*b*) For $n = 2, 3, 4$, find the conditional probability that he made the first shot given $E(n)$.

31. A time-conscious traveler is considering flying from New York to Los Angeles, and she reviews the on-time performance of Best Air, East-West Air, and Bi-Coastal Airlines. She finds that Best Air has 2 flights each day, East-West Air has 4 flights, and Bi-Coastal Airlines has 5 flights. Data show that Best Air is on time 50 percent of the time, East-West Air is on time 70 percent of the time, and Bi-Coastal Airlines is on time 40 percent of the time. She selects a flight at random, and she arrives on time. Find the probabilities that she flew on each of the three airlines.

32. The Alumni Association of GSU has conducted a survey of 1990 graduates. That year the university awarded 5000 undergraduate degrees and 3000 graduate degrees, and no student received both a graduate and an undergraduate degree. Of the graduate degrees, 40 percent were in technical fields and 60 percent were in nontechnical fields. Of the undergraduate degrees, 20 percent were in technical fields and 80 percent in nontechnical fields. Among those who earned graduate degrees, 98 percent of those with technical degrees and 95 percent of those with nontechnical degrees are employed, and the remainder are unemployed. Among those who earned undergraduate degrees, 95 percent of those with technical degrees and 90 percent of those with nontechnical degrees are employed, and the remainder are unemployed. Find the probability that a randomly selected employed graduate earned a graduate degree from GSU.

33. In the setting of Exercise 32, which is more likely, that a randomly selected employed graduate earned a graduate degree or an undergraduate degree?

34. The class standing and residency status of undergraduates at GSU are shown in Table 3.7. A randomly selected student is a state resident. Find the probability that the student is a freshmen.

35. Using the data of Table 3.7, if a randomly selected student is not a state resident, find the most likely class standing of the student selected.

TABLE 3.7

Class Standing	Percentage in Class	% Resident
Freshman	26	75
Sophomore	24	73
Junior	22	73
Senior	28	70

36. Suppose you have cards numbered 1, 2, 3, and 4. An experiment consists of selecting a card at random, noting its number, and setting it aside. Next, another card is selected from the remaining cards with higher numbers, its number is noted and it is set aside. Continue until the card numbered 4 is selected. If the card numbered 3 is selected at some stage, find the probability that it was selected as the first card.

IMPORTANT TERMS AND CONCEPTS

You should be able to describe, define, or give examples of each of the following:

Axioms of a probability measure
Properties of a probability measure
Conditional probability
Independence
Probabilities on trees
Stochastic process
Bayes probabilities

REVIEW EXERCISES

1. An experiment has the sample space $S = \{\mathcal{O}_1, \mathcal{O}_2, \mathcal{O}_3, \mathcal{O}_4, \mathcal{O}_5\}$ and probabilities $w_1 = .09$, $w_2 = .23$, $w_3 = .41$, $w_4 = .14$, and $w_5 = .13$. Define $E_1 = \{\mathcal{O}_1, \mathcal{O}_2, \mathcal{O}_4\}$, $E_2 = \{\mathcal{O}_3, \mathcal{O}_4, \mathcal{O}_5\}$, $E_3 = \{\mathcal{O}_2, \mathcal{O}_3\}$. Find:
   (*a*) $\Pr[E_1']$ (*b*) $\Pr[E_1 \cup E_2]$
   (*c*) $\Pr[E_1 \cap E_3]$ (*d*) $\Pr[E_2 \cap E_3']$
2. A sample space contains events E and F with $\Pr[E] = .35$, $\Pr[F] = .30$, and $\Pr[E \cap F] = .20$. Find:
   (*a*) $\Pr[E']$ (*b*) $\Pr[E \cup F]$ (*c*) $\Pr[E \cap F']$
3. A sample space contains events E and F with $\Pr[E] = .3$, $\Pr[F] = .6$, and $\Pr[E \cap F] = .25$. Find
   (*a*) $\Pr[E']$ (*b*) $\Pr[E \cup F]$ (*c*) $\Pr[E \cap F']$ (*d*) $\Pr[E' \cap F']$
4. A sample space contains events E, F, and G with E and G disjoint, $\Pr[E] = .3$, $\Pr[F] = .6$, $\Pr[G] = .45$, $\Pr[F \cap G] = .2$, and $\Pr[E \cap F] = .25$. Find
   (*a*) $\Pr[E \cup G]$ (*b*) $\Pr[E \cup G']$ (*c*) $\Pr[E \cap G']$ (*d*) $\Pr[G \cap F']$
5. An experiment has outcomes $\mathcal{O}_1$, $\mathcal{O}_2$, and $\mathcal{O}_3$. If $\mathcal{O}_1$ is twice as likely as $\mathcal{O}_2$, and $\mathcal{O}_3$ is 3 times as likely as $\mathcal{O}_2$, find the probability of $\mathcal{O}_1$.

6. Suppose that events E_1, E_2, E_3 form a partition of a sample space S and that $\Pr[E_1] = 2\Pr[E_2]$, $\Pr[E_3] = 3\Pr[E_1]$. Find the probabilities of events E_1, E_2, and E_3.
7. Suppose E and F are events in a sample space with $\Pr[E \cup F] = .8$, $\Pr[E \cap F] = .3$, and $\Pr[E'] = .4$.
   (*a*) Find $\Pr[E]$. (*b*) Find $\Pr[F]$. (*c*) Find $\Pr[E|F]$.
8. For two events E and F in a sample space S, it is known that $\Pr[E|F] = .5$, $\Pr[E] = .4$, and $\Pr[F'] = .4$. Find $\Pr[E|F']$.
9. Eighty percent of the freshmen at GSU plan to live in the residence halls, and 60 percent have their phone plan through ATT. If living in the residence halls and having an ATT phone plan are independent, find the probability that a randomly selected freshman lives in a residence hall or has an ATT phone plan but not both.
10. A sample space contains the events E, F, and G, with $\Pr[E] = .3$, $\Pr[F] = .4$, and $\Pr[G] = .5$. If $\Pr[E \cap F] = .12$, $\Pr[E \cap G] = .1$, and $\Pr[F \cup G] = .7$, decide which (if any) of the following pairs are independent.
    (*a*) E and F (*b*) E and G (*c*) F and G
11. Homer watches Monday Night Football with probability .6, he has pizza on Monday night with probability .45, and he does both with probability .25. When you call him on Monday night, you learn that he is watching Monday Night Football. What is the probability that he is having pizza?
12. A multistage experiment has outcomes X and Y at the first stage and outcomes A, B, and C at the second stage. Suppose $\Pr[X] = .2$, $\Pr[Y] = .8$, $\Pr[A|X] = .3$, $\Pr[B|X] = \Pr[A|Y] = \Pr[C|Y] = .2$ Find $\Pr[X|B]$.
13. There are 5 Toyotas and 4 Hondas in the company motor pool. Three cars are selected at random and assigned to sales representatives. If both makes are included, find the probability that exactly 2 are Hondas.
14. Let E and F be events in a sample space S with $\Pr[E] = .40$, $\Pr[F] = .60$.
    (*a*) If $\Pr[E \cap F] = .25$, find $\Pr[E|F]$.
    (*b*) If $\Pr[E \cap F'] = .25$, find $\Pr[E|F]$.
    (*c*) If E and F are independent, find $\Pr[E \cap F]$.
15. There are 8 mice in a cage: 3 white males, 3 gray females, and 2 gray males. Two mice are selected simultaneously and at random, and their colors are noted. Find the probability that at least one mouse is a male, given that exactly one is gray.
16. Weather records for the town of Mulberry show that during November it rains on 40 percent of the days, the high temperature is below 40 degrees on 60 percent of the days, and both of these conditions hold on 25 percent of the days. A resident of Mulberry looks out of the window on a November afternoon and notes that it is raining. What is the probability that the high temperature that afternoon will be at least 40 degrees?
17. The Human Factors Group at the Joltmobile Corporation is assigned the task of designing the interior of a new automobile. A preliminary design is tested by asking a sample of 100 people to evaluate various aspects. The data shown in Table 3.8 are collected. An evaluation sheet is selected at random. What is the probability that it evaluates favorably *exactly one* of the items—seats, instruments, pedals?

TABLE 3.8

Percentage Responding Favorably	Feature
35	Seats
42	Instruments
28	Pedals
22	Seats and instruments
18	Seats and pedals
8	All three
39	None of the three

18. There are 3 quarters, 2 dimes, and 3 nickels in a drawer. An experiment consists of selecting two coins, simultaneously and at random, and noting their values. Find the conditional probability that the value of the two coins is at least 20 cents given that at most one coin is a quarter.
19. At the local Rent-A-Reck car rental company the fleet consists of Audi, BMW, and Mercedes cars: 20 percent are Audi, 45 percent BMW, and 35 percent Mercedes. Half of the Mercedes, 70 percent of the BMW, and 90 percent of the Audi cars have over 100,000 miles on the odometer. A car selected from the fleet at random has over 100,000 on the odometer. Find the probability that it is an Audi.
20. In the setting of Exercise 19, if a randomly selected car does not have over 100,000 miles on the odometer, find the probability it is either an Audi or a BMW.
21. A box contains 3 red balls, 2 blue balls, and 1 white ball. A ball is selected at random, its color is noted and it is replaced. This experiment is repeated 4 additional times. Let E be the event that all balls selected are the same color. Find $\Pr[E']$.
22. Let E and F be independent events in a sample space with $\Pr[E] = .3$ and $\Pr[F] = .6$. If G is the set of outcomes which are in neither E nor F, find $\Pr[G]$.
23. A parking lot contains 2 Chevrolets, 3 Fords, and 1 Toyota. Two cars leave at random, one after another; the make of each car is noted as it leaves. Draw a tree diagram to represent this situation, and find the probabilities of all outcomes.
24. In the situation described in Exercise 23, find:
    (*a*) The probability that the second car to leave is a Ford.
    (*b*) The probability that the first car to leave is a Chevrolet given that the second car to leave is a Ford or Toyota.
25. In a class of 100 students there are 70 freshmen and 30 sophomores. Of the freshmen, 50 are Indiana residents and of the sophomores 20 are Indiana residents. A student is selected at random. Find the probability that a freshman is selected given that the student selected is not an Indiana resident.
26. Two fair dice are rolled, and the result on each die is noted. Find the probability that:
    (*a*) The sum is 8, given that at least one of the numbers is even.
    (*b*) At least one of the numbers is even, given that the sum is 8.
    (*c*) At least one of the number is even, given that the sum is 7.

27. A 3-digit number is formed from the digits 1, 2, 4, 6, 9 by using 3 different digits. If the digits are selected and ordered at random, what is the probability that:
    (*a*) The number is even.
    (*b*) The number is less than 500.
    (*c*) The number is even, given that it is less than 500.
    (*d*) The number is less than 500, given that it is even.
28. You have 3 nickels, 3 dimes, and 2 quarters. An experiment is as follows. A coin is selected at random, its value is noted, and it is set aside. If it is a nickel, then 2 additional coins are selected, one after another without replacement, and their values are noted. If it is a dime, then select 1 more coin and note its value. If the first coin is a quarter, then the experiment stops.
    (*a*) Find the probability that at least one of the coins selected is a nickel.
    (*b*) Find the probability that at least two coins are selected and the second is a dime.
    (*c*) Find the probability the first is a nickel given that at least two coins are selected and the second is a dime.
29. A box contains 1 green ball, 2 blue balls, and 3 red balls. Three balls are selected at random, one after another without replacement, and their colors are noted.
    (*a*) Find the probability that the third ball selected is red.
    (*b*) Find the conditional probability that the third ball selected is red given that exactly one red ball is selected.
30. Each Monday morning a student decides whether to attend economics class that day. She attends randomly with probability .6, and each decision is independent of what has been done in the past. For a period of 3 consecutive weeks, find the probability that she attended on at least one Monday given that she did not attend on all Mondays.
31. A box contains 3 red balls, 1 blue ball and 1 white ball. A ball is selected at random, its color is noted and it is set aside. This experiment is repeated 2 additional times (so a total of 3 balls are selected). Let E be the event that the third ball selected is white, and let F be the event that the first ball selected is blue. Find $\Pr[E|F]$ and $\Pr[F|E]$.
32. At Gigantic State University 40 percent of the biology classes have laboratories, 30 percent have discussion sections, and 15 percent have both. A biology course is selected at random.
    (*a*) Find the probability that it has neither a laboratory nor a discussion section.
    (*b*) Find the probability that it has a laboratory, given that it has a discussion section.
    (*c*) Find the probability that it has a laboratory, given that it has exactly one of these features.
33. The Student Affairs office at GSU surveyed a group of students about their participation in selected cultural activities: visit the art museum, attend a concert, and attend a play. The following data were obtained:

    25 percent of the students participated in none of these activities
    No student who visited the art museum also attended a play
    50 percent of the students participated in exactly one type of activity
    40 percent of the students attended a concert

    Find the probability that a randomly selected student in the survey group attended only a concert.

34. In the situation described of Exercise 33, suppose that in addition:
20 percent of the students who attended either a concert or visited the art museum visited only the museum.
 (*a*) Find the probability that a randomly selected student in the survey group visited only the art museum.
 (*b*) Find the probability that a randomly selected student in the survey group attended only a play.
35. Suppose E and F are events in a sample space S, with $\Pr[E] = \frac{2}{5}$, $\Pr[F|E] = \frac{1}{2}$, and $\Pr[E' \cap F'] = \frac{3}{15}$. Find $\Pr[F']$ and $\Pr[E \cap F]$.
36. There are three \$10 bills and five \$20 bills in a drawer. An experiment consists of selecting bills, one after another without replacement, and noting the value of each bill selected. The experiment ends after two bills with the same denomination have been selected. If the total value of the bills selected was \$40, find the probability that a \$20 bill was selected first.

CHAPTER 4

Bernoulli Trials, Random Variables, and Expected Values

4.0 THE SETTING AND OVERVIEW

This chapter forms a bridge between the study of probability and the application of the concepts of probability theory in the field of statistics. We will apply the methods of Chapters 2 and 3 to study several topics which are very useful in business, the life and social sciences, and everyday life.

We begin with a special type of stochastic process, the Bernoulli process that can be used to model many situations which occur in applications. Another topic is the study of the values or costs which are sometimes associated with the outcomes of experiments. A common problem in such situations, a problem which occurs frequently in decision making, is to determine an ''average'' value to associate with an experiment. To solve such problems we introduce the concepts of random variable, mean, and standard deviation.

4.1 BERNOULLI TRIALS

A stochastic process is an experiment defined as a sequence of subexperiments, and such situations occur frequently in applications of probability to problems arising in a variety of settings. In Section 3.3, we studied stochastic processes by using tree diagrams and by assigning probabilities to the branches. This approach works fine if there are only a small number of subexperiments and each has only a small number of possible outcomes. However, if the tree becomes large, then it may be difficult to draw and to analyze. In such cases, we need other tools to compute the probabilities of outcomes. Such tools are available for special stochastic processes, and this section considers one such process. Here we study the case where the process consists of independent repetitions of a single experiment with exactly two possible outcomes. The independence condition means that the probabilities of the two outcomes are the same on each repetition of the experiment.

This type of experiment with two possible outcomes is called a *Bernoulli*[1] *trial*. The two possible outcomes are usually called *success* (s) and *failure* (f). Examples of experiments with these properties are common: guessing on a true-false test, s = correct and f = incorrect; testing a light bulb, s = it lights up and f = it does not light; attempting a basketball free-throw, s = the ball goes through the hoop, f = it does not. A *Bernoulli process* is a sequence of repetitions of the same Bernoulli trial, and the probability of success is the same at each repetition.

Example 4.1 Suppose an experiment consists of two repetitions of a Bernoulli trial with the probability of success equal to $\frac{1}{3}$ and the probability of failure equal to $\frac{2}{3}$. What is the probability that exactly one success is obtained in the two trials?

Solution We solve this problem with the aid of the tree diagram for the experiment (Figure 4.1). The assumption of independence is used in assigning the conditional probabilities on the tree. Thus we assume that the probabilities of the two possible outcomes (s and f) on the second trial are independent of the outcome (s or f) on the first trial. In other words, the second trial is identical (in terms of probabilities) to the first trial. Accordingly, each fork

FIGURE 4.1

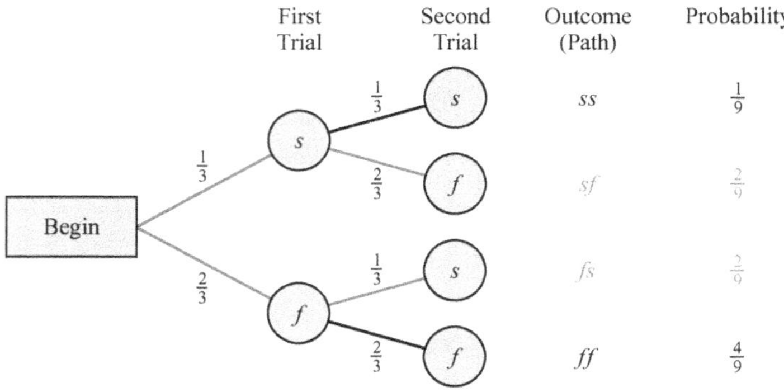

[1]After Jakob Bernoulli (1654–1705), a Swiss mathematician and one of the founders of probability theory.

of the tree has two branches, one leading to s, which has probability $\frac{1}{3}$, and another leading to f, which has probability $\frac{2}{3}$.

The outcomes of the experiment which are of interest to us are sf and fs. Using the probabilities shown at the right of the tree diagram, we conclude that

$$\Pr[\text{exactly 1 success}] = \Pr[\{sf, fs\}] = \tfrac{2}{9} + \tfrac{2}{9} = \tfrac{4}{9}$$ ■

An example of an experiment which can be modeled by Example 4.1 is the following. A fair die is rolled twice, and the result is noted each time. On a single roll of the die, the result is said to be a success if a 1 or a 6 comes up, and the result is said to be a failure otherwise. Since the die is fair,

$$\Pr[s] = \Pr[\{1, 6\}] = \tfrac{1}{3} \qquad \text{and} \qquad \Pr[f] = \Pr[\{2, 3, 4, 5\}] = \tfrac{2}{3}$$

Two rolls of the die can be modeled as two repetitions of a Bernoulli trial, and this is precisely the experiment described in Example 4.1.

Throughout this section we will denote the probability of success in a single Bernoulli trial by p and the probability of failure by $q = 1 - p$. In general, we will be interested in computing the probability of obtaining a certain number of successes (say, r) in a given number of trials (say, n). We begin with a special case.

Example 4.2 An experiment consists of four Bernoulli trials. Compute the probabilities of obtaining exactly r successes for $r = 0, 1, 2, 3, 4$.

Solution In Figure 4.1 the Bernoulli process with two trials described in Example 4.1 is represented by a tree diagram. In this example the experiment consists of four Bernoulli trials instead of two, and hence the tree has four sets of forks instead of two. Otherwise, the tree for this example, shown in Figure 4.2, can be constructed in the same way as the tree in Figure 4.1. The conditional probabilities on the tree result from the fundamental assumption that the probability of success (s) is *always* p and the probability of failure (f) is *always* q. In particular, these probabilities do not depend on which trial in the sequence is being considered.

An examination of Figure 4.2 shows that for a Bernoulli process with 4 trials, the probability of any outcome which has r successes and $4 - r$ failures is $p^r q^{4-r}$. Indeed, each path which starts at "Begin" and includes a result for each of the 4 trials consists of r branches leading to an s, each with probability p, and $4 - r$ branches leading to an f, each with probability q. Consequently, to determine the probability that the experiment has an outcome consisting of r successes and $4 - r$ failures, it remains for us to count the number of such outcomes. We know the probability of each one.

For example, suppose we let $r = 1$. There are 4 paths with outcomes that consist of exactly 1 success and 3 failures. Each of these outcomes has

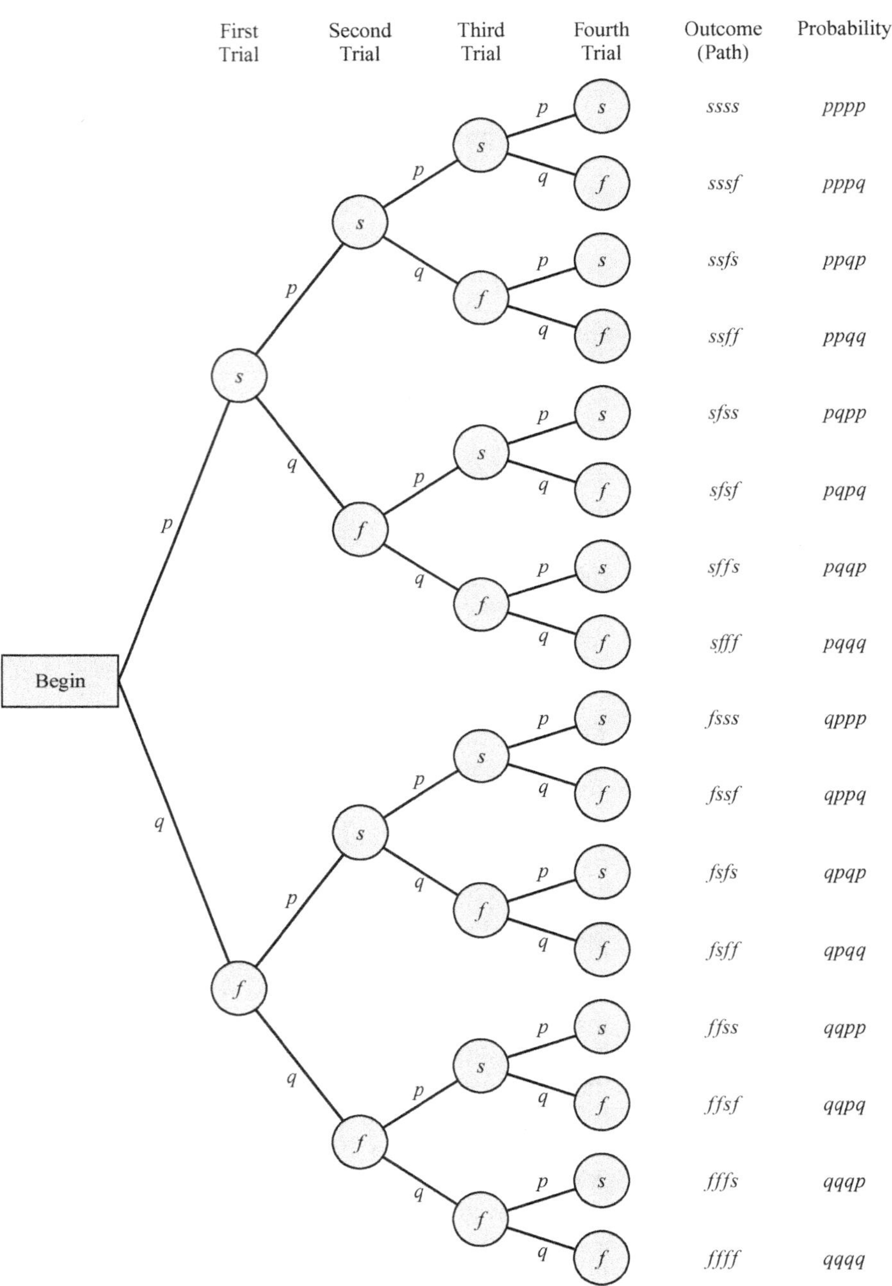

First Trial
Second Trial
Third Trial
Fourth Trial
Outcome (Path)
Probability
Begin
ssss pppp
sssf pppq
ssfs ppqp
ssff ppqq
sfss pqpp
sfsf pqpq
sffs pqqp
sfff pqqq
fsss qppp
fssf qppq
fsfs qpqp
fsff qpqq
ffss qqpp
ffsf qqpq
fffs qqqp
ffff qqqq

FIGURE 4.2

probability pq^3. Hence,

$$\Pr[1 \text{ success and } 3 \text{ failures }] = 4pq^3$$

In a similar way (using Figure 4.2), we obtain the following:

$$\begin{aligned}
\Pr[0 \text{ successes and } 4 \text{ failures}] &= q^4 \\
\Pr[2 \text{ successes and } 2 \text{ failures}] &= 6p^2q^2 \\
\Pr[3 \text{ successes and } 1 \text{ failure}] &= 4p^3q \\
\Pr[4 \text{ successes and } 0 \text{ failures}] &= p^4
\end{aligned}$$

■

Although the method used in Example 4.2 is a relatively simple one (draw a tree and count outcomes), it is clear that for more than 4 trials, the tree and the method will become unwieldy. Fortunately, it is possible to use a rather simple formula to obtain the same results.

To justify our formula, let us compute the probability that we have exactly r successes in a Bernoulli process with n trials. First we note that we can represent each element of the sample space by a list of n letters, each of which is an s or an f. For example, three elements of the sample space are

$$\underbrace{ff\ldots f}_{n \text{ times}}, \quad \underbrace{ss\ldots s}_{n \text{ times}}, \quad \text{and} \quad \underbrace{ss\ldots s}_{k \text{ times}}\,\underbrace{ff\ldots f}_{n-k \text{ times}}$$

Those outcomes of the experiment that have r successes and $n - r$ failures are represented by elements in the sample space in which the letter s appears exactly r times and the letter f appears $n - r$ times. Note that on the tree diagram the path corresponding to such an outcome must have r branches with probability p (the successes) and $n - r$ branches with probability q (the failures). Since the probability of the outcome is the product of the conditional probabilities on the branches, the probability of this outcome is $p^r q^{n-r}$. Finally, since each outcome of r successes and $n - r$ failures has probability $p^r q^{n-r}$, we need only compute the number of such outcomes to find the probability of r successes in n trials.

To determine the number of outcomes with exactly r successes, we note that each such outcome corresponds to a selection of r positions from n in which to place the letter s. For example, two such selections are

$$\underbrace{ss\ldots s}_{\substack{r\\ \text{letters}\\ s}}\,\underbrace{ff\ldots f}_{\substack{n-r\\ \text{letters}\\ f}} \quad \text{and} \quad \underbrace{ff\ldots f}_{\substack{n-r\\ \text{letters}\\ f}}\,\underbrace{ss\ldots s}_{\substack{r\\ \text{letters}\\ s}}$$

and in general there are many more. Thus to count the number of ways to have r successes in n trials, we simply count the number of ways to select r objects from a set of n. We recognize this number to be $C(n, r)$ (recall Section 2.3). Combining these facts, we have this formula:

The probability of obtaining exactly r successes in a Bernoulli process consisting of n trials with success probability p and failure probability $q = 1 - p$ is

$$\Pr[r \text{ successes}] = C(n, r)p^r q^{n-r} \tag{4.1}$$

for $r = 0, 1, 2, \ldots, n$.

We illustrate formula (4.1) by applying it to the experiment described in Example 4.1. It consists of 2 Bernoulli trials with success probability $p = \frac{1}{3}$. Therefore $n = 2, p = \frac{1}{3}, q = \frac{2}{3}$. The problem asks for the probability of exactly 1 success. Therefore $r = 1$ in Equation (4.1). We have

$$\begin{aligned}\Pr[1 \text{ success}] = C(2, 1)p^1q^1 &= \frac{2!}{1!1!}\left(\frac{1}{3}\right)^1\left(\frac{2}{3}\right)^1\\ &= 2 \cdot \tfrac{1}{3} \cdot \tfrac{2}{3} = \tfrac{4}{9}\end{aligned}$$

as we obtained in Example 4.1.

Example 4.3 There are balls labeled 1 through 5 in a box, and a game of chance involves selecting a ball at random from the box, noting the label on the ball and replacing it. One play of the game consists of selecting 4 balls in this manner and recording the total number of balls selected that are labeled 1, 3, or 5.

Problem Find the probability that in one play of the game exactly three of the balls have labels in the set $S = \{1, 3, 5\}$.

Solution We view a play of the game as a sequence of 4 Bernoulli trials in which a success is selecting a ball with label in the set $\{1, 3, 5\}$. Since we are making a random selection from a set of 5 balls $\{1, 2, 3, 4, 5\}$, the probability of selecting a ball in the S is $\frac{3}{5}$. That is, success probability $p = \frac{3}{5}$. Using Equation (4.1) we have

$$\begin{aligned}\Pr[3 \text{ successes}] = C(4, 3)\left(\frac{3}{5}\right)^3\left(\frac{2}{5}\right)^1 &= \frac{4!}{3!1!}\left(\frac{3}{5}\right)^3\left(\frac{2}{5}\right)^1\\ &= \frac{4 \cdot 27}{5^4} = \frac{108}{625}\end{aligned}$$

■

Example 4.4 Solve the problem posed in Example 4.2 by using Equation (4.1). Assume $p = \frac{1}{4}$, so $q = \frac{3}{4}$.

Solution In Example 4.2 we have $n = 4$. We are interested in the probabilities of 0, 1, 2, 3, and 4 successes. Using Equation (4.1) with $p = \frac{1}{4}$ and $q = \frac{3}{4}$, we find

$$\begin{aligned}
\Pr[0 \text{ successes}] &= C(4,0)\left(\frac{1}{4}\right)^0\left(\frac{3}{4}\right)^4 = \frac{4!}{4!0!}\cdot 1\cdot\frac{3^4}{4^4} = 1\cdot 1\cdot\tfrac{81}{256} = \tfrac{81}{256}\\
\Pr[1 \text{ success}] &= C(4,1)\left(\frac{1}{4}\right)^1\left(\frac{3}{4}\right)^3 = \frac{4!}{3!1!}\cdot\frac{1}{4}\cdot\frac{3^3}{4^3} = 4\cdot\tfrac{1}{4}\cdot\tfrac{27}{64} = \tfrac{108}{256} = \tfrac{27}{64}\\
\Pr[2 \text{ successes}] &= C(4,2)\left(\frac{1}{4}\right)^2\left(\frac{3}{4}\right)^2 = \frac{4!}{2!2!}\cdot\frac{1}{4^2}\cdot\frac{3^2}{4^2} = 6\cdot\tfrac{1}{16}\cdot\tfrac{9}{16} = \tfrac{54}{256} = \tfrac{27}{128}\\
\Pr[3 \text{ successes}] &= C(4,3)\left(\frac{1}{4}\right)^3\left(\frac{3}{4}\right)^1 = \frac{4!}{1!3!}\cdot\frac{1}{4^3}\cdot\frac{3}{4} = 4\cdot\tfrac{1}{64}\cdot\tfrac{3}{4} = \tfrac{12}{256} = \tfrac{3}{64}\\
\Pr[4 \text{ successes}] &= C(4,4)\left(\frac{1}{4}\right)^4\left(\frac{3}{4}\right)^0 = \frac{4!}{0!4!}\cdot\frac{1}{4^4}\cdot 1 = 1\cdot\tfrac{1}{256}\cdot 1 = \tfrac{1}{256}
\end{aligned}$$ ■

We note that in Example 4.4 the events 0 successes, 1 success, 2. successes, 3 successes, and 4 successes form a partition of the sample space S. Thus the sum of the probabilities for these events should be 1.

Indeed, we have

$$\begin{aligned}
\Pr[0 \text{ successes}] &+ \Pr[1 \text{ success}] + \Pr[2 \text{ successes}]\\
&+ \Pr[3 \text{ successes}] + \Pr[4 \text{ successes}]\\
&= \tfrac{81}{256} + \tfrac{108}{256} + \tfrac{54}{256} + \tfrac{12}{256} + \tfrac{1}{256}\\
&= \tfrac{256}{256} = 1
\end{aligned}$$

In fact, in any binomial experiment with n trials, the events 0 successes, 1 success, 2 successes, ..., n successes form a partition of the sample space, and the sum of their probabilities must be 1.

In any Bernoulli process with n trials,

$$\Pr[0 \text{ successes}] + \Pr[1 \text{ success}] + \ldots + \Pr[n \text{ successes}] = 1 \qquad (4.2)$$

Formula (4.2) can frequently be used to reduce the amount of computation needed to solve a problem.

Example 4.5 A National Football League kicker knows that he makes one-fourth of his field goal attempts from more than 50 yards. He also knows that they are independent trials. In a certain game he attempts 5 field goals of more than 50 yards.

Problem What is the probability that he will make at least 2 of the 5 attempts?

Solution The probability of at least 2 successes (the kicker made at least 2 field goals) is the sum of the probabilities of the disjoint events: exactly 2 successes, exactly 3 successes, exactly 4 successes, and exactly 5 successes. That is, Pr[at least 2 made] = Pr[2 made] + Pr[3 made] + Pr[4 made] + Pr[5 made]. Thus, one method of obtaining the solution to this problem is to use formula (4.1) to compute Pr[2 successes], Pr[3 successes], Pr[4 successes], and Pr[5 successes] and then to add these 4 numbers. Using formula (4.1) with $n = 5, p = \frac{1}{4}, q = \frac{3}{4}$, and $r = 2, 3, 4, 5$, we obtain

$$\begin{aligned}\Pr[\text{at least 2 made}] &= C(5,2)\left(\frac{1}{4}\right)^2\left(\frac{3}{4}\right)^3 + C(5,3)\left(\frac{1}{4}\right)^3\left(\frac{3}{4}\right)^2 \\ &\quad + C(5,4)\left(\frac{1}{4}\right)^4\left(\frac{3}{4}\right)^1 + C(5,5)\left(\frac{1}{4}\right)^5\left(\frac{3}{4}\right)^0 \\ &= \frac{270}{1024} + \frac{90}{1024} + \frac{15}{1024} + \frac{1}{1024} \\ &= \frac{376}{1024}\end{aligned}$$

A second method of solving our problem is to use formula (4.2) for the case $n = 5$. Using a field goal made as a success, we have

$$\Pr[0 \text{ made}] + \Pr[1 \text{ made}] + \Pr[2 \text{ made}] + \Pr[3 \text{ made}] + \Pr[4 \text{ made}] + \Pr[5 \text{ made}] = 1$$

This can also be stated as

$$\Pr[0 \text{ made}] + \Pr[1 \text{ made}] + \Pr[\text{at least 2 made}] = 1$$

which gives

$$\Pr[\text{at least 2 made}] = 1 - \Pr[0 \text{ made}] - \Pr[1 \text{ made}]$$

Now if we use formula (4.1), we have

$$\begin{aligned}\Pr[\text{at least 2 made}] &= 1 - C(5,0)\left(\frac{1}{4}\right)^0\left(\frac{3}{4}\right)^5 - C(5,1)\left(\frac{1}{4}\right)^1\left(\frac{3}{4}\right)^4 \\ &= 1 - \frac{243}{1024} - \frac{405}{1024} = \frac{376}{1024}\end{aligned}$$

■

In the first method illustrated in Example 4.5, we partitioned the event "at least 2 made" into 4 events and used formula (4.1) 4 times. In the second method we partitioned the entire sample space into the disjoint events "0 made," "1 made," and "at least 2 made"; and [using formula (4.2)] we applied formula (4.1) only 2 times. The difference in the two methods would be even more striking if there were more trials. In 10 trials the probability of at least 2 successes can be obtained by using formula (4.2) and *two* applications of (4.1), or it can be obtained by directly applying (4.1) *nine times* and adding the results. Clearly, in some cases the method based on formula (4.2) is preferable.

In some interesting problems involving Bernoulli trials, the number of trials n is unknown. We solve such problems by a trial-and-error method.

Example 4.6 An investor makes money on approximately 70 percent of her investments. She would like to have at least 3 profitable investments in the coming year. How many investments should she make so that the probability of having *at least* 3 profitable investments is at least .8?

Solution We solve the problem by assuming that her investments are Bernoulli trials with $p = .7$. Here a success is a profitable investment. The precise mathematical question is the following: Find n such that

$$\Pr[3 \text{ or more successes in } n \text{ trials}] \geq .8$$

We proceed by using a "guess and test" strategy. Clearly there must be at least 3 investments.

If $n = 3$, then

$$\Pr[3 \text{ successes in } 3 \text{ trials}] = C(3, 3)(.7)^3(.3)^0 = .343$$

This is much too small, and consequently more than 3 investments are required.

If $n = 4$, then

$$\begin{aligned}\Pr[3 \text{ or more successes in } 4 \text{ trials}] &= \Pr[3 \text{ successes}] + \Pr[4 \text{ successes}] \\ &= C(4, 3)(.7)^3(.3)^1 + C(4, 4)(.7)^4(.3)^0 \\ &= .412 + .240 = .652\end{aligned}$$

If $n = 5$, then

$$\begin{aligned}&\Pr[3 \text{ or more successes in } 5 \text{ trials}] \\ &\quad = \Pr[3 \text{ successes}] + \Pr[4 \text{ successes}] + \Pr[5 \text{ successes}] \\ &\quad = C(5, 3)(.7)^3(.3)^2 + C(5, 4)(.7)^4(.3)^1 + C(5, 5)(.7)^5(.3)^0 \\ &\quad = .309 + .360 + .168 = .837\end{aligned}$$

We conclude that the investor should plan on making at least 5 investments to be sure that the probability of making money on 3 or more investments is at least .8. ■

Example 4.7 There are 5 red balls, 3 blue balls, and 2 green balls in a box. An experiment consists of selecting a ball at random, noting its color, and replacing it. The process continues until a total of five balls are selected.

Problem Find the probability that exactly 2 of the balls selected are blue.

Solution The color of the selected ball may be red, blue, or green. However, to answer the question, we are interested only in whether the ball is blue or not. Accordingly, we call a result a success if the selected ball is blue and a failure if it is not blue—that is, if it is red or green. With this definition of success and failure and the given data of the problem, $p = .3$ and $q = .7$, we apply formula (4.1) and we have

$$\Pr[\text{exactly 2 balls are blue}] = C(5, 2)(.3)^2(.7)^3 = 10(0.09)(0.343)$$ ■

Exercises for Section 4.1

1. For Bernoulli trials compute the following probabilities.
   (*a*) 1 success in 3 trials with $p = .4$
   (*b*) 1 success in 5 trials with $p = .2$
   (*c*) 3 successes in 5 trials with $p = \frac{1}{3}$
2. For Bernoulli trials compute the following probabilities.
   (*a*) 2 successes in 4 trials with $p = .8$
   (*b*) 3 successes in 4 trials with $p = .2$
   (*c*) 0 successes in 3 trials with $p = \frac{1}{5}$
3. For Bernoulli trials compute the following probabilities.
   (*a*) 4 successes in 6 trials with $q = .4$
   (*b*) 2 failures in 5 trials with $q = .6$
4. For Bernoulli trials compute the following probabilities.
   (*a*) 3 successes in 6 trials with $q = .5$
   (*b*) 3 failures in 5 trials with $q = .7$
5. For Bernoulli trials compute the following probabilities.
   (*a*) At least 3 successes in 6 trials with $p = .2$
   (*b*) At least 3 failures in 5 trials with $p = .8$
6. An experiment consists of rolling a fair die 4 times and noting the number that lands uppermost on each roll.
   (*a*) Find the probability that 3 lands uppermost at least twice.
   (*b*) Find the probability that an odd number lands uppermost at least twice.
7. For a Bernoulli process with $n = 5$ and $p = \frac{2}{5}$, find the probability of at least 1 success and at least 1 failure.
8. A basketball player makes each of his shots with probability .5. If he takes 6 shots and if the results of his shots are independent, find the probability that he makes at least 4.
9. An unfair coin with $\Pr[H] = .4$ is flipped 5 times. If the results of the flips are independent, find the probability that there are exactly 2 heads or exactly 2 tails.

10. An unfair coin with $\Pr[H] = .6$ is flipped 6 times. If the results of the flips are independent, find the probability that at least 2 heads and at least 2 tails occur.
11. A coin is weighted so that a head is twice as likely to occur as is a tail. The coin is flipped 4 times and the result of each flip is noted. Find the probability that both heads and tails occur.
12. Homer has studied for his mathematics exam, and he believes that if he has to guess at a question, then he will be twice as likely to select the correct answer as to select an incorrect answer. Suppose that he guesses on 5 questions, and each guess is independent.
    (*a*) Find the probability that he answers exactly 2 correctly.
    (*b*) Find the probability that he answers at least 3 correctly.
13. Henry skips breakfast in the morning at random. Suppose that each day he eats breakfast with probability .6 and skips breakfast with probability .4, and his decisions each day are independent.
    (*a*) Find the probability that for the next five days he will eat breakfast exactly once.
    (*b*) Find the probability that for the next five days he will eat breakfast every day.
    (*c*) Find the probability that for the next five days he will eat breakfast at most once.
14. Suppose Maggie guesses each answer independently on a 5 question true-false quiz. Find the probability that she answers the first 2 questions correctly and the next 3 incorrectly.
15. In a 20-question true-false test, what is the probability of answering exactly 18 questions correctly just by guessing?
16. In a 10-question true-false test, find the probability of answering at least 8 questions correctly just by guessing.
17. In an 8-question multiple-choice test, each question has 4 choices, and you are told that one and only one is correct. If you guess at all 8 questions, what is the probability that you get *exactly* 2 right?
18. In the setting of Exercise 17, find the probability of answering at least 7 questions correctly just by guessing.
19. In the inventory of Good Vehicles, Inc., 1 car in 10 is defective and will not start. At different times 3 individuals randomly select cars for test drives. What is the probability that at least 1 of them selects a car that will not start?
20. A streaming music service plays tracks from its library at random, and the library contains 20 percent jazz tracks. Find the probability that of the first 5 tracks played one evening, there are exactly 2 jazz tracks and they are played consecutively.
21. A deep-sea fisherman estimates that if he uses 4 lines, then the probability of making a catch on any line is .7; if he uses 5 lines, then the probability of making a catch on any line is .6; and if he uses 6 lines, then the probability of making a catch on any line is .5. If his objective is to catch at least 4 fish, how many lines should he use to maximize the probability of achieving his goal?
22. A soft drink machine malfunctions randomly, with probability .05 it will accept your money but fail to deliver a soft drink. Assume the results of depositing money at different times are independent.
    (*a*) If you deposit money 3 different times, find the probability that your soft drink is delivered twice.

(*b*) If you deposit money 3 different times, find the probability that you receive a soft drink the first 2 times you try.

23. A high school basketball player makes one-third of his three-point shots. If we assume that his shots are Bernoulli trials, how many must he shoot to have a probability at least .7 of making at least 1 of them?
24. In the setting of Exercise 23, suppose the player only makes a three-point shot with probability $\frac{1}{4}$. Now how many must he shoot to have probability at least .75 of making at least 1 shot?
25. A used car saleswoman estimates that each time she shows a customer a car, there is probability .1 that the customer will buy the car. The saleswoman would like to sell at least 1 car per week. If showing a car is a Bernoulli trial, how many cars must the saleswoman show per week to have a probability at least .95 of making at least 1 sale?
26. An unfair die has the property that when rolled each of the odd numbers is equally likely to land uppermost, each of the even numbers is equally likely to land uppermost, and each odd number is twice as likely to land uppermost as an even number. The die is rolled 4 times. Assume that the results of the rolls are independent, and find the probability that 2 even and 2 odd numbers land uppermost.
27. In a large city 50 percent of the voters consider themselves Democrats, 25 percent consider themselves Independents, and 25 percent consider themselves Republicans. A poll taker asks 10 people at random for their party affiliations. What is the probability that at least 7 are Democrats?
28. Your pizza delivery service promises delivery in 20 minutes or your pizza is free. You find that they fail to deliver within 20 minutes at random with probability .05. Assume late pizza deliveries are independent. You plan to order pizzas repeatedly until you receive your first free pizza. How many times do you need to place an order before the probability that you receive a free pizza first exceeds .2?
29. A professor who intends to bring her briefcase to the office each morning forgets it one-quarter of the time. Assume that forgetting the briefcase is a Bernoulli trial, and find the probability that she forgets it at least twice a week (5 days).
30. Zelda and Friend take a multiple-choice examination consisting of 10 questions. Each question has 5 choices for an answer, and each question has exactly one correct answer. Zelda answers each question by working the problem (sometimes she gets it correct, sometimes not). Friend answers each question by picking one of the answers at random, and her choices are independent. Find the probability that Friend has the answer for each question the same as Zelda.
31. A multiple-choice examination consists of 10 questions, each question with 5 choices for an answer, and each question has exactly 1 correct answer. Two students answer the questions by guessing. Assume the answer sheets are prepared independently, and find the probability that each student answers exactly 4 questions correctly.
32. In the setting of Exercise 31, find the probability that the 2 students answer *the same* 4 questions correctly just by guessing.
33. North Fork River Expeditions, Inc., operates white-water rafting trips on the North Fork of the Trout River. Data from past years indicate that about 60 percent of the people who come on such trips prefer to paddle rafts and the remainder prefer to paddle one-person kayaks. A specific trip has 20 people, and there are 6 kayaks. If

the preferences of the people on the trip can be viewed as the result of a Bernoulli trials process, find the probability that everyone who prefers to paddle a kayak can be accommodated.

34. In the setting of Exercise 33, how many kayaks would be needed so that everyone who prefers to paddle a kayak can do so with probability at least .9?
35. In the setting of Exercise 33, suppose that data from past years indicate that 50 percent of the people prefer to paddle in rafts, 30 percent prefer to paddle a kayak, and 20 percent are willing to do either. Find the probability that everyone is satisfied with her or his paddling opportunity.
36. There are cards numbered 1 through 9 in a bowl. Cards are selected at random, one after another with replacement, and the number on each card is noted.
    (*a*) Find the probability that exactly 5 of the first 8 cards selected have number 9.
    (*b*) Find the probability that exactly 5 of the first 8 cards selected have either number 8 or number 9.
37. In the situation of Exercise 36, find the probability that exactly 5 of the first 8 cards have numbers in either the set $\{1, 2\}$ or the set $\{8, 9\}$.

4.2 RANDOM VARIABLES AND PROBABILITY DENSITY FUNCTIONS

In many situations that involve uncertainty, we are interested in a numerical quantity whose value depends on the outcome of an experiment. For instance, gamblers are interested in the amount of money won or lost on each play of a game; business managers are interested in the day-to-day demand for products; and students are interested in semester-to-semester grade-point averages. Each of these quantities (winnings, demands, grade-point averages) is a number, and in general it is not known in advance what the number will be. We will use probability to help us understand such situations.

Example 4.8 Consider the following simple lottery. You pay \$1 to play, and then you select an integer in the set $\{0, 1, 2, 3, 4, 5, 6, 7, 8, 9\}$. Next the person running the lottery randomly picks an integer from the same set. If the number picked is the same as yours, you win \$5; if not, you win nothing. If you play this game many times, how much should you expect to win (or lose)?

Solution In playing this game, you will sometimes be lucky and win \$5, but most of the time you will not win anything. Since it costs you \$1 to play, in most cases you lose that \$1. In a few cases you gain \$4 (the \$5 you win, minus the \$1 you paid to play). In addition to how much you win or lose, you need to know how often you will win or lose. Once you select a number in the given set of 10 integers, your chance of winning is $\frac{1}{10}$, because your number is 1 of 10 and in a random selection it has 1 chance in 10 of being selected by the person running the lottery. Thus, in playing 10 times, you would expect to win 1 time and lose 9 times. Of course, this is just an average. You might not win at all, or you might win more than once, but on average you win 1 time in 10 tries. When you win, you end up \$4 ahead; and when you lose, you end up short \$1. Thus, on average, when you play 10 times, you lose \$9 and gain \$4, for a net loss of \$5. In other words, your average loss is \$.50 per play. ■

In Example 4.8, we are not able to predict the result of the lottery on any specific play of the game. However, we know that if we play many times, then we lose an average of 50 cents per play. In many situations in life, we cannot predict a specific outcome, but we can compute an "average" value. Of course, we need to be precise about our meaning of the term "average." We work one more example and then develop the general setting.

Example 4.9 Suppose that the following game is proposed by a friend: A fair die is to be rolled, and if an outcome of 2, 3, 4, or 5 occurs, then your friend will pay you \$1.50. If either a 1 or a 6 occurs, then you pay your friend an amount in dollars equal to the outcome. That is, you pay \$1.00 if a 1 occurs and \$6.00 if a 6 occurs.

Problem If you play the game many times, how much gain (or loss) should you expect?

Solution We begin an analysis of this game by viewing each play as an experiment. We construct a table that shows the outcomes of the experiment, the gain or loss to you associated with each outcome, and the probability that each outcome occurs. Table 4.1 contains this information.

It is impossible to predict with certainty the outcome of any specific play of this game. Sometimes you will lose \$1.00, sometimes you will lose \$6.00, and sometimes you will win \$1.50. Although it is impossible to predict a single outcome of the game, it is possible to make predictions about the results of many plays of the game. If there are many plays of the game (rolls of the die), then we expect each of about one-sixth of these plays (rolls) to result in a loss of \$1.00, each of another one-sixth to result in a loss of \$6.00, and each of the remaining four-sixths of the outcomes to result in a win of \$1.50. These values reflect the probabilities of the various outcomes given in Table 4.1.

Suppose that you play this game 600 times and each outcome of the die occurs exactly 100 times. Then 100 times you lose \$1.00, 100 times you lose \$6.00, and on each of the other 400 times you win \$1.50. Your losses would add up to \$700, and your gains would add up to \$600; so your net return would be $-\$100$ (a loss of \$100). Since you played 600 times, your average return per play would be $-\$100/600 = -(\$1)/6$. Summarizing these computations, we see that the average return is

$$V = \frac{100(-\$1.00) + 400(+\$1.50) + 100(-\$6.00)}{600}$$

$$= \frac{-\$100 + \$600 - \$600}{6} = -\frac{\$1}{6}$$

TABLE 4.1

Outcome	Gain (+) or Loss (−)	Probability
1	−1.0	$\frac{1}{6}$
2	+1.5	$\frac{1}{6}$
3	+1.5	$\frac{1}{6}$
4	+1.5	$\frac{1}{6}$
5	+1.5	$\frac{1}{6}$
6	−6.0	$\frac{1}{6}$

In 600 actual plays of this game, it is unlikely that each outcome on the die will occur exactly 100 times. However, it is likely that each outcome will occur about 100 times, and thus a net return of $-\$1/6$ is about what you would expect for a fair die. Without reference to the number of plays, we expect that each outcome on the die will occur one-sixth of the time. Then the net return per play, called the *expected return*, is (in dollars)

$$\begin{aligned} V &= (-1.00)\left(\tfrac{1}{6}\right) + (1.50)\left(\tfrac{1}{6}\right) + (1.50)\left(\tfrac{1}{6}\right) + (1.50)\left(\tfrac{1}{6}\right) \\ &\quad + (1.50)\left(\tfrac{1}{6}\right) + (-6.00)\left(\tfrac{1}{6}\right) \\ &= \frac{-7+6}{6} = -\tfrac{1}{6} \end{aligned}$$

Therefore, in any number of plays of this game, you expect to lose one-sixth of a dollar per play of the game. Your ''friend'' has a definite advantage! ■

The method of Example 4.9 can be used in any experiment where numbers are attached to outcomes. An assignment of numbers to outcomes is a *random variable.* In Example 4.9 the elements in the sample space are the outcomes of the die (1, 2, 3, 4, 5, 6), and the random variable attaches -1 to outcome 1, -6 to outcome 6, and 1.5 to each of the outcomes 2, 3, 4, and 5. A general definition follows:

A *random variable* defined on a sample space S, is an assignment of real numbers to the elements of S, exactly one number assigned to each outcome.

In mathematical terms a random variable on S is a real-valued function with domain S.

To illustrate further the idea of a random variable, consider the experiment of flipping a coin four times and noting each time whether it lands heads or tails. If to each outcome of this experiment we assign the *number of heads* obtained in the four flips, then we have defined a random variable. The *values* of the random variable are the numbers assigned to the outcomes. In this case the value of the random variable can be 0, 1, 2, 3, or 4, since these are the possible numbers of heads obtained in four flips. If we think of obtaining a head as a success in the Bernoulli trial of flipping a coin, then our random variable counts the total number of successes in four trials. A random variable of this type occurs often, and it has its own name.

A random variable which assigns to each outcome of a Bernoulli process the number of successes is called a *binomial random variable*.

Random variables are usually represented by uppercase letters such as X and Y. The values of the random variable X will be denoted by the lowercase letters $x_1, x_2, \ldots, x_k$. Following convention, we will list these values in increasing order: $x_1 < x_2 < \cdots < x_k$. Also, in most problems we will specify a random variable by using a table in which each row corresponds to a single value of the random variable.

We illustrate this with two examples: first, the binomial random variable which assigns the number of heads to each outcome of four flips of a fair coin. The values, labeled by our convention, are $x_1 = 0, x_2 = 1, x_3 = 2, x_4 = 3$, and $x_5 = 4$. The appropriate table is Table 4.2. The first and third columns of this table will be discussed after we give another example.

TABLE 4.2

Event E_j	Value of Random Variable X, x_j	Probability $\Pr[E_j]$
No heads	0	$\frac{1}{16}$
One head	1	$\frac{4}{16}$
Two heads	2	$\frac{6}{16}$
Three heads	3	$\frac{4}{16}$
Four heads	4	$\frac{1}{16}$

As a second example, we use the random variable of Example 4.9. The random variable X has three values ($-6, -1$, and 1.5), and using our convention, we set $x_1 = -6, x_2 = -1$, and $x_3 = 1.5$. Forming a table in which each value of X is listed once, we represent the data of Table 4.1 in Table 4.3.

TABLE 4.3

Event E_j	Value of Random Variable X, x_j	Probability $\Pr[E_j]$
{6}	−6.0	$\frac{1}{6}$
{1}	−1.0	$\frac{1}{6}$
{2, 3, 4, 5}	+1.5	$\frac{4}{6}$

It is important to note that in Table 4.3 the column at the left consists of events and *not* of single outcomes, as in Table 4.1. This is necessary because we are using only one row of the table for each value of the random variable, and it is often the case (as in Example 4.9) that more than one outcome is assigned the same value of the random variable.

The technique of grouping together all outcomes for which a random variable assumes a specific value is an important and useful one. We next introduce terminology and notation which describe the process of grouping more precisely. We consider only sample spaces which contain a finite number of elements, and consequently on random variables which assume a finite number of values.

Suppose that the values assumed by a random variable X are $x_1, x_2, \ldots, x_k$. For $j = 1, 2, \ldots, k$ let E_j be the event consisting of all outcomes to which the random variable X assigns the number x_j. That is, E_j is the event such that X takes the value x_j for each outcome in E_j and it takes the value x_j for no other outcomes. In the game of Example 4.9, the random variable takes the three values -6, -1, and 1.5, so $k = 3$. If we let

$$x_1 = -6 \qquad x_2 = -1 \qquad x_3 = 1.5$$

then

$$E_1 = \{6\} \qquad E_2 = \{1\} \qquad E_3 = \{2, 3, 4, 5\}$$

Notice that x_j is the value of the random variable assigned to each outcome in event E_j, which is a set of outcomes. The first column in tables such as Tables 4.2 and 4.3 lists the events E_j corresponding to the distinct values x_j of the random variable.

The third column in Table 4.2 lists the probabilities assigned to events E_j. Since E_j consists of those outcomes for which X takes the value x_j, we have

$$\Pr[X = x_j] = \Pr[E_j]$$

Thus we have a correspondence between values x_j and probabilities p_j defined by $p_j = \Pr[X = x_j]$. This correspondence is of sufficient interest and importance to have a name of its own.

The *probability density function*, or simply *density function*, of a random variable X assigns probabilities p_j to values of x_j of X, where p_j is the probability of event E_j on which the random variable X takes the value x_j, $j = 1, 2, \ldots, k$.

We note that since the events E_j are always a partition of the sample space S,

$$p_1 + p_2 + \cdots + p_k = 1$$

In the setting described in Example 4.9 and shown in Table 4.3, we have $p_1 = \frac{1}{6}, p_2 = \frac{1}{6}$, and $p_3 = \frac{4}{6}$. Thus, even though the values x_j are always different for different values of j, it is possible that some of the probabilities p_j are the same.

Remark In Example 4.8, we considered a simple lottery, and we computed the average loss per play without using the concepts of random variable or density function. However, it is natural to define a random variable X to be the net return on each play of the lottery. Then X takes values of -1 (you lose your dollar) and 4 (you win \$5, but paid \$1 to play). Also, the probability of the value -1 is $\frac{9}{10}$, and the probability of the value 4 is $\frac{1}{10}$. Hence the density function for X is as shown in Table 4.4.

TABLE 4.4

Value of X	Probability
-1	$\frac{9}{10}$
4	$\frac{1}{10}$

Example 4.10 Max has an alarm clock that goes off at the time he sets with probability .8, and on Sunday he sets it for the following Monday, Wednesday, and Friday. View the situation as an experiment with results ''alarm goes off'' and ''alarm does not go off'' for each of the 3 days. A random variable X is defined as the number of days the alarm goes off at the time set.

Problem Assume that this is a Bernoulli process, and find the density function of X.

Solution We define a success for the Bernoulli process to be the alarm's going off as set, and consequently we have $p = .8$. The probability of the event for which X takes the value 0, that is, the set of outcomes with the alarm's never

TABLE 4.5

Value of X	Probability
0	.008
1	.096
2	.384
3	.512

going off as set, can be obtained by using (4.1) with $n = 3$, $r = 0$, and $p = .8$. We have

$$\Pr[X = 0] = C(3, 0)(.8)^0(.2)^3 = .008$$

Likewise,

$$\Pr[X = 1] = C(3, 1)(.8)^1(.2)^2 = .096$$
$$\Pr[X = 2] = C(3, 2)(.8)^2(.2)^1 = .384$$
$$\Pr[X = 3] = C(3, 3)(.8)^3(.2)^0 = .512$$

The values of X and the associated values of the density function for X are shown in Table 4.5. ■

Example 4.11 A student is responsible for creating and maintaining the data files for a group project, and she formats 8 files to receive data. At the end of the project, she has 5 files with data and 3 files without data. Suppose 3 files are selected at random, and a random variable X is defined as the number of files which contain data.

Problem Find the density function of X.

Solution The random variable X takes the values 0, 1, 2, and 3, so we set $x_1 = 0$, $x_2 = 1$, $x_3 = 2$, and $x_4 = 3$. The probabilities of the associated events can be obtained using the methods of Chapter 2, and we have

$$p_1 = \Pr[E_1] = \Pr[X = 0] = \frac{C(5, 0) \times C(3, 3)}{C(8, 3)} = \frac{1}{56}$$

$$p_2 = \Pr[E_2] = \Pr[X = 1] = \frac{C(5, 1) \times C(3, 2)}{C(8, 3)} = \frac{15}{56}$$

$$p_3 = \Pr[E_3] = \Pr[X = 2] = \frac{C(5, 2) \times C(3, 1)}{C(8, 3)} = \frac{30}{56}$$

$$p_4 = \Pr[E_4] = \Pr[X = 3] = \frac{C(5, 3) \times C(3, 0)}{C(8, 3)} = \frac{10}{56}$$

The density function is shown in Table 4.6. ■

TABLE 4.6

Value of X	Probability
0	$\frac{1}{56}$
1	$\frac{15}{56}$
2	$\frac{30}{56}$
3	$\frac{10}{56}$

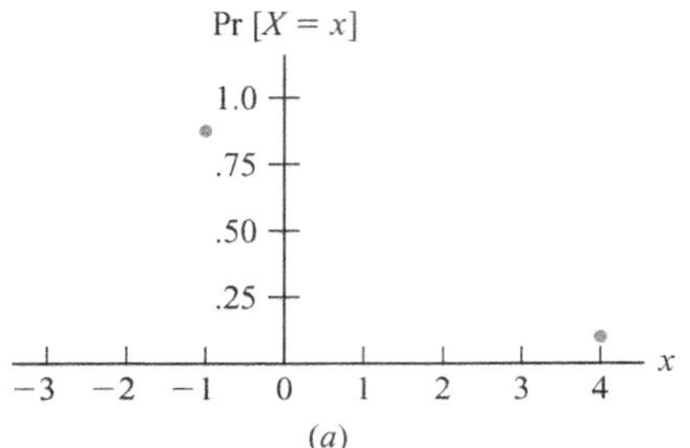

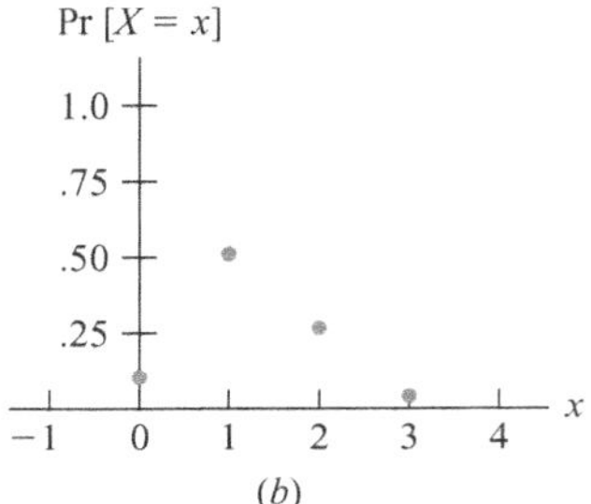

FIGURE 4.3

In addition to using tables to represent random variables and density functions, it is often useful to represent them graphically. This is done by using a coordinate system for which the horizontal coordinates represent the values of the random variable, and the vertical coordinates are the probabilities associated with these values. In Figure 4.3, we display the graphs associated with the random variables of Table 4.4 (part (*a*) of the graph) and Table 4.6 (part (*b*) of the graph).

Exercises for Section 4.2

1. An unfair coin with $\Pr[H] = .4$ is flipped 3 times. A random variable X is defined as the number of heads plus twice the number of tails.
   (*a*) Find the values of X.
   (*b*) Find the density function of X.
2. An unfair coin with $\Pr[H] = .3$ is flipped 4 times and the result of each flip is noted. A random variable X is defined to be 3 times the number of heads minus 2 times the number of tails.
   (*a*) Find the values of X
   (*b*) Find the density function of X.
3. A team of students working on a project consists of 3 juniors and 2 seniors. Two students are selected at random and a random variable X is defined to be the number of juniors selected. Find $\Pr[X = 2]$.
4. A box contains 2 nickels and 3 quarters. Two coins are selected simultaneously and at random, and a random variable X is defined as the value of the two coins selected. Find $\Pr[X = 30]$.

5. A student committee has 6 members, 4 females and 2 males. Two students are selected at random, and a random variable X is defined to be the number of females selected. Find the density function of X.
6. Joe has 3 \$1 bills, 1 \$5 bill, and 6 \$10 bills. He selects 2 bills at random and notes their values. A random variable X is defined to be the total value (in dollars) of the two bills selected. Find the density function for X.
7. There are 5 women and 3 men waiting on standby for a flight to New York. Suppose 3 of these 8 people are selected at random, and a random variable X is defined to be the number of women selected. Find $\Pr[X = 2]$.
8. An unfair coin with $\Pr[H] = .6$ is flipped four times and the result of each flip is noted. A random variable X is defined as follows: X takes the value zero if the number of heads is 2 or 3, and otherwise X is equal to the total number of heads. Find the density function of X.
9. A vending machine yields the item selected 80 percent of the time and no item at all 20 percent of the time. Three individuals attempt to use the machine. Let the random variable X be defined as the number of individuals who obtain the item selected. Find the values taken by X and the density function of X, under the assumption that the attempts to use the machine form a Bernoulli process.
10. Two fair dice, red and green, are rolled. A random variable X is defined as follows.
    - If the number on the red die is 1, then $X =$ number on the green die.
    - If the number on the red die is not 1, then $X =$ sum of numbers on red and green dice.

    Find $\Pr[X = 5]$.
11. You have one card marked 1, two cards marked 3, and one card marked 5. Two cards are selected simultaneously and at random, and the numbers on the cards are noted. A random variable X is defined as the sum of the numbers on the two cards. Find the density function of X.
12. An experiment consists of randomly drawing 2 cards from a standard deck (without replacement). The random variable X is defined to be the number of aces drawn. Find the density function of X.
13. A box contains 5 balls, one is blue and 4 are red. An experiment consists of selecting balls at random, one after another (without replacement) and noting the color of each ball selected. The experiment ends when a blue ball is selected or after a total of 3 balls have been selected. A random variable X is defined as the total number of balls selected when the experiment ends. Find the density function of X.
14. A ticket broker has 4 tickets to a concert, one on the main level and 3 in the balcony. She selects tickets at random, one after another without replacement until the main level ticket is selected. A random variable X is defined to be the total number of tickets selected. Find the density function of X.
15. A box contains 2 red balls and 3 green balls. A ball is selected at random and its color is noted. If it is red, it is not replaced in the box and a second ball is drawn and its color is noted. If the first ball is green, then it is replaced in the box, a second ball is drawn at random, and its color is noted. A random variable X is defined as the total number of red balls selected. Find the density function of X.
16. In a box of 6 markers, 4 contain ink and 2 do not contain ink. Three markers are selected simultaneously and at random and each is checked to determine whether

it contains ink. A random variable X is defined as the number of markers which do contain ink. Find the values of X and its density function.

17. There are 3 cans of regular cola and 4 cans of diet cola in the refrigerator, and you select 3 cans at random to take to the beach. A random variable X is defined to be the number of cans of regular cola selected. Find the values of X and its density function.
18. There are 20 balls labeled 1 through 20 in a box. A ball with an even number is worth \$1, and a ball with an odd number is worth \$2. Three balls are selected simultaneously and at random. A random variable X is defined to be the total value (in dollars) of the 3 balls selected. Find the probability density function of X.
19. Five cards are selected at random from an ordinary deck, and a random variable X is defined as the number of aces. Find the probability density function of X.
20. A track coach has 8 stopwatches: 5 are accurate, 1 is slow, and 2 are fast. Three stopwatches are selected at random and tested for accuracy. A random variable X is defined to be the number of accurate stopwatches in the sample. Find the values assumed by X and its density function.
21. Box A contains 3 red and 2 green balls and box B contains 4 red balls and 1 green ball. An unfair coin with $\Pr[H] = .4$ is flipped, and if it is heads, then two balls are selected at random from box A, and if it is tails, then two balls are selected at random from box B. A random variable X is defined as the number of green balls selected. Find the density function of X.
22. An unfair coin is weighted so that $\Pr[H] = \frac{2}{3}$. The coin is flipped until a head appears or 4 consecutive tails appear. The random variable X is defined to be the total number of flips of the coin. Find the values assumed by X and the density function of X.
23. A student is planning to present the results of a class research project, and she has 3 slides of numerical data and 5 slides of graphical data. She will have time to use only 3 slides, and she selects the 3 to be used at random. Define a random variable X to be the number of graphical slides selected, and find the density function of X.
24. A student is planning to present the results of a class research project, and she has 3 slides of numerical data and 5 slides of graphical data. She selects slides, one after another (without replacement) and at random until she has at least one slide of each type or a total of 4 slides. Define a random variable X to be the number of slides selected, and find the density function of X.
25. An experiment consists of rolling a fair die until the sum of all numbers which have appeared exceeds 3. A random variable X is defined to be the total number of rolls. Find the density function of X.
26. A fair coin is flipped until either 3 heads have appeared or 3 tails have appeared. A random variable X is defined to be the total number of flips. Find the density function of X.
27. Each week cars in the motor pool of the Department of Environmental Management are assigned to employees at random. The motor pool has 20 cars and 4 of them have all-wheel drive. For 5 consecutive weeks the motor pool manager records a "Yes" if the first car assigned has all-wheel drive and "No" otherwise. Let the random variable X be defined as the number of times a "Yes" is recorded. Find the density function of X.

28. A sales representative has probability .1 of making a sale on a "cold call," that is, when the sales representative has no prior relationship with the customer. Suppose that 10 cold calls are made and the results of successive calls are independent. A sales bonus is awarded as follows: no bonus unless there are at least 2 sales, \$1000 for 2 sales, and \$5000 for more than 2 sales. If a random variable X is defined as the value of the bonus (in dollars), find the density function of X.
29. You have two coins: One is fair and the other is unfair with $\Pr[H] = \frac{2}{3}$. An experiment consists of selecting a coin at random and flipping it twice, noting the result of each flip. Define a random variable X to be the number of heads. Find the density function of X.
30. You have 3 coins: 2 are fair and 1 is unfair with $\Pr[H] = \frac{1}{3}$. An experiment consists of selecting a coin at random and flipping it twice, noting the result of each flip. Define a random variable X to be the number of heads. Find the density function of X.
31. An experiment consists of randomly choosing two 4-digit numbers from the set of consecutive integers from 0000 through 9999. The selection is with replacement, and we assume the selections are independent. Thus, possible selections are 0135 and 2553. If the two numbers selected are the same, you win \$500; and if they are not the same, you lose \$1. Find the density function of the random variable which gives your gain or loss.
32. Kirsten plays a lottery with the following rules. She selects a set of six distinct 2-digit numbers from the set of consecutive integers from 01 through 45. Thus one possible selection is $\{09, 23, 24, 25, 44, 45\}$. At the end of the week, a computer selects six distinct numbers independently and at random from the set of consecutive integers from 01 through 45. She pays \$1 for a ticket, and she wins \$1,000,000 if the set of numbers selected by the computer is the same as hers. Define a random variable to have the value \$999,999 if the computer selects the same set as Kirsten (this is the \$1,000,000 she wins minus the \$1 cost of a ticket), and to have the value $-\$1$ if the sets are not the same (this is the cost of the lottery ticket). Find the density function of this random variable.
33. A box contains 4 green balls and 2 blue balls. A ball is selected at random and its color is noted. If it is blue, it is replaced; if it is green, it is not replaced. Continue until a total of 5 balls has been drawn. A random variable X is defined as the number of blue balls selected. Find the density function of X.
34. There are three \$10 bills and five \$20 bills in a drawer. An experiment consists of selecting bills, one after another without replacement, and noting the value of each bill selected. The experiment ends after two bills with the same denomination have been selected. A random variable X is defined as the total value of the bills selected. Find the values of X and its density function.
35. There are three cards in a bowl, and each of the cards has exactly one of the letters A, B, and C. An experiment consists of selecting 4 cards at random one after another with replacement and noting the letter on each card. A random variable X is defined as the number of different letters on the four cards selected. Find the density function of X.
36. An experiment consists of creating random computer passwords of 4 letters using the 6 letters N, K, Y, F, R, and P. A letter may occur once, more than once or not at all in each password. A random variable X is defined as the number of different letters in a password. Find $\Pr[X = 3]$.

4.3 EXPECTED VALUES AND STANDARD DEVIATIONS OF RANDOM VARIABLES

In the discussion of Example 4.8, we concluded that it was reasonable to expect to lose \$.50 per play of the game. We obtained this average loss by noting that in each 10 plays of the game, we expect to win 1 time (\$4) and lose 9 times ($9 \times \$1 = \$9$). Thus, in 10 plays we lose \$5 or, on average, \$.50 per play. Similarly, in Example 4.9, we decided the average return per play is $-\$1/6$. This followed from the fact that a loss of \$6.00 occurred with probability $\frac{1}{6}$, a loss of \$1.00 with probability $\frac{1}{6}$, and a gain of \$1.50 with probability $\frac{4}{6}$:

$$\text{Expected gain (in dollars)} = (-6)\left(\tfrac{1}{6}\right) + (-1)\left(\tfrac{1}{6}\right) + (1.5)\left(\tfrac{4}{6}\right) = -\tfrac{1}{6}$$

This concept of an average or expected gain can be extended to any random variable.

Let X be a random variable with values $x_1, x_2, \ldots, x_k$. Also, let $p_i = \Pr[X = x_i]$ for $i = 1, 2, \ldots, k$. The expected value of X, $E[X]$, is defined to be

$$E[X] = x_1p_1 + x_2p_2 + \cdots + x_kp_k \tag{4.3}$$

The expected value of X is also called the *mean* of X.

The probabilities p_i are given by the probability density function for the random variable X. Thus a necessary step in determining the expected value of X is to find the density function of X.

Example 4.12 A ticket broker has 8 concert tickets available for sale, 3 on the main level and 5 in the balcony. The broker sells tickets on the main level for \$100 each and tickets on the balcony for \$60 each. Two tickets are selected at random and a random variable X is defined as the cost of the 2 tickets selected.

Problem Find the expected value of the random variable X.

Solution In general we will apply formula (4.3) by using a table. In this first example, however, we apply the formula directly to emphasize the meaning of each term.

We first determine the values assumed by X. If tickets for 2 balcony seats are selected, then the cost is \$120; if one balcony seat and one main level seat are selected, then the cost is \$160; and if 2 main level seats are selected, then the cost is \$200. Thus we set $x_1 = 120$, $x_2 = 160$, and $x_3 = 200$. We determine the density function (using the techniques of Chapter 2) to be

$$p_1 = \Pr[X = x_1] = \frac{C(5, 2)}{C(8, 2)} = \frac{(5 \cdot 4)/(1 \cdot 2)}{(8 \cdot 7)/(1 \cdot 2)} = \frac{20}{56}$$

$$p_2 = \Pr[X = x_2] = \frac{C(5, 1)C(3, 1)}{C(8, 2)} = \frac{(5/1)(3/1)}{(8 \cdot 7)/(1 \cdot 2)} = \frac{30}{56}$$

$$p_3 = \Pr[X = x_3] = \frac{C(3, 2)}{C(8, 2)} = \frac{(3 \cdot 2)/(1 \cdot 2)}{(8 \cdot 7)/(1 \cdot 2)} = \frac{6}{56}$$

Applying the definition of expected value, formula (4.3), we have

$$E[X] = x_1p_1 + x_2p_2 + x_3p_3 = 120\left(\tfrac{20}{56}\right) + 160\left(\tfrac{30}{56}\right) + 200\left(\tfrac{6}{56}\right) = \tfrac{8400}{56} = 150$$

In terms of the original setting, the expected value of the cost of two tickets is \$150. ■

Remarks

1. In Example 4.12, we computed the expected value of a cost. In such a case we frequently shorten the phrase "expected value of the cost" to "expected cost." Similarly, we say "expected grade-point average" for "expected value of the grade point average," etc.
2. Note that in Example 4.12 the expected value of X (which is 150) is *not* one of the values taken by X (which are 120, 160, and 200). This is often, but not always, the case.

In Section 4.2 we saw how to form a table (Table 4.6 for instance) giving the density function of a random variable. It is easy and frequently useful to modify such a table for use in finding the expected value of a random variable. Indeed, such a table already contains the values of X and their associated probabilities. We add another column labeled "product" in which we multiply each value of X by its associated probability. The expected value of X is, by Equation (4.3), the sum of these products. Using this idea in Example 4.12, we have Table 4.7. The table is completed by adding the entries in the column labeled "product." This sum is the expected value of X.

Example 4.13 A friend invites you to play the following game: 2 coins are to be selected at random from 6 coins: 2 nickels, 3 dimes, and 1 quarter. If the sum of the values of the coins is 10, 20, or 30 cents, your friend pays you 25 cents. Otherwise you must pay your friend the value of the coins. What is your expected gain per play of the game?

Solution Let N, D, and Q denote nickel, dime, and quarter, respectively. Since the order in which the coins are drawn is unimportant, the sample space

TABLE 4.7

Value of X x_1	Probability p_i	Product $x_i p_i$
120	$\frac{20}{56}$	$\frac{2400}{56}$
160	$\frac{30}{56}$	$\frac{4800}{56}$
200	$\frac{6}{56}$	$\frac{1200}{56}$
		$E[X] = \frac{8400}{56} = 150$

of the experiment can be represented as $\{DQ, DN, DD, NQ, NN\}$. The gain to you is -35 cents for DQ, -15 cents for DN, and $+25$ cents for the other three outcomes. Let X denote the random variable which assigns to each outcome its value to you in cents. The density function of X is given in Table 4.8, and we have

$$E[X] = -\frac{105}{15} - \frac{90}{15} + \frac{150}{15} = -\frac{45}{15} = -3$$

You should expect to lose 3 cents to your friend on each play of the game. ■

TABLE 4.8

Value	Probability	Product
-35	$\frac{C(3,1)C(1,1)}{C(6,2)} = \frac{3}{15}$	$-\frac{105}{15}$
-15	$\frac{C(2,1)C(3,1)}{C(6,2)} = \frac{6}{15}$	$-\frac{90}{15}$
$+25$	$\frac{C(2,2)}{C(6,2)} + \frac{C(3,2)}{C(6,2)} + \frac{C(2,1)C(1,1)}{C(6,2)} = \frac{6}{15}$	$+\frac{150}{15}$
		$E[X] = -\frac{45}{15} = -3$

Example 4.14 A sales representative makes sales to 20 percent of the customers on which he calls. His commissions are \$100 each for the first 3 sales each week, \$200 each for every sale above 3. In a certain week the sales representative calls on 8 customers.

Problem Find the expected value of the total income of the sales representative that week.

TABLE 4.9

Value, $	Probability	Product
0	.1678	0
100	.3355	33.55
200	.2936	58.72
300	.1468	44.04
500	.0459	22.95
700	.0092	6.44
900	.0011	.99
1100	.0001	.11
1300	.0000	.00
		$E[X] = 166.80$

Solution Define a random variable X to be the total income of the sales representative. We view the calls made by the sales representative as Bernoulli trials. There are 8 trials, and each has success probability $p = .2$. There is no income for no sales. The total income for 1, 2, or 3 sales is \$100, \$200, or \$300, respectively. Each sale above 3 adds \$200 to the total income. Thus for 4, 5, 6, 7, and 8 sales the total income is \$500, \$700, \$900, \$1100, and \$1300, respectively. The values and probability density function for X (taken from Appendix B) are shown in Table 4.9. Using the definition of expected value, we add the entries in the product column, and we conclude that the expected value of X is (in dollars)

$$E[X] = 166.80$$

Thus the expected total income of the sales representative for that week is \$166.80. ■

In computing the mean or expected value of a random variable, it is usually necessary to use the process just described. However, for the important special case of a binomial random variable (introduced in Section 4.2) there is a formula which greatly simplifies the task.

Consider a Bernoulli process consisting of n trials, and let X be the random variable which assigns to each outcome the number of successes. Suppose p is the probability of success on a single trial. The random variable X takes the values $0, 1, 2, \ldots, n$. The probability associated with each of these values was determined in formula (4.1); it is

$$\Pr[X = r] = C(n, r)p^r(1 - p)^{n-r}$$

for $r = 0, 1, 2, \ldots, n$. According to the definition of expected value, we have

$$\begin{aligned} E[X] &= 0 \cdot \Pr[X = 0] + 1 \cdot \Pr[X = 1] + 2 \cdot \Pr[X = 2] \\ &\quad + \cdots + n \cdot \Pr[X = n] \\ &= 0 \cdot C(n, 0)p^0(1-p)^n + 1 \cdot C(n, 1)p(1-p)^{n-1} \\ &\quad + 2 \cdot C(n, 2)p^2(1-p)^{n-2} + \cdots + n \cdot C(n, n)p^n \end{aligned}$$

Although the formula for $E[X]$ appears to be a complicated sum, it can be written in a very simple form. We illustrate the simplification for $n = 1$ and $n = 2$. First, suppose $n = 1$. Then

$$E[X] = 0 \cdot p^0(1-p)^1 + 1 \cdot p^1(1-p)^0 = p$$

Next, if $n = 2$, then

$$E[X] = 0 \cdot p^0(1-p)^2 + 1 \cdot 2 \cdot p^1(1-p)^1 + 2 \cdot 1 \cdot p^2(1-p)^0 = 2p$$

The argument can be continued and an analogous result can be established for any value of n by using mathematical induction.

Expected Value of a Binomial Random Variable

If X is a binomial random variable for a Bernoulli process consisting of n trials with success probability p, then

$$E[X] = np \tag{4.4}$$

Example 4.15 A political poll is to be taken by mailing 1000 questionnaires. It is known that the probability that any given questionnaire will be returned is .14.

Problem Find the expected number of questionnaires that will be returned (assume that each return or nonreturn of a questionnaire is a Bernoulli trial).

Solution We use formula (4.4). We define a success to be a returned questionnaire, so $p = .14$. Since $n = 1000$, the expected number of returned questionnaires is $1000 \times .14 = 140$. ■

Example 4.16 An NBA basketball player makes 30 percent of his 3-point shots and 45 percent of his 2-point shots. If each year he attempts 300 three-point shots and 800 two-point shots, what is the average number of points he makes per year on field goals? You may assume that his 3-point shots and his 2-point shots are both Bernoulli trial experiments.

Solution The total number of points on field goals is the sum of the points from 3-point shots and the points from 2-point shots. If we consider the 3-point shots as a Bernoulli process with 300 trials and $p = .30$, the expected number of points from 3-point shots is $3 \times 300 \times .30 = 270$. Similarly, the expected number of points from 2-point shots is $2 \times 800 \times .45 = 720$. Thus, the expected total number of points from field goals is $270 + 720 = 990$. ■

Remark In the solution of Example 4.16, we used a powerful fact about the expected value of a random variable. In that problem we began with two random variables—the number of points from 3-point shots made in a year and the number of points from 2-point shots made in a year. We were interested in a third random variable, namely, the total number of points from field goals. Using the formula for the expected value of a random variable (4.4), we obtained the expected number of successful 3-point shots ($300 \times .3 = 90$) and the expected number of successful 2-point shots ($800 \times .45 = 360$). This gave us $270 = 3 \times 90$ expected points from 3-point shots and $720 = 2 \times 360$ expected points from 2-point shots. Finally, we added these to obtain the expected number of total points, $990 = 270 + 720$. The powerful result that we are using is that the steps combining these numbers are legitimate operations. In particular, if a random variable Z is equal to $aX + bY$, where X and Y are random variables and a and b are numbers, then

$$E[Z] = aE[X] + bE[Y]$$

In our case, X is the number of 3-point shots made, Y is the number of 2-point shots made, $a = 3$, and $b = 2$.

Example 4.17 Suppose we have experiments labeled A, B, C and corresponding random variables X_A, X_B, and X_C. Moreover, suppose that the probability functions of these random variables are as shown in Table 4.10.

TABLE 4.10

X_A		X_B		X_C	
Value	**Probability**	**Value**	**Probability**	**Value**	**Probability**
+5	.5	+1	.25	+5	.1
−5	.5	0	.5	0	.8
		−1	.25	−5	.1

Problem Find the mean of each of these random variables and draw graphs of their density functions. To draw a graph, you plot the points (value, probability of that value) on a coordinate system.

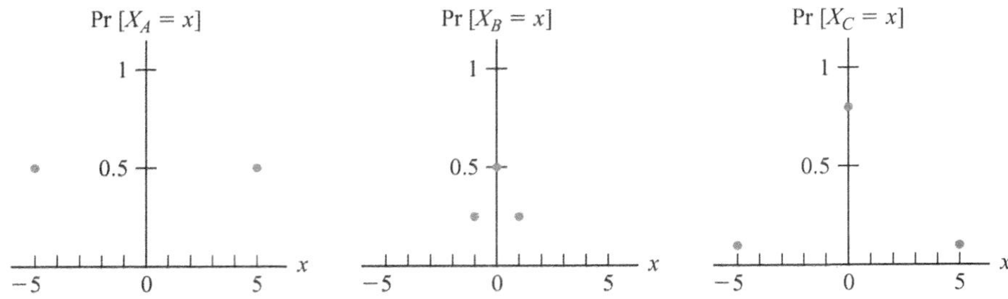

FIGURE 4.4

Solution The graphs of the density functions are shown in Figure 4.4. Using Equation (4.3), we find

$$E[X_A] = (5)(.5) + (-5)(.5) = 0$$
$$E[X_B] = (1)(.25) + (0)(.5) + (-1)(.25) = 0$$
$$E[X_C] = (5)(.1) + (0)(.8) + (-5)(.1) = 0$$

■

In Example 4.17 each of the three random variables X_A, X_B, and X_C has mean 0. However, it is clear from Table 4.10 and Figure 4.4 that these random variables are quite different. For instance, X_A never takes the value 0 and in fact takes each of the values +5 and −5 with probability .5. On the other hand, X_B takes only values relatively close to 0 and in fact takes the value 0 with probability .5. Finally, X_C also takes the values +5 and −5, but it is far more likely to take the value 0. Since these quite different random variables have the same mean, it is clear that another measure is needed to help distinguish one from another. One approach is to measure the dispersion of the values of X about the mean, i.e., how the values of X are spread out. To do so, we shall use the *variance* and *standard deviation*. It is common to adopt notation using the Greek letters μ (mu) and σ (sigma) for the mean and standard deviation, respectively.

Let X be a random variable which takes the values $x_1, x_2, \ldots, x_n$ with probabilities $p_1, p_2, \ldots, p_n$, respectively. Let $\mu = E[X]$ denote the *mean* of X. The *variance* of X is the number

$$\text{Var}[X] = (x_1 - \mu)^2 p_1 + (x_2 - \mu)^2 p_2 + \cdots + (x_n - \mu)^2 p_n \qquad (4.5)$$

The *standard deviation* of X is the number

$$\sigma[X] = \sqrt{\text{Var}[X]} \qquad (4.6)$$

Equation (4.6) simply says that once we have the variance of X, we obtain the standard deviation by taking the square root of the variance.

Example 4.18 Determine the variance and standard deviation of the random variables X_A, X_B, and X_C of Example 4.17.

Solution Using definitions (4.5) and (4.6), we have

$$\begin{aligned}
\text{Var}[X_A] &= (5-0)^2(.5) + (-5-0)^2(.5) = 25 \\
\text{Var}[X_B] &= (1-0)^2(.25) + (0-0)^2(.5) + (-1-0)^2(.25) = .5 \\
\text{Var}[X_C] &= (5-0)^2(.1) + (0-0)^2(.8) + (-5-0)^2(.1) = 5
\end{aligned}$$

and therefore for X_A we have $\sigma = 5$, for X_B we have $\sigma = \sqrt{.5} = .71$, and for X_C we have $\sigma = \sqrt{5} = 2.2$, where the square roots are correct to two digits. ■

Notice that in this example the variances of X_A, X_B, and X_C correspond in a qualitative way to the distribution of the values about the mean. That is, the random variable with the largest variance, X_A, takes values relatively far from the mean (0) with high probability, and the random variable with the smallest variance, X_B, takes only values relatively close to the mean.

Just as there is a simple formula for the mean of a binomial random variable, there is a corresponding formula for the variance.

Variance of a Binomial Random Variable

If X is a binomial random variable for a Bernoulli process consisting of n trials with success probability p, then the variance of X, $\text{Var}[X]$, is

$$\text{Var}[X] = np(1-p) \tag{4.7}$$

and the standard deviation of X, $\sigma[X]$, is

$$\sigma[X] = \sqrt{np(1-p)}$$

Example 4.19 Sales information provided by a vegetable seed company asserts that the germination rate for its best-selling Robust Red Tomato seeds is 98 percent. Suppose 2000 seeds are planted. Let X denote a random variable which assigns to each outcome, for the "experiment" of planting 2000 seeds, the number of seeds which germinate. Assume that this is a Bernoulli process and that the assertion is correct.

Problem Find the expected value and variance of X.

Solution The random variable X is a binomial random variable with $n = 2000$ and $p = .98$. (A success is a germinated seed.) Using (4.4) and (4.7), we have

$$E[X] = 2000(.98) = 1960 \quad \text{and} \quad \text{Var}[X] = 2000(.98)(.02) = 39.2 \quad ■$$

Exercises for Section 4.3

1. A random variable X has the density function shown below. Find the expected value of X.

Value of *X*	Probability
1	.5
3	.2
8	.3

2. A random variable X has the density function shown below. Find the expected value of X.

Value of *X*	Probability
−1	.2
0	.4
2	.1
5	.3

3. A random variable X has the density function shown below. What is the expected value of X?

Value of *X*	Probability
1	$\frac{1}{21}$
2	$\frac{2}{21}$
3	$\frac{3}{21}$
4	$\frac{4}{21}$
5	$\frac{5}{21}$
6	$\frac{6}{21}$

4. A random variable X has the values and probabilities shown below. What is the expected value of X?

Value of *X*	Probability
−1	$\frac{1}{21}$
2	$\frac{2}{21}$
−3	$\frac{3}{21}$
4	$\frac{4}{21}$
−5	$\frac{5}{21}$
6	$\frac{6}{21}$

5. A random variable X has the density function shown below. Find the expected value of X.

Value of *X*	Probability
−5	.4
−1	.2
2	.3
5	.1

6. A random variable X has the density function shown below. Find the missing entries in the table and the expected value of X?

Value of *X*	Probability	Product
?	.2	−2
−1	.3	?
2	?	?
10	.1	?

7. A random variable X has the density function shown below. Find the missing entries in the table and the expected value of X.

Value of *X*	Probability	Product
−1	?	−.3
−2	?	−.4
?	.2	.3
2	.3	.6

8. A random variable X has the density function shown below. Find the missing entries in the table.

Value of X	Probability	Product
?	?	?
1	.2	.2
?	.3	.6
3	?	.3
4	?	1.2
		$E[X] = 2.1$

9. A drawer contains 3 nickels, 2 dimes, and 4 quarters. One coin is randomly selected from the drawer. What is the expected value of the coin selected?
10. Suppose X is a random variable which takes values 1, 2, and 5. If $\Pr[X = 2] = .3$, and $E[X] = 2.9$, find $\Pr[X = 5]$.
11. A box contains 4 blue and 3 green balls. Four balls are selected simultaneously and at random and their colors are noted. A random variable X is defined as the number of blue balls minus the number of green balls. Find the expected value of X.
12. For a certain baseball player, hitting against left-handed pitchers is a Bernoulli process with the probability of a hit equal to .3, while hitting against a right-handed pitcher is a Bernoulli process with the probability of a hit equal to .25. One month this player bats 20 times against left-handed pitchers and 70 times against right-handed pitchers. What is the expected number of hits the batter obtains that month?
13. A coin is weighted so that $\Pr[H] = \frac{2}{5}$. The coin is flipped 10 times. A random variable X is defined by assigning to each outcome the number of heads obtained in the 10 flips. Find $E[X]$.
14. There are 3 red and 2 blue balls in a box. You select 2 balls, one after another at random and without replacement and note the colors of the balls selected. Each ball is worth \$2 except:

    - if you select a red ball followed by a blue ball, the red ball is worth \$5 and
    - if you select a red ball following a blue ball then the red ball is worth \$1.

    Find the expected total value of the balls selected.
15. You have two coins; one is fair and one is unfair with $\Pr[H] = \frac{2}{3}$. An experiment consists of selecting a coin at random and flipping it twice, noting the result of each flip. Find the expected numbers of heads.
16. There are three \$1 bills, one \$5 bill, and one \$10 bill in a drawer. An experiment consists of selecting bills, one at a time at random without replacement, and noting the value of each bill selected. The experiment ends when the \$10 bill is selected or when 3 bills have been selected. A random variable X is defined as the total value (in dollars) of the bills selected. Find the expected value of X.

17. An experiment consists of flipping an unfair coin with $\Pr[H] = .6$ repeatedly until a head first appears or there are a total of 4 flips. A random variable X is defined as the total number of flips. Find the expected value of X.
18. A golfer makes 60 percent of her putts when they are less than 10 feet and 30 percent when they are 10 feet or more in length. Assume that her putts are Bernoulli trials and in one tournament she takes 32 putts from less than 10 feet and 78 from 10 feet or more. What is the expected number of putts made?
19. The probability of winning \$10,000 in the lottery is .00002, the probability of winning \$100,000 is .000004, and the probability of winning \$1,000,000 is .0000001. A ticket costs \$10. Find your expected gain or loss on each ticket you buy.
20. A game is played as follows: A fair coin is flipped 5 times. If there are fewer than 3 heads, you win nothing. If there are 3 or 4 heads, you win \$1, and if there are five heads, you win \$5. Define a random variable X as the amount you win on one play of the game and find the expected value of X. Find the variance and standard deviation of X.
21. A shopper has two \$1 bills, two \$5 bills, and three \$10 bills. Three bills are selected simultaneously and at random and a random variable X is defined as the total value (in dollars) of the 3 bills selected. Find the expected value of X.
22. At a local carnival a game can be played with a fishpond containing 100 fish; 90 are white, 9 are red, and 1 is blue. A contestant randomly catches a fish and receives payment as follows:

White:	\$.30
Red:	\$1.00
Blue:	\$10.00

    If it costs \$.60 to play this game, how much (on the average) does the carnival gain on each play?
23. A bag contains 1 green ball, 2 blue balls, and 3 orange balls. Two balls are selected simultaneously and at random, and their colors are noted. The green ball is worth \$23, each blue ball is worth \$5, and each orange ball is worth \$1. Find the expected total value and standard deviation of the value of the two balls selected.
24. There are 5 white mice and 3 gray mice in a cage. Three mice are selected at random and their colors are noted. Find the expected number of white mice.
25. An examination consists of 2 true-false questions and 2 multiple choice questions (5 options per question), each with exactly 1 correct answer. If a student selects answers at random, one answer per each question, what is the expected number of correct answers?
26. In a Bernoulli process with $n = 1{,}000$ and $p = .1$, find the expected number of successes and the standard deviation of the number of successes.
27. A foundry worker is assigned bonus points for producing castings without defects. In a typical day the worker produces 10 castings, and he expects that 90 percent of the time he can produce a casting without defects. The reward system assigns 100 points if none of the 10 castings has defects, 80 points if 1 or 2 castings have defects, 50 points if 3 or 4 castings have defects, and no bonus points if 5 or more castings have defects. Find the expected number of bonus points per day for the worker. (*Hint*: View this as a Bernoulli process and use Table B.1 in Appendix B.)

28. Suppose the free throws of a basketball player can be viewed as Bernoulli trials with success probability $p = .4$. If she takes four free throws in a game, find the expected number of points scored, one point per free throw.
29. A Bernoulli process consists of 10 trials with $p = .2$. A random variable X is defined by assigning to each outcome 3 times the number of successes minus the number of failures. Find the expected value of X. (*Hint*: Use Table B.1)
30. You have two baskets labeled H and T. The basket labeled H has two \$5 bills and one \$10 bill, the basket labeled T has three \$5 bills and two \$10 bills. You flip a fair coin, and according to the side that lands uppermost you select 2 bills simultaneously and at random from the basket with that label. Find the expected value of the bills selected.
31. Joe has 2 quarters and 1 dime in his right-hand pocket and 1 quarter and 1 dime in his left-hand pocket. He selects a coin at random from his right-hand pocket, notes its value, and puts it in his left-hand pocket. Then he selects a coin at random from his left-hand pocket. A random variable X is defined as the total number of quarters selected. Find the expected value of X.
32. A box contains 2 green and 3 blue balls. A ball is selected at random and its color is noted. If it is green, it is not replaced, and another ball is selected and its color is noted. If the first ball is blue, then it is replaced, and a second ball is drawn and its color is noted. A random variable X is defined as the total number of green balls selected. Find the expected value and standard deviation of X.
33. A box contains 5 balls, one is blue and 4 are red. An experiment consists of selecting balls at random, one after another (without replacement) and noting the color of each ball selected. The experiment ends when a blue ball is selected or after 3 balls have been selected. A random variable X is defined as the total number of balls selected when the experiment ends. Find the expected value and standard deviation of X. (This is the setting of Exercise 13, Section 4.2).
34. Data for visits to the Student Health Service at GSU show the following for one day in November. For each student registering for treatment at most two concerns were recorded, and the results are: 38 percent of the students listed "injury", 39 percent listed a "respiratory infection", and 23 percent listed "other", 4 percent listed "injury and other", and 12 percent listed "respiratory infection and other." No students listed "respiratory infection and injury." The records of 10 students were selected at random and the number of concerns recorded for each record selected. Find the expected value and variance of the number of concerns.
35. There are two \$10 bills and five \$20 bills in a drawer. An experiment consists of selecting bills, one after another without replacement, and noting the value of each bill selected. The experiment ends after two consecutive bills with the same denomination have been selected. A random variable X is defined as the total value of the bills selected. Find the expected value of X.
36. Find the variance and standard deviation of the random variable X of Exercise 1.
37. Find the variance and standard deviation of the random variable X of Exercise 5.
38. Find the variance and standard deviation of the random variable X of Exercise 13.

IMPORTANT TERMS AND CONCEPTS

You should be able to describe, define, or give examples and use each of the following:

Bernoulli trial
Bernoulli process
Random variable
Binomial random variable
Density function
Mean or expected value
Variance
Standard deviation

REVIEW EXERCISES

1. A fair die is rolled, and a random variable X is defined to be -1 if the result is a 1, 2 if the result is a 2 or a 3, and 5 if the result is a 4, 5, or 6. Find the density function of X.
2. Suppose you have 6 playing cards numbered 2 through 7. Two cards are selected simultaneously and at random and their numbers are noted. A random variable X is defined as the sum of the numbers on the cards selected. Find $\Pr[X = 8]$.
3. A box contains 3 red balls and 2 blue balls. Three balls are selected simultaneously and at random, and a random variable is defined to be the number of blue balls. Find the density function of X.
4. Suppose that you have 4 cards numbered 3 through 6. Two cards are selected simultaneously and at random, and their numbers are noted. A random variable X is defined as the sum of the numbers on the cards. Find the probability density function of X.
5. A box contains 6 balls, one is blue and 5 are red. An experiment consists of selecting balls at random, one after another without replacement and noting the color of each ball selected. The experiment ends when a blue ball is selected or after 4 balls have been selected. Define a random variable X to be the total number of red balls selected. Find $\Pr[X = 3]$.
6. Suppose Homer attends math class at random, and the probability of attending each day is .6. The instructor takes attendance 3 times and awards 10 points to students who attend at least twice, and no points to students who attend less than twice. A random variable X is defined as the number of points Homer receives based on attendance. Find the probability density function of X.
7. A carnival game consists of selecting 3 balls simultaneously and at random from a box containing 5 red balls and 3 green balls. Each red ball selected pays \$.20, and each green ball pays \$.50. It costs \$1.00 to play the game. A random variable X is defined by associating with each play of the game the *net* payoff to the player. Find the density function of X.

8. A fair die is rolled 10 times. A roll is called a success if either a 1 or a 2 comes up. What is the probability that there are exactly 3 successes or exactly 3 failures in the 10 rolls?
9. A box contains 8 green balls and 2 blue balls. A ball is selected at random and its color is noted. If it is green, you *win* \$5, and if it is blue, then you *lose* \$8. What is your expected gain (in dollars) per play of the game?
10. A basketball player makes 80 percent of her free throws, 50 percent of her 2-point field goal attempts, and 30 percent of her 3-point field goal attempts. In a typical game the player attempts 10 free throws, 12 two-point field goals, and 5 three-point field goals. If we assume that each type of shot is a Bernoulli process, find the expected number of points the player will score.
11. An aquarium contains 7 fish: 3 of the fish weigh 200 grams each, 2 weigh 150 grams each, and the remaining 2 weigh 100 grams each. A sample of 3 fish is selected at random. A random variable Y is defined by associating with each outcome the total weight of the 3 fish.
    (*a*) Find the density function of Y. (*b*) Find the mean of Y.
    (*c*) Find the variance and standard deviation of Y.

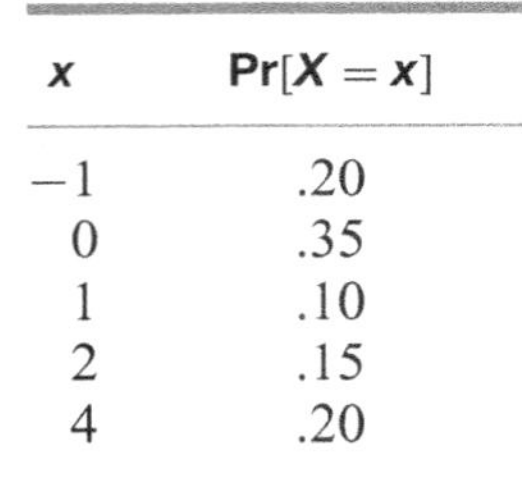

x	$\Pr[X = x]$
-1	.20
0	.35
1	.10
2	.15
4	.20

12. Let X be a random variable whose density function is given at the left.
    (*a*) Find the mean of X.
    (*b*) Find the variance of X.
    (*c*) Find the standard deviation of X.
    (*d*) Find the probability that X takes a value in the interval from $\mu - \sigma$ to $\mu + \sigma$.
13. My morning paper is delivered late 40 percent of the time. Suppose deliveries can be described as a Bernoulli process, and let a random variable X be defined by counting the number of late deliveries in a year (365 days).
    (*a*) Find the mean of X.
    (*b*) Find the standard deviation of X.
14. A biased coin with $\Pr[H] = .6$ is flipped 5 times, and the result of each flip is noted. A random variable X is defined to be 20 if there are exactly 4 heads, 5 if there are 5 heads, and 0 otherwise. Find the expected value and standard deviation of X.
15. A shopper has one \$10 bill, two \$5 bills, and three \$1 bills in his pocket. An experiment consists of selecting bills at random one after another (without replacement) and noting the denomination of each. The experiment ends when a \$10 bill is selected or a total of 3 bills are selected. Define a random variable X to be the total number of bills selected. Find the density function of X.
16. An automatic counter on a machine is supposed to reset itself each time the machine is turned off. However, it fails to do so at random 35 percent of the time. If it fails to reset, then it must be reset by hand. The machinery

is turned off at the end of each day and only then. Assume the reset failures can be viewed as Bernoulli trials, and find how many days must pass before the expected number of hand resets is at least 10.

17. A binomial random variable X has $n = 100$ and $p = .6$. Another binomial random variable Y has $n = 150$.
    (*a*) What must be the value of p for Y so that the two random variables have the same mean?
    (*b*) Using this value of p for Y, decide which random variable has the larger variance.
18. A box contains 3 red balls, 2 blue balls, and one white ball. A ball is selected at random, its color is noted and it is replaced. This experiment is repeated 4 additional times. Let E be the event that all balls selected are the same color. Find $\Pr[E']$.
19. A coin with $\Pr[H] = p > 0$ is flipped 10 times. If the probability of exactly 4 heads is equal to the probability of exactly 5 heads, what is the value of p?
20. A student takes a multiple choice exam consisting of 10 questions, each with four possible answers, exactly one of which is correct. If the student selects answers independently and at random, find the probability that she gets at least 7 correct given that she gets at least two correct.
21. Ten percent of the laboratory tests for a certain disease give ''false-positive'' results. That is, the test indicates that the patient has the disease when, in fact, the patient does not. Five patients are tested, and we assume that the tests can be viewed as Bernoulli trials.
    (*a*) Find the probability that exactly 2 tests give false-positive results.
    (*b*) Find the probability that the first test and the last test give false-positive results.
22. In the setting of Exercise 21, find the probability that there are exactly 2 false-positives given that there are at least 2 false-positives.
23. In the setting of Exercise 21, find the probability that there are exactly 2 false-positives given that the first test and the last test are false-positives.
24. An inspector checks the seals on the doors of microwave ovens on an assembly line. Experience shows that doors with defective seals occur at random and with probability .2. How many doors must the inspector check so that the expected number of ovens with nondefective door seals is at least 1000? Assume that each oven is checked exactly once.
25. A major league baseball player has a batting average (number of hits divided by number of times at bat) of .200. If the player's turns at bat are viewed as Bernoulli trials with $p = .2$, what is the probability that in 200 times at bat he has at least 50 hits?
26. One-fifth of the holes punched on a high-speed punching machine in an automobile plant are more than 1 millimeter out of place. If the positions of 400 randomly selected holes are checked, what is the probability that

the number of holes more than 1 millimeter out of place is no more than 60?

27. A student takes a 100-question true-false test. A passing grade is 70 or more correct answers.
    (*a*) What is the probability that the student passes the test by guessing? When the student is guessing, the probability of a correct answer on any question is .5.
    (*b*) If the student studies and has probability .8 of answering each question correctly, what is the probability that she does *not* pass the test?
28. The quality control group for a firm manufacturing laptop computers runs battery tests by playing video games continuously on a laptop until the battery is drained. Data for the tests show that on average 20 percent of the batteries are drained before 8 hours have elapsed and the remainder retain a charge at 8 hours. View each laptop test as a Bernoulli trial with outcomes battery drained or not drained at 8 hours. With this assumption, find the probability that in a test of 10 laptops no more than 3 will have the battery drained before 8 hours of continuous use.
29. A sales representative estimates that on each call there is a probability $\frac{1}{4}$ of making a sale. A bonus of \$100 is paid for the first and second sale each day, and a bonus of \$200 is paid for each additional sale. If it is possible to make 3 calls each day, what is the expected income from bonuses? What is the standard deviation of income from bonuses?
30. A carnival game has a tank of water containing 6 plastic fish. Each fish has a payoff marked on the bottom. Three of the fish are worth \$0.25, 2 are worth \$0.50, and 1 is worth \$2.00. It costs \$1.00 to play the game, and it is played as follows: A fish is selected at random. If it is worth \$0.50 or \$2.00, the game ends. If it is worth \$0.25, then another fish is selected (the first is not returned to the tank) and the game ends. You receive the total amount on the fish you select. Find your expected *net* gain (the amount you receive minus the amount you pay) per play of the game.
31. A box contains 3 red balls and 2 blue balls. Three balls are selected one after another without replacement, and the color of each ball is noted. A random variable X is defined to be 5 if the first ball is blue and 0 otherwise; a random variable Y is defined to be the number of red balls drawn on the second and third selections. Find the expected value of the random variable $X + Y$.
32. A cage of rats in a psychology laboratory contains 8 rats of which 3 are fully trained, 1 is partially trained, and the rest are untrained. A sample of 4 rats is selected at random. A random variable X is defined by associating with each outcome the number of fully trained rats.
    (*a*) Find the density function of X. (*b*) Find the mean of X.
    (*c*) Find the variance of X.

33. Eric is an expert blackjack player, but he suffers from chronic insomnia and he is superstitious. On 60% of those nights when he plays blackjack, he has slept the night before and he wears his lucky baseball cap. On those nights he wins \$100. On the nights he plays and wears his lucky baseball cap but has not been able to sleep the night before, he wins \$20. He forgets his lucky baseball cap with probability .2, and his forgetfulness is independent of whether he has slept the night before or not. If he forgets his lucky baseball cap, then he wins half as much as if he has it. Let X be a random variable whose value is the amount Eric wins on a random night of playing blackjack. Find the expected value of X.
34. The current population of Metroburg is 120,000. Projections are that in 10 years the population will increase 10 percent with probability .6, it will increase 5 percent with probability .3, and it will decline 2 percent with probability .1. Find the expected population of Metroburg in 10 years.
35. A person plays a state lottery by selecting 5 numbers in the set of integers from 1 through 50, with no repetitions allowed. The selections are not ordered, so {10, 20, 30, 40, 50} and {50, 20, 30, 40, 10} are the same selection. The winning numbers are selected at random by a computer. In a given week, 500,000 people play this lottery, and we assume that each person selects 5 numbers at random. It costs \$2 to play this lottery, and there is a prize of \$1,000,000 if you match all 5 numbers. Find the expected gain to the state.
36. Each morning Tom decides whether to attend economics class. He attends randomly with probability .6, and each decision is independent of what he has done in the past. That is, his decision process can be viewed as a Bernoulli process. Find the probability that he attends at least 6 of 10 classes given that he attends at least 1 but not all of the 10 classes.

PART

2

Linear Models

Glow Images

© Ingram Publishing/Alamy

Malcolm Fife/age fotostock

CHAPTER 5

Systems of Linear Equations

5.0 THE SETTING AND OVERVIEW: LINEAR MODELS

The first step in most applications of mathematics involves determining an appropriate mathematical model of the system being studied. A mathematical model consists of both symbolic notation (i.e., symbols and an agreement as to what the symbols mean) and relations among the symbols. The relations we propose depend on what we are willing to assume about the situation being studied.

Many of the situations in which mathematical concepts and methods are applied in the management, social, and life sciences involve quantities which are assumed to be related to each other through one or more linear equations. To illustrate the ideas, suppose we have two quantities, and let them be denoted by x and y. A linear expression or linear function of the variables x and y is an expression of the form $Ax + By$, where A and B are numbers. We say that x and y satisfy a *linear equation* if there are numbers A, B, and C such that $Ax + By = C$. For instance, $4x - 3y$ is a linear expression, and $3x + 2y = 6$ is a linear equation. On the other hand, $4x^2 - 2y$ and $x + (3/y)$ are not linear expressions in variables x and y. Mathematical models in which the assumptions lead to linear expressions and linear equations are included in a class known as *linear models*. The term "linear" refers to the geometric concept of a line.

As an example, suppose we have a manufacturing plant which uses electricity in the manufacturing process as well as in the administrative office. Suppose that the office uses 6000 kilowatthours each month and production requires 400 kilowatthours for each unit of product produced. Then if x denotes the number of units of product produced in a month and y denotes the amount of electricity used in that month, then x and y are related by $y = 400x + 6000$. Since this is equivalent to $-400x + y = 6000$, which is of the form $Ax + By = C$ with $A = -400$, $B = 1$, and $C = 6000$, we see that x and y satisfy a linear equation.

Notice that we have made several implicit assumptions in this discussion. First, we are assuming that the amount of electricity used in the office does not depend on the amount of manufacturing done. This is reasonable if the level of activity in the office is approximately the same no matter how much product is produced. Such an assumption is likely to be legitimate over a range of manufacturing levels, but is unlikely to be valid for all levels. For instance, if the manufacturing level is very low for an extended period, then the office staff may be reduced and electricity use would decline. Also, if the manufacturing level increases beyond that which can be supported by the present office staff, then new staff would be added, and this would involve a new level of office electricity use. Also, we are assuming that the same amount of electricity is needed to produce one unit of product independent of the level of production. This may not always be a legitimate assumption. For example, the manufacturing process may use less electricity to produce a unit of product when the process is operating at one level than at other levels. Indeed, it is common for manufacturing processes to have so-called optimal operating levels which are more efficient than levels either above or below. Another implicit assumption is that we know exactly how much electricity will be used by the office and in the manufacturing process. In practice, it would be rare indeed to have no variation in these quantities from one month to another. The fact that we take them to be constants is an assumption that needs to be carefully considered in light of the data actually available. In this example the relation $y = 400x + 6000$ is a mathematical model because it represents an idealized situation, a situation using precise notation and described by specific assumptions.

Another situation in which linear equations are common involves linear, or straight-line, depreciation. Suppose that you have a building whose original value is \$250,000 and whose useful life is 30 years and whose salvage value, i.e., the value after its useful life is over, is \$10,000. The depreciable value of the building is \$250,000 – \$10,000 = \$240,000. By using linear depreciation, one of several options available in most cases, the depreciation which can be claimed each year is the depreciable value of the building divided by its useful life, \$240,000 divided by 30, or \$8000. It follows that if we let y denote the depreciated value of the building measured in dollars after x years, then y and x are related by $y = 250{,}000 - 8000x$.

As we shall see, it is frequently useful to find values of variables which satisfy several linear equations simultaneously. Each such equation describes a specific relation among the variables, and satisfying several equations means that several relations hold simultaneously.

5.1 REVIEW OF EQUATIONS AND GRAPHS OF LINES

The basic expressions used in this chapter are linear equations and their graphs. In this section we review briefly the concepts for expressions with two variables, and we introduce similar ideas for expressions with three variables in Section 5.3.

For expressions with two variables, we use the familiar cartesian coordinate system shown in Figure 5.1*a* to associate pairs of numbers with points in a plane. If P is the label of the point (x, y), then the numbers x and y are the *coordinates* of point P. For example, for the point $P = (2, 1)$, 2 is the x coordinate and 1 is the y coordinate. Several other examples are shown in Figure 5.1*b*. We are especially interested in pairs (x, y) where x and y satisfy a linear equation, as illustrated in the following example.

Example 5.1 An instructor gives weekly quizzes in her mathematics course, and she seeks to find a relationship between the time required to prepare and grade a quiz and the number of students in the class. Her experience is that the average time required to prepare a quiz—to create the questions and write multiple versions—is 30 minutes, and the average time to grade each paper is 2 minutes. With this data, the relationship can be expressed as

Average time (in minutes) required = 30 + 2 (number of students in the class)

Problem Using the formula given above, graph average time required for classes with 20, 30, 50, and 100 students.

Solution We use a standard coordinate system, and we let

$$x = \text{number of students in the class}$$
$$y = \text{average time required in minutes}$$

FIGURE 5.1

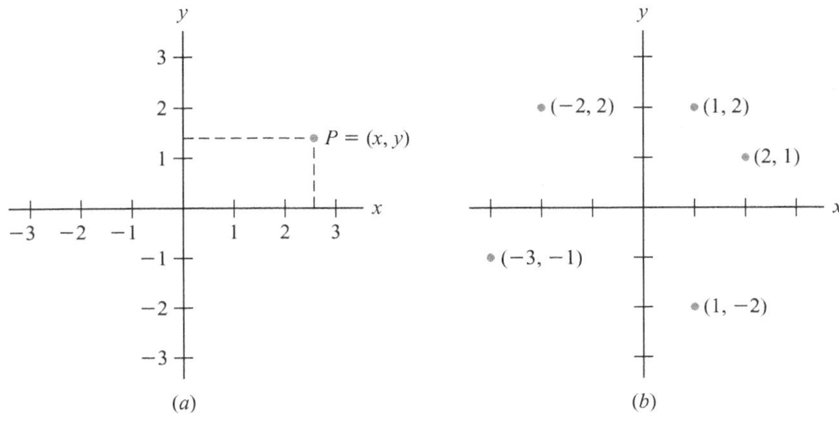

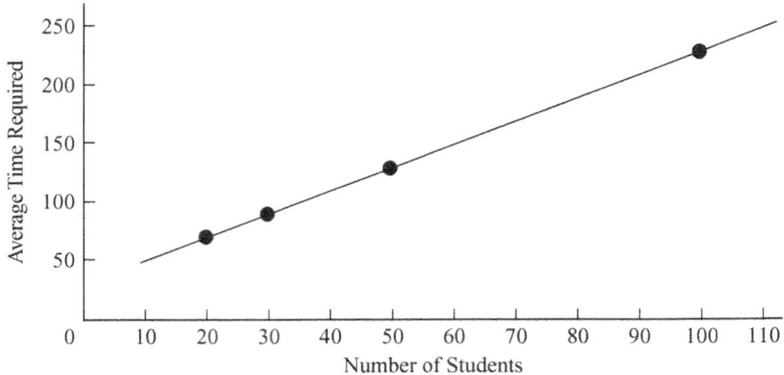

FIGURE 5.2

Then, the above relationship is $y = 30 + 2x$, and for $x = 20$, the formula predicts an average time of $30 + 2(20) = 70$ minutes. The points representing the pairs (x, y) for $x = 20$, 30, 50, and 100 are shown in Figure 5.2 as large dots, and the line $y = 30 + 2x$ is shown as a thin line for all values of x between 10 and 100. ■

Note that the formula used in Example 5.1 ($y = 30 + 2x$) is an example of a linear model with one variable, in this case x, the number of students. This model may or may not provide good predictions: it depends on the data used to create the model. Also, the predictions involve averages, and thus the formula may not give useful information about a specific quiz. Some quizzes may require more time and some may require less, and yet the model (the equation) may provide useful information when viewed as representative of a ''typical'' quiz.

The formula given in Example 5.1 is called a *linear model* because the graph of this equation is a line. To make our discussion precise, we define the term ''line'' in an algebraic way as a set of points which satisfy a certain type of equation. The geometric representation is the graph of this set on a cartesian coordinate system.

For any numbers A, B, and C with A and B not both zero, the set points

$$\{(x, y) : Ax + By = C\}$$

is a *line*. If (x_1, y_1) and (x_2, y_2) are two points on this line, i.e., if $Ax_1 + By_1 = C$ and $Ax_2 + By_2 = C$, then the line is referred to as the *line through* (x_1, y_1) *and* (x_2, y_2).

We emphasize that the point (x_1, y_1) lies on the line $Ax + By = C$ if $Ax_1 + By_1 = C$ and that the point does not lie on the line if $Ax_1 + By_1 \neq C$.

Example 5.2 The set of points (x, y) which satisfy the equation $x - 3y = 6$ is a line (take $A = 1, B = -3, C = 6$ in the above definition).

Problem Graph the line on a cartesian coordinate system.

Solution We recall that a line is determined by two points, and our approach to solving the problem is to find two points which lie on the line. That is, we find two points each of which satisfies the equation $x - 3y = 6$. To find points which satisfy the equation, we select a value of x and then find the value of y which satisfies $x - 3y = 6$. We have

$$y = \frac{x - 6}{3}$$

To illustrate the method, we take $x = 0$ and $x = 3$. For $x = 0$ we have $y = -2$, and for $x = 3$ we have $y = -1$. The points $(0, -2)$ and $(3, -1)$ and the line through them are shown on Figure 5.3. ■

It is customary to refer to the equation $Ax + By = C$ as a *line*, and we shall retain this custom where it is convenient. We mean, of course, the set of points $\{(x, y)\colon Ax + By = C\}$. The equation $Ax + By = C$ is known as the *general equation of a line* and as a linear equation in two variables.

It is often necessary to determine values for coefficients A, B, and C by using given information about the line, especially the x and y *intercepts* and the *slope*. If a line has the equation $Ax + By = C$ with $A \neq 0$, then it intersects the x axis in exactly one point, and that point is the x intercept. Likewise, if $B \neq 0$, then the line intersects the y axis in exactly one point, the y intercept. We obtain the x intercept by setting $y = 0$ in the equation of the line and solving for x, and

FIGURE 5.3

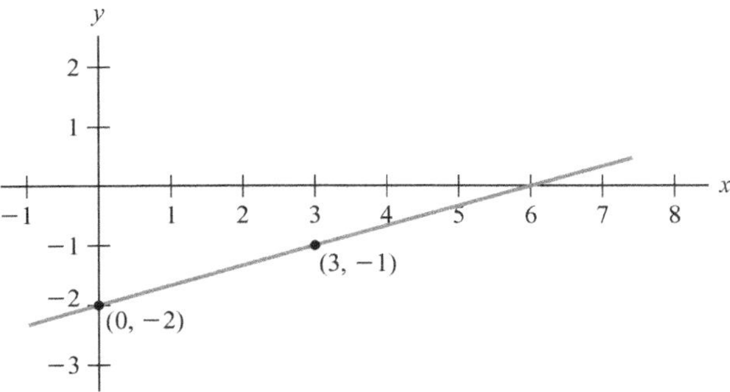

we obtain the y intercept by setting $x = 0$ and solving for y. In Example 5.2, we have the line $x - 3y = 6$, and to find the x intercept we set $y = 0$. The x intercept is 6. Similarly, the y intercept is -2. Using the same method on a line whose general equation is $Ax + By = C$, we have the following result.

The line $Ax + By = C$ has an x intercept if $A \neq 0$ and the x intercept is C/A. The line has a y intercept if $B \neq 0$, and the y intercept is C/B.

If $C = 0$ and both intercepts exist ($A \neq 0$ and $B \neq 0$), then both intercepts are 0. If $C \neq 0$ and $A = 0$, then the line does not intersect the x axis and therefore has no x intercept. If $C \neq 0$ and $B = 0$, then the line does not intersect the y axis and therefore has no y intercept.

Note The intercept of a line on an axis can be denoted by a single number, such as the x intercept is 2, or by the pair (2, 0) giving the point of intersection in the plane.

Example 5.3 Find the x and y intercepts of the line $3x + 2y = 12$, and graph the line.

Solution We set $y = 0$ to find the x intercept:

$$\begin{aligned} 3x + 2(0) &= 12 \\ 3x &= 12 \\ x &= 4 \end{aligned}$$

Similarly, the y intercept is $y = 6$. The line is determined by two points, and we know that the points (4, 0) and (0, 6) lie on the line. The line is shown in Figure 5.4. ■

FIGURE 5.4

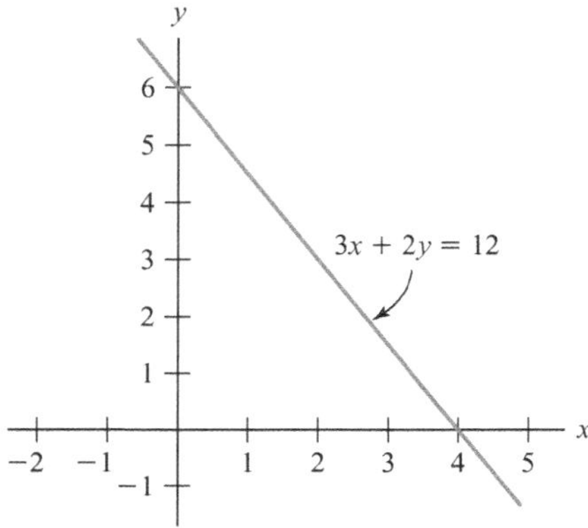

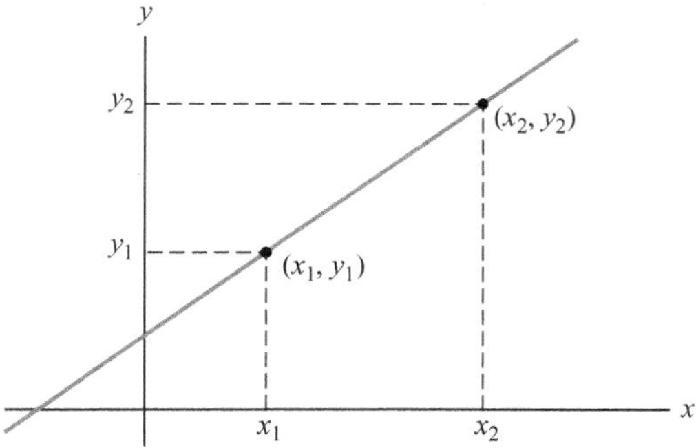

FIGURE 5.5

A line is determined by two distinct points, for instance, (x_1, y_1) and (x_2, y_2) in Figure 5.5. It is also determined by one point and its inclination or slope.

The *slope* of a line is the ratio of the difference of the y coordinates to the difference of the x coordinates of any two distinct points on the line, whenever the latter difference is not zero. That is, if (x_1, y_1) and (x_2, y_2) are two distinct points on a line, with $x_1 \neq x_2$, then the slope m of the line is

$$m = \frac{y_2 - y_1}{x_2 - x_1} \tag{5.1}$$

If $x_2 = x_1$ and $y_2 \neq y_1$, then the line is vertical and its slope is not defined. The slope m of a line does not depend on the choice of the points (x_1, y_1) and (x_2, y_2) used in formula (5.1).

Example 5.4 Find the slope of the line with the equation $x + 2y = 4$.

Solution The intercepts of $x + 2y = 4$ are (4, 0) and (0, 2). Thus, using these two points in Equation (5.1), we compute the slope to be

$$m = \frac{0 - 2}{4 - 0} = -\frac{1}{2}$$ ■

In Example 5.4 we showed that the line whose equation is $x + 2y = 4$ has slope $-\frac{1}{2}$. This number can be obtained directly from the equation by taking $-A/B$, where $A = 1$ and $B = 2$. Such a technique always works, and we have

If $B \neq 0$, the slope of the line $Ax + By = C$ is $m = -A/B$. If $B = 0$, the slope is not defined.

Both methods of determining the slope of a line (using two points and using the formula $-A/B$) always give the same value.

Example 5.5 Find the slope of the line $x - 3y = 6$

(a) By using the formula $m = -A/B$

(b) By using Equation (5.1) and the two points $(1, -\frac{5}{3})$ and $(2, -\frac{4}{3})$

Solution (a) In the equation $x - 3y = 6$, we have $A = 1$ and $B = -3$. Hence the slope is $m = (-1)/(-3) = \frac{1}{3}$.

(b) We label the first of the given points as (x_1, y_1) and the second as (x_2, y_2). Then we get

$$m = \frac{y_2 - y_1}{x_2 - x_1} = \frac{-\frac{5}{3} - (-\frac{4}{3})}{1 - 2} = \frac{-\frac{1}{3}}{-1} = \frac{1}{3}$$

■

Remark We would obtain the same result if we labeled the first point as (x_2, y_2) and the second as (x_1, y_1). That is, the way the points used in Formula (5.1) are labeled does not affect the answer obtained.

Another useful form of the equation of a line is the *slope-intercept* form $y = mx + b$. To derive this form of the equation, we begin with the general equation $Ax + By = C$ and assume $B \neq 0$, so the slope is defined. Dividing the equation by B, we obtain $(A/B)x + y = C/B$. Next, subtracting $(A/B)x$ from both sides, we have

$$y = -\frac{A}{B}x + \frac{C}{B}$$

Notice here that $-A/B$ is the slope of the line and C/B is the y intercept. Thus we have

$$y = -\frac{A}{B}x + \frac{C}{B} = mx + b$$

In the equation $y = mx + b$, the number m is always the slope of the line and b is always the y intercept.

We emphasize that there is exactly one line through two points and there is exactly one line through a point with a specified slope. Another way of saying this is that a line is uniquely determined by two points or by one point and a slope.

We use the concept of slope to define the term "parallel."

Two lines are *parallel* if they have the same slope or if the slope is undefined for both.

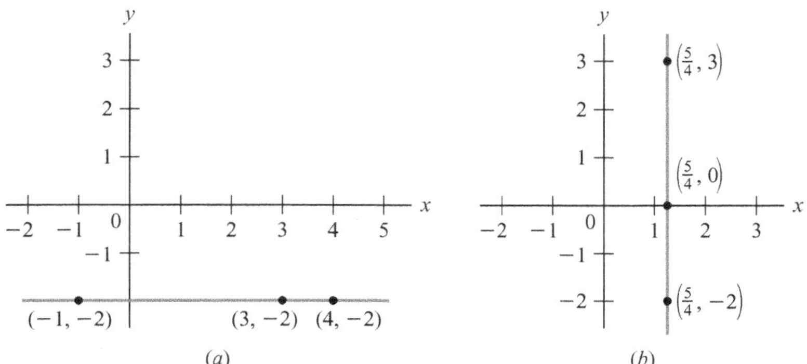

FIGURE 5.6

In Section 5.2 we will relate this definition of parallel to the geometric notion that parallel lines do not cross. If two lines are not parallel, then they intersect. The problem of determining the point (or points) of intersection is considered in the next section.

To complete our study of the slope of a line, we must consider the case of a line $Ax + By = C$ when either $A = 0$ or $B = 0$. According to the definition of a line, at least one of A and B must be different from 0 (Exercise 24 of this section). The equation of a line with $A = 0$ is $By = C$ with $B \neq 0$. Every point of the form $(x, C/B)$ satisfies this equation. Thus if the equation is $-3y = 6$, then $(-1, -2)$, $(3, -2)$, and $(4, -2)$ are all solutions. The graph determined by the equation $-3y = 6$ is a line parallel to the x axis which intersects the y axis at the point -2 (Figure 5.6*a*). The slope is 0.

It remains to consider the equation $Ax = C$, $A \neq 0$. Every point of the form $(C/A, y)$ satisfies the equation. Thus if the equation is $4x = 5$, the points $(\frac{5}{4}, -2)$, $(\frac{5}{4}, 0)$, and $(\frac{5}{4}, 3)$ are solutions of the equation. The graph determined by $4x = 5$ is the line parallel to the y axis which intersects the x axis at the point $\frac{5}{4}$ (Figure 5.6*b*). Since $B = 0$, the slope is not defined.

We conclude our discussion of lines with three typical problems.

Example 5.6 Find the equation of the line through the points (3, 2) and (−1, 0).

Solution Using the given points, we find that the line has the slope

$$m = \frac{2 - 0}{3 - (-1)} = \frac{2}{4} = \frac{1}{2}$$

Therefore, in slope-intercept form, the equation of the line is

$$y = \tfrac{1}{2}x + b$$

To find b, the y intercept, we use the fact that the point (3, 2) is on the line. That is, $x = 3$ and $y = 2$ must satisfy $y = \frac{1}{2}x + b$. It follows that

$$2 = \tfrac{1}{2}(3) + b$$

and therefore $b = \frac{1}{2}$. The desired equation is

$$y = \tfrac{1}{2}x + \tfrac{1}{2}$$

Other forms of the same equation are $2y = x + 1$ and $x = 2y - 1$. ■

Example 5.7 Find the general equation of the line which is parallel to the line $4x - 2y = 3$ and which has x intercept equal to $\frac{1}{2}$.

Solution Using the formula $m = -A/B$, we find that the slope of the line $4x - 2y = 3$ is $(-4)/(-2) = 2$. Thus the line we seek also has slope 2, and the equation has the form $y = 2x + b$. Since the x intercept is $\frac{1}{2}$, the point $(\frac{1}{2}, 0)$ is on the line. Using this, we find $0 = 2(\frac{1}{2}) + b = 1 + b$, and thus $b = -1$. The equation is $y = 2x - 1$. Written in general form, it is $-2x + y = -1$. ■

Example 5.8 Suppose that the cost of an airline ticket is related to the distance traveled by a linear equation. The cost of a 200-mile flight is \$76, and the cost of a 350-mile flight is \$100.

Problem Find the equation relating cost and distance, and find the cost of a 275-mile flight.

Solution Let

$$x = \text{distance of the flight in miles}$$
$$y = \text{cost of the flight in dollars}$$

The slope of the line through the points (200, 76) and (350, 100) is $\frac{4}{25}$, and therefore the slope-intercept form of the equation of the line through these points is $y = \frac{4}{25}x + b$. Using the fact that (200, 76) satisfies this equation, we can evaluate b. We find $b = 44$. Since y = cost (in dollars) and x = distance (in miles),

$$\text{Cost} = \tfrac{4}{25}(\text{distance}) + 44$$

The cost of a 275-mile flight (in dollars) is

$$\tfrac{4}{25}(275) + 44 = 88$$ ■

It frequently happens that we are interested in a situation in which there is one linear relation between the quantities being studied for certain values of the variables x and y, and another relation for other values of the variables. For example, there might be one relation for values of x satisfying $x \leq 1$ and another relation for values of x satisfying $x > 1$. This idea is illustrated in the following example.

Example 5.9 An internet service provider offers web hosting services at a rate of \$20 per web page for the first 10 web pages purchased. Orders for more than 10 web pages receive a discount of 15 percent on each web page purchased beyond the tenth.

Problem Find an expression for the cost of an order of x web pages, graph that cost as a function of x, and use that expression to find the cost of an order for 18 web pages.

Solution Let y denote the cost of purchasing x web pages. From the given information, for orders of 10 web pages or less, the cost is \$20 for each web page, and therefore a total of \$20x. Each web page beyond 10 costs $20 - 20(.15) =$ \$17 per web page, and if the order x is greater than 10, then the cost of \$17 applies to $x - 10$ web pages. Therefore, for orders of more than 10 web pages, the cost is \$200 for the first 10 web pages plus \$17 for each web page beyond 10. If we let y denote the total cost of an order, then we have

$$y = \begin{cases} 20x, & \text{for } x \leq 10 \\ 200 + 17(x - 10) & \text{for } x > 10 \end{cases}$$

The graph of this relation is a straight line for values of x at most 10, and a different straight line for values of x greater than 10. The straight lines are shown in Figure 5.7 for $0 \leq x \leq 22$. The cost for an order of 18 web pages is

$$200 + 17(18 - 10) = 200 + 136 = 336.$$

■

FIGURE 5.7

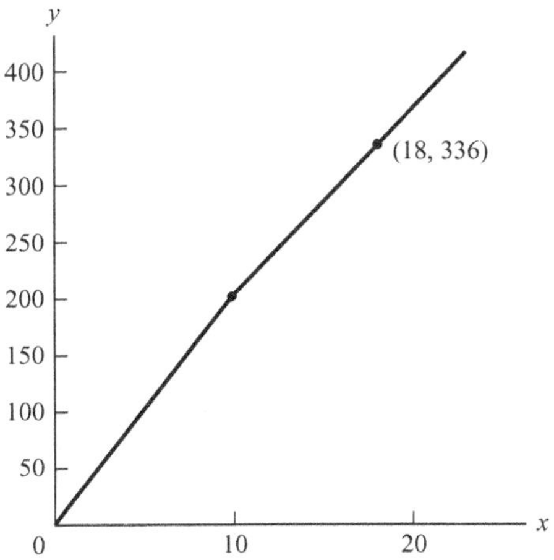

Exercises for Section 5.1

1. Graph the line whose equation is
   (*a*) $3x - 4y = 12$ (*b*) $2x + 6y = 6$
2. Graph the line whose equation is
   (*a*) $-5x - 2y = 20$ (*b*) $x - 3y = 0$
3. Find the x and y intercepts of each of the following lines and graph the lines:
   (*a*) $2x - y = 4$ (*b*) $y - 5 = 0$
   (*c*) $-x + 3y = 9$ (*d*) $x = -2$
4. On a cartesian coordinate system, draw the line through the points $(-4, 9)$ and $(4, -3)$.
5. On a cartesian coordinate system, draw the line through the points $(-3, 3)$ and $(1, 1)$. Also draw the line through the points $(-3, -3)$ and $(1, 1)$.
6. Find the x and y intercepts of each of the following lines and graph the lines.
   (*a*) $2x - y = 1$ (*b*) $2x - y = 0$
   (*c*) $y = 3x + 7$ (*d*) $x = 5$
7. Find the slope of the line through each of the following pairs of points.
   (*a*) $(2, -2), (5, 3)$ (*b*) $(-1, 3), (0, 5)$
8. Find the slope, x intercept, and y intercept of the line whose equation is $3x - 6y = -24$.
9. Find the slope, x intercept, and y intercept of the line whose equation is $x = 4y - 6$.
10. Find the slope of the line through each of the following pairs of points.
    (*a*) $(7, 3), (-1, 2)$ (*b*) $(3, -5), (1, 2)$
11. Find the equation of the line through each of the following pairs of points and graph each line.
    (*a*) $(1, 3), (4, 1)$ (*b*) $(-3, -1), (1, 3)$
12. Suppose that the cost of a truck rental is related to the number of days the truck is rented by a linear equation: the cost of a 2-day rental is \$105 and the cost of a 6-day rental is \$285.
    (*a*) Find the cost of a 7-day rental.
    (*b*) If a particular rental costs \$510, then for how many days was the truck rented?
13. Suppose that the weight of a cargo ship is linearly related to the number of storage crates that are onboard: the weight of the ship is 70 tons if there are 200 storage crates onboard, and the weight of the ship is 100 tons if there are 350 storage crates onboard. Find the weight of the ship when there are 400 storage crates onboard.
14. State the equation of the line with
    (*a*) Slope -3 and containing the point $(1, 0)$
    (*b*) Slope 0 and containing the point $(1, -2)$
    (*c*) Slope not defined and containing the point $(3, 2)$
15. Find the equation of the line through the point $(-2, -1)$ and parallel to the line through the points $(2, 3)$ and $(4, 1)$. Graph both lines.
16. The cost of paving a parking lot is linearly related to the area paved. Suppose that the cost of paving a 1,000 square foot lot is \$1,200 and the cost of paving a 1,500 square foot lot is \$1,600.
    (*a*) If the cost of paving a lot is \$840, then how large is that lot?
    (*b*) Find the cost of paving an 1,800 square foot lot.

17. Production records indicate that the number of defective basketballs produced on a certain production line is related by a linear equation to the total number of basketballs produced. Suppose that 10 defective balls are produced on a day when a total of 300 balls are produced, and 15 defective balls are produced on a day when a total of 425 balls are produced.
    (*a*) How many defective balls will there be on a day when a total of 500 balls are produced?
    (*b*) The production manager wants to produce as many basketballs as possible without producing more than 25 defective balls. What total production should be scheduled?
18. A customer service phone operator for a large software company is paid a base salary of \$750 per week plus \$15 for every customer helped.
    (*a*) Find an equation that expresses the relationship between the worker's weekly salary and the number of customers helped during a given week.
    (*b*) If the worker helps 40 customers one week, then how much will he be paid?
    (*c*) If the worker makes \$1,650 one week, then how many customers did he help that week?
19. Find the equation of the line through the points (32, 0) and (212, 100), and graph this line. What is the slope of this line? This graph can be related to temperature scales. How should the axes be labeled to illustrate this relationship?
20. The following data give the year-by-year resale value of a car which costs \$30,000 when new.

Age, years	1	2	3	4	5
Resale value, \$	24,000	19,500	15,000	10,500	6,000

    (*a*) Is the function that relates the value of the car to the age of the car linear?
    (*b*) How much will the car be worth 5 years and 6 months after purchase (i.e., 5.5 years after purchase)?
21. A certain car can be rented at either of two different rates. Rate A is \$40 per day plus \$0.30 per mile driven, and Rate B is \$30 per day plus \$0.50 per mile driven.
    (*a*) Write equations which describe the cost (in dollars) of driving x miles in one day for each rate.
    (*b*) Which rate is less expensive for someone who plans to drive 30 miles in a single day?
    (*c*) Which rate is less expensive for someone who plans to drive 225 miles over a three day period?
    (*d*) How far must someone plan to drive on a single day for the cost of the two rates to be equal?
22. A linear equation of the form $Ax + By = C$ is such that $A = 2B = 3C$, where $A \neq 0$. Find an equation of the line.
23. Suppose a linear equation relates the cost of operating a duplicating machine to the number of copies produced. The cost for a month in which 20,000 copies are made is \$565.00, and the cost for a month in which 35,000 copies are made is \$940.00. If 14,000 copies are made in a month, find the monthly operating cost.

24. Suppose that the cost of leasing temporary office space is related to the length of the lease by a linear equation. Also, suppose that the cost of a 60-day lease is \$5000 and the cost of a 90-day lease is \$7250. If a start-up corporation has \$11,000 to use for office space, what length lease can be obtained?
25. The community of Mulberry is experiencing a water shortage, and the utilities board has implemented a surcharge to reduce water usage. The standard rate is \$4.00 per thousand gallons, and that rate will continue to apply to the first 3,000 gallons each month. However, for all water used beyond 3,000 gallons, customers will be charged \$5.50 per thousand gallons. Find an expression for the monthly cost for using x gallons of water, and graph that cost as a function of x.
26. At a particular track, a NASCAR driver is able to drive at a pace of 10 seconds for each one half mile driven. Write an equation that gives the distance, d, in miles, in terms of the time, t, in minutes, that the driver has been driving. How long will it take this driver to complete a 300 mile race when driving at this pace?
27. WiFi service at an airport costs \$0.25 per minute for the first 10 minutes of use. For each 10 minute period after the first 10 minutes, the price of service is doubled until 40 minutes of use is reached, at which time the service ends (that is, from 10 to 20 minutes, the cost is \$0.50 per minute, from 20 to 30 minutes, the cost is \$1.00 per minute, etc.).
    (*a*) Find an expression for the cost of using x minutes of WiFi service, and graph that cost as a function of x.
    (*b*) Find the cost of 37 minutes of WiFi service.
28. Suppose that the cost of leasing warehouse space is related to the amount of space by a linear equation. Also, suppose that the cost of leasing 6000 square feet is \$50,000 for one year and the cost of leasing 9000 square feet is \$72,500 for one year. Find the cost of leasing 8,000 square feet for one year.
29. Suppose that a line is defined by the equation $Ax + By = C$ with $B \neq 0$. Show that if (x_1, y_1) and (x_2, y_2) are two distinct points on this line, then $x_1 \neq x_2$.
30. Using the general equation of a line, suppose $A = B = 0$.
    (*a*) If $C = 0$, show that the solution set of $Ax + By = C$ is the entire xy plane.
    (*b*) If $C \neq 0$, show that the solution set of $Ax + By = C$ is the empty set.
    (Thus in neither case is the solution set a line.)

5.2 FORMULATION AND SOLUTION OF SYSTEMS OF LINEAR EQUATIONS IN TWO VARIABLES

An important part of the skill of using mathematics to solve problems is the ability to translate verbal expressions into mathematical expressions, usually equations. In this section, we consider several problems which can be translated into linear equations in two variables. We formulate these problems, and then we solve them. We begin with the following example.

Example 5.10 Burt's Beds decides to make giant rectangular beds for which the length is 20 percent longer than the width and for which the perimeter is 330 inches. What are the length and width of these beds?

Solution The length and width of the beds are unknowns, so it is natural to use these as our variables. Thus, let

$$x = \text{the length of the bed in inches}$$

and

$$y = \text{the width of the bed in inches}$$

Next, since the length x is to be 20 percent longer than the width y, we have the equation

$$x = y + .2y \tag{5.2}$$

Also, the perimeter of the bed $2x + 2y$ is known to be 330 inches, so we have the second equation

$$2x + 2y = 330 \tag{5.3}$$

Together, Equations (5.2) and (5.3) form a system of two equations in the two variables x and y. If we rewrite Equation (5.2) by adding the two terms in y, then an equivalent form of the two equations is

$$x = 1.2y \tag{5.4}$$
$$2x + 2y = 330 \tag{5.5}$$

We are interested in the solution of this system of equations, i.e., a pair of numbers (x, y) which satisfies both equations. Since each equation is the equation of a line, we are interested in a point on both lines, i.e., the point of intersection of the lines. A direct way of finding this point is to substitute Equation (5.4) into Equation (5.5) to obtain a single equation in the variable y and then solve for y. We obtain the following:

$$\begin{aligned} 2(1.2y) + 2y &= 330 \\ 4.4y &= 330 \\ y &= 75 \end{aligned}$$

Since $y = 75$, using Equation (5.4), we obtain $x = (1.2)(75) = 90$. Thus the length of the giant bed is 90 inches, and the width is 75 inches. ■

A graph of the lines in Example 5.10 is shown in Figure 5.8.

Example 5.11 Murphy's Muffin Shoppe makes two sizes of raisin muffins using prepackaged dough and raisins. Each large muffin uses 5 ounces of dough and 2 ounces of raisins, and each small muffin uses 2 ounces of dough and 1 ounce of raisins. Each day the shop receives 450 ounces of dough and 200 ounces of raisins.

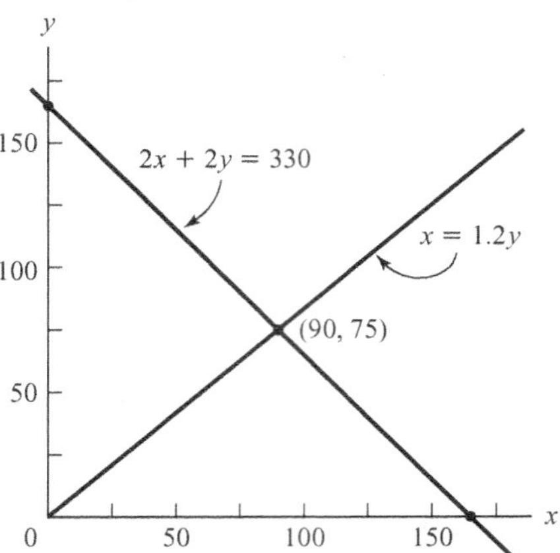

FIGURE 5.8

How many large muffins and small muffins should be baked each day to use up all the dough and all the raisins?

Solution The unknowns in this problem are the number of large muffins to be baked and the number of small muffins to be baked. Thus, we specify variables x and y as follows:

$x =$ the number of large muffins to be baked each day
$y =$ the number of small muffins to be baked each day

Next, we describe the conditions that x and y must satisfy due to the limited amounts of dough and raisins. Each large muffin uses 5 ounces of dough, so x large muffins require $5x$ ounces of dough. Also, each small muffin uses 2 ounces of dough, so y small muffins require $2y$ ounces of dough. Thus, the total amount of dough used by x large muffins and y small muffins is $5x + 2y$. Since 450 ounces of dough are available each day, x and y must satisfy the equation

$$5x + 2y = 450 \tag{5.6}$$

Reasoning in the same way for raisins, we see that x large muffins and y small muffins use a total of $2x + y$ ounces of raisins. There are 200 ounces of raisins available each day, so x and y must satisfy

$$2x + y = 200 \tag{5.7}$$

Equations (5.6) and (5.7) must be satisfied at the same time, and since they are both equations of lines, we are looking for a point, i.e., a pair (x, y), which lies on both lines. To find the values of x and y at the intersection of these two lines, we once again express one of the variables in terms of the other and then substitute to obtain a single equation in one variable. Using (5.7), we have $y = 200 - 2x$, and substituting this into Equation (5.6) gives $5x + 2(200 - 2x) = 450$ or, equivalently, $5x + 400 - 4x = 450$, which in turn gives $x = 50$. Finally, using Equation (5.7) with $x = 50$, we have $y = 200 - 2(50) = 100$. Thus, Murphy should bake 50 large muffins and 100 small muffins in order to use all the dough and all the raisins. ■

Note In Example 5.11, the values obtained for variables x and y are integers, 50 and 100. However, it is easy to modify the problem so that this is not the case, and in such situations the answer would not be a practical one for the baker.

Example 5.12 Two communications satellites are launched simultaneously and are circling the earth following the same circular orbital path, which has a length of 24,000 miles. One satellite is traveling at a rate of 3,000 miles per one half hour, and the other satellite is travelling at 3,600 miles per one half hour.

Problem How far has the slower satellite travelled at the time when the faster satellite catches up to the slower satellite?

Solution The faster satellite covers 3,600 miles in 30 minutes, or 3600/30 miles/minute, so a formula that relates distance covered in miles to time of travel in minutes, for the faster satellite, is

$$d = \frac{3600}{30} t \tag{5.8}$$

where t is measured in minutes and d is measured in miles. A similar formula for the slower satellite gives

$$d = \frac{3000}{30} t \tag{5.9}$$

To solve the problem posed, we need to find the distance d traveled by the faster satellite when it has made exactly one more revolution (i.e., traveled exactly 24,000 miles farther) than the slower satellite. To find this distance, we first find the time that the satellites have been traveling when the faster satellite catches the slower satellite. To do this, we add 24,000 miles to Equation (5.9), the distance traveled by the slower satellite plus one orbital revolution, and then we set this equal to the distance traveled by the faster satellite. This gives

$$\frac{3000}{30}t + 24,000 = \frac{3600}{30}t$$

Solving this equation for t gives $t = 1,200$ minutes. To complete the solution, we use $t = 1,200$ minutes in Equation (5.9), and this gives $d = (3000/30)1200 = 120,000$ miles. Note that the faster satellite has travelled $d = (3600/30)1200 = 144,000$ miles, which is the distance travelled by the slower satellite, plus one orbital revolution. ■

In Examples 5.10, 5.11, and 5.12, we used basic algebraic techniques to solve two equations in two variables. In each case, we obtained a single value for x and a single value for y, and we noted that since each equation represented a line, we had found the point of intersection of the two lines. However, not all pairs of lines intersect in a single point. If the lines are parallel but different, then they do not intersect—they have no points in common; and if the two algebraic equations represent the same geometric line (set of points), then the two equations have infinitely many points in common. Our goal is to develop a method to solve all systems of linear equations, including those with more than two variables and/or more than two equations. Here by the word ''solve'' we mean that we find the set of points which satisfy all the equations of the system. Of course, one possibility is that this set is empty, in which case we say that the system has no solution. In this section we consider the case of two variables, and in Section 5.3 we consider the general case.

There are several methods for solving systems of equations in two variables, and we used one of them above in solving the systems of Examples 5.10, 5.11, and 5.12. This method is called the *substitution method* since it is based on using one equation to obtain an expression for one variable in terms of the other variable and then substituting that expression into the other equation to obtain a new equation with only one variable. The substitution method is simple and easy to use, and most students have used it in high school. However, the method is not a general one, and it is of limited value for the more general systems studied later in this chapter and in Chapter 8. Therefore, we also present a second method, called the *reduction method*, which can be used for all linear systems. First, however, we illustrate the substitution method with two more examples.

Example 5.13 Solve the system of equations

$$\begin{aligned} x - y &= 6 \\ -2x + 2y &= 5 \end{aligned} \tag{5.10}$$

and graph the lines described by these equations.

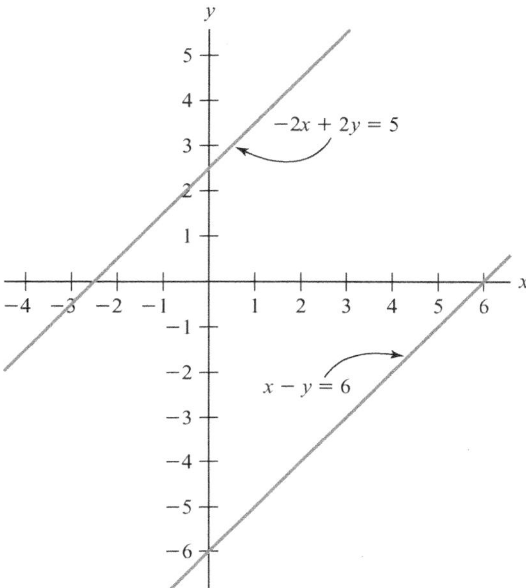

FIGURE 5.9

Solution We solve the first equation for x in terms of y. This gives

$$x = 6 + y$$

That is, if (x, y) is a solution of the system, then x and y must be related as $x = 6 + y$. Now use this expression for x in the left-hand side of the second equation:

$$-2x + 2y = -2(6 + y) + 2y = -12 - 2y + 2y = -12$$

We have shown that if (x, y) satisfies the first equation, then for that (x, y) the left-hand side of the second equation is -12. But the right-hand side of the second equation is 5. Therefore, we have shown that if (x, y) satisfies the first equation, it *cannot* satisfy the second ($-12 \neq 5$). The system has no solution (no point of intersection), and the lines described by Equations (5.10) are parallel. They are shown in Figure 5.9. ■

We note that if Equations (5.10) are written in slope-intercept form, we have

$$y = x - 6$$
$$y = x + \tfrac{5}{2}$$

Thus both lines have slope $m = 1$, and we see immediately that they are parallel.

There is one more case that can arise.

Example 5.14 Solve the system of equations

$$x - y = 3$$
$$-3x + 3y = -9$$

Solution We solve the first equation for x:

$$x = 3 + y$$

Substituting this expression for x into the left-hand side of the second equation, we have

$$-3x + 3y = -3(3 + y) + 3y = -9 - 3y + 3y = -9$$

That is, if (x, y) satisfies the first equation, then the left-hand side of the second equation is -9 and the second equation is automatically satisfied. Therefore, all points which satisfy the first equation also satisfy the second equation. This fact also follows from the observation that the second equation is simply -3 times the first equation. We conclude that for *every value of* y the pair $(x, y) = (3 + y, y)$ is a solution of both equations. Thus there are infinitely many solutions, and the two equations describe the same line. It is shown in Figure 5.10. ■

To summarize our last three examples, we have now shown that there are at least three types of results that arise when we solve a system of two equations in two variables. In fact, these are the only possible results. First, the system

FIGURE 5.10

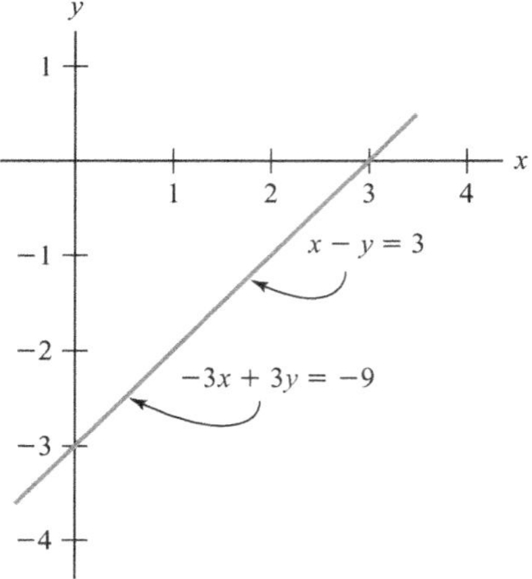

may describe two lines which intersect in a single point (as in Example 5.12). This point is the solution of the system. Second, the system may describe two parallel lines, line which do not meet (as in Example 5.13). In this case the system is said to be *inconsistent*, and the solution set is empty. Third, the system may consist of two equations which describe the same line (as in Example 5.14). The solution set in this case consists of infinitely many points, namely, all points on this line. In the first and third cases (one point common and infinitely many points common to the two lines), the system is said to be *consistent*.

The substitution method is useful primarily for systems of two equations in two variables. For more general systems, another method is needed. The *reduction method*, which is developed in Section 5.3 for systems with more than two variables, can also be used to solve systems of two equations in two variables. The basic idea of the method is to transform the given system into one new system after another until we obtain a system whose solution is obvious. In particular, our goal will be a system in which each equation contains a single variable. Since the number of variables in each equation has been reduced, our method is called the reduction method.

To carry out the reduction method, we use two basic operations:

1. Multiply any equation (both sides of the equals sign) by a number different from zero.
2. Replace any equation by the sum of that equation and any multiple of another equation.

That is, operation 1 means that if E is an equation in a system, then E can be replaced by kE, where k is any number different from 0. Operation 2 means that if E and F are equations in a system, then F can be replaced by $F + kE$, where k is any number. These operations form the basis of the methods discussed in Section 5.3.

The reduction method works because the use of these two operations does not change the set of solutions of a system of equations.

Example 5.15 Solve the system of equations

$$\begin{aligned} 2x + 4y &= 6 \\ 3x - 6y &= 1 \end{aligned} \tag{5.11}$$

Solution We solve this system by converting it into one new system after another, using operations 1 and 2. Our goal is to reach a system whose solution is obvious, i.e., one in which each equation contains a single variable.

First we obtain a system in which the second equation contains a single variable. We begin our conversion process by multiplying the first equation of (5.11) by $\frac{1}{2}$, an operation of type 1. Our goal is to replace the original system by one in which the coefficient of x (the number multiplied by x) in the first equation is 1. We have

$$\begin{aligned} x + 2y &= 3 \\ 3x - 6y &= 1 \end{aligned}$$

Next, we multiply the first equation in this new system by -3 and add the result to the second equation. We obtain an equation which contains only the variable y:

$$-12y = -8$$

We obtain a new system by replacing the second equation by $-12y = -8$.

$$\begin{aligned} x + 2y &= 3 \\ -12y &= -8 \end{aligned}$$

This second replacement has been accomplished by an operation of type 2. We have succeeded in converting the original system to a new system in which the second equation contains a single variable. Now we divide both sides of the second equation in the last system by -12 to obtain the system

$$\begin{aligned} x + 2y &= 3 \\ y &= \tfrac{2}{3} \end{aligned}$$

Now we convert the last system to one in which the first equation also contains a single variable. To do so, we multiply the second equation by -2 and add the result to the first equation. We obtain an equation which contains only the variable x:

$$x = \tfrac{5}{3}$$

Finally, we replace the first equation by $x = \frac{5}{3}$, and hence we have converted the original system to one in which each equation contains a single variable:

$$\begin{aligned} x &= \tfrac{5}{3} \\ y &= \tfrac{2}{3} \end{aligned}$$

The solution of this system is obvious. The point $(x, y) = (\frac{5}{3}, \frac{2}{3})$ is the only solution of the original system. In other words, there is only one point common to the two lines, and it is $P = (\frac{5}{3}, \frac{2}{3})$. The lines (5.11) and the point P are shown in Figure 5.11. ■

The reduction method also enables us to identify those systems which have no solutions.

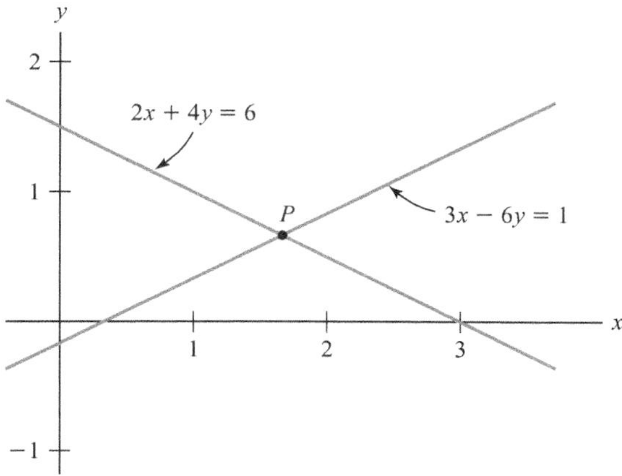

FIGURE 5.11

Example 5.16 Solve the system of equations

$$\begin{aligned} 8x - 4y &= 16 \\ 2x - y &= 0 \end{aligned} \tag{5.12}$$

Solution We begin our conversion of the system (5.12) by dividing the first equation by 8 (the coefficient is x) and using the result as a new first equation. The resulting system is

$$\begin{aligned} x - \tfrac{1}{2}y &= 2 \\ 2x - y &= 0 \end{aligned} \tag{5.13}$$

The next step is to eliminate the variable x from the second equation in the system (5.13). We do this by multiplying the first equation by -2, adding it to the second equation, and using this sum as a new second equation. We have

$$\begin{aligned} x - \tfrac{1}{2}y &= 2 \\ 0 &= -4 \end{aligned} \tag{5.14}$$

At this stage we stop the process because $0 \neq -4$, and we conclude that the system (5.14) *has no solutions*. Since the solution set of the system remains unchanged during the conversions from one system to another, we conclude that the original system has no solutions. The lines described by the system (5.12) are parallel. ■

Finally, the reduction method also enables us to identify those systems which have infinitely many solutions and to obtain the solution sets for such systems.

We conclude with a final example of the use of the reduction method.

Example 5.17 Margaret's Mountain Shop prepares two types of trail mix—Hiker's Special mix and Mountain Mix. One package of Hiker's Special mix requires 40 grams of peanuts and 20 grams of raisins. One package of Mountain Mix requires 20 grams of peanuts and 60 grams of raisins. Margaret has 800 grams of peanuts and 1200 grams of raisins.

Problem Find the number of packages of each type of trail mix Margaret should prepare to use all the peanuts and all the raisins.

Solution There are two unknown quantities to determine: the number of packages of each type of trail mix to prepare. Let

$x =$ the number of packages of Hiker's Special mix to prepare
$y =$ the number of packages of Mountain Mix to prepare

Since each package of Hiker's Special mix requires 40 grams of peanuts, x packages will require $40x$ grams of peanuts, and since each package of Mountain Mix requires 20 grams of peanuts, y packages requires $20y$ grams. There are 800 grams of peanuts available, and if all are used, then we must have

$$40x + 20y = 800$$

Using the same reasoning for raisins, we have

$$20x + 60y = 1200$$

Thus the problem is to find values of x and y that satisfy the system of equations

$$\begin{aligned} 40x + 20y &= 800 \\ 20x + 60y &= 1200 \end{aligned}$$

From the setting, we are interested only in solutions for which $x \geq 0$ and $y \geq 0$.

Using the reduction method, we transform the system successively as follows: Multiply the first equation by $\frac{1}{40}$ and use the result as a new first equation.

$$\begin{aligned} x + .5y &= 20 \\ 20x + 60y &= 1200 \end{aligned}$$

Next, multiply the first equation by -20, add it to the second equation, and use the result as a new second equation:

$$\begin{aligned} x + .5y &= 20 \\ 50y &= 800 \end{aligned}$$

Continuing, multiply the second equation by $\frac{1}{50}$, and use the result as a new second equation.

$$\begin{aligned} x + .5y &= 20 \\ y &= 16 \end{aligned}$$

Finally, multiply the second equation by $-.5$, add it to the first equation, and use the result as a new first equation:

$$\begin{aligned} x &= 12 \\ y &= 16 \end{aligned}$$

We conclude that Margaret should prepare 12 packages of Hiker's Special mix and 16 packages of Mountain Mix to use all the peanuts and raisins available. ■

Exercises for Section 5.2

For Exercises 1 through 4, formulate the problem as a system of linear equations in two variables. Be sure to define your variables.

1. Suppose that Burt's Beds makes a rectangular children's bed for which the length is 30 percent longer than the width and the sum of the length plus the width is 115 inches. Formulate a system of equations which can be used to find the length and width of the bed.
2. Suppose that Murphy's Muffin Shoppe decides to make both large and small bran muffins. Each large muffin uses 4 ounces of dough and 2 ounces of bran, while a small muffin uses 1 ounce of dough and 1 ounce of bran. Suppose also that there are 300 ounces of dough available each day and 160 ounces of bran. Formulate a system of equations to determine how many muffins of each size should be baked each day to use up all the dough and all the bran.
3. University Games, Inc., produces two types of computer games—adventure games and fantasy games. One adventure game requires 200 hours of time from the creative staff and 500 hours of time from the technical staff. One fantasy game requires 400 hours of time from the creative staff and 100 hours of time from the technical staff. The company has 16,800 hours of time from the creative staff and 6,000 hours of time from the technical staff. Formulate a system of equations to determine how many games of each type should be produced to use all staff time available.
4. A terrarium contains only spiders, which have 8 legs each, and beetles, which have six legs each. If there are 19 creatures and 128 legs in the terrarium, then how many spiders and how many beetles are in the terrarium?
5. In the setting of Example 5.17, suppose that Margaret also has sunflower seeds available, and that in addition to peanuts and raisins, she proposes to add 6 grams of sunflower seeds to each package of Hiker's Special mix and 5 grams of sunflower seeds to each package of Mountain Mix. Suppose that she has 12 kilograms of peanuts, 18 kilograms of raisins, and 2.7 kilograms of sunflower seeds to be used. Margaret would like to know whether she can use all the peanuts, raisins, and sunflower seeds to produce these types of trail mix. Formulate a system of equations

that expresses Margaret's goal. That is, a system of equations whose solution provides the number of packages of each type of trail mix that should be produced to use all the peanuts, raisins, and sunflower seeds.

For Exercises 6 through 10, solve each of the two systems of equations and graph the lines.

6. (*a*) $\begin{aligned} 5x \quad\quad &= 20 \\ 3x + 2y &= 16 \end{aligned}$ (*b*) $\begin{aligned} 3x + 2y &= 16 \\ 3x - 2y &= 16 \end{aligned}$

7. (*a*) $\begin{aligned} 4x + 2y &= 3 \\ 6x + 3y &= -2 \end{aligned}$ (*b*) $\begin{aligned} x + 2y &= -1 \\ 3x - 6y &= 3 \end{aligned}$

8. (*a*) $\begin{aligned} 3x - 2y &= 3 \\ 3x - 8y &= -6 \end{aligned}$ (*b*) $\begin{aligned} 3x + y &= 8 \\ 3x - y &= 10 \end{aligned}$

9. (*a*) $\begin{aligned} 10x + 5y &= 20 \\ 6x + 3y &= 12 \end{aligned}$ (*b*) $\begin{aligned} -x + y &= 7 \\ 2x - y &= -8 \end{aligned}$

10. (*a*) $\begin{aligned} 3x - y &= -1 \\ -x + 3y &= 1 \end{aligned}$ (*b*) $\begin{aligned} 3x + 2y &= 16 \\ 12x + 8y &= 16 \end{aligned}$

11. Solve the problem formulated in Exercise 1.
12. Solve the problem formulated in Exercise 2.
13. Solve the problem formulated in Exercise 3.
14. Solve the problem formulated in Exercise 4.
15. A rapidly growing suburb has a population of 50,000 and is growing at the rate of 7500 people per year. The adjacent declining city has a population of 1,000,000 and is decreasing at a rate of 125,000 people per year. If these rates continue, in how many years will the population of the suburb equal the population of the city?
16. In calendar 2004, Division A of MegaStore increased its sales from \$1.5 billion to \$1.8 billion, and Division B increased its sales from \$600 million to \$1.0 billion. If each division continues to increase sales by these amounts, when will the two divisions have equal sales? What will be the common value of sales?
17. A lottery winner plans to invest part of her \$1,000,000 in utility bonds paying 12 percent per year and the rest in a savings account paying 8 percent per year.
    (*a*) How much should be allocated to each investment if the yearly incomes from the two investments are to be the same?
    (*b*) How much should be allocated to each investment if the income from the savings account is to be twice the income from the utility bonds?
    (*c*) How much should be allocated to each investment if the income from utility bonds is to be \$10,000 more than the income from the savings account?
18. At a zoo, a baby elephant weighs 140 pounds and is gaining 12 pounds per week. One of the zoo keepers at the zoo weighs 220 pounds and is losing 4 pounds per week. In how many weeks will their weights be equal?
19. Stewart Dent's backpack holds 270 cubic inches of supplies, and he has \$146 to spend on camp food at the local outfitter. He only needs two things: dehydrated camp dinners, each of which costs \$8 and takes up 10 cubic inches of space; and

water bottles, each of which costs \$5 and takes up 15 cubic inches of space. How many camp dinners and water bottles should Stewart buy if he wants to spend all of his money and use all of the available space in his backpack?

20. Two cars start from the same place and begin traveling east along a road at noon, one at 60 mph, and the other at 80 mph. What time will it be when the faster car is exactly 90 miles ahead of the slower car.
21. On January 1, 2015, Carly wins \$100,000 in the lottery, and she invests the entire amount in two stocks, stock X and stock Y. At the end of 2015, she sells both stocks for a total profit of \$24,000. If she earned 10 percent on stock X and 30 percent of stock Y, how much did she invest in each stock?
22. In the situation of Exercise 21, suppose that on January 1, 2016, Carly invests the \$124,000 in the same two stocks, and at the end of 2016, she sells both stocks and finds she has lost \$24,000. In 2016, she loses 10 percent on stock X, and she loses 30 percent on stock Y. How much did she invest in each stock in 2016?
23. Janet and Michael decide to pool their money for investments. They will invest a total of \$10,000,000, and it is all to be in stocks, bonds, and real estate. Suppose that the amount in stocks must be twice the amount in bonds, and the amount in stocks and bonds together must be 3 times the amount in real estate. How should their money be distributed among the three areas?
24. For what numbers a and b is this system of equations satisfied for $x = b$ and $y = a$?

$$\begin{aligned} x - 3y &= a \\ 2x + 7y &= 5 \end{aligned}$$

25. For what numbers a and b is this system of equations satisfied by $x = 1$ and $y = b$?

$$\begin{aligned} ax + y &= 3 \\ -x + 2y &= 4 \end{aligned}$$

26. The system of equations

$$\begin{aligned} 3x - 2y &= -4 \\ -6x + ay &= 8 \end{aligned}$$

has a unique solution for all but one value of the number a. What is this exceptional value of a? How many solutions does the system have for this value of a?

27. Tom, Dick, and Harry are being questioned by the police after a robbery at a local fruit market. All three fit the descriptions of the fruit thief, and all three were seen at the market. The police ask each what he bought and how much he paid. Tom says he bought 20 apples and 20 oranges and paid \$8.00. Dick says he bought 15 apples and 5 oranges and paid \$6.75. Harry says he bought 10 apples and 25 oranges and paid \$11.00. After a short pause for computational purposes, the police released Dick and Harry but kept Tom for additional questioning. Why?
28. Murphy's Muffin Shoppe makes large and small apple-raisin muffins. A large apple-raisin muffin requires 5 ounces of dough, 2 ounces of apples, and 0.5 ounce of raisins. A small apple-raisin muffin requires 3 ounces of dough, 1 ounce of apples, and 0.3 ounce of raisins. Murphy has 270 ounces of dough, 100 ounces

of apples, and 30 ounces of raisins. How many muffins of each type can Murphy make to use all the dough and apples? If he does so, how many ounces of raisins remain unused?

29. In the setting of Exercise 28, suppose Murphy has only 25 ounces of raisins. Will he have enough raisins to use all the dough and apples? If not, find the number of large and small muffins he should make to use all the raisins.
30. In the situation described in Exercise 5, how many packages of each type of trail mix should be produced to use up all the peanuts and raisins? With this production, how many sunflower seeds remain unused?
31. River West Expeditions runs raft trips on the North Fork of the Trout River and through the Blue River Gorge. One trip on the North Fork requires 20 days of guide time and 50 hours of time from the support staff. One trip through the Blue Gorge requires 40 days of guide time and 10 hours of time from the support staff. The company has 1680 days of guide time and 600 hours of time from the support staff. There is a commitment to have at least 6 trips down the North Fork. Can the management schedule trips to use all of the time available and also meet a commitment for 6 trips down the North Fork?
32. In the setting of Exercise 31, suppose the management can arrange for additional time from the support staff. How many hours are necessary to enable the commitment to be met and all time used up?

5.3 FORMULATION AND SOLUTION OF SYSTEMS OF LINEAR EQUATIONS IN THREE OR MORE VARIABLES

Most problems involving linear equations have more than two unknown quantities. Consequently, it is important to develop methods to solve systems of equations with more than two variables. Our methods will be primarily algebraic, though we do discuss the geometry of the three-variable situation. In this section we formulate some problems with more than two variables, and we develop an algorithm (i.e., a step-by-step method) which will produce all solutions of a system of linear equations when there are solutions.

Example 5.18 Nan's Nursery sells bushes, trees, and perennial flowers. Each bush costs \$20, each tree costs \$40, and each flower costs \$2. To plant these bushes, trees, and flowers, Nan's charges \$10 per bush, \$10 per tree, and \$1 per flower. Also, Nan will insure the items she plants for 1 year at a charge of \$4 per bush, \$6 per tree, and \$0.20 per flower. A new homeowner has budgeted \$1000 for purchases, \$400 for planting the purchases, and \$150 for insuring purchases from Nan's. How many bushes, trees, and flowers should the homeowner buy to exactly use up the money budgeted?

Problem Formulate the homeowner's problem as a system of linear equations.

Solution Since the homeowner is interested in the number of bushes, trees, and flowers to buy, we let

$$\begin{aligned} x &= \text{the number of bushes to buy} \\ y &= \text{the number of trees to buy} \\ z &= \text{the number of flowers to buy} \end{aligned}$$

Next, since \$1000 is budgeted for purchases, and since bushes, trees, and flowers cost \$20, \$40, and \$2, respectively, we know that variables x, y, and z must satisfy the equation

$$20x + 40y + 2z = \$1000 \tag{5.15}$$

Similarly, since the planting budget is \$400, and since planting each bush, tree, and flower costs \$10, \$10, and \$1, respectively, we also know that variables x, y, and z must satisfy

$$10x + 10y + z = \$400 \tag{5.16}$$

Finally, since \$150 is budgeted for insurance for the first year, we have

$$4x + 6y + .2z = \$150 \tag{5.17}$$

The variables x, y, and z must satisfy Equations (5.15), (5.16), and (5.17) simultaneously, and these three equations form the desired system. Also, because of the meanings of x, y, and z, we are only interested in integer solutions which satisfy $x \geq 0$, $y \geq 0$, and $z \geq 0$. ■

Example 5.19 Salvador's Custom Paint Shop mixes Red, Yellow, and Blue paint to create shades of orange, violet and green paint. Orange paint is made from a mixture of 2 parts red paint to 1 part yellow paint, violet paint uses a mixture of 2 parts blue paint to 1 part red paint, and green paint uses a mixture of 1 part yellow paint to 1 part blue paint. Salvador has on hand 4 gallons of red paint, 6 gallons of yellow paint, and 12 gallons of blue paint.

Problem Formulate a mathematical problem whose solution will give the amounts of orange, green, and violet paint to be made so that the mixtures satisfy the conditions above and completely use up all of the yellow, red, and blue paint on hand.

Solution Let

$$\begin{aligned} x &= \text{amount (in gallons) of orange paint} \\ y &= \text{amount (in gallons) of violet paint} \\ z &= \text{amount (in gallons) of green paint} \end{aligned}$$

Now consider the information concerning red paint. Since orange paint uses a 2-to-1 mixture of red paint to yellow paint, each gallon of orange paint requires 2/3 of a gallon of red paint. Similarly, each gallon of violet paint requires 1/3 gallon of red paint. Since there are 4 gallons of red paint available, x and y are to be selected so that

$$\left(\tfrac{2}{3}\right)x + \left(\tfrac{1}{3}\right)y = 4$$

Next, we use the information concerning yellow paint. The 2-to-1 ratio in orange paint means that each gallon of orange paint requires 1/3 gallon of yellow paint, and the 1-to-1 ratio in green paint means that each gallon of green paint uses 1/2 gallon of yellow paint. There are 6 gallons of yellow paint on hand, and consequently we have the equation

$$\left(\tfrac{1}{3}\right)x + \left(\tfrac{1}{2}\right)z = 6$$

By the same type of argument, the information concerning blue paint leads to the equation

$$\left(\tfrac{2}{3}\right)y + \left(\tfrac{1}{2}\right)z = 12$$

The mathematical problem whose solution gives the amounts of the various mixtures which satisfy the mixing ratios and use all of the available paint is the following: Find x, y, and z which satisfy

$$\begin{aligned}\left(\tfrac{2}{3}\right)x + \left(\tfrac{1}{3}\right)y &= 4\\ \left(\tfrac{1}{3}\right)x + \left(\tfrac{1}{2}\right)z &= 6\\ \left(\tfrac{2}{3}\right)y + \left(\tfrac{1}{2}\right)z &= 12\end{aligned} \tag{5.18}$$

Again, because of the meanings of x, y, and z, we are only interested in solutions which satisfy $x \geq 0$, $y \geq 0$, and $z \geq 0$. ■

In Examples 5.18 and 5.19, the formulation of the problem resulted in a system of three linear equations with three variables. In Section 5.2, when we discussed solving linear systems of equations with two variables, we noted that the equations represented lines in the plane, and, in seeking a solution, we were really seeking a point common to these lines.

Geometrically speaking, a similar situation holds with equations in three variables, but now the equations represent planes instead of lines and we are seeking a point common to these planes.

In addition, the concepts developed in this section can be given meaning for linear functions of more than three variables. For instance, the set of points $(x_1, x_2, \ldots, x_n)$ which satisfy an equation of the form $A_1x_1 + A_2x_2 + \cdots + A_nx_n = B$ is called a *hyperplane* in n-dimensional space. However, to introduce these ideas would take us astray from the main goals of this chapter, and we omit them.

The primary goal of this section is to develop methods of solving problems like those posed in Examples 5.18 and 5.19. Since we also want to solve similar systems with more than three variables, it is useful to begin by introducing a general notation.

In Examples 5.18 and 5.19, the problems were formulated using the three variables x, y, and z. In general, if the problem involves n variables, it is customary to label them $x_1, x_2, \ldots, x_n$, particularly when $n > 3$. With this notation, a system of m linear equations in n variables can be written in the form

$$\begin{aligned} a_{11}x_1 + a_{12}x_2 + \cdots + a_{1n}x_n &= b_1 \\ a_{21}x_1 + a_{22}x_2 + \cdots + a_{2n}x_n &= b_2 \\ \vdots \qquad \vdots \qquad\quad \vdots \quad &\quad \vdots \\ a_{m1}x_1 + a_{m2}x_2 + \cdots + a_{mn}x_n &= b_m \end{aligned} \tag{5.19}$$

It is assumed that the a_{ij}'s and b_j's are known numbers. That is, the values of these numbers are given in the problem. The values of the variables are to be determined.

A solution of system (5.19) is an ordered set of n numbers which when substituted into Equations (5.19) for $x_1, x_2, \ldots, x_n$, respectively, results in numerical equalities.

Example 5.20 Show that $x = \frac{6}{5}, y = \frac{48}{5}, z = \frac{56}{5}$ is a solution of the system (5.18).

Solution On the left-hand side of system (5.18) we replace x by $\frac{6}{5}$, y by $\frac{48}{5}$, and z by $\frac{56}{5}$. We have

$$\begin{aligned} \tfrac{2}{3}x + \tfrac{1}{3}y &= \tfrac{2}{3}(\tfrac{6}{5}) + \tfrac{1}{3}(\tfrac{48}{5}) = \tfrac{4}{5} + \tfrac{16}{5} = \tfrac{20}{5} = 4 \\ \tfrac{1}{3}x + \tfrac{1}{2}z &= \tfrac{1}{3}(\tfrac{6}{5}) + \tfrac{1}{2}(\tfrac{56}{5}) = \tfrac{2}{5} + \tfrac{28}{5} = \tfrac{30}{5} = 6 \\ \tfrac{2}{3}y + \tfrac{1}{2}z &= \tfrac{2}{3}(\tfrac{48}{5}) + \tfrac{1}{2}(\tfrac{56}{5}) = \tfrac{32}{5} + \tfrac{28}{5} = \tfrac{60}{5} = 12 \end{aligned}$$

After making the substitution, we see that the left-hand side of each expression is equal to the right-hand side. In other words, the substitution yields three numerical equalities. ■

In Examples 5.18 and 5.19, the labels we used to denote the unknown quantities, i.e., the variables, are unimportant. We used x, y, z. We could equally well have used x_1, x_2, x_3 or u, v, w. The important information of system (5.18) is contained in the coefficients of the variables in the equations. This information can be extracted and represented in an array of numbers.

In particular, we write the coefficients of the variables x, y, z in the first equation in order in the first row of the array. We write the coefficients of x, y, z in the second equation as the second row of the array; the coefficients of the third equation form the third row, and we enclose the array in brackets.

$$\begin{bmatrix} \frac{2}{3} & \frac{1}{3} & 0 \\ \frac{1}{3} & 0 & \frac{1}{2} \\ 0 & \frac{2}{3} & \frac{1}{2} \end{bmatrix} \tag{5.20}$$

Notice that the first entry in each row is a coefficient of variable x, the second entry in each row is a coefficient of variable y, and the third entry in each row is a coefficient of variable z. Each equation must be viewed as containing *all* variables; a missing variable is considered to have a zero coefficient. For example, the first equation in (5.18) has only x and y terms, but it can be written equivalently as

$$\tfrac{2}{3}x + \tfrac{1}{3}y + 0z = 4$$

The array of numbers in (5.20) with the coefficients of each variable aligned in a column is an example of a *coefficient matrix*. In general:

The array

$$\begin{bmatrix} a_{11} & a_{12} & \cdots & a_{1n} \\ a_{21} & a_{22} & \cdots & a_{2n} \\ \vdots & \vdots & & \vdots \\ a_{m1} & a_{m2} & \cdots & a_{mn} \end{bmatrix} \tag{5.21}$$

in which the entries are the coefficients that appear in system (5.19) is called the *coefficient matrix* of the system. The entries in a horizontal line in this matrix form a *row*, and the entries in a vertical line form a *column*. For instance, $[a_{21}\ a_{22}\ \cdots\ a_{2n}]$ is the second row, and the third column is

$$\begin{bmatrix} a_{13} \\ a_{23} \\ \vdots \\ a_{m3} \end{bmatrix}$$

In determining the coefficient matrix of a system of equations, it is important to remember that the variables must appear in the same order in every equation and that every variable must have a coefficient, possibly zero, in each equation. The array (5.20) is the coefficient matrix of the system (5.18).

It is convenient to have a shorthand notation for the coefficient matrix of a system of equations. We use the boldface letter **A** to denote the matrix (5.21).

Example 5.21 Find the coefficient matrix **A** of the following system of equations:

$$\begin{aligned} 3x_2 - 4x_1 - x_4 &= 6 \\ x_3 + x_2 - x_1 &= 2 \end{aligned}$$

Solution First we rewrite the system of equations, placing the variables in the same order in both equations and inserting missing variables with zero coefficients:

$$\begin{aligned} -4x_1 + 3x_2 + 0x_3 - x_4 &= 6 \\ -x_1 + x_2 + x_3 + 0x_4 &= 2 \end{aligned}$$

From this it is easy to find the coefficient matrix:

$$\mathbf{A} = \begin{bmatrix} -4 & 3 & 0 & -1 \\ -1 & 1 & 1 & 0 \end{bmatrix}$$

■

We now turn to the task of describing an algorithm which will enable us to solve all systems of the form (5.19) which have solutions. For notational convenience we write the system (5.19) symbolically as $\mathbf{AX} = \mathbf{B}$. Here **A**, **B**, and **X** are just symbols. In Chapter 6 we will attach a meaning to the symbols and see that the representation $\mathbf{AX} = \mathbf{B}$ is more than just notation.

As we saw in Section 5.2, there are systems of equations which have a unique solution, there are systems which have infinitely many solutions, and there are systems which have no solutions.

A system of equations that has at least one solution is said to be *consistent*, and a system that has no solution is said to be *inconsistent*.

The solution algorithm introduced here is based on the following idea: We successively transform the original system into simpler and simpler systems *without changing the set of solutions* until we obtain a system whose solutions are clear. The technique is the same as that used in Section 5.2 to solve systems of two equations in two variables. The method rests on the following important fact about systems of linear equations.

Theorem on Transforming Systems of Equations

If a system of equations is transformed into a new system by any one of the following operations

1. Interchange two equations.
2. Multiply any equation by a nonzero number.
3. Replace any equation by the sum of that equation and a multiple of any other equation.

then the set of solutions of the transformed system is the same as the set of solutions of the original system.

Our goal in transforming a system is to obtain a new system in which each equation contains only one variable. For such a system the solution can be obtained by reading the value of each variable from the equation containing only that variable. We saw in Section 5.2, however, that even in the special case of two equations and two variables, we could not always achieve this goal. The best that we can do is to always obtain a new system with a special form, called the *reduced form*, that enables us to find the solutions of that system easily. The coefficient matrix we seek has the following properties:

A. The entry in the first row and first column of the coefficient matrix is a 1, and the first nonzero entry in each row is 1. These entries are called *leading ones* (1s).

B. If a column of the coefficient matrix contains a leading 1, then all other entries in that column are 0.

C. As you move from left to right through the columns of the coefficient matrix, the leading 1s occur in successive rows. In particular, all rows with only 0s are at the bottom of the matrix.

Condition C is sometimes phrased in descriptive terms as "The leading 1s march downward and to the right." Matrix **A** shown below is an example of a matrix which satisfies conditions A, B, and C.

$$\mathbf{A} = \begin{bmatrix} 1 & 0 & 0 & 0 \\ 0 & 1 & 1 & 0 \\ 0 & 0 & 0 & 1 \\ 0 & 0 & 0 & 0 \end{bmatrix}$$

Notice that the leading 1s occur successively in row 1, row 2, and row 3.

A coefficient matrix which has the form described by conditions A, B, and C is said to be in *reduced form*.

Example 5.22 Which of the following matrices are in reduced form? If a matrix is not in reduced form, determine which of the conditions A, B, or C are violated.

(*a*) $\begin{bmatrix} 1 & 2 & 2 & 0 \\ 0 & 1 & 3 & 0 \\ 0 & 0 & 0 & 1 \end{bmatrix}$ (*b*) $\begin{bmatrix} 1 & 0 & 0 & 0 \\ 0 & 0 & 1 & 3 \\ 0 & 1 & 0 & 0 \end{bmatrix}$

(*c*) $\begin{bmatrix} 1 & 0 & 0 & 2 \\ 0 & 1 & 0 & -1 \\ 0 & 0 & 1 & 3 \end{bmatrix}$ (*d*) $\begin{bmatrix} 1 & 2 & 0 & 0 \\ 0 & 0 & 1 & 0 \\ 0 & 0 & 0 & 1 \end{bmatrix}$

Solution (*a*) This matrix is not in reduced form. The first nonzero entry in each row is a 1; however, in the second column there is a leading 1 and a nonzero entry, the 2 immediately above the 1.

(*b*) This matrix is not in reduced form. Conditions A and B are met, but condition C is violated. Indeed, as you move from left to right through the columns of the matrix, the leading 1s appear in row 1, then row 3, then row 2. They do *not* appear in successive rows.

(*c*) and (*d*) Both are in reduced form. ■

The first step in our method of solving a system of equations is to transform it into a new system with a 1 as the upper left entry in the coefficient matrix, as required by condition A. We continue to transform the system until all of the conditions A, B, and C are satisfied.

Example 5.23 Solve the system of equations

$$\begin{aligned} 2x_1 + 4x_2 + 2x_3 &= -4 \\ 3x_1 + 6x_2 + 4x_3 &= -5 \\ x_2 + 2x_3 &= 1 \end{aligned} \tag{5.22}$$

Solution We begin by transforming the system into one in which the coefficient of x_1 in the first equation is 1, so that condition A is satisfied for the first row. To accomplish this, we multiply the first equation by $\frac{1}{2}$ (an operation of type 2). We obtain

$$\begin{aligned} x_1 + 2x_2 + x_3 &= -2 \\ 3x_1 + 6x_2 + 4x_3 &= -5 \\ x_2 + 2x_3 &= 1 \end{aligned}$$

To satisfy condition B, we must transform the system into one in which the coefficients of x_1 in the second and third equations are zero. Since the coefficient of x_1 in the third equation is already 0, we need to consider only the second equation. We multiply the first equation by -3, add it to the second, and use the result to replace the second equation (an operation of type 3). We now have

$$\begin{aligned} x_1 + 2x_2 + x_3 &= -2 \\ x_3 &= 1 \\ x_2 + 2x_3 &= 1 \end{aligned}$$

The leading coefficient in each row is now a 1; however, these leading coefficients do not march down and to the right. To obtain such a form, we need to interchange the second and third equations. After the interchange we have

$$\begin{aligned} x_1 + 2x_2 + x_3 &= -2 \\ x_2 + 2x_3 &= 1 \\ x_3 &= 1 \end{aligned}$$

Our system of equations has now been transformed into one which satisfies two of the three conditions for reduced form (A and C). To satisfy condition B, we wish to keep the coefficient of x_3 as a 1 in the third equation and eliminate x_3 (obtain a zero coefficient) in the other two equations. To accomplish this, we multiply the third equation by -2, add it to the second equation, and use the result as a new second equation. We have

$$\begin{aligned} x_1 + 2x_2 + x_3 &= -2 \\ x_2 &= -1 \\ x_3 &= 1 \end{aligned}$$

Next, we multiply the third equation by -1, add it to the first, and use the result as a new first equation. We have

$$\begin{aligned} x_1 + 2x_2 &= -3 \\ x_2 &= -1 \\ x_3 &= 1 \end{aligned}$$

Finally, we multiply the second equation by -2, add it to the first, and use the result as a new first equation. We have

$$\begin{aligned} x_1 &= -1 \\ x_2 &= -1 \\ x_3 &= 1 \end{aligned} \tag{5.23}$$

The coefficient matrix of this last system is

$$\begin{bmatrix} 1 & 0 & 0 \\ 0 & 1 & 0 \\ 0 & 0 & 1 \end{bmatrix}$$

which clearly satisfies conditions A, B, and C. That is, it is in reduced form.

A solution (in fact, the only solution) of system (5.23) is obvious: $x_1 = -1$, $x_2 = -1$, $x_3 = 1$. According to the theorem, this is also a solution (and again the only solution) of the original system (5.22). ■

It is important to realize that the system of Example 5.23 could have been solved by using other sequences of transformations. However, each sequence of transformation (if correctly carried out) will lead to the same set of solutions.

It is clear that in Example 5.23 the variables x_1, x_2, and x_3 were just "carried along for the ride." That is, the entire process can be carried out by working with only the entries in the coefficient matrix and the numbers on the right-hand side, the numbers b_j in Equation (5.19). To take advantage of this simplification we introduce the idea of an augmented matrix.

The *augmented matrix* of a system of equations **AX** = **B** of the form (5.19) is the array of numbers

$$\left[\begin{array}{cccc|c} a_{11} & a_{12} & \cdots & a_{1n} & b_1 \\ a_{21} & a_{22} & \cdots & a_{2n} & b_2 \\ \cdot & \cdot & \cdot & \cdot & \cdot \\ \cdot & \cdot & \cdot & \cdot & \cdot \\ \cdot & \cdot & \cdot & \cdot & \cdot \\ a_{m1} & a_{m2} & \cdots & a_{mn} & b_m \end{array}\right]$$

The vertical line between the two columns on the right indicates that the column on the far right is not a part of the coefficient matrix, but instead represents the right-hand side of Equation (5.19).

Example 5.24 Find the augmented matrix for system (5.22).

Solution

$$\left[\begin{array}{ccc|c} 2 & 4 & 2 & -4 \\ 3 & 6 & 4 & -5 \\ 0 & 1 & 2 & 1 \end{array}\right]$$

■

In working the next example, we show each step in two forms: the form displaying the variables and the form utilizing the augmented matrix.

Example 5.25 Solve the system posed in Example 5.18.

$$\begin{aligned} 20x + 40y + 2z &= 1000 \\ 10x + 10y + z &= 400 \\ 4x + 6y + .2z &= 150 \end{aligned} \tag{5.24}$$

Solution The augmented matrix for system (5.24) is

$$\left[\begin{array}{ccc|c} 20 & 40 & 2 & 1000 \\ 10 & 10 & 1 & 400 \\ 4 & 6 & .2 & 150 \end{array}\right]$$

We begin by multiplying the first equation in system (5.24) by $\frac{1}{20}$, in order to make the first coefficient in the first equation a 1. In matrix terms, we multiply the first row by $\frac{1}{20}$. The new system and the corresponding augmented matrix are

$$\begin{aligned} 1x + 2y + .1z &= 50 \\ 10x + 10y + z &= 400 \\ 4x + 6y + .2z &= 150 \end{aligned} \qquad \left[\begin{array}{ccc|c} 1 & 2 & .1 & 50 \\ 10 & 10 & 1 & 400 \\ 4 & 6 & .2 & 150 \end{array}\right]$$

Next, we replace the second equation—row 2 in the augmented matrix—by the sum of the second equation and -10 times the first equation. This yields a second equation with a first coefficient of 0. The new system and augmented matrix are

$$\begin{aligned} 1x + 2y + .1z &= 50 \\ 0x + (-10)y + 0z &= -100 \\ 4x + 6y + .2z &= 150 \end{aligned} \qquad \left[\begin{array}{ccc|c} 1 & 2 & .1 & 50 \\ 0 & -10 & 0 & -100 \\ 4 & 6 & .2 & 150 \end{array}\right]$$

We now replace the third equation (row 3 of the matrix) by the sum of the third equation and -4 times the first equation. This gives the following system and augmented matrix:

$$\begin{aligned} 1x + 2y + .1z &= 50 \\ 0x + (-10)y + 0z &= -100 \\ 0x + (-2)y + (-.2)z &= -50 \end{aligned} \qquad \left[\begin{array}{ccc|c} 1 & 2 & .1 & 50 \\ 0 & -10 & 0 & -100 \\ 0 & -2 & -.2 & -50 \end{array}\right]$$

At this stage of the reduction process we have completed work on the first column of the augmented matrix. In terms of the equations, there is only one equation, the first one, that contains variable x. In the second and third equations the coefficient of x is 0. Next, we need to form a leading 1 in the second row of the augmented matrix. Since the first nonzero entry in the second row is -10, we multiply the second row (equation) by $-\frac{1}{10}$. This gives the following system and augmented matrix:

$$\begin{aligned} 1x + \quad 2y + \quad .1z &= \ \ 50 \\ 0x + \quad 1y + \quad 0z &= \ \ 10 \\ 0x + (-2)y + (-.2)z &= -50 \end{aligned} \qquad \left[\begin{array}{ccc|c} 1 & 2 & .1 & 50 \\ 0 & 1 & 0 & 10 \\ 0 & -2 & -.2 & -50 \end{array}\right]$$

Since we now have a leading 1 in the second row, we need to create 0s above and below this entry. Accordingly, we replace the first row by the sum of the first row and -2 times the second row, and we replace the third row by the sum of the third row and 2 times the second row. This gives the following:

$$\begin{aligned} 1x + 0y + \quad .1z &= \ \ 30 \\ 0x + 1y + \quad 0z &= \ \ 10 \\ 0x + 0y + (-.2)z &= -30 \end{aligned} \qquad \left[\begin{array}{ccc|c} 1 & 0 & .1 & 30 \\ 0 & 1 & 0 & 10 \\ 0 & 0 & -.2 & -30 \end{array}\right]$$

The first and second rows now have leading 1s, and we need to form a leading 1 in the third row. Since the first nonzero entry in the third row is $-.2$, we multiply row 3 by $-1/.2 = -5$ to obtain

$$\begin{aligned} 1x + 0y + .1z &= \ \ 30 \\ 0x + 1y + \ 0z &= \ \ 10 \\ 0x + 0y + \ 1z &= 150 \end{aligned} \qquad \left[\begin{array}{ccc|c} 1 & 0 & .1 & 30 \\ 0 & 1 & 0 & 10 \\ 0 & 0 & 1 & 150 \end{array}\right]$$

The final step in obtaining reduced form for this augmented matrix is to transform all the entries above the leading 1 in the third column into 0s. The only such entry is in the first row, so we replace row 1 by the sum of row 1 and $-.1$ times row 3. This gives the reduced form

$$\begin{aligned} 1x + 0y + 0z &= \ \ 15 \\ 0x + 1y + 0z &= \ \ 10 \\ 0x + 0y + 1z &= 150 \end{aligned} \qquad \left[\begin{array}{ccc|c} 1 & 0 & 0 & 15 \\ 0 & 1 & 0 & 10 \\ 0 & 0 & 1 & 150 \end{array}\right]$$

The solution of the problem posed in Example 5.17 is given by this last system of equations, namely,

$$\begin{aligned} x \qquad\qquad &= \ \ 15 \\ y \qquad &= \ \ 10 \\ z &= 150 \end{aligned}$$

To check our work, we verify that this solution satisfies the original system (5.24). We have

$$\begin{aligned} 20(15) + 40(10) + \ 2(150) &= 1000 \\ 10(15) + 10(10) + \ 1(150) &= \ \ 400 \\ 4(15) + \ \ 6(10) + .2(150) &= \ \ 150 \end{aligned}$$

This verifies that our solution is correct, and thus the homeowner should buy 15 bushes, 10 trees, and 150 flowers. ■

If a system of equations has any solutions, then the technique illustrated in Examples 5.23 and 5.25 will produce all solutions. Also, if a system has no solutions, then the technique will show that fact as well.

Example 5.26 Find the solutions (if any) of the system of equations

$$\begin{aligned} 3x_1 - x_2 &= 4 \\ 6x_1 - 2x_2 &= 3 \end{aligned}$$

Solution To illustrate the method, we again proceed by using both the equations and the augmented matrix. The augmented matrix for the given system is

$$\left[\begin{array}{cc|c} 3 & -1 & 4 \\ 6 & -2 & 3 \end{array}\right]$$

We multiply the first equation by -2, add it to the second equation, and use the result as a new second equation. We have

$$\begin{aligned} 3x_1 - x_2 &= 4 \\ 0 &= -5 \end{aligned} \qquad \left[\begin{array}{cc|c} 3 & -1 & 4 \\ 0 & 0 & -5 \end{array}\right]$$

Thus there is an equation of the form $0x_1 + 0x_2 = -5$ in the transformed system. Since this is true for *no choice* of x_1 and x_2, we conclude that the original system has no solution. ■

Inconsistent Systems

If in using this technique it ever happens that a transformed system has an equation with zero on the left-hand side and a nonzero number on the right, then the original system has no solutions, i.e., it is inconsistent.

In terms of the augmented matrix (or its transform) this condition is as follows: If there is a row with only 0s to the left of the vertical line and a nonzero entry in that row to the right of the vertical line, then the system has no solutions.

The remainder of this section is concerned with systems which have more than one solution. A system of linear equations has *no solutions*, *exactly one solution*, or *infinitely many solutions*. There are no other possibilities.

The solution set of a single linear equation in three variables is a plane in three-dimensional space. The set of points which are simultaneously the solution of two linear equations in three variables will be empty if the planes associated with the two equations are parallel; it will be a line if the planes intersect but are not coincident; and it will be a plane if the planes are coincident. The set of points that are simultaneously the solution of three linear equations in three variables can be empty, a single point, a line, or a plane. In the first case, the system has no solution; in the second case, a unique solution; and in the third and fourth cases, infinitely many solutions—either all points on a line or all points in a plane. Thus, there are infinitely many solutions associated with intersections which are either lines or planes. We conclude that there can be different kinds of solution sets with infinitely many elements. We look further into this situation after our next example, and we make the ideas precise in a theorem.

A graph of one of the cases, three equations which have a unique solution, is shown in Figure 5.12. Suppose we have three equations, denoted Equation 1, Equation 2, and Equation 3, in three-dimensional space where the coordinate axes are denoted by x_1, x_2, and x_3. The graph of the solution set of Equation 1 might appear as in Figure 5.12*a*. The solution set of the single equation is a plane. The graphs of the solutions of Equations 1 and 2 might appear as in Figure 5.12*b*. Here the solution set of the two equations is a line. Finally, the solution set of all three equations, a point, might appear as in Figure 5.12*c*.

FIGURE 5.12

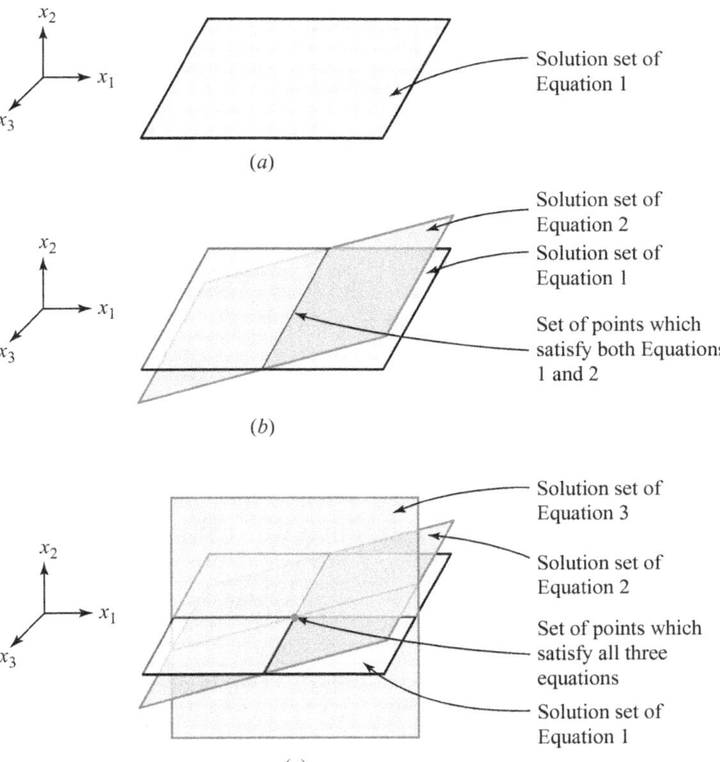

Example 5.27 Find all solutions of the system

$$\begin{aligned} x_1 + 2x_2 - x_3 &= 5 \\ 2x_1 + 3x_2 - 3x_3 &= 8 \\ x_2 + x_3 &= 2 \end{aligned} \tag{5.25}$$

Solution In this example, and in general, we will work only with the augmented matrix. We begin by interchanging the second and third rows to obtain a leading 1 as the entry in the second row and second column of the matrix. We have

$$\left[\begin{array}{ccc|c} 1 & 2 & -1 & 5 \\ 0 & 1 & 1 & 2 \\ 2 & 3 & -3 & 8 \end{array}\right]$$

Next, we multiply the first row by -2, add it to the third row, and use the result as a new third row. We have

$$\left[\begin{array}{ccc|c} 1 & 2 & -1 & 5 \\ 0 & 1 & 1 & 2 \\ 0 & -1 & -1 & -2 \end{array}\right]$$

Next, we add the second row to the third row and use the result as a new third row. We have

$$\left[\begin{array}{ccc|c} 1 & 2 & -1 & 5 \\ 0 & 1 & 1 & 2 \\ 0 & 0 & 0 & 0 \end{array}\right]$$

Finally, we multiply the second row by -2, add it to the first row, and use the result as a new first row. We have

$$\left[\begin{array}{ccc|c} 1 & 0 & -3 & 1 \\ 0 & 1 & 1 & 2 \\ 0 & 0 & 0 & 0 \end{array}\right] \tag{5.26}$$

The augmented matrix is now in reduced form.

The system of equations with the augmented matrix (5.26) is

$$\begin{aligned} x_1 - 3x_3 &= 1 \\ x_2 + x_3 &= 2 \end{aligned}$$

Suppose $x_3 = 0$. Then the system becomes

$$\begin{aligned} x_1 &= 1 \\ x_2 &= 2 \end{aligned}$$

Thus one solution of the system (5.25) is $x_1 = 1, x_2 = 2, x_3 = 0$. Likewise, if $x_3 = -1$, then the system becomes

$$\begin{aligned} x_1 - 3(-1) &= 1 \\ x_2 + \ (-1) &= 2 \end{aligned}$$

with the solution $x_1 = -2, x_2 = 3, x_3 = -1$. The same method works when x_3 is set equal to any number. That is, for any choice of x_3 we can determine x_1 and x_2. We have

$$\begin{aligned} x_1 - 3x_3 &= 1 \\ x_2 + \ x_3 &= 2 \end{aligned} \qquad \text{or} \qquad \begin{aligned} x_1 &= 1 + 3x_3 \\ x_2 &= 2 - \ x_3 \end{aligned}$$

For each number x_3, a solution of (5.25) is given by $x_1 = 1 + 3x_3, x_2 = 2 - x_3$, x_3. Since there are infinitely many choices for x_3—any number will do—and since each choice of x_3 gives a different solution of the system, there are infinitely many solutions of the system (5.25). Moreover, every solution of the system is given in this form for some value of x_3, and consequently the solution set is specified by

$$x_1 = 1 + 3x_3, \qquad x_2 = 2 - x_3, \qquad x_3 \text{ arbitrary}$$ ■

In Example 5.27 one of the variables (x_3) could be assigned an arbitrary value. The geometry in this case is that the solution set of system (5.25) is a line in three-dimensional space. It may happen that two or more of the variables can be assigned arbitrary values. For example, if the solution set of a system of three equations in three variables is a plane in three-dimensional space, then two of the variables can be specified arbitrarily. There is a means of determining precisely those variables which can be specified arbitrarily.

Theorem on the Solution Set of a System of Linear Equations

Suppose that a consistent system of linear equations in n variables has been transformed into reduced form with k nonzero rows. Then there are solutions in which $n - k$ of the variables can be specified arbitrarily. In particular, each of the $n - k$ variables associated with a column in the reduced coefficient matrix which does *not* contain a leading 1 can be specified arbitrarily. If $n > k$, then there are infinitely many solutions.

Example 5.28 A system of equations is given by

$$\begin{aligned} 2x_1 - 2x_2 + 3x_3 &= -4 \\ x_1 - x_2 + 3x_3 &= \ \ 2 \end{aligned} \tag{5.27}$$

Problem

(*a*) Find all solutions of the system (5.27).
(*b*) Find the solutions (if there are any) which satisfy $x_2 = 2$.
(*c*) Find the solutions (if there are any) which satisfy $x_3 = 2$.

Solution The augmented matrix for the system is

$$\left[\begin{array}{ccc|c} 2 & -2 & 3 & -4 \\ 1 & -1 & 3 & 2 \end{array}\right]$$

We begin by multiplying the first row by $\frac{1}{2}$ to obtain a leading 1 in the first row, and we have

$$\left[\begin{array}{ccc|c} 1 & -1 & \frac{3}{2} & -2 \\ 1 & -1 & 3 & 2 \end{array}\right]$$

Next, we multiply the first row by -1, add the result to the second row, and use the result as a new second row. We have

$$\left[\begin{array}{ccc|c} 1 & -1 & \frac{3}{2} & -2 \\ 0 & 0 & \frac{3}{2} & 4 \end{array}\right]$$

We continue by multiplying the second row by $\frac{2}{3}$.

$$\left[\begin{array}{ccc|c} 1 & -1 & \frac{3}{2} & -2 \\ 0 & 0 & 1 & \frac{8}{3} \end{array}\right]$$

Finally, we multiply the second row by $-\frac{3}{2}$, add it to the first row, and use the result as a new first row. We have

$$\left[\begin{array}{ccc|c} 1 & -1 & 0 & -6 \\ 0 & 0 & 1 & \frac{8}{3} \end{array}\right]$$

The last augmented matrix is in reduced form. We see that there is no leading 1 in the column corresponding to the variable x_2, and consequently, x_2 can be specified arbitrarily. Also, we see that $x_3 = \frac{8}{3}$, and $x_1 - x_2 = -6$. Therefore, the solution set of the system is given by

$$x_1 = x_2 - 6, \quad x_2 \text{ arbitrary}, \quad x_3 = \frac{8}{3}.$$

For part (*b*), we use the expression $x_1 = x_2 - 6$ and the condition $x_2 = 2$, and we find the desired solution to be: $x_1 = -4, x_2 = 2, x_3 = \frac{8}{3}$.

For part (*c*), we note that every solution of the system has $x_3 = \frac{8}{3}$, and consequently, there are no solutions with $x_3 = 2$. ■

Example 5.29 Find the specific solution of the system of Example 5.27 with $x_2 = 1$.

Solution The reduction process in Example 5.27 leads to the augmented matrix shown in (5.26). This augmented matrix shows that x_3 can be specified arbitrarily and the set of all solutions is given by

$$x_1 = 1 + 3x_3, \quad x_2 = 2 - x_3, \quad x_3 \text{ arbitrary}$$

If $x_2 = 1$, then x_3 must satisfy $1 = 2 - x_3$, so x_3 must be 1. If $x_3 = 1$, then $x_1 = 1 + 3 = 4$. Therefore, the desired solution is $x_1 = 4, x_2 = 1$, and $x_3 = 1$. ■

We close this section with an explicit statement of the method we have developed to solve systems of linear equations.

Algorithm for Solving a System of Linear Equations

1. Form the augmented matrix.
2. Use row operations to transform the augmented matrix into reduced form.
3. Interpret the reduced form to obtain information about the solution set.
   a. If there is a row with zeros to the left of the vertical line and a nonzero entry to the right, then the system has no solutions.
   b. If the system has n equations in n variables and the reduced form has a leading 1 in each row, then there is a unique solution.
   c. If a consistent system has n variables and the reduced form has k, $k < n$, nonzero rows, then there are infinitely many solutions in which $n - k$ of the variables can be specified arbitrarily.

Exercises for Section 5.3

For Exercises 1 through 4, formulate the problem as a system of linear equations. Be sure to define your variables carefully.

1. Ted's Toys makes toy airplanes, boats, and cars. The materials used are plastic, wood strips, and steel. Each airplane uses 100 grams of plastic, 10 inches of wood strips, and 200 grams of steel. Each boat uses 50 grams of plastic, 100 inches of wood strips, and 50 grams of steel; and each car uses 50 grams of plastic and 150 grams of steel. If Ted's has on hand 10,500 grams of plastic, 1500 inches of wood strips, and 25,500 grams of steel, how many planes, boats, and cars should be made to use up all these supplies?
2. Rachel, Stephanie, and Tina are investing for retirement, using stocks, bonds, and money market funds. They use the following guidelines: Rachel wants half of her money in stocks and the rest split equally in bonds and money market funds. Stephanie wants her money split equally among all three areas, and Tina wants her money split equally between stocks and bonds. If the annual return on stocks is 9 percent, on bonds 6 percent, and on money market funds 3 percent, what is

the total that each women should invest in order that each of them gain \$10,000 from her investment?

3. Mike's Mountain Shop prepares 3 types of trail mix—Hiker's Mix, Biker's Mix, and Mike's Special Mix. One package of Hiker's Mix uses 60 grams of raisins, 20 grams of peanuts, and 10 grams of chocolate chips. One package of Biker's Mix uses 40 grams of raisins, 40 grams of peanuts, and 20 grams of chocolate chips. One package of Mike's Special Mix uses 30 grams of raisins, 30 grams of peanuts, and 30 grams of chocolate chips. Mike has 18,000 grams of raisins, 14,000 grams of peanuts, and 7000 grams of chocolate chips. How many packages of each type of tail mix should Mike produce to use all the raisins, peanuts, and chocolate chips?
4. Raskins and Bobbins Ice Cream Shop makes three kinds of ice cream using skim milk, cream, vanilla, and cacao. Each gallon of Deluxe Vanilla uses 3 quarts of milk, 1 quart of cream, and 2 ounces of vanilla. Each gallon of Regular Vanilla uses 3.5 quarts of milk, 0.5 quart of cream, and 1 ounce of vanilla. Each gallon of Deluxe Chocolate uses 3.25 quarts of milk, 0.75 quart of cream, and 2 ounces of cacao. How many gallons of each type of ice cream should be made in order to use up 100 gallons of milk, 25 gallons of cream, 5 pounds of vanilla, and 10 pounds of cacao?
5. Decide which of the following matrices are in reduced form and which are not. If a matrix is not in reduced form, tell why it is not.

   (*a*) $\begin{bmatrix} 0 & 1 \\ 1 & 1 \end{bmatrix}$ (*b*) $\begin{bmatrix} 1 & 1 \\ 0 & 0 \end{bmatrix}$ (*c*) $\begin{bmatrix} 1 & 1 \\ 1 & 1 \end{bmatrix}$
6. Decide which of the following matrices are in reduced form and which are not. If a matrix is not in reduced form, tell why it is not.

   (*a*) $\begin{bmatrix} 1 & -2 & 0 \\ 0 & 0 & 1 \\ 0 & 0 & 0 \end{bmatrix}$ (*b*) $\begin{bmatrix} 0 & 1 & 2 \\ 1 & 0 & 3 \\ 0 & 0 & 0 \end{bmatrix}$ (*c*) $\begin{bmatrix} 1 & 0 & 2 & 3 \\ 0 & 0 & 2 & 7 \\ 0 & 1 & 4 & 9 \\ 0 & 0 & 0 & 1 \end{bmatrix}$
7. Find the augmented matrix for each of the following systems of equations.

   (*a*) $\begin{aligned} 2x_1 - x_2 - x_3 &= 2 \\ x_1 + x_2 + 2x_3 &= 4 \end{aligned}$ (*b*) $\begin{aligned} 3x &= 4 + 2y \\ x + 3y + 1 &= 0 \end{aligned}$
8. Find the augmented matrix for each of the following systems of equations.

   (*a*) $\begin{aligned} 3x_1 + 2x_2 - x_3 &= 8 \\ x_1 + x_2 + x_3 &= 2 \\ 2x_1 + x_2 - x_3 &= 5 \end{aligned}$ (*b*) $\begin{aligned} 2x_2 - x_1 &= 5 \\ 3x_3 - x_1 &= 2 \\ 2x_1 - x_3 &= 6 \end{aligned}$

   (*c*) $\begin{aligned} 3z - 2y + x &= 5 \\ x + z - y &= 3 \\ y + 2x - 4z &= -2 \end{aligned}$
9. For the following system of equations

$$\begin{aligned} 3x_1 - x_2 + 6x_3 &= 8 \\ 2x_1 + x_2 + 4x_3 &= 7 \end{aligned}$$

   (*a*) find the augmented matrix of the system;
   (*b*) show that $x_1 = -1,\ x_2 = 1,\ x_3 = 2$ is a solution of the system;
   (*c*) show that there are no solutions with $x_2 = 0$.

10. Suppose that

$$\left[\begin{array}{rrr|r} 2 & 1 & 3 & 11 \\ 6 & -3 & 4 & 12 \\ 4 & -4 & 1 & 1 \end{array}\right]$$

is the augmented matrix of a system of equations.
(*a*) Write the system in the form (5.19).
(*b*) Verify that $x_1 = \frac{1}{2}, x_2 = 1, x_3 = 3$ is a solution of the system.
(*c*) Show that there are no solutions with $x_1 = \frac{1}{2}$ and $x_2 = 0$.

In Exercises 11 through 20, find all solutions of the given system of equations.

11. $$\begin{aligned} 2x - 6z &= 1 \\ x + 3y + 2z &= 3 \\ 3y + 8z &= 4 \end{aligned}$$

12. $$\begin{aligned} -x + 3y + 2z &= 2 \\ 4x + 2y + z &= 4 \\ -2x + 4y - z &= 6 \end{aligned}$$

13. $$\begin{aligned} 2x - 4y + z &= 7 \\ 4y + 2z &= -3 \end{aligned}$$

14. $$\begin{aligned} 2x - 8y + 3z &= 8 \\ 3x - 9y + 6z &= 12 \\ x - 3y + 2z &= 4 \end{aligned}$$

15. $$\begin{aligned} x - 2y &= 3 \\ x + 2y + 2z &= 3 \\ x + 6y + 4z &= 3 \end{aligned}$$

16. $$\begin{aligned} 3x_1 + 5x_2 - x_3 + 2x_4 &= 2 \\ 2x_1 - x_3 &= 0 \\ 2x_2 - x_4 &= -3 \\ x_1 - 3x_2 - x_3 &= 1 \end{aligned}$$

17. $$\begin{aligned} x - y + z &= 3 \\ 2x - 2y + z &= 7 \\ x - 2y + 3z &= 3 \end{aligned}$$

18. $$\begin{aligned} 3x + 2y - 13z &= 25 \\ 2x - 2y - 12z &= 10 \end{aligned}$$

19. $$\begin{aligned} 2x + y + 3z &= 1 \\ 3x - 2y + 4z &= -1 \\ 2x - 4y + 2z &= -2 \end{aligned}$$

20. $$\begin{aligned} x - y + 2z &= 2 \\ x - 5y + 5z &= -2 \\ x + 3y &= 2 \end{aligned}$$

21. $$\begin{aligned} 2x + y + 8z &= 14 \\ 3x - y + 17z &= 31 \end{aligned}$$

22. $$\begin{aligned} 2x + 2y - z &= 8 \\ -2x + y + z &= 4 \\ 4x - y + 2z &= -4 \end{aligned}$$

23. Solve the problem formulated in Exercise 1.
24. Solve the problem formulated in Exercise 2.
25. Solve the problem formulated in Exercise 3.
26. Solve the problem formulated in Exercise 4.
27. A small businessman allocates his time among sales (both new clients and old clients), office management, and long-range planning. He decides that he should devote half his time to sales and twice as much time to old clients as to new clients. Also, he decides to devote twice as much time to new clients as to long-range planning. Assume he works 40 hours each week.
(*a*) Find a system of four equations in four variables that represents this information in mathematical form.
(*b*) Solve the system and determine how the businessman should allocate his time to meet his goals.

28. A student is trying to decide how to allocate her study time among mathematics, English, biology, and economics. She decides to spend a total of 45 hours per week studying and to spend twice as much time on mathematics and biology combined as on English and economics combined. Also, she will spend twice as much time on economics as on English and the same amount of time on mathematics as on biology. How much time will she spend on each subject per week?
29. (*a*) Find all solutions of the system

$$\begin{aligned} 3x_1 - 2x_2 + x_3 + 2x_4 &= 6 \\ 2x_1 + 4x_2 - 2x_3 + 3x_4 &= 2 \end{aligned}$$

    (*b*) Find all solutions with $x_1 = 0$.
30. (*a*) Find all solutions of the system

$$\begin{aligned} 3x - 2y + z - w &= 8 \\ 2x + y - z &= 6 \\ x - 3y + w &= 2 \end{aligned}$$

    (*b*) Find all solutions with $w = 0$.
    (*c*) Find all solutions with $y = 0$.
31. Find all solutions of the system

$$\begin{aligned} 3x - 2y + z - w &= 8 \\ 4x - 5y + w &= 8 \\ 2x + y - z &= 6 \\ x - 3y + w &= 2 \end{aligned}$$

32. (*a*) Find all solutions of the system

$$\begin{aligned} x_1 - x_2 + 2x_3 - x_4 &= 7 \\ x_1 + x_2 - 4x_3 + x_4 &= 3 \\ x_1 - x_3 &= 5 \\ 2x_2 + 6x_3 - 2x_4 &= 4 \end{aligned}$$

    (*b*) Find a specific solution with $x_1 = 0$ and $x_2 = 0$.
    (*c*) Are there any solutions with $x_1 = 0$ and $x_3 = 0$?
33. (*a*) Find all solutions of the system

$$\begin{aligned} 5x + 5y + 2z &= 20 \\ 3x + y &= 6 \end{aligned}$$

    (*b*) Find a specific solution to the system in which $x = y$.
34. Robin makes bows and arrows using wood, string, and feathers. Each bow uses 5 feet of wood and 4 feet of string, while each arrow uses 3 feet of wood and 4 feathers. If Robin has 100 feet of wood and 32 feet of string, how many feathers does he need so that he can use up all the wood, string, and feathers making bows and arrows?

35. Consider the setting of Exercise 3.
    (*a*) Suppose that Mike has 8000 grams of chocolate chips. How many packages of each type of trail mix should he produce to use up all the raisins, peanuts, and chocolate chips?
    (*b*) Suppose that Mike has 6000 grams of chocolate chips and solve the resulting system of equations. What do you conclude in this case?
    (*c*) Suppose that Mike has 6000 grams of chocolate chips and that he decides to use the raisins, peanuts, and chocolate chips to produce only two types of trail mix. If he produces only Hiker's Mix and Biker's Mix and uses up all the raisins and chocolate chips, how many grams of peanuts remain unused?
36. Consider the following system of equations:

$$\begin{aligned} 2w - 2y - 4z &= -10 \\ -3w + x + 7z &= 21 \end{aligned}$$

    (*a*) Find the general solution to the system of equations.
    (*b*) Find a specific solution for the system in which $w = x = 0$.
37. Consider the following system of equations:

$$\begin{aligned} w + 2y - z &= 5 \\ x - y + z &= -2 \\ w + x + y &= 3 \\ w - x + 3y - 2z &= 7 \end{aligned}$$

    (*a*) Find all solutions to the system of equations.
    (*b*) If a specific solution is such that $w = x = 0$, then what is the value of y in that solution?
    (*c*) If a specific solution is such that $x = y$, then what is the value of z in that solution?

IMPORTANT TERMS AND CONCEPTS

You should be able to describe, define, or give examples of and use each of the following:

Coordinates in the plane
Line
General equation of a line
Intercept
Slope
Slope-intercept equation of a line
Equation of a plane
System of linear equations
Consistent system
Inconsistent system
Solution of a system of linear equations
Algorithm for solving a system of linear equations
Coefficient matrix
Augmented matrix
Reduced form

REVIEW EXERCISES

1. An economist reviews recent economic growth and inflation, and she concludes that both economic growth and inflation appear to be linear functions of time. Economic growth is now 3.0 percent per year, and it is increasing 0.6 percent

per year. Inflation is now 2.0 percent per year, and it is increasing 1 percent per year. If the economist's assumptions continue to hold, when will economic growth and inflation be equal?

2. At the Bureau of Motor Vehicles, suppose that the length of time you must wait before speaking to a customer service representative is linearly related to the number of people who are in line in front of you. If there are 8 people in line in front of you, you will wait 44 minutes, and if there are 14 people in front of you, you will wait 68 minutes. Find the waiting time if there are 10 people in line in front of you.
3. Suppose that the number of pages an author produces is related to the time she spends writing by a linear equation. To produce 9 pages requires 120 minutes of writing, and to produce 17 pages requires 200 minutes. If she writes for 360 minutes, how many pages will she produce?
4. The cost of downloading data is linearly related to the size of the file downloaded. The cost of downloading a 100MB file is \$0.70 and the cost of downloading a 500MB file is \$2.50.
   (*a*) If a file costs \$4.30 to download, then how large is the file?
   (*b*) Find the cost of downloading a 300MB file.
5. Find all solutions of the system of equations

$$\begin{aligned} 5x + 2y &= 16 \\ 6x + 3y &= 21 \end{aligned}$$

6. Find all solutions of the system of equations

$$\begin{aligned} 3x + 2y &= -1 \\ 5x + 4y &= 0 \end{aligned}$$

7. Find all solutions of the system of equations

$$\begin{aligned} -2x - 4y &= 6 \\ 6x + 6y &= -3 \end{aligned}$$

8. To prepare an advertising brochure requires 5 hours of marketing time to select the products and 10 hours of design time to create the brochure. Also, to prepare a newspaper supplement requires 4 hours of marketing time to select the products and 11 hours of design time to create the supplement. A manager has 300 hours of marketing time and 750 hours of design time available. If all the time is to be used, how many brochures and how many newspaper supplements can be prepared?
9. Shirley, Mary, and Flo go hiking in the Circuitous Mountain Range. Although they do not realize it, they are hiking on a trail that forms a 6 mile loop. Shirley hikes at a pace of 30 minutes per mile, Mary hikes at a pace of 20 minutes per mile, and Flo hikes at a pace of 15 minutes per mile. If they begin hiking at the same place and travel in the same direction, how far will Mary have hiked when Flo catches up with Shirley?
10. A car which cost \$18,900 when new is depreciated linearly for a period of 10 years. At the end of 10 years, the salvage value is \$350.
    (*a*) If v is the book value of the car and t is the number of years since the car was purchased, find a formula which expresses the relationship between v and t.
    (*b*) What is the depreciated value (called the *book value*) of the car after 4 years?

11. A data processing company has a computer which cost \$1,000,000 when new and which depreciates linearly to a salvage value of \$50,000 over 10 years. The company also has a computer which cost \$2,225,000 when new and which depreciates linearly to a salvage value of \$75,000 over a period of 10 years. If the computers were purchased at the same time, when will the book value of the more expensive computer be exactly twice the book value of the less expensive computer?
12. Find the coefficient matrix of each of the following systems of equations.
    (*a*)
    $$\begin{aligned} x_1 + x_2 \qquad + 3x_4 &= 4 \\ x_2 - x_3 \qquad &= 4 \\ x_1 \qquad + x_3 - 2x_4 &= 5 \end{aligned}$$
    (*b*)
    $$\begin{aligned} x_1 + x_3 &= 3 \\ x_1 - x_2 &= 2 \\ x_2 - x_3 &= 3 \end{aligned}$$
13. (*a*) Verify that $x_1 = 4$, $x_2 = 3$, $x_3 = -1$, $x_4 = -1$ is a solution of the system in Exercise 12(*a*).
    (*b*) Verify that $x_1 = 4$, $x_2 = 2$, $x_3 = -1$ is a solution of the system in Exercise 12(*b*).
14. Find all solutions of the system of equations
$$\begin{aligned} 2x + 4y + z &= 6 \\ x + 3y + z &= 4 \\ 2x - 2y - z &= 4 \end{aligned}$$
15. Find all solutions of the system of equations
$$\begin{aligned} 2x_1 + 4x_2 &= 8 \\ 4x_1 - 2x_2 &= 4 \\ 6x_1 + 2x_2 &= 12 \end{aligned}$$
16. Find all solutions of the system of equations
$$\begin{aligned} 2x_1 + 2x_2 - 4x_3 &= 12 \\ x_1 + x_2 + x_3 &= 6 \\ 3x_1 + 3x_2 - 3x_3 &= 3 \end{aligned}$$
17. Find all solutions of the system of equations
$$\begin{aligned} 2x - 5y \qquad &= 0 \\ x - 3y - z &= -1 \\ -x + 2y - z &= -1 \end{aligned}$$
18. Find all solutions of the system of equations
$$\begin{aligned} x_1 + 5x_2 + 2x_3 &= 0 \\ 2x_1 + 7x_2 + x_3 &= -3 \\ 2x_2 + 3x_3 &= 3 \end{aligned}$$

19. Find all solutions of the system of equations

$$\begin{aligned} x_1 - x_3 &= 2 \\ 2x_1 - x_2 - x_3 &= 3 \\ 2x_2 - 3x_3 &= 4 \end{aligned}$$

20. Find all solutions of the system of equations

$$\begin{aligned} 2x_1 + x_2 + x_3 + 2x_4 &= 4 \\ 2x_1 - x_2 + 4x_3 + 2x_4 &= 2 \end{aligned}$$

21. Find all solutions of the system

$$\begin{aligned} 5x_1 - 2x_2 + 2x_3 + x_4 &= 17 \\ 5x_1 - 2x_2 - 10x_3 - 5x_4 &= 5 \end{aligned}$$

22. (*a*) Find all solutions of the system

$$\begin{aligned} 2x_1 - x_2 - 3x_3 &= 6 \\ x_1 + 2x_3 &= 1 \\ x_1 + x_2 + 3x_3 &= -3 \end{aligned}$$

(*b*) Are there any solutions with $x_1 = 1$?

23. A shipping crate on a boat is badly damaged by a storm. The label on the shipping crate states that there were a total of 42 string instruments in the crate and that the crate contained only violins, which have four strings and weigh 1.0 pound each, banjoes, which have five strings and weigh 2.0 pounds each, and guitars, which have six strings and weigh 2.0 pounds each. All of the instruments in the crate were smashed into small pieces during the storm, but a total of 202 strings were recovered from the remains, and the total weight of the remains was found to be 64 pounds. Based on this information, how many of each type of instrument were in the crate?

24. A ticket promoter at a small auditorium that seats 5,000 people is selling tickets for an upcoming concert. They sell three types of tickets—Early Bird tickets, which cost \$60 each, General Admission Tickets, which cost \$80 each, and Late Arrival tickets, which cost \$40 each. The promoter plans to fill every seat in the auditorium, and they need to make exactly \$300,000 to cover cost. They plan to determine the number of General Admission Tickets and Late Arrival Tickets to sell only after the number of Early Bird tickets sold has been determined.

Let

x = number of General Admission tickets to be sold.
y = number of Late Arrival tickets sold, and
z = number of Early Bird tickets sold

(*a*) Write an expression for the number (x) of General Admission tickets to be sold for a given number (z) of Early Bird tickets sold.

(*b*) Write an expression for the number (y) of Late Arrival tickets to be sold for a given number (z) of Early Bird tickets sold.

(*c*) If 1500 Early Bird tickets are sold, how many General Admission tickets and Later Arrival tickets must they sell to fill all of the seats and meet the financial obligations of the promoter?

In Exercises 25 through 29, the augmented matrix shown has been obtained by a sequence of row operations. In each case determine which of the following statements is true about the associated system of equations.

(*a*) The system has a unique solution.

(*b*) The system has no solution.

(*c*) The system has an infinite number of solutions in which one variable can be selected arbitrarily.

(*d*) The system has an infinite number of solutions in which two variables can be selected arbitrarily.

25. $\left[\begin{array}{ccc|c} 1 & 0 & 5 & 5 \\ 0 & 1 & -3 & 4 \\ 0 & 2 & -6 & -8 \end{array}\right]$

26. $\left[\begin{array}{ccc|c} 1 & 0 & 4 & 4 \\ 0 & 1 & -3 & 4 \\ 0 & 2 & -6 & 8 \end{array}\right]$

27. $\left[\begin{array}{ccc|c} 1 & 0 & 3 & 3 \\ 0 & 1 & -3 & 4 \\ 0 & 2 & -5 & 8 \end{array}\right]$

28. $\left[\begin{array}{cccc|c} 1 & 0 & 0 & 0 & 2 \\ 0 & 1 & -3 & 4 & 0 \\ 0 & 2 & -6 & -8 & 1 \\ 0 & 0 & 1 & 1 & 2 \end{array}\right]$

29. $\left[\begin{array}{cccc|c} 1 & 0 & 0 & 0 & 2 \\ 0 & 1 & -3 & 4 & 1 \\ 0 & 2 & -6 & 8 & 2 \\ 0 & 0 & 1 & 1 & 2 \end{array}\right]$

30. A system of equations is given by

$$\begin{aligned} 3x + y - z &= 6 \\ 2x - z &= 2 \\ y + kz &= 3 \end{aligned}$$

where k is a number. For what values of k (if any) does the system have infinitely many solutions?

31. Find all solutions of each of the following systems of equations.

(*a*)

$$\begin{aligned} x_1 + 2x_2 - x_3 &= 3 \\ 2x_1 + 3x_2 - x_3 &= 5 \\ 2x_1 + 4x_2 - 4x_3 &= 5 \end{aligned}$$

(*b*)

$$\begin{aligned} x_1 + 2x_2 - x_3 &= 3 \\ 2x_1 + 3x_2 - x_3 &= 5 \\ 2x_1 + 4x_2 - 2x_3 &= 5 \end{aligned}$$

(*c*)

$$\begin{aligned} x_1 + 2x_2 - x_3 &= 3 \\ 2x_1 + 3x_2 - x_3 &= 5 \\ 3x_1 + 5x_2 - 2x_3 &= 8 \end{aligned}$$

32. For what values (if any) of the number k does the system of equations

$$\begin{aligned} x_1 - 2x_2 + x_3 - 2x_4 &= 5 \\ x_1 - 3x_2 + x_3 - kx_4 &= 2 \end{aligned}$$

have a solution with $x_2 = 2$?

33. A FredEx Delivery Truck is filled with four different sized boxes—small, medium, large, and extra large. Each small box weighs 2 pounds and is valued at \$10, each medium box weighs 5 pounds and is valued at \$20, each large box weighs 10 pounds and is valued at \$40, and finally each extra large box weighs 20 pounds and is valued at \$80. There is a combined total of 46 boxes on the truck with a total combined weight of 280 pounds and a total combined monetary value of \$1,160. In addition, there are twice as many small boxes on the truck as large boxes. How many boxes of each size are on the truck?

34. Find all solutions to the system of equations whose augmented matrix is given below:

$$\left[\begin{array}{ccccc|c} 1 & 0 & 1 & 0 & 1 & 9 \\ 0 & 1 & 0 & 1 & 0 & 6 \\ 0 & 1 & 1 & 0 & 1 & 8 \\ 1 & 0 & 1 & 1 & 0 & 10 \\ 1 & 1 & 0 & 0 & 1 & 10 \end{array}\right]$$

CHAPTER 6

Matrix Algebra and Applications

6.0 THE SETTING AND OVERVIEW

Matrices are mathematical objects which are useful in the study of systems of linear equations, the topic of Chapter 5, as well as in many other areas of mathematics. Matrices are arrays of numbers, and they can be manipulated and combined in much the same way as we handle numbers. In this chapter we develop an ''algebra'' of matrices, i.e., a method of adding, subtracting, multiplying, and dividing matrices when these operations make sense. Also, we illustrate the use of the ideas in this chapter combined with those in Chapter 5 in an important model from economic analysis. This model is useful in theoretical studies as well as in very practical situations.

6.1 MATRIX NOTATION AND ALGEBRA

A *matrix* is a rectangular array. If the array has m (horizontal) rows and n (vertical) columns, the matrix is said to be of dimension $m \times n$, read "m by n." The entry in the ith row and the jth column of the matrix is said to be the (i, j) entry in the matrix. Matrix **A** with entries a_{ij} is

$$\mathbf{A} = \begin{bmatrix} a_{11} & a_{12} & \cdots & a_{1n} \\ a_{21} & a_{22} & \cdots & a_{2n} \\ \cdot & \cdot & & \cdot \\ \cdot & \cdot & & \cdot \\ \cdot & \cdot & & \cdot \\ a_{m1} & a_{m2} & \cdots & a_{mn} \end{bmatrix}$$

We also use the shorthand notation $\mathbf{A} = [a_{ij}]$.

Example 6.1

$$\mathbf{A} = \begin{bmatrix} 1 & 2 & 3 \\ 4 & 5 & 6 \end{bmatrix} \qquad \mathbf{B} = \begin{bmatrix} -1 & 0 \\ .5 & 2 \end{bmatrix} \qquad \mathbf{C} = \begin{bmatrix} 1 \\ -2 \\ 5 \end{bmatrix}$$

$$\mathbf{D} = [-.2 \quad .4 \quad .6 \quad 1.8]$$

Problem Find the dimensions of **A**, **B**, **C**, and **D**. Also find the (2, 1) entry of **A**, the (1, 2) entry of **B**, the (3, 1) entry of **C**, and the (1, 1) entry of **D**.

Solution

A is 2×3; the (2, 1) entry of **A** is 4.
B is 2×2; the (1, 2) entry of **B** is 0.
C is 3×1; the (3, 1) entry of **C** is 5.
D is 1×4; the (1, 1) entry of **D** is $-.2$. ■

A matrix with one column is a *column vector*, and a matrix with one row is a *row vector*. The entries in a vector are called *coordinates*. A column (or row) vector with n coordinates is referred to as a *column* (or *row*) n-*vector*, and n is the *dimension* of the vector. We use boldface letters such as **X**, **Y**, and **U** to denote vectors.

A row vector **U** with m coordinates can be represented as

$$\mathbf{U} = [u_1 \quad u_2 \quad \cdots \quad u_m]$$

and a column vector **X** with n coordinates can be represented as

$$\mathbf{X} = \begin{bmatrix} x_1 \\ x_2 \\ \cdot \\ \cdot \\ \cdot \\ x_n \end{bmatrix}$$

The number of coordinates or the dimension of a vector will always be clear from the way it arises.

Example 6.2 $\mathbf{W} = [1 \quad 3 \quad 8 \quad -5 \quad -2]$

$$\mathbf{X} = \begin{bmatrix} -1 \\ 1 \\ 5 \end{bmatrix} \qquad \mathbf{Y} = \begin{bmatrix} 1 & 2 \\ 3 & -1 \\ 0 & 2 \end{bmatrix} \qquad \mathbf{Z} = [1]$$

Problem Decide whether **W**, **X**, **Y**, and **Z** are vectors; if so, give their dimensions. Also find the second coordinate of each vector.

Solution

W is a row vector of dimension 5, and the second coordinate of **W** is 3.

X is a column vector of dimension 3, and its second coordinate is 1.

Y is neither a row vector nor a column vector.

Z is both a row vector and a column vector of dimension 1, and **Z** has no second coordinate. ■

Example 6.3 At a three-day long fencing competition, each of five competitors scores points by competing against each other in each of three events—the epée, foil, and saber. The winner of each event is the competitor with the highest combined total points for that event over the three days of competition. The scores for each fencer on Day 1 of competition are displayed in Table 6.1.

TABLE 6.1

	Competitor				
Event	**Arianna**	**Elisa**	**Laura**	**Britta**	**Danuta**
Epée	13	11	12	9	10
Foil	6	4	7	3	9
Saber	15	12	9	11	14

If we agree to remember the meaning of the entry in each location, then we can represent the scores on Day 1 in a 3×5 matrix; call it $\mathbf{A}$:

$$\mathbf{A} = \begin{bmatrix} 13 & 11 & 12 & 9 & 10 \\ 6 & 4 & 7 & 3 & 9 \\ 15 & 12 & 9 & 11 & 14 \end{bmatrix}$$

The corresponding matrix for another day of the competition would be viewed as equal to that for Day 1 only if each of its entries was the same as that for Day 1. If the corresponding matrix for Day 2 is

$$\mathbf{B} = \begin{bmatrix} 10 & 14 & 12 & 11 & 7 \\ 9 & 5 & 8 & 7 & 4 \\ 14 & 15 & 11 & 9 & 12 \end{bmatrix}$$

then the matrix which represents the combined scores for Day 1 and Day 2 of the competition is given by

$$\begin{bmatrix} 23 & 25 & 24 & 20 & 17 \\ 15 & 9 & 15 & 10 & 13 \\ 29 & 27 & 20 & 20 & 26 \end{bmatrix}$$

This new matrix represents the sum of $\mathbf{A}$ and $\mathbf{B}$. The entry 17 in the upper right-hand corner, the (1, 5) entry, is the sum of Danuta's scores in the Epée event over Day 1 and Day 2 of the competition. We denote this new matrix, the matrix formed by adding the corresponding entries of matrices $\mathbf{A}$ and $\mathbf{B}$, by $\mathbf{A} + \mathbf{B}$. Also, suppose that Day 3 of the competition is canceled and it is decided that the scores on Day 2 of the competition will be doubled for the purposes of determining a winner in each event. In this case, the scores for Day 2 can be represented by the matrix

$$\begin{bmatrix} 20 & 28 & 24 & 22 & 14 \\ 18 & 10 & 16 & 14 & 8 \\ 28 & 30 & 22 & 18 & 24 \end{bmatrix}$$

Since the original Day 2 score matrix is denoted by $\mathbf{B}$, it is reasonable to denote this new matrix as $2\mathbf{B}$. ■

Example 6.3 illustrates the following definitions of *equality of matrices*, *matrix addition*, and *scalar multiplication*.

Equality of Matrices

Let $\mathbf{A} = [a_{ij}]$ and $\mathbf{B} = [b_{ij}]$ be two $m \times n$ matrices. Matrix **A** is said to be *equal* to matrix **B**, written $\mathbf{A} = \mathbf{B}$, if $a_{ij} = b_{ij}$ for $1 \le i \le m$, $1 \le j \le n$.

That is, two matrices **A** and **B** are equal if they are the same size and if their corresponding entries are all equal.

Addition of Matrices

With **A** and **B** as above, the sum $\mathbf{A} + \mathbf{B}$ of matrices **A** and **B** is defined to be the matrix $\mathbf{C} = [c_{ij}]$, where $c_{ij} = a_{ij} + b_{ij}$, $1 \le i \le m$, $1 \le j \le n$.

That is, the sum of two $m \times n$ matrices is the $m \times n$ matrix whose entries are each the sum of the corresponding entries of **A** and **B**. Addition of matrices is defined only for matrices of the same size, i.e., with the same number of rows and the same number of columns.

The sum of three or more $m \times n$ matrices, **A**, **B**, **C**, . . . can be computed by first computing the sum $\mathbf{A} + \mathbf{B}$, then $(\mathbf{A} + \mathbf{B}) + \mathbf{C}$, and so on. In fact, the parentheses are unnecessary: The sum $(\mathbf{A} + \mathbf{B}) + \mathbf{C}$ is the same matrix as the sum $\mathbf{A} + (\mathbf{B} + \mathbf{C})$. Therefore there is no ambiguity in writing simply $\mathbf{A} + \mathbf{B} + \mathbf{C}$ for the sum, and we shall do so in the future.

Scalar Multiplication

If c is a number and **A** is an $m \times n$ matrix, then the *scalar multiple* $c\mathbf{A}$ is defined to be the matrix $\mathbf{D} = [d_{ij}]$, where $d_{ij} = ca_{ij}$, $1 \le i \le m$, $1 \le j \le n$.

That is, the scalar multiple of a matrix **A** is the matrix whose entries are each the corresponding entry of **A** multiplied by the scalar.

Example 6.4 Let

$$\mathbf{A} = \begin{bmatrix} 3 & 2 \\ 1 & -1 \\ 0 & 2 \end{bmatrix} \qquad \mathbf{B} = \begin{bmatrix} 2 & 1 \\ 0 & 2 \\ -1 & -3 \end{bmatrix} \qquad \mathbf{C} = \begin{bmatrix} a & 2 \\ b & -1 \\ 0 & c \end{bmatrix}$$

Problem Find $\mathbf{A} + \mathbf{B}$, $2\mathbf{A}$, $(-1)\mathbf{B}$, and the conditions on a, b, and c such that $\mathbf{A} = \mathbf{C}$.

Solution

$$\mathbf{A}+\mathbf{B}=\begin{bmatrix}3 & 2\\ 1 & -1\\ 0 & 2\end{bmatrix}+\begin{bmatrix}2 & 1\\ 0 & 2\\ -1 & -3\end{bmatrix}=\begin{bmatrix}5 & 3\\ 1 & 1\\ -1 & -1\end{bmatrix}$$

$$2\mathbf{A}=2\begin{bmatrix}3 & 2\\ 1 & -1\\ 0 & 2\end{bmatrix}=\begin{bmatrix}6 & 4\\ 2 & -2\\ 0 & 4\end{bmatrix}$$

$$(-1)\mathbf{B}=(-1)\begin{bmatrix}2 & 1\\ 0 & 2\\ -1 & -3\end{bmatrix}=\begin{bmatrix}-2 & -1\\ 0 & -2\\ 1 & 3\end{bmatrix}$$

$$\mathbf{A}=\mathbf{C} \qquad \text{or} \qquad \begin{bmatrix}3 & 2\\ 1 & -1\\ 0 & 2\end{bmatrix}=\begin{bmatrix}a & 2\\ b & -1\\ 0 & c\end{bmatrix}$$

if and only if $a = 3$, $b = 1$, and $c = 2$. ■

There are several features of matrix addition and scalar multiplication which will be useful to us.

Properties of Matrix Algebra

If **A** and **B** are $m \times n$ matrices and c and d are numbers, then

$$\mathbf{A}+\mathbf{B}=\mathbf{B}+\mathbf{A}$$
$$c\mathbf{A}+d\mathbf{A}=(c+d)\mathbf{A}$$
$$c\mathbf{A}+c\mathbf{B}=c(\mathbf{A}+\mathbf{B})$$
$$(cd)\mathbf{A}=c(d\mathbf{A})$$

In the work which follows in this and later chapters, we use these properties freely without specifically mentioning them. At times more than one may be combined into a single step in a computation. We write $-\mathbf{A}$ for the matrix $(-1)\mathbf{A}$ and $\mathbf{A}-\mathbf{B}$ for $\mathbf{A}+(-\mathbf{B})$.

Matrix Multiplication

We now turn to the topic of multiplying matrices. We begin with a special case which is important in the study of systems of equations, and then we continue by using this special case to define general matrix multiplication. First we define the product of a row n-vector **U** by a column n-vector **X**, to obtain **UX**. Then we use this idea to define the product of an $m \times n$ matrix **A** and an $n \times k$ matrix **B**, to obtain **AB**.

Row-by-Column Multiplication

If

$$\mathbf{U} = [u_1 \quad u_2 \quad \cdots \quad u_n]$$

is a row n-vector and

$$\mathbf{X} = \begin{bmatrix} x_1 \\ x_2 \\ \cdot \\ \cdot \\ \cdot \\ x_n \end{bmatrix}$$

is a column n-vector, then the product **UX** is defined and

$$\mathbf{UX} = u_1x_1 + u_2x_2 + \cdots + u_nx_n \tag{6.1}$$

The row vector in (6.1) is always written to the left of the column vector. The product of a row k-vector and a column n-vector with $n \neq k$ is not defined.

Example 6.5 Let

$$\mathbf{U} = [1 \quad -1 \quad 3] \quad \text{and} \quad \mathbf{X} = \begin{bmatrix} 4 \\ 2 \\ -1 \end{bmatrix}$$

Find **UX**.

Solution

$$\mathbf{UX} = 1(4) + (-1)(2) + 3(-1) = -1$$

■

Example 6.6 Let

$$\mathbf{U} = [2 \quad 3 \quad -4 \quad 5] \quad \text{and} \quad \mathbf{X} = \begin{bmatrix} x_1 \\ x_2 \\ x_3 \\ x_4 \end{bmatrix}$$

Find **UX**.

Solution In the column vector **X**, the entries x_1, x_2, x_3, and x_4 are variables which represent unknown numbers. By formula (6.1) the product **UX** has the form

$$\mathbf{UX} = 2x_1 + 3x_2 - 4x_3 + 5x_4$$

Thus, **UX** is a linear expression in the variables x_1, x_2, x_3, and x_4. ■

Matrix Multiplication

If $\mathbf{A} = [a_{ij}]$ is an $m \times n$ matrix and $\mathbf{B} = [b_{ij}]$ is an $n \times k$ matrix, then the *matrix product* **AB** is defined to be the $m \times k$ matrix $\mathbf{C} = [c_{ij}]$, where

$$c_{ij} = a_{i1}b_{1j} + a_{i2}b_{2j} + \cdots + a_{in}b_{nj} \qquad 1 \le i \le m, 1 \le j \le k \tag{6.2}$$

Notice that the product **AB** is defined only between matrices **A** and **B** where the number of columns of **A** is equal to the number of rows of **B**. Since the (i, j) entry of the product **AB** is determined by the ith row of matrix **A** and the jth column of matrix **B**, the (i, j) entry is said to be obtained through *row-by-column* multiplication. For example,

$$\begin{aligned} c_{32} &= [\text{third row of } \mathbf{A}] \begin{bmatrix} \text{second} \\ \text{column} \\ \text{of } \mathbf{B} \end{bmatrix} \\ &= a_{31}b_{12} + a_{32}b_{22} + \cdots + a_{3n}b_{n2} \end{aligned}$$

Example 6.7 Find the matrix products **AB** and **BC**, where

$$\mathbf{A} = \begin{bmatrix} 2 & 3 & -1 \\ -1 & 0 & 2 \end{bmatrix} \qquad \mathbf{B} = \begin{bmatrix} 1 & -1 \\ -1 & 0 \\ 1 & 2 \end{bmatrix} \qquad \mathbf{C} = \begin{bmatrix} 1 & -1 \\ -3 & 2 \end{bmatrix}$$

Solution Since **A** is 2×3 and **B** is 3×2, the product **AB** is defined and is a 2×2 matrix. Likewise, **BC** is defined and is a 3×2 matrix.

$$\begin{aligned} \mathbf{AB} &= \begin{bmatrix} 2(1) + 3(-1) + (-1)(1) & 2(-1) + 3(0) + (-1)(2) \\ (-1)(1) + 0(-1) + 2(1) & (-1)(-1) + 0(0) + 2(2) \end{bmatrix} \\ &= \begin{bmatrix} -2 & -4 \\ 1 & 5 \end{bmatrix} \end{aligned}$$

$$\mathbf{BC} = \begin{bmatrix} 1(1) + (-1)(-3) & 1(-1) + (-1)(2) \\ (-1)(1) + 0(-3) & (-1)(-1) + 0(2) \\ 1(1) + 2(-3) & 1(-1) + 2(2) \end{bmatrix}$$

$$= \begin{bmatrix} 4 & -3 \\ -1 & 1 \\ -5 & 3 \end{bmatrix}$$

■

Multiplication of three or more matrices can be defined by grouping the matrices and computing the product in steps by multiplying two matrices at a time. For example, the product of an $m \times n$ matrix **A**, an $n \times r$ matrix **B**, and an $r \times s$ matrix **C** (in that order) can be defined as (**AB**)**C**. This is to be interpreted as the result of multiplying the $m \times r$ matrix **AB** (which is defined by the definition of multiplication of two matrices) by the $r \times s$ matrix **C**. It can be shown that this is the same as the product of the $m \times n$ matrix **A** and the $n \times s$ matrix **BC**. That is, $(\mathbf{AB})\mathbf{C} = \mathbf{A}(\mathbf{BC})$, and in the future we write simply **ABC** since there is no possible ambiguity.

In contrast to the freedom we have in grouping matrices in a product in different ways, we cannot in general change the order of the factors in a matrix product. If the product **AB** of matrices **A** and **B** in that order is defined, it may be that the product of these matrices in the reverse order is not defined. Even if **AB** and **BA** are both defined, they may not be equal.

Example 6.8 If

$$\mathbf{A} = \begin{bmatrix} 2 & 0 \\ 1 & 3 \\ 0 & -1 \end{bmatrix} \quad \text{and} \quad \mathbf{B} = \begin{bmatrix} 1 & 1 \\ -1 & -1 \end{bmatrix}$$

then **AB** is defined since **A** is 3×2 and **B** is 2×2. The product **AB** is 3×2. However, the product **BA** is not defined since **B** has 2 columns and **A** has 3 rows.

With **B** as above and $\mathbf{C} = \begin{bmatrix} 2 & 2 \\ 1 & 1 \end{bmatrix}$, we have both **CB** and **BC** defined, but

$$\mathbf{CB} = \begin{bmatrix} 0 & 0 \\ 0 & 0 \end{bmatrix} \quad \text{and} \quad \mathbf{BC} = \begin{bmatrix} 3 & 3 \\ -3 & -3 \end{bmatrix}$$

This shows that in general $\mathbf{AB} \neq \mathbf{BA}$. It also illustrates that the product of a matrix **A** that is not all zeros and a matrix **B** that is not all zeros can be a matrix with all zeros. Thus the familiar result "if $ab = 0$, then either $a = 0$ or $b = 0$," which holds for numbers, does *not* hold for matrices. ■

There is a matrix **I** which plays the same role in matrix multiplication that the number 1 plays with respect to multiplication of numbers.

The $n \times n$ matrix **I** defined by

$$\mathbf{I} = \underbrace{\begin{bmatrix} 1 & 0 & 0 & \cdots & 0 \\ 0 & 1 & 0 & \cdots & 0 \\ 0 & 0 & 1 & \cdots & 0 \\ \cdot & \cdot & \cdot & & \cdot \\ \cdot & \cdot & \cdot & & \cdot \\ \cdot & \cdot & \cdot & & \cdot \\ 0 & 0 & 0 & \cdots & 1 \end{bmatrix}}_{n \text{ columns}} \Bigg\} n \text{ rows}$$

is said to be the $n \times n$ *identity* matrix.

We shall not distinguish notationally between identity matrices of different sizes. When we write **IA**, we assume that **I** has the correct size for the product to be defined.

For every matrix **A** and the identity matrices **I** for which the products **AI** and **IA** are defined, we have

$$\mathbf{AI} = \mathbf{A} \quad \text{and} \quad \mathbf{IA} = \mathbf{A}$$

We use $\mathbf{A} = \begin{bmatrix} 1 & 3 \\ 2 & -1 \end{bmatrix}$ and $\mathbf{I} = \begin{bmatrix} 1 & 0 \\ 0 & 1 \end{bmatrix}$ to illustrate the equality $\mathbf{AI} = \mathbf{A}$. We have

$$\begin{aligned} \mathbf{AI} = \begin{bmatrix} 1 & 3 \\ 2 & -1 \end{bmatrix} \begin{bmatrix} 1 & 0 \\ 0 & 1 \end{bmatrix} &= \begin{bmatrix} 1(1) + 3(0) & 1(0) + 3(1) \\ 2(1) + (-1)(0) & 2(0) + (-1)(1) \end{bmatrix} \\ &= \begin{bmatrix} 1 & 3 \\ 2 & -1 \end{bmatrix} \\ &= \mathbf{A} \end{aligned}$$

Example 6.9 Let

$$\mathbf{A} = \begin{bmatrix} 2 & 3 & 4 & 5 \\ -1 & 2 & 0 & 4 \\ 3 & -2 & 1 & -3 \end{bmatrix} \quad \text{and} \quad \mathbf{X} = \begin{bmatrix} x_1 \\ x_2 \\ x_3 \\ x_4 \end{bmatrix}$$

Problem Find **AX**.

Solution Since $\mathbf{A}$ is 3×4 and $\mathbf{X}$ is 4×1, the product $\mathbf{AX}$ is defined and is a 3×1 matrix. As in Example 6.6, the entries in the column vector $\mathbf{X}$ represent variables, and using definition (6.2), we obtain

$$\mathbf{AX} = \begin{bmatrix} 2x_1 + 3x_2 + 4x_3 + 5x_4 \\ -x_1 + 2x_2 + 4x_4 \\ 3x_1 - 2x_2 + x_3 - 3x_4 \end{bmatrix}$$

We see that each entry in the 3×1 matrix $\mathbf{AX}$ is a linear expression in the variables x_1, x_2, x_3, and x_4. ■

Using the ideas of Example 6.9, we now show that systems of linear equations, such as those studied in Chapter 5, can be conveniently represented in matrix form. If a system of m equations and n variables has the form

$$\begin{array}{ccccccccc} a_{11}x_1 & + & a_{12}x_2 & + & \cdots & + & a_{1n}x_n & = & b_1 \\ a_{21}x_1 & + & a_{22}x_2 & + & \cdots & + & a_{2n}x_n & = & b_2 \\ \vdots & & \vdots & & & & \vdots & & \vdots \\ a_{m1}x_1 & + & a_{m2}x_2 & + & \cdots & + & a_{mn}x_n & = & b_m \end{array} \tag{6.3}$$

then, as in Chapter 5, we let $\mathbf{A}$ represent the coefficient matrix. Thus,

$$\mathbf{A} = \begin{bmatrix} a_{11} & a_{12} & \cdots & a_{1n} \\ a_{21} & a_{22} & \cdots & a_{2n} \\ \vdots & \vdots & & \vdots \\ a_{m1} & a_{m2} & \cdots & a_{mn} \end{bmatrix}$$

We also define the column vectors $\mathbf{X}$ and $\mathbf{B}$ as follows:

$$\mathbf{X} = \begin{bmatrix} x_1 \\ x_2 \\ \vdots \\ x_n \end{bmatrix} \qquad \mathbf{B} = \begin{bmatrix} b_1 \\ b_2 \\ \vdots \\ b_m \end{bmatrix}$$

Then, using the definitions of matrix multiplication and matrix equality, we see that the system (6.3) is identical to the matrix equation $\mathbf{AX} = \mathbf{B}$. This justifies the shorthand notation used in Chapter 5.

Example 6.10 Let

$$\mathbf{B} = \begin{bmatrix} 8 \\ 6 \\ -5 \end{bmatrix}$$

Using the matrix A of Example 6.9, show that for

$$\mathbf{X} = \begin{bmatrix} \frac{10}{9}(1-a) \\ \frac{1}{9}(32-23a) \\ -\frac{11}{9}(1-a) \\ a \end{bmatrix},$$

we have $AX = B$ for every choice of the parameter a.

Solution Using the definition of matrix multiplication, we have

$$\mathbf{AX} = \begin{bmatrix} 2 & 3 & 4 & 5 \\ -1 & 2 & 0 & 4 \\ 3 & -2 & 1 & -3 \end{bmatrix} \begin{bmatrix} \frac{10}{9}(1-a) \\ \frac{1}{9}(32-23a) \\ -\frac{11}{9}(1-a) \\ a \end{bmatrix}$$

$$= \begin{bmatrix} 2(\frac{10}{9})(1-a) & +3(\frac{1}{9})(32-23a) & +4(-\frac{11}{9})(1-a) & +5a \\ -1(\frac{10}{9})(1-a) & +2(\frac{1}{9})(32-23a) & +0(-\frac{11}{9})(1-a) & +4a \\ 3(\frac{10}{9})(1-a) & -2(\frac{1}{9})(32-23a) & +1(-\frac{11}{9})(1-a) & -3a \end{bmatrix}$$

$$= \begin{bmatrix} 8 \\ 6 \\ -5 \end{bmatrix}$$

■

We see from Example 6.10 that the system of equations $AX = B$ has an infinite number of solutions, one for each value of the parameter a. In particular, for $a = 1$ we have the solution

$$\mathbf{X} = \begin{bmatrix} 0 \\ 1 \\ 0 \\ 1 \end{bmatrix}.$$

Exercises for Section 6.1

1. Find the dimension of each of the following matrices, and decide which are vectors.

$$(a) \begin{bmatrix} 1 & 2 & 3 \\ 0 & 1 & 5 \\ 2 & -1 & 6 \end{bmatrix} \qquad (b) \begin{bmatrix} -1 & 0 \\ .2 & .8 \\ .5 & 2 \end{bmatrix} \qquad (c) \begin{bmatrix} -1 \\ 2 \\ .5 \end{bmatrix}$$

2. Find the dimension of each of the following matrices, and decide which are vectors.

(a) $\begin{bmatrix} 1 \\ 0 \\ 1 \\ 0 \end{bmatrix}$ (b) $\begin{bmatrix} 1 & x \\ 0 & y \\ 1 & z \\ 0 & w \end{bmatrix}$ (c) $\begin{bmatrix} 1 & x \\ y & 2 \end{bmatrix}$

3. Let

$$\mathbf{A} = \begin{bmatrix} 5 & 2 \\ 1 & 0 \end{bmatrix} \quad \text{and} \quad \mathbf{B} = \begin{bmatrix} 1 & 4 \\ 2 & 3 \end{bmatrix}$$

Find $\mathbf{A} + \mathbf{B}$ and $\mathbf{A} - \mathbf{B}$.

4. Let

$$\mathbf{A} = \begin{bmatrix} 2 & 3 \\ 1 & -2 \end{bmatrix} \quad \text{and} \quad \mathbf{B} = \begin{bmatrix} 2 & -1 \\ 4 & -3 \end{bmatrix}$$

Find the following:

(a) $2\mathbf{A} + \mathbf{B}$ (b) $2\mathbf{A} - \mathbf{B}$ (c) $3\mathbf{B} - \left(\frac{1}{2}\right)\mathbf{A}$

5. Let

$$\mathbf{A} = \begin{bmatrix} 3 & -1 & 3 \\ 0 & 2 & 1 \\ 4 & -2 & -2 \end{bmatrix} \quad \text{and} \quad \mathbf{B} = \begin{bmatrix} -1 & 2 & -1 \\ 2 & -1 & 0 \\ 0 & -4 & 3 \end{bmatrix}$$

Find $3\mathbf{A} + 2\mathbf{B}$ and $2\mathbf{A} - \mathbf{B}$.

6. Find the product $\mathbf{AB}$ in each of the following cases.
   (a) $\mathbf{A}$ and $\mathbf{B}$ defined as in Exercise 3
   (b) $\mathbf{A}$ and $\mathbf{B}$ defined as in Exercise 4
   (c) $\mathbf{A}$ and $\mathbf{B}$ defined as in Exercise 5

7. Let

$$\mathbf{A} = \begin{bmatrix} 2 & -1 & 0 \\ 4 & -2 & 3 \end{bmatrix} \quad \mathbf{B} = \begin{bmatrix} -1 & 2 \\ 2 & 1 \\ 3 & 2 \end{bmatrix} \quad \mathbf{C} = \begin{bmatrix} -1 & 0 & -1 & 1 \\ 2 & -2 & 0 & 3 \end{bmatrix} \quad \mathbf{D} = \begin{bmatrix} 3 & -1 \\ 0 & 4 \\ -1 & 3 \end{bmatrix}$$

Decide which of the following operations are defined, and carry out those which are defined.

(a) $\mathbf{A} + \mathbf{B}$ (b) $\mathbf{AB}$ (c) $\mathbf{BC}$ (d) $\mathbf{ABC}$ (e) $(\mathbf{B} + \mathbf{D})\mathbf{C}$

8. For matrices $\mathbf{A}$, $\mathbf{B}$, $\mathbf{C}$ and $\mathbf{D}$ given in Exercise 7, decide which of the following operations are defined, and carry out those operations that are defined.

(a) $3\mathbf{D} - \mathbf{B}$ (b) $\mathbf{DCD}$ (c) $\mathbf{ABAB}$ (d) $\mathbf{A}(\mathbf{D} + \mathbf{B})\mathbf{C}$

9. Let $\mathbf{A} = \begin{bmatrix} 4 & -2 \\ 2 & 2 \\ 5 & -3 \end{bmatrix}$ and $\mathbf{B} = \begin{bmatrix} -1 & 3 \\ 4 & 1 \\ 2 & -2 \end{bmatrix}$.

   A matrix **C** satisfies $3\mathbf{A} + \mathbf{C} = 2\mathbf{B}$. Find **C**.

10. Matrices **A** and **B** are defined as

$$\mathbf{A} = \begin{bmatrix} 4 & 1 & 2 \\ 2 & -2 & c \\ 2 & c & 6 \end{bmatrix} \quad \text{and} \quad \mathbf{B} = \begin{bmatrix} 5 & c & -3 \\ -1 & 2 & 0 \\ 3 & c & 4 \end{bmatrix}.$$

   For what value of c is the (1,2) entry in the matrix product **AB** equal to 8?

11. In the situation described in Example 6.3, Day 3 is canceled, and the winner of each event will be determined by adding together the competitors' scores on Day 1 for that event and twice the competitors' scores on Day 2 for that event. Determine the winner of each event in the competition.

12. A car dealership has two salesmen, Rob (R) and Steve (St). The dealership sells cars (C), vans (V), SUVs (S), and trucks (T). Sales figures can be viewed in the form of the following matrices:

$$\text{January} \quad \begin{array}{c} \\ C \\ V \\ S \\ T \end{array}\begin{array}{c} \begin{array}{cc} R & St \end{array} \\ \begin{bmatrix} 4 & 3 \\ 2a & 2 \\ 6 & 4a \\ 1 & 4 \end{bmatrix} \end{array} \qquad \text{February} \quad \begin{array}{c} \\ C \\ V \\ S \\ T \end{array}\begin{array}{c} \begin{array}{cc} R & St \end{array} \\ \begin{bmatrix} 1 & 4 \\ 3b & 2 \\ 5 & b \\ 6 & 4 \end{bmatrix} \end{array} \qquad \text{Jan./Feb. combined} \quad \begin{array}{c} \\ C \\ V \\ S \\ T \end{array}\begin{array}{c} \begin{array}{cc} R & St \end{array} \\ \begin{bmatrix} 5 & 7 \\ 18 & 4 \\ 11 & 16 \\ 7 & 8 \end{bmatrix} \end{array}$$

   (*a*) How many vans did Rob sell during the month of January?
   (*b*) How many SUVs did Steve sell in February?

13. Let

$$\mathbf{A} = \begin{bmatrix} 2 & 2 \\ 3 & 1 \end{bmatrix} \quad \mathbf{B} = \begin{bmatrix} 3 & 1 \\ -1 & 0 \\ 4 & 2 \end{bmatrix} \quad \mathbf{C} = \begin{bmatrix} 4 & 0 & 1 \\ 1 & -1 & 2 \\ 3 & 1 & 1 \end{bmatrix} \quad \mathbf{D} = \begin{bmatrix} -1 & 0 \\ 2 & 1 \end{bmatrix}$$

   Find: (*a*) **2B** (*b*) **BA** (*c*) **CBA**

14. A matrix **C** satisfies $4\mathbf{A} - 2\mathbf{C} = 3\mathbf{B}$, where **A** and **B** are defined as

$$\mathbf{A} = \begin{bmatrix} 4 & -2 & 1 \\ 2 & 0 & -2 \\ 2 & -5 & 6 \end{bmatrix} \quad \text{and} \quad \mathbf{B} = \begin{bmatrix} 5 & 0 & -3 \\ 3 & -1 & 2 \\ 3 & 0 & 4 \end{bmatrix}.$$

   Find the matrix **C**.

15. Let matrices **A**, **B**, and **C** be defined by

$$\mathbf{A} = \begin{bmatrix} 2 & 0 & -3 \\ 1 & 4 & 6 \end{bmatrix} \quad \mathbf{B} = \begin{bmatrix} -1 & 2 & 0 \\ 1 & 4 & 3 \end{bmatrix} \quad \mathbf{C} = \begin{bmatrix} 3 & 1 \\ 2 & 0 \end{bmatrix}$$

Decide which of the following operations are defined, and carry out those which are defined.

(*a*) $3\mathbf{A} - \mathbf{B}$ (*b*) $\mathbf{CA}$
(*c*) $(\mathbf{A} - 2\mathbf{B})\mathbf{C}$ (*d*) $\mathbf{ABC}$

16. Let matrices **A**, **B**, and **C** be as in Exercise 15, and let

$$\mathbf{X} = \begin{bmatrix} 1 \\ 0 \\ 4 \end{bmatrix} \qquad \mathbf{Y} = \begin{bmatrix} 2 \\ -1 \end{bmatrix}$$

Decide which of the following are defined, and evaluate those which are defined.

(*a*) $2\mathbf{X} - \mathbf{Y}$ (*b*) $\mathbf{AX}$
(*c*) $\mathbf{AX} + \mathbf{CY}$ (*d*) $\mathbf{CAX}$

17. Let

$$\mathbf{A} = \begin{bmatrix} 3 & 1 \\ 2 & 1 \end{bmatrix}$$

For what value of c does the matrix

$$\mathbf{B} = \begin{bmatrix} 1 & -1 \\ -2 & c \end{bmatrix}$$

satisfy $\mathbf{AB} = \mathbf{I}$?

18. For what values of c and d does the following matrix equation hold?

$$c\begin{bmatrix} 3 \\ 1 \end{bmatrix} + d\begin{bmatrix} -1 \\ 2 \end{bmatrix} = \begin{bmatrix} 7 \\ 0 \end{bmatrix}$$

19. Let

$$\mathbf{A} = \begin{bmatrix} 2 & -1 \\ 4 & 0 \end{bmatrix} \quad \text{and} \quad \mathbf{B} = \begin{bmatrix} -2 & 3 \\ -1 & 2 \end{bmatrix}$$

(*a*) Find a matrix **C** which satisfies $2\mathbf{A} + \mathbf{C} = \mathbf{B}$.
(*b*) Find a matrix **D** which satisfies $\mathbf{A} + \mathbf{B} + \mathbf{D} = \mathbf{I}$.

20.

$$\text{Let a matrix } \mathbf{A} = \begin{bmatrix} a & 1 \\ -1 & b \end{bmatrix} \quad \text{Suppose } \mathbf{A}\begin{bmatrix} 2 \\ 3 \end{bmatrix} = \begin{bmatrix} 4 \\ 7 \end{bmatrix}$$

Find a and b.

21. Find three 2×2 matrices, **A**, **B**, and **C** (**C** not all zeros) such that $\mathbf{AC} = \mathbf{BC}$ but $\mathbf{A} \neq \mathbf{B}$.
22. Find a 2×2 matrix **A** whose entries are all different from zero but for which **AA** has all zero entries. Also, find a 2×2 matrix **A**, so that $\mathbf{AA} = \mathbf{I}$ and **A** has no zero entries.
23. For a square matrix **A** (equal numbers of rows and columns), the product **AA** is always defined. This product is denoted $\mathbf{A}^2$. Likewise, $\mathbf{A}^3 = \mathbf{AAA}$, and for any

positive integer n, the product of $\mathbf{AAA} \cdots \mathbf{A}$ with n factors is denoted $\mathbf{A}^n$. For

$$\mathbf{A} = \begin{bmatrix} 2 & 1 \\ 1 & 0 \end{bmatrix}$$

find $\mathbf{A}^2$ and $\mathbf{A}^3$.

24. Let $\mathbf{P} = \begin{bmatrix} .5 & .5 \\ 1 & 0 \end{bmatrix}$. Using the definitions of Exercise 23, find $\mathbf{P}^2$, $\mathbf{P}^4$, and $\mathbf{P}^8$.
25. Let $\mathbf{P}$ be as in Exercise 24, and let $\mathbf{X} = [2 \quad 1]$. Show that $\mathbf{XP} = \mathbf{X}$ and $\mathbf{XP}^2 = \mathbf{X}$.
26. Let $\mathbf{P}$ be as in Exercise 24, and let $\mathbf{X} = \begin{bmatrix} .5 \\ .5 \end{bmatrix}$. Show that $\mathbf{PX} = \mathbf{X}$ and $\mathbf{P}^2\mathbf{X} = \mathbf{X}$.
27. Let

$$\mathbf{P} = \begin{bmatrix} 0 & 1 & 0 \\ 0 & 0 & 1 \\ \frac{2}{3} & 0 & \frac{1}{3} \end{bmatrix}$$

Using the definitions of Exercise 23, find $\mathbf{P}^2$ and $\mathbf{P}^4$.

28. Let $\mathbf{P}$ be as in Exercise 27, and let $\mathbf{X} = [\,1 \quad 1 \quad \frac{3}{2}\,]$. Show that $\mathbf{XP} = \mathbf{X}$. In fact, by using mathematical induction, one can show $\mathbf{XP}^n = \mathbf{X}$ for any positive integer n. Show that $\mathbf{XP}^4 = \mathbf{X}$.
29. Let $\mathbf{P}$ be as in Exercise 27, and let $\mathbf{X}$ satisfy $\mathbf{XP} = \mathbf{X}$.
    (*a*) Show that if $\mathbf{Y} = k\mathbf{X}$ for any number k, then $\mathbf{Y}$ satisfies $\mathbf{YP} = \mathbf{Y}$.
    (*b*) Find a vector $\mathbf{Y}$ the sum of whose coordinates is 1 which satisfies $\mathbf{YP} = \mathbf{Y}$. (*Hint*: Use Exercise 28.)
30. Let $\mathbf{P} = \begin{bmatrix} 0 & 1 \\ .5 & .5 \end{bmatrix}$. Find a vector $\mathbf{X}$ which satisfies $\mathbf{XP} = \mathbf{X}$.
31. Let $\mathbf{P} = \begin{bmatrix} 0 & 1 & 0 \\ 0 & 0 & 1 \\ \frac{1}{4} & \frac{1}{4} & \frac{1}{2} \end{bmatrix}$. Find a vector $\mathbf{X}$ which satisfies $\mathbf{XP} = \mathbf{X}$.
    (*Hint*: Use the techniques of Chapter 5.)
32. Write the following systems of equations in the matrix form $\mathbf{AX} = \mathbf{B}$. Thus, find $\mathbf{A}$, $\mathbf{X}$, and $\mathbf{B}$.
    (*a*) $\begin{aligned} 3x_1 + 4x_2 &= 5 \\ -x_1 + 2x_2 &= 3 \end{aligned}$
    (*b*) $\begin{aligned} -2x_1 + \phantom{4x_2 +{}} x_3 &= 7 \\ 4x_2 + 9x_3 &= 19 \\ 4x_1 - x_2 &= 29 \end{aligned}$
33. Let

$$\mathbf{A} = \begin{bmatrix} 1 & 2 & 1 \\ 2 & 3 & 1 \\ -2 & 4 & 6 \end{bmatrix} \qquad \mathbf{X} = \begin{bmatrix} 2+t \\ 1-t \\ t \end{bmatrix} \qquad \mathbf{B} = \begin{bmatrix} 4 \\ 7 \\ 0 \end{bmatrix}$$

Use the definition of matrix multiplication to show that for each value of the variable t, $\mathbf{X}$ is a solution of the matrix equation $\mathbf{AX} = \mathbf{B}$.

34. Find a 2×2 matrix $\mathbf{B}$ such that $\mathbf{AB} = \mathbf{I}$, where $\mathbf{A} = \begin{bmatrix} 1 & 2 \\ 3 & 7 \end{bmatrix}$ and $\mathbf{I} = \begin{bmatrix} 1 & 0 \\ 0 & 1 \end{bmatrix}$.

35. Find a 2×2 matrix **B** such that $\mathbf{AB} = \mathbf{C}$, where

$$\mathbf{A} = \begin{bmatrix} 1 & -2 \\ -3 & 4 \end{bmatrix} \quad \text{and} \quad \mathbf{C} = \begin{bmatrix} 10 & -7 \\ -22 & 15 \end{bmatrix}$$

36. Write the system of equations below in the form $\mathbf{AX} = \mathbf{B}$ and solve the system for **X** using the methods of Section 5.3

$$\begin{aligned} x + y + z &= 8 \\ x + 2y + 3z &= 13 \\ y + 3z &= 6 \end{aligned}$$

37. Write the system of equations below in the form $\mathbf{AX} = \mathbf{C}$ and solve the system for **X** using the methods of Section 5.3

$$\begin{aligned} x + y + z &= 10 \\ x + 2y + 3z &= 21 \\ y + 3z &= 14 \end{aligned}$$

NOTE The coefficient matrix **A** is the same in Exercises 36 and 37, the only difference between the two is that $\mathbf{B} \neq \mathbf{C}$. In section 6.2, we develop a method of solving systems of equations such as these that will allow us to solve both systems very efficiently.

6.2 MATRIX INVERSES

Linear equations in a single scalar variable are especially easy to solve. For instance, to find x for which $5x = 3$, we multiply both sides of the equation by $\frac{1}{5}$ (the reciprocal of 5) to obtain

$$\tfrac{1}{5}(5x) = 1 \cdot x = \tfrac{1}{5} \cdot 3 = \tfrac{3}{5}$$

or $x = \frac{3}{5}$. Superficially, a system of equations written in matrix form as $\mathbf{AX} = \mathbf{B}$ appears much like the above scalar equation $5x = 3$. It would be useful to have a reciprocal of matrix **A** which could be used to solve the equation $\mathbf{AX} = \mathbf{B}$ in the same way as $\frac{1}{5}$ was used to solve the scalar equation $5x = 3$. Unfortunately, in general, a matrix **A** will not have a reciprocal which is analogous to the reciprocal of a nonzero number. There is, however, a special case in which the method described above can be applied to matrix equations.

Inverse of a Matrix

An $n \times n$ matrix **A** is said to be *invertible* if there is an $n \times n$ matrix **B** such that $\mathbf{BA} = \mathbf{AB} = \mathbf{I}$. The matrix **B** with this property is said to be the *inverse* of **A** and is written $\mathbf{A}^{-1}$.

Not all square matrices are invertible; some are and others are not. If a matrix is invertible, then *there is only one* matrix $\mathbf{A}^{-1}$ such that $\mathbf{A}^{-1}\mathbf{A} = \mathbf{I} = \mathbf{A}\mathbf{A}^{-1}$; that is, the inverse of a square matrix is unique.

If $\mathbf{A}$ is invertible, then the solution of the system of equations $\mathbf{AX} = \mathbf{B}$ is straightforward. Indeed, if $\mathbf{A}^{-1}$ is the inverse of $\mathbf{A}$, then

$$\mathbf{A}^{-1}\mathbf{AX} = \mathbf{IX} = \mathbf{X}$$

Therefore, if we multiply the equation $\mathbf{AX} = \mathbf{B}$ on the left by $\mathbf{A}^{-1}$, then we obtain

$$\mathbf{A}^{-1}\mathbf{AX} = \mathbf{A}^{-1}\mathbf{B} \qquad \text{or} \qquad \mathbf{X} = \mathbf{A}^{-1}\mathbf{B}$$

Since $\mathbf{A}^{-1}$ and $\mathbf{B}$ are known matrices, this provides a vector $\mathbf{X}$ which satisfies the equation $\mathbf{AX} = \mathbf{B}$.

In general, one would not solve a single system $\mathbf{AX} = \mathbf{B}$ by computing the inverse of $\mathbf{A}$ since this computation frequently involves more labor than the direct solution of $\mathbf{AX} = \mathbf{B}$ by the methods described in Section 5.3. However, if one is asked to solve several systems with the same coefficient matrix, e.g.,

$$\mathbf{AX} = \mathbf{B} \qquad \mathbf{AX} = \mathbf{B}' \qquad \mathbf{AX} = \mathbf{B}''$$

then it may be desirable to compute $\mathbf{A}^{-1}$. Indeed, once we have $\mathbf{A}^{-1}$, we can obtain the solutions of these equations immediately as $\mathbf{A}^{-1}\mathbf{B}$, $\mathbf{A}^{-1}\mathbf{B}'$, and $\mathbf{A}^{-1}\mathbf{B}''$, respectively. Also there are important uses of the inverse matrix other than its use in solving systems of equations. One such use will be discussed in our study of Markov chains (Chapter 8).

Our method for computing the inverse of a matrix is essentially the same as the method described in Section 5.3 for solving a system of linear equations. This method consists of systematically transforming a certain augmented matrix into reduced form. Since it may seem somewhat mysterious that this method should be useful in computing inverse matrices, first we describe briefly *why* the method works, then we show *how* it works.

Given a matrix $\mathbf{A}$, our problem is to find a matrix $\mathbf{B}$ such that $\mathbf{AB} = \mathbf{I}$. If we write $\mathbf{B}^{(1)}, \mathbf{B}^{(2)}, \ldots, \mathbf{B}^{(n)}$ for the columns of $\mathbf{B}$ in order, then the equation $\mathbf{AB} = \mathbf{I}$ is equivalent to n systems of equations for unknown vectors $\mathbf{B}^{(1)}, \mathbf{B}^{(2)}, \ldots, \mathbf{B}^{(n)}$:

$$\mathbf{AB}^{(1)} = \begin{bmatrix} 1 \\ 0 \\ \cdot \\ \cdot \\ \cdot \\ 0 \end{bmatrix}, \quad \mathbf{AB}^{(2)} = \begin{bmatrix} 0 \\ 1 \\ \cdot \\ \cdot \\ \cdot \\ 0 \end{bmatrix}, \quad \ldots, \quad \mathbf{AB}^{(n)} = \begin{bmatrix} 0 \\ 0 \\ \cdot \\ \cdot \\ \cdot \\ 1 \end{bmatrix} \tag{6.4}$$

For example, given the matrix

$$\mathbf{A} = \begin{bmatrix} 3 & 2 \\ 4 & 3 \end{bmatrix}$$

the problem of finding the inverse $\mathbf{B} = [\mathbf{B}^{(1)}, \mathbf{B}^{(2)}]$ of $\mathbf{A}$ is equivalent to solving

$$\mathbf{AB} = \mathbf{I} = \begin{bmatrix} 1 & 0 \\ 0 & 1 \end{bmatrix} \quad \text{or} \quad \mathbf{AB}^{(1)} = \begin{bmatrix} 1 \\ 0 \end{bmatrix} \quad \mathbf{AB}^{(2)} = \begin{bmatrix} 0 \\ 1 \end{bmatrix}$$

In the general case, if we solve the n systems (6.4) for the vectors $\mathbf{B}^{(1)}$, $\mathbf{B}^{(2)}, \ldots, \mathbf{B}^{(n)}$, then we have matrix $\mathbf{B}$, that is, the inverse of $\mathbf{A}$. If $\mathbf{A}$ is invertible, then each of the systems (6.4) can be solved by the method of Section 5.3. In particular, we can use the operations of types 1, 2, and 3 on the augmented matrices

$$\left[\begin{array}{c|c} & 1 \\ & 0 \\ \mathbf{A} & \vdots \\ & \vdots \\ & 0 \end{array}\right], \quad \left[\begin{array}{c|c} & 0 \\ & 1 \\ \mathbf{A} & \vdots \\ & \vdots \\ & 0 \end{array}\right], \quad \ldots, \quad \left[\begin{array}{c|c} & 0 \\ & 0 \\ \mathbf{A} & \vdots \\ & \vdots \\ & 1 \end{array}\right]$$

However, since the coefficient matrices are the same in each case, we can solve all n systems simultaneously! We simply set up the "augmented" matrix

$$\left[\begin{array}{c|cccc} & 1 & 0 & \cdots & 0 \\ & 0 & 1 & \cdots & 0 \\ \mathbf{A} & \cdot & \cdot & \cdots & \cdot \\ & 0 & 0 & \cdots & 1 \end{array}\right] \quad \text{or} \quad [\mathbf{A}|\mathbf{I}] \tag{6.5}$$

and then we use the operations of types 1, 2, and 3 to successively replace this by simpler systems until the $n \times n$ matrix on the left of (6.5) is the identity matrix. Now the matrix on the right of the new augmented matrix is $\mathbf{A}^{-1}$.

Method of Determining Invertibility and Computing the Inverse of a Square Matrix A

1. Form the matrix $[\mathbf{A}|\mathbf{I}]$.
2. Use operations of types 1, 2, and 3 to successively transform this matrix.
   a. If $[\mathbf{A} \mid \mathbf{I}]$ can be so transformed into $[\mathbf{I} \mid \mathbf{B}]$, then $\mathbf{A}$ is invertible and $\mathbf{A}^{-1} = \mathbf{B}$.
   b. If $[\mathbf{A} \mid \mathbf{I}]$ cannot be transformed into the form $[\mathbf{I} \mid \mathbf{B}]$, then $\mathbf{A}$ is not invertible. Matrix $\mathbf{A}$ is not invertible if and only if one of the matrices obtained from $[\mathbf{A} \mid \mathbf{I}]$ by these transformations has a row consisting entirely of zeros to the left of the vertical line.

Example 6.11 Find the inverse (if it exists) of the matrix

$$\mathbf{A} = \begin{bmatrix} 2 & 1 \\ 5 & 3 \end{bmatrix}$$

Solution We form the augmented matrix $[\mathbf{A} \mid \mathbf{I}]$:

$$\left[\begin{array}{cc|cc} 2 & 1 & 1 & 0 \\ 5 & 3 & 0 & 1 \end{array}\right]$$

Our goal is to transform the left-hand side of this augmented matrix into an identity matrix. First, we multiply the first row by $\frac{1}{2}$ to obtain

$$\left[\begin{array}{cc|cc} 1 & \frac{1}{2} & \frac{1}{2} & 0 \\ 5 & 3 & 0 & 1 \end{array}\right]$$

Next, we multiply the first row by -5, add it to the second row, and use the result as a new second row:

$$\left[\begin{array}{cc|cc} 1 & \frac{1}{2} & \frac{1}{2} & 0 \\ 0 & \frac{1}{2} & -\frac{5}{2} & 1 \end{array}\right]$$

Continuing, we multiply the second row by 2:

$$\left[\begin{array}{cc|cc} 1 & \frac{1}{2} & \frac{1}{2} & 0 \\ 0 & 1 & -5 & 2 \end{array}\right]$$

Finally, we multiply the second row by $-\frac{1}{2}$, add it to the first row, and use the result as a new first row:

$$\left[\begin{array}{cc|cc} 1 & 0 & 3 & -1 \\ 0 & 1 & -5 & 2 \end{array}\right]$$

The left-hand side is now an identity matrix. We conclude that the matrix $\mathbf{A}$ is invertible and that

$$\mathbf{A}^{-1} = \begin{bmatrix} 3 & -1 \\ -5 & 2 \end{bmatrix}$$

■

Example 6.12 Find the inverse (if it exists) of the matrix

$$\mathbf{A} = \begin{bmatrix} 2 & 0 & 1 \\ 2 & 1 & -1 \\ 3 & 1 & -1 \end{bmatrix}$$

Solution We form the augmented matrix

$$\left[\begin{array}{ccc|ccc} 2 & 0 & 1 & 1 & 0 & 0 \\ 2 & 1 & -1 & 0 & 1 & 0 \\ 3 & 1 & -1 & 0 & 0 & 1 \end{array}\right]$$

First, we multiply the first row by $\frac{1}{2}$ to obtain

$$\left[\begin{array}{ccc|ccc} 1 & 0 & \frac{1}{2} & \frac{1}{2} & 0 & 0 \\ 2 & 1 & -1 & 0 & 1 & 0 \\ 3 & 1 & -1 & 0 & 0 & 1 \end{array}\right]$$

Next we multiply the first row by -2 and add it to the second row and multiply the first row by -3 and add it to the third row. The next matrix is

$$\left[\begin{array}{ccc|ccc} 1 & 0 & \frac{1}{2} & \frac{1}{2} & 0 & 0 \\ 0 & 1 & -2 & -1 & 1 & 0 \\ 0 & 1 & -\frac{5}{2} & -\frac{3}{2} & 0 & 1 \end{array}\right]$$

The next step is to multiply the second row by -1 and add it to the third row. The resulting matrix is

$$\left[\begin{array}{ccc|ccc} 1 & 0 & \frac{1}{2} & \frac{1}{2} & 0 & 0 \\ 0 & 1 & -2 & -1 & 1 & 0 \\ 0 & 0 & -\frac{1}{2} & -\frac{1}{2} & -1 & 1 \end{array}\right]$$

Multiplying the third row by -2, we obtain

$$\left[\begin{array}{ccc|ccc} 1 & 0 & \frac{1}{2} & \frac{1}{2} & 0 & 0 \\ 0 & 1 & -2 & -1 & 1 & 0 \\ 0 & 0 & 1 & 1 & 2 & -2 \end{array}\right]$$

Finally, multiplying the third row by 2 and adding it to the second row and multiplying the third row by $-\frac{1}{2}$ and adding it to the first row, we obtain

$$\left[\begin{array}{ccc|ccc} 1 & 0 & 0 & 0 & -1 & 1 \\ 0 & 1 & 0 & 1 & 5 & -4 \\ 0 & 0 & 1 & 1 & 2 & -2 \end{array}\right]$$

We conclude that the matrix $\mathbf{A}$ is invertible and that

$$\mathbf{A}^{-1} = \begin{bmatrix} 0 & -1 & 1 \\ 1 & 5 & -4 \\ 1 & 2 & -2 \end{bmatrix}$$

Although it is not a necessary part of the method, we verify our work in this example by showing that $\mathbf{A}^{-1}\mathbf{A} = \mathbf{I}$. We have

$$\begin{bmatrix} 0 & -1 & 1 \\ 1 & 5 & -4 \\ 1 & 2 & -2 \end{bmatrix} \begin{bmatrix} 2 & 0 & 1 \\ 2 & 1 & -1 \\ 3 & 1 & -1 \end{bmatrix}$$

$$= \begin{bmatrix} 0(2)+(-1)(2)+1(3) & 0(0)+(-1)(1)+1(1) & 0(1)+(-1)(-1)+1(-1) \\ 1(2)+5(2)+(-4)(3) & 1(0)+5(1)+(-4)(1) & 1(1)+5(-1)+(-4)(-1) \\ 1(2)+2(2)+(-2)(3) & 1(0)+2(1)+(-2)(1) & 1(1)+2(-1)+(-2)(-1) \end{bmatrix}$$

$$= \begin{bmatrix} 1 & 0 & 0 \\ 0 & 1 & 0 \\ 0 & 0 & 1 \end{bmatrix}$$

■

It is worthwhile to consider an example which illustrates how we can infer from the failure of the method proposed here that a matrix is not invertible.

Example 6.13 Find the inverse (if it exists) of the matrix

$$\mathbf{A} = \begin{bmatrix} 2 & 0 & 1 \\ 3 & 1 & -1 \\ -2 & -2 & 4 \end{bmatrix}$$

Solution We form the augmented matrix

$$\left[\begin{array}{ccc|ccc} 2 & 0 & 1 & 1 & 0 & 0 \\ 3 & 1 & -1 & 0 & 1 & 0 \\ -2 & -2 & 4 & 0 & 0 & 1 \end{array}\right]$$

We multiply the first row by $\frac{1}{2}$ to obtain

$$\left[\begin{array}{ccc|ccc} 1 & 0 & \frac{1}{2} & \frac{1}{2} & 0 & 0 \\ 3 & 1 & -1 & 0 & 1 & 0 \\ -2 & -2 & 4 & 0 & 0 & 1 \end{array}\right]$$

Next we multiply the first row by -3 and add it to the second row, and we multiply the first row by 2 and add it to the third row. The new matrix is

$$\left[\begin{array}{ccc|ccc} 1 & 0 & \frac{1}{2} & \frac{1}{2} & 0 & 0 \\ 0 & 1 & -\frac{5}{2} & -\frac{3}{2} & 1 & 0 \\ 0 & -2 & 5 & 1 & 0 & 1 \end{array}\right]$$

We continue by multiplying the second row by 2 and adding it to the third row. We have

$$\left[\begin{array}{ccc|ccc} 1 & 0 & \frac{1}{2} & \frac{1}{2} & 0 & 0 \\ 0 & 1 & -\frac{5}{2} & -\frac{3}{2} & 1 & 0 \\ 0 & 0 & 0 & -2 & 2 & 1 \end{array}\right]$$

Notice the third row of this matrix. It has only zeros to the left of the vertical line. Therefore, $\mathbf{A}$ is not invertible. In particular, since there is a nonzero entry in the (3, 4) spot of the augmented matrix, we conclude that the system of equations

$$\mathbf{AX} = \begin{bmatrix} 1 \\ 0 \\ 0 \end{bmatrix} \tag{6.6}$$

has no solutions. In fact, in this case neither do the systems

$$\mathbf{AX} = \begin{bmatrix} 0 \\ 1 \\ 0 \end{bmatrix} \quad \text{and} \quad \mathbf{AX} = \begin{bmatrix} 0 \\ 0 \\ 1 \end{bmatrix}$$

■

It is important to remember the connection between the invertibility of a matrix $\mathbf{A}$ and the solvability of a system of equations $\mathbf{AX} = \mathbf{B}$. We have seen that if $\mathbf{A}$ has an inverse, then $\mathbf{AX} = \mathbf{B}$ always has a unique solution, given by $\mathbf{X} = \mathbf{A}^{-1}\mathbf{B}$. On the other hand, if $\mathbf{A}$ does not have an inverse, then $\mathbf{AX} = \mathbf{B}$ may or may not have a solution; it depends on the particular $\mathbf{A}$ and $\mathbf{B}$. For instance, with matrix $\mathbf{A}$ of Example 6.13, which we have just shown to be noninvertible, the equation

$$\mathbf{AX} = \begin{bmatrix} 1 \\ 2 \\ -2 \end{bmatrix}$$

is solvable, and the vector

$$\mathbf{X} = \begin{bmatrix} 1 \\ -2 \\ -1 \end{bmatrix}$$

is a solution. We saw that Equation (6.6) with the same matrix $\mathbf{A}$ had no solutions.

Example 6.14 Let

$$\mathbf{A} = \begin{bmatrix} 2 & -1 \\ 4 & 3 \end{bmatrix}$$

Problem Use the inverse of matrix **A** to solve the equations

$$\mathbf{AX} = \begin{bmatrix} 1 \\ 3 \end{bmatrix} \qquad \mathbf{AX} = \begin{bmatrix} 3 \\ 2 \end{bmatrix} \qquad \mathbf{AX} = \begin{bmatrix} 1 \\ -1 \end{bmatrix}$$

Solution We begin by computing $\mathbf{A}^{-1}$. First we form the augmented matrix $[\mathbf{A}|\mathbf{I}]$:

$$\left[\begin{array}{cc|cc} 2 & -1 & 1 & 0 \\ 4 & 3 & 0 & 1 \end{array}\right]$$

We proceed to use row reduction operations to determine $\mathbf{A}^{-1}$.

$$\left[\begin{array}{cc|cc} 1 & -\frac{1}{2} & \frac{1}{2} & 0 \\ 4 & 3 & 0 & 1 \end{array}\right]$$

$$\left[\begin{array}{cc|cc} 1 & -\frac{1}{2} & \frac{1}{2} & 0 \\ 0 & 5 & -2 & 1 \end{array}\right]$$

$$\left[\begin{array}{cc|cc} 1 & -\frac{1}{2} & \frac{1}{2} & 0 \\ 0 & 1 & -\frac{2}{5} & \frac{1}{5} \end{array}\right]$$

$$\left[\begin{array}{cc|cc} 1 & 0 & \frac{3}{10} & \frac{1}{10} \\ 0 & 1 & -\frac{2}{5} & \frac{1}{5} \end{array}\right]$$

Therefore,

$$\mathbf{A}^{-1} = \begin{bmatrix} \frac{3}{10} & \frac{1}{10} \\ -\frac{2}{5} & \frac{1}{5} \end{bmatrix}$$

The solution of $\mathbf{AX} = \begin{bmatrix} 1 \\ 3 \end{bmatrix}$ is

$$\mathbf{X} = \mathbf{A}^{-1}\begin{bmatrix} 1 \\ 3 \end{bmatrix} = \begin{bmatrix} \frac{3}{10} & \frac{1}{10} \\ -\frac{2}{5} & \frac{1}{5} \end{bmatrix} \begin{bmatrix} 1 \\ 3 \end{bmatrix} = \begin{bmatrix} \frac{3}{5} \\ \frac{1}{5} \end{bmatrix}$$

The solution of $\mathbf{AX} = \begin{bmatrix} 3 \\ 2 \end{bmatrix}$ is

$$\mathbf{X} = \mathbf{A}^{-1}\begin{bmatrix} 3 \\ 2 \end{bmatrix} = \begin{bmatrix} \frac{11}{10} \\ -\frac{4}{5} \end{bmatrix}$$

and the solution of $\mathbf{AX} = \begin{bmatrix} 1 \\ -1 \end{bmatrix}$ is

$$\mathbf{X} = \mathbf{A}^{-1}\begin{bmatrix} 1 \\ -1 \end{bmatrix} = \begin{bmatrix} \frac{1}{5} \\ -\frac{3}{5} \end{bmatrix}$$

■

Example 6.15 Let

$$\mathbf{A} = \begin{bmatrix} 2 & 1 \\ 5 & 3 \end{bmatrix} \quad \text{and} \quad \mathbf{C} = \begin{bmatrix} 2 & 1 \\ 1 & -1 \end{bmatrix}$$

Problem Find a matrix **B** which satisfies **AB** = **C**.

Solution If **A** is invertible, then the equation **AB** = **C** is the same as $\mathbf{B} = \mathbf{A}^{-1}\mathbf{C}$. (Why?) Therefore, if we can invert **A**, then we can solve the problem. But we have already found (in Example 6.11) that **A** is invertible and that

$$\mathbf{A}^{-1} = \begin{bmatrix} 3 & -1 \\ -5 & 2 \end{bmatrix}$$

Consequently we have

$$\mathbf{B} = \mathbf{A}^{-1}\mathbf{C} = \begin{bmatrix} 3 & -1 \\ -5 & 2 \end{bmatrix}\begin{bmatrix} 2 & 1 \\ 1 & -1 \end{bmatrix} = \begin{bmatrix} 5 & 4 \\ -8 & -7 \end{bmatrix}$$

as the desired matrix. ■

Exercises for Section 6.2

1. Let $\mathbf{A} = \begin{bmatrix} 1 & 0 \\ 2 & 1 \end{bmatrix}$ and $\mathbf{B} = \begin{bmatrix} 1 & 0 \\ -2 & 1 \end{bmatrix}$. Decide whether $\mathbf{B} = \mathbf{A}^{-1}$ by computing **AB** and **BA**.
2. Let $\mathbf{A} = \begin{bmatrix} 1 & 2 \\ 3 & 4 \end{bmatrix}$ and $\mathbf{B} = \begin{bmatrix} -2 & 1 \\ \frac{3}{2} & -\frac{1}{2} \end{bmatrix}$. Decide whether $\mathbf{B} = \mathbf{A}^{-1}$ by computing **AB** and **BA**.

3. Let $\mathbf{A}$ and its inverse be $\mathbf{A} = \begin{bmatrix} 2 & 1 & 0 \\ 4 & 2 & 1 \\ 5 & 2 & 1 \end{bmatrix}$ and $\mathbf{A}^{-1} = \begin{bmatrix} 0 & -1 & 1 \\ 1 & 2 & -2 \\ -2 & 1 & 0 \end{bmatrix}$.

   If $\mathbf{X} = \begin{bmatrix} x \\ y \\ z \end{bmatrix}$ is a solution of $\mathbf{AX} = \begin{bmatrix} -1 \\ 4 \\ 1 \end{bmatrix}$, find the number y.

4. Let $\mathbf{A} = \begin{bmatrix} 1 & 1 & 0 \\ 0 & 1 & 0 \\ 1 & 1 & 1 \end{bmatrix}$ and $\mathbf{B} = \begin{bmatrix} 1 & -1 & 0 \\ 0 & 1 & 0 \\ -1 & 0 & 1 \end{bmatrix}$. Decide whether $\mathbf{B} = \mathbf{A}^{-1}$ by computing $\mathbf{AB}$ and $\mathbf{BA}$.

5. Let $\mathbf{A} = \begin{bmatrix} 3 & 2 \\ 4 & 3 \end{bmatrix}$. Verify that $\mathbf{A}^{-1} = \begin{bmatrix} 3 & -2 \\ -4 & 3 \end{bmatrix}$.

6. Let $\mathbf{A} = \begin{bmatrix} 2 & 0 & 1 \\ 2 & 1 & -1 \\ 3 & 1 & -1 \end{bmatrix}$. Verify that $\mathbf{A}^{-1} = \begin{bmatrix} 0 & -1 & 1 \\ 1 & 5 & -4 \\ 1 & 2 & -2 \end{bmatrix}$.

7. Find $\mathbf{C}^{-1}$ and $\mathbf{D}^{-1}$ for

$$\mathbf{C} = \begin{bmatrix} 1 & -1 \\ 2 & 3 \end{bmatrix} \quad \text{and} \quad \mathbf{D} = \begin{bmatrix} .3 & .4 \\ .5 & .8 \end{bmatrix}$$

8. Let

$$\mathbf{A} = \begin{bmatrix} 1 & -1 \\ 2 & 2 \end{bmatrix} \quad \text{and} \quad \mathbf{B} = \begin{bmatrix} 1 & 1 \\ 2 & c \end{bmatrix}$$

   For which value of c is it the case that $\mathbf{AB}$ does not have an inverse?

9. Let $\mathbf{A} = \begin{bmatrix} 2 & 0 \\ 3 & 1 \end{bmatrix}$. Find the inverse of $\mathbf{A}$ and use it to solve the systems of equations

$$\mathbf{AX} = \begin{bmatrix} 1 \\ 0 \end{bmatrix} \quad \text{and} \quad \mathbf{AX} = \begin{bmatrix} 1 \\ -1 \end{bmatrix}$$

10. Let $\mathbf{A} = \begin{bmatrix} 2 & 3 \\ 5 & 9 \end{bmatrix}$. Find the inverse of $\mathbf{A}$ and use it to solve the systems of equations

$$\mathbf{AX} = \begin{bmatrix} 3 \\ 2 \end{bmatrix} \quad \text{and} \quad \mathbf{AX} = \begin{bmatrix} 4 \\ -1 \end{bmatrix}$$

11. Find the inverse (if it exists) of the matrix

$$\mathbf{A} = \begin{bmatrix} 3 & -2 \\ -6 & 4 \end{bmatrix}$$

12. Let k be a number and let

$$\mathbf{H} = \begin{bmatrix} 1 & 1 & 2 \\ 1 & 0 & k \\ 0 & 1 & 0 \end{bmatrix}$$

Which of the following is a true statement?

(a) The matrix **H** has an inverse for all values of k.
(b) The matrix **H** has an inverse for no values of k.
(c) The matrix **H** has an inverse for all k except $k = 2$.
(d) The matrix **H** has an inverse for all k except $k = 1$.

13. Find the inverse (if it exists) of the matrix

$$\mathbf{A} = \begin{bmatrix} 0 & 1 & 1 \\ 2 & 0 & 1 \\ 0 & 0 & 1 \end{bmatrix}$$

14. Find the inverse (if it exists) of the matrix

$$\mathbf{A} = \begin{bmatrix} 0 & 2 & 4 \\ 1 & 0 & 1 \\ 3 & 0 & 1 \end{bmatrix}$$

15. (a) Express the following system of equations in matrix form:

$$\begin{aligned} 2x_1 + 4x_2 &= -2 \\ x_1 + 3x_2 &= 4 \end{aligned}$$

(b) Use the inverse of the coefficient matrix in part a to solve the system of equations.

16. (a) Express the following system of equations in matrix form:

$$\begin{aligned} 2x_1 - 2x_2 &= 2 \\ 3x_1 - 2x_3 &= 4 \\ 2x_2 - x_3 &= -2 \end{aligned}$$

(b) Find the inverse of the coefficient matrix of (a).
(c) Use the inverse of the coefficient matrix determined in (b) to solve the system of equations.

17. Let there be two matrices $\mathbf{A} = \begin{bmatrix} 1 & -2 & 1 \\ -1 & x & -1 \\ -1 & 2 & 0 \end{bmatrix}$ and $\mathbf{B} = \begin{bmatrix} 2 & 2 & -1 \\ 1 & 1 & 0 \\ 1 & 0 & 1 \end{bmatrix}$.

For what value of x is $\mathbf{B} = \mathbf{A}^{-1}$?

18. Let $\mathbf{A} = \begin{bmatrix} 5 & 2 \\ 2 & 1 \end{bmatrix}$ and $\mathbf{B} = \begin{bmatrix} 1 & 3 \\ 2 & 5 \end{bmatrix}$. Find $\mathbf{A}^{-1}$, $\mathbf{B}^{-1}$, $(\mathbf{AB})^{-1}$, and $(\mathbf{BA})^{-1}$.

19. Using the results of Exercise 18, find $\mathbf{A}^{-1}\mathbf{B}^{-1}$ and $\mathbf{B}^{-1}\mathbf{A}^{-1}$. What is the relationship among $(\mathbf{AB})^{-1}$, $(\mathbf{BA})^{-1}$, $\mathbf{A}^{-1}\mathbf{B}^{-1}$, and $\mathbf{B}^{-1}\mathbf{A}^{-1}$?
20. Let **A**, **B**, and **C** be 2×2 matrices, and suppose

$$\mathbf{A} = \begin{bmatrix} 2 & 1 \\ -3 & 1 \end{bmatrix} \quad \text{and} \quad \mathbf{C} = \begin{bmatrix} 2 & 6 \\ 1 & -3 \end{bmatrix}$$

(*a*) Find **B** such that $\mathbf{AB} = \mathbf{C}$.
(*b*) Find **B** such that $\mathbf{BA} = \mathbf{C}$.

21. Let $\mathbf{A} = \begin{bmatrix} .2 & 0 & -.6 \\ 0 & .5 & -.8 \\ -.2 & 0 & .4 \end{bmatrix}$.

(*a*) Find $\mathbf{A}^{-1}$.
(*b*) Evaluate $\mathbf{AA}^{-1}\mathbf{A}$.

22. Using matrices **A** and **B** of Exercise 18 and the results of that exercise, decide whether $(\mathbf{A} + \mathbf{B})^{-1}$ is equal to $\mathbf{A}^{-1} + \mathbf{B}^{-1}$.

23. Let a matrix $\mathbf{A} = \begin{bmatrix} 1 & -1 & 2 \\ -1 & 3 & -2 \\ -1 & 2 & x \end{bmatrix}$.

(*a*) For what value of x does $\mathbf{A}^{-1}$ not exist?
(*b*) If x is such that $\mathbf{A}^{-1}$ does exist, what is the (2, 2) entry of $\mathbf{A}^{-1}$?

24. Find the inverse (if it exists) of the matrix

$$\mathbf{A} = \begin{bmatrix} 0 & 1 & 2 & 1 \\ 1 & 0 & -1 & -1 \\ 1 & 2 & 0 & 0 \\ 1 & 0 & -2 & 0 \end{bmatrix}$$

25. Find the inverse of matrix **A** and use it to solve the equations

$$\mathbf{AX} = \begin{bmatrix} 1 \\ 3 \\ 1 \end{bmatrix} \quad \text{and} \quad \mathbf{AX} = \begin{bmatrix} 2 \\ 1 \\ 0 \end{bmatrix}$$

where

$$\mathbf{A} = \begin{bmatrix} 2 & 1 & 0 \\ -1 & 1 & 1 \\ 0 & -1 & 1 \end{bmatrix}$$

26. Find the inverse of matrix **A** and use it to solve the equations

$$\mathbf{AX} = \begin{bmatrix} 1 \\ 1 \\ 1 \end{bmatrix} \quad \text{and} \quad \mathbf{AX} = \begin{bmatrix} 1 \\ -1 \\ 1 \end{bmatrix}$$

where

$$\mathbf{A} = \begin{bmatrix} 2 & 0 & 1 \\ 2 & 1 & -1 \\ 3 & 1 & -1 \end{bmatrix}$$

27. Use the concept of a matrix inverse to solve the following systems of equations:

(a) $\begin{aligned} x + y + z &= 15 \\ y - z &= 1 \\ x \quad + z &= 10 \end{aligned}$

(b) $\begin{aligned} x + y + z &= 9 \\ y - z &= 0 \\ x \quad + z &= 6 \end{aligned}$

(c) $\begin{aligned} x + y + z &= 0 \\ y - z &= 1 \\ x \quad + z &= 0 \end{aligned}$

28. Let a matrix $\mathbf{A} = \begin{bmatrix} 1 & -1 & 1 \\ -1 & 2 & (-1+a) \\ -2 & 2 & -1 \end{bmatrix}$. Find the (3, 1) entry of $\mathbf{A}^{-1}$.

29. Let $\mathbf{A} = \begin{bmatrix} 1 & 3 \\ 1 & 5 \end{bmatrix}$. Compute $\mathbf{AA} = \mathbf{A}^2$, $\mathbf{A}^{-1}$, $(\mathbf{A}^{-1})(\mathbf{A}^{-1})$, and $(\mathbf{AA})^{-1}$. Is $(\mathbf{A}^2)^{-1}$ the same as $(\mathbf{A}^{-1})^2$?

30. (Continuation of Exercise 29) Use the definition of a matrix inverse to show that for any square matrix **A**, if **A** has an inverse, then

$$(\mathbf{A}^n)^{-1} = (\mathbf{A}^{-1})^n \qquad \text{for} \qquad n = 1, 2, \ldots$$

31. Let $\mathbf{A} = \begin{bmatrix} 1 & b \\ 0 & 1 \end{bmatrix}$, where $b \neq 0$. Find $\mathbf{A}^{-1}$.

32. Let $\mathbf{A} = \begin{bmatrix} 1 & b \\ c & 1 \end{bmatrix}$, where $b \neq 0$, $c \neq 0$, and $bc \neq 1$. Find $\mathbf{A}^{-1}$.

33. Let $\mathbf{A} = \begin{bmatrix} a & b \\ c & d \end{bmatrix}$, where $ad \neq bc$. Find $\mathbf{A}^{-1}$.

34. Let $\mathbf{A} = \begin{bmatrix} a & 0 & 0 \\ 0 & b & 0 \\ 0 & 0 & c \end{bmatrix}$, where $a \neq 0, b \neq 0, c \neq 0$. Find $\mathbf{A}^{-1}$.

35. Let $\mathbf{A} = \begin{bmatrix} 1 & a & b \\ 0 & 1 & c \\ 0 & 0 & 1 \end{bmatrix}$. Find $\mathbf{A}^{-1}$.

36. Examine the following matrices.

$$\mathbf{A} = \begin{bmatrix} 1 & 0 & 1 \\ -1 & 1 & 2 \end{bmatrix} \qquad \mathbf{B} = \begin{bmatrix} -1 \\ 0 \\ 2 \end{bmatrix} \qquad \mathbf{C} = \begin{bmatrix} x & 1 \end{bmatrix}$$

Is there any value of x such that $(\mathbf{ABC})^{-1}$ exists?

37. Let $\mathbf{A} = \begin{bmatrix} 1 & -2 \\ -3 & 5 \end{bmatrix}$, and $\mathbf{B} = \begin{bmatrix} 13 & -2 \\ -3 & 17 \end{bmatrix}$. Do there exist values for x and y such that $x\mathbf{A} + y\mathbf{A}^{-1} = \mathbf{B}$ is a true statement?

38. Suppose $\mathbf{A} = \begin{bmatrix} 1 & 0 & x \\ 0 & 1 & y \\ 0 & 0 & z \end{bmatrix}$. If $3\mathbf{A}^{-1} = \begin{bmatrix} 3 & 0 & -9 \\ 0 & 3 & -12 \\ 0 & 0 & 1 \end{bmatrix}$, then what are the values of x, y, and z?

39. Find the inverse (if it exists) of the matrix $\mathbf{A}$ below.

$$\mathbf{A} = \begin{bmatrix} 1 & 0 & 0 & 0 & 1 \\ 0 & 1 & 2 & 0 & 0 \\ 0 & 0 & 1 & 0 & 1 \\ 0 & 0 & 0 & 1 & 0 \\ 0 & 0 & -1 & 1 & 0 \end{bmatrix}$$

40. Find the inverse of the coefficient matrix $\mathbf{A}$ in Exercise 36 of Section 6.1 and use it to solve the system of equations in Exercise 36 and 37 of Section 6.1.

6.3 A LINEAR ECONOMIC MODEL

In 1973 Professor Wassily Leontief was awarded the Nobel Prize for Economics in recognition of his development of mathematical methods to study economic systems in terms of inputs and outputs. In practice, these models are quite complicated because of the very large number of variables involved and because of modifications made to increase the accuracy of the predictions. In their simplest form, however, Leontief input-output models are very straightforward.

As an introduction, suppose we have an economy with a single good.

Example 6.16 Consider an economy with a single good which we take to be lumber. We suppose here, and in the general case as well, that some of the good being produced is consumed in the production process. For this example, suppose .2 unit of lumber is consumed in the production of 1 unit of lumber. Finally, suppose we have an order for 10 units of lumber.

Problem How many units of lumber must be produced to fill this order?

Solution To answer the question, let x denote the number of units of lumber produced by the economy. Then, for each unit produced, .2 unit is consumed. Net production is $x - .2x$. The problem is to find x such that

$$x - .2x = 10 \qquad \text{or} \qquad .8x = 10$$

We conclude that $x = 12.5$. The production process must produce 12.5 units of lumber to fill an order for 10 units. ■

The ideas introduced in this simple one-good example can be applied in more general situations. We consider first the case of two goods and then the case of n goods.

Economies with Two Goods

Suppose we have an economy with two industries, each of which produces a single good, and suppose the economy operates over a specific time period (e.g., a year). Consider a situation where each of the industries may use some of both goods in the production processes. For example, if the two goods are lumber and steel, then some lumber and some steel are used in the production of lumber, and likewise both goods are used in the production of steel. Let x_1 be the amount of good 1 produced in this economy, and let x_2 be the amount of good 2 produced. In studying this simple economy, we also need to know—and represent—the amounts of each good used in the production of the two goods. To represent this information, we let

a_{11} = the amount of good 1 used to produce one unit of good 1
a_{12} = the amount of good 1 used to produce one unit of good 2
a_{21} = the amount of good 2 used to produce one unit of good 1
a_{22} = the amount of good 2 used to produce one unit of good 2

Also suppose there is an external demand d_1 for good 1 and an external demand d_2 for good 2. By an *external demand* we mean an order for goods from outside the production processes.

Next, since it takes a_{11} units of good 1 to produce one unit of good 1, we assume that it takes $a_{11}x_1$ units of good 1 to produce x_1 units of good 1. Also we assume it will take $a_{12}x_2$ units of good 1 to produce x_2 units of good 2. Thus, the total amount of good 1 used in production is $a_{11}x_1 + a_{12}x_2$. Since there are x_1 units of good 1 produced and d_1 units are needed for external demand, we have the following equation

$$x_1 = a_{11}x_1 + a_{12}x_2 + d_1 \tag{6.7}$$

Similarly, for good 2, we have the equation

$$x_2 = a_{21}x_1 + a_{22}x_2 + d_2 \tag{6.8}$$

Equations (6.7) and (6.8) form a system of two equations in two variables (x_1 and x_2); and if we let

$$\mathbf{A} = \begin{bmatrix} a_{11} & a_{12} \\ a_{21} & a_{22} \end{bmatrix} \qquad \mathbf{X} = \begin{bmatrix} x_1 \\ x_2 \end{bmatrix} \qquad \mathbf{D} = \begin{bmatrix} d_1 \\ d_2 \end{bmatrix}$$

then this system of equations can be written in matrix form as

$$\mathbf{X} = \mathbf{AX} + \mathbf{D} \tag{6.9}$$

The matrix **A** in (6.9) is called the *technology matrix* for the economy, **X** is called the *production schedule*, and **D** is called the *demand vector*.

Example 6.17 Consider a Leontief input-output model for an economy with two goods, steel and coal. Suppose .1 unit of steel and 2 units of coal are required to produce 1 unit of steel, and .3 unit of steel is required to produce 1 unit of coal.

Problem Find the technology matrix **A**.

Solution Let x_1 and x_2 denote the number of units of steel and coal, respectively, produced in the economy. The amount of steel necessary to produce 1 unit of steel is .1, and the amount of steel required to produce 1 unit of coal is .3. Therefore, we have

$$x_1 = .1x_1 + .3x_2$$

Likewise, the amount of coal necessary to produce 1 unit of steel is 2, and no coal is required in the production of coal. Therefore, we have

$$x_2 = 2x_1 + 0x_2 = 2x_1$$

The technology matrix **A** is the matrix which arises when these equations are written in matrix form. We have

$$\begin{bmatrix} x_1 \\ x_2 \end{bmatrix} = \begin{bmatrix} .1 & .3 \\ 2 & 0 \end{bmatrix} \begin{bmatrix} x_1 \\ x_2 \end{bmatrix}$$

and consequently the technology matrix **A** is

$$\mathbf{A} = \begin{bmatrix} .1 & .3 \\ 2 & 0 \end{bmatrix}$$

■

Warning

A common error which occurs in forming technology matrices is to mix up the rows and columns of the matrix. To avoid this error you should be careful that, when you form the system of equations, you are representing only one good per equation. For example, in the equation $x_1 = .1x_1 + .3x_2$ (of Example 6.17), the left side is the amount of steel produced and the right side is the sum of the amount of steel needed for production of steel ($.1x_1$) and the amount of steel needed for production of coal ($.3x_2$). Both sides of the equation represent amounts of steel.

In most applications of Leontief models, one is interested in the relationship between the demand vector **D** and the production **X**. Using the matrix algebra tools of Sections 6.1 and 6.2, we can convert (6.9) to the form

$$(\mathbf{I} - \mathbf{A})\mathbf{X} = \mathbf{D} \qquad \text{where } \mathbf{I} = \begin{bmatrix} 1 & 0 \\ 0 & 1 \end{bmatrix}$$

Therefore, if the square matrix $\mathbf{I} - \mathbf{A}$ has an inverse, then we can express **X** in terms of **D** as follows:

$$\mathbf{X} = (\mathbf{I} - \mathbf{A})^{-1}\mathbf{D} \tag{6.10}$$

Equation (6.10) is especially useful when one is interested in the effect of various demands on production. For example, if a government has a goal of stimulating the economy, then it can use (6.10) to evaluate the effect of specific stimulus actions, different demand vectors **D**, on the level of economic activity. For this reason it is common to determine the production schedule **X** by using (6.10). However, it is also possible to solve (6.9) for **X** by using the techniques of Chapter 5. In Example 6.18 we illustrate both methods; from then on we use (6.10).

Example 6.18 Consider a Leontief input-output model for an economy with two goods, steel and coal, and the technology matrix (as derived in Example 6.17)

$$\mathbf{A} = \begin{bmatrix} .1 & .3 \\ 2 & 0 \end{bmatrix}$$

Recall that the first row (and column) is identified with steel and the second row (and column) with coal. Suppose that the external demand vector is $\begin{bmatrix} 12 \\ 3 \end{bmatrix}$.

Problem Find the production schedule which meets this demand.

Solution We illustrate both methods of finding the production schedule: First we solve the system (6.9), and then we find $(\mathbf{I} - \mathbf{A})^{-1}$ and use (6.10).

To use the techniques of Chapter 5 on Equation (6.9), we write it in the form $(\mathbf{I} - \mathbf{A})\mathbf{X} = \mathbf{D}$, and we form the augmented matrix for this system. The left-hand side of the augmented matrix is determined by computing $\mathbf{I} - \mathbf{A}$:

$$\mathbf{I} - \mathbf{A} = \begin{bmatrix} 1 & 0 \\ 0 & 1 \end{bmatrix} - \begin{bmatrix} .1 & .3 \\ 2 & 0 \end{bmatrix} = \begin{bmatrix} .9 & -.3 \\ -2 & 1 \end{bmatrix}$$

Since $\mathbf{D} = \begin{bmatrix} 12 \\ 3 \end{bmatrix}$, the augmented matrix is

$$\left[\begin{array}{rr|r} .9 & -.3 & 12 \\ -2 & 1 & 3 \end{array}\right]$$

Using elementary row operations, we have successively

$$\left[\begin{array}{rr|r} 1 & -\frac{1}{3} & \frac{40}{3} \\ -2 & 1 & 3 \end{array}\right]$$

$$\left[\begin{array}{rr|r} 1 & -\frac{1}{3} & \frac{40}{3} \\ 0 & \frac{1}{3} & \frac{89}{3} \end{array}\right]$$

$$\left[\begin{array}{rr|r} 1 & 0 & 43 \\ 0 & 1 & 89 \end{array}\right]$$

From this we conclude that $\begin{bmatrix} 43 \\ 89 \end{bmatrix}$ is the production schedule required to produce the demand vector $\begin{bmatrix} 12 \\ 3 \end{bmatrix}$.

Next, we use Equation (6.10) to determine the demand vector, and to do so, we must determine $(\mathbf{I} - \mathbf{A})^{-1}$. Using the methods of Section 6.2, we find

$$(\mathbf{I} - \mathbf{A})^{-1} = \begin{bmatrix} \frac{10}{3} & 1 \\ \frac{20}{3} & 3 \end{bmatrix}$$

Using (6.10), we have

$$\mathbf{X} = (\mathbf{I} - \mathbf{A})^{-1}\mathbf{D} = \begin{bmatrix} \frac{10}{3} & 1 \\ \frac{20}{3} & 3 \end{bmatrix} \begin{bmatrix} 12 \\ 3 \end{bmatrix} = \begin{bmatrix} 43 \\ 89 \end{bmatrix}$$

Interpreting these results in the original setting, we see that it is necessary to produce 43 units of steel and 89 units of coal to meet the external demand. We know from the demand vector that 12 units of steel and 3 units of coal are used outside the production system, and therefore we see that $43 - 12 = 31$ units of steel and $89 - 3 = 86$ units of coal are used within the economy. ■

Economies with *n* Goods

The discussion preceding Examples 6.17 and 6.18 described a Leontief model for an economy in which two goods were produced. Such a model consists of assumptions and equations. We turn now to a similar model for an economy in which many goods are produced.

Suppose we have an economy in which there are n industries, each of which produces a single good. We assume that each industry utilizes the goods produced by some or all of the industries in the production process.

Let x_i denote the amount of the ith good (measured in appropriate units) produced in unit time. We suppose that this output is used in the production of the ith good, in the production of other goods, and in the satisfaction of the demand external to the economic system being considered. Thus

$$\begin{aligned} x_i = {} & \text{amount of } i\text{th good used to produce goods} \\ & + \text{amount used to satisfy external demand} \end{aligned} \tag{6.11}$$

That is, a portion of the amount of good i produced goes outside the system (it satisfies the external demand), and a portion remains in the system (it is used in the production processes). The amount of good i used in the production processes can be further subdivided into the amounts used to produce good 1, good 2, . . . , good n, respectively. We repeat for emphasis that the situation in which good i is used in the production of good i is included in the model.

We set a_{ij} equal to the amount of good i used to produce one unit of good j, and we assume that the amount of good i needed to produce x_j units of good j is $a_{ij}x_j$. We also assume that the various production processes are unrelated in the sense that the amount of good i used to produce x_1 units of good 1 and x_2 units of good 2 and . . . and x_n units of good n is the sum of the amounts of good i needed to produce those quantities of the goods individually:

$$a_{i1}x_1 + a_{i2}x_2 + \cdots + a_{in}x_n$$

These assumptions enable us to use the methods of this chapter to study the model. Now, if we let d_i denote the external demand for good i, then the representation of x_i given in Equation (6.11) has the form

$$x_i = a_{i1}x_1 + a_{i2}x_2 + \cdots + a_{in}x_n + d_i$$

We assume that all the goods produced in the economy can be described by similar equations. It follows that we have a system of linear equations in the variables $x_1, x_2, \ldots, x_n$:

$$\begin{aligned} x_1 &= a_{11}x_1 + a_{12}x_2 + \cdots + a_{1n}x_n + d_1 \\ x_2 &= a_{21}x_1 + a_{22}x_2 + \cdots + a_{2n}x_n + d_2 \\ &\;\vdots \\ x_n &= a_{n1}x_1 + a_{n2}x_2 + \cdots + a_{nn}x_n + d_n \end{aligned}$$

In matrix-vector notation, this system of equations has the form

$$\mathbf{X} = \mathbf{AX} + \mathbf{D}$$

where **A** is the $n \times n$ matrix whose (i, j) entry is a_{ij}, and **X** and **D** are column n-vectors whose coordinates are $x_1, \ldots, x_n$ and $d_1, \ldots, d_n$, respectively.

In a Leontief input-output model represented by the equation $\mathbf{X} = \mathbf{AX} + \mathbf{D}$, the matrix **A** is the *technology* or *input-output* matrix, the vector **D** is the *external demand* vector, and the vector **X** is a *production schedule* (a list of amounts of goods to be produced).

Since the coordinates of a production schedule are the amounts of various goods produced, each of these coordinates must be nonnegative.

As a result of our assumption that each industry produces a single good (the jth industry produces the jth good only), it follows that $a_{jk} \geq 0$ for $j \neq k$. Indeed, if there were industries j and k with $a_{jk} < 0$, then the effect of producing x_k units of good k would be to reduce the amount of good j required by an amount $|a_{jk}x_k|$. Thus, if this were the case, the production of good k would be equivalent to the production of good j. We assume that this is not the case.

Finally, we assume that all the coordinates of the demand vector **D** are nonnegative. This assumption reflects the fact that we are assuming **D** to be a genuine demand vector, and demands ought not to decrease the amount of a good required.

The problem we consider is that of finding a production schedule **X** which satisfies the demand **D** with a given technology matrix **A**. Thus we seek **X** with nonnegative coordinates such that

$$\mathbf{X} = \mathbf{AX} + \mathbf{D} \qquad \text{or} \qquad (\mathbf{I} - \mathbf{A})\mathbf{X} = \mathbf{D}$$

We assume that $\mathbf{I} - \mathbf{A}$ is invertible. This assumption can be given economic justification. Indeed, the failure of $\mathbf{I} - \mathbf{A}$ to be invertible would imply a particular and exact relationship among the coefficients a_{ij} of **A**. Since the coefficients of **A** are usually estimated and consequently not known precisely, it is not unduly restrictive to assume that $\mathbf{I} - \mathbf{A}$ is invertible.

For the remainder of this discussion we shall assume that **A** has nonnegative entries, that $\mathbf{I} - \mathbf{A}$ is invertible, and that $(\mathbf{I} - \mathbf{A})^{-1}$ has nonnegative entries. We can make additional assumptions about the nature of the economic system that will guarantee that $(\mathbf{I} - \mathbf{A})^{-1}$ has nonnegative entries, but we shall not discuss this assumption in economic terms. With these assumptions, the equation $(\mathbf{I} - \mathbf{A})\mathbf{X} = \mathbf{D}$ can be solved for the production schedule **X** by multiplying both sides by $(\mathbf{I} - \mathbf{A})^{-1}$. We conclude that

$$\mathbf{X} = (\mathbf{I} - \mathbf{A})^{-1}\mathbf{D} \tag{6.12}$$

Since **D** and $(\mathbf{I} - \mathbf{A})^{-1}$ contain only nonnegative entries, it follows that **X** has only nonnegative entries, and consequently **X** is a legitimate production schedule.

Example 6.19 Suppose an economy has three goods—cement, electricity, and steel—and a technology matrix

$$\mathbf{A} = \begin{bmatrix} .2 & .6 & .2 \\ 0 & .1 & .4 \\ .6 & 0 & .3 \end{bmatrix}$$

In **A**, the first row (and column) corresponds to cement, the second to electricity, and the third to steel.

Problem Find the external demand **D** which will be met by the production schedule

$$\mathbf{X} = \begin{bmatrix} 30 \\ 20 \\ 40 \end{bmatrix}$$

Solution The technology matrix **A**, demand **D**, and production schedule **X** are related by

$$\mathbf{X} = \mathbf{AX} + \mathbf{D}$$

Since we are to determine **D** given **A** and **X**, it is helpful to rewrite this equation in the form

$$\mathbf{D} = \mathbf{X} - \mathbf{AX}$$

Using the values given for **A** and **X**, we have

$$\mathbf{D} = \begin{bmatrix} 30 \\ 20 \\ 40 \end{bmatrix} - \begin{bmatrix} .2 & .6 & .2 \\ 0 & .1 & .4 \\ .6 & 0 & .3 \end{bmatrix} \begin{bmatrix} 30 \\ 20 \\ 40 \end{bmatrix} = \begin{bmatrix} 4 \\ 2 \\ 10 \end{bmatrix}$$

■

Example 6.20 Consider an economy which produces three goods: hydro-electric power, propane, and titanium. Suppose the production of 1 unit of hydro-electric power requires .5 unit of hydro-electric power, .2 unit of propane, and 1 unit of titanium. Also the production of 1 unit of propane requires .8 unit of propane and .4 unit of titanium, and the production of 1 unit of titanium requires .2 unit of hydro-electric power and .12 unit of propane.

Problem Find the technology matrix for this economy, and find a production schedule which will satisfy an external demand for 5 units of hydro-electric power, 3 units of propane, and 4 units of titanium.

Solution Since we are interested in the amounts of hydro-electric power, propane, and titanium to be produced, we let

$x_1 =$ the number of units of hydro-electric power produced
$x_2 =$ the number of units of propane produced
$x_3 =$ the number of units of titanium produced

Then, using the information given about the amount of hydro-electric power used in producing hydro-electric power, propane, and titanium, and the external demand for hydro-electric power, we have

$$x_1 = .5x_1 + 0x_2 + .2x_3 + 5$$

Similarly, we obtain the equations

$$\begin{aligned} x_2 &= .2x_1 + .8x_2 + .12x_3 + 3 \\ x_3 &= 1x_1 + .4x_2 + 0x_3 + 4 \end{aligned}$$

for propane and titanium, respectively. To use matrix-vector notation, we let

$$\mathbf{X} = \begin{bmatrix} x_1 \\ x_2 \\ x_3 \end{bmatrix} \qquad \mathbf{A} = \begin{bmatrix} .5 & 0 & .2 \\ .2 & .8 & .12 \\ 1 & .4 & 0 \end{bmatrix} \qquad \mathbf{D} = \begin{bmatrix} 5 \\ 3 \\ 4 \end{bmatrix}$$

and we have the equation

$$\mathbf{X} = \mathbf{AX} + \mathbf{D}$$

Again, we proceed by determining $(\mathbf{I} - \mathbf{A})^{-1}$ and using Equation (6.12). In this case

$$\mathbf{I} - \mathbf{A} = \begin{bmatrix} .5 & 0 & -.2 \\ -.2 & .2 & -.12 \\ -1 & -.4 & 1 \end{bmatrix}$$

and

$$(\mathbf{I} - \mathbf{A})^{-1} = \begin{bmatrix} 7.6 & 4 & 2 \\ 16 & 15 & 5 \\ 14 & 10 & 5 \end{bmatrix}$$

The production vector $\mathbf{X}$ can be obtained from (6.12):

$$\mathbf{X} = (\mathbf{I} - \mathbf{A})^{-1}\mathbf{D} = \begin{bmatrix} 7.6 & 4 & 2 \\ 16 & 15 & 5 \\ 14 & 10 & 5 \end{bmatrix} \begin{bmatrix} 5 \\ 3 \\ 4 \end{bmatrix} = \begin{bmatrix} 58 \\ 145 \\ 120 \end{bmatrix}$$

To satisfy the external demand, it is necessary to produce 58 units of hydro-electric power, 145 units of propane, and 120 units of titanium. ■

Example 6.21 Consider an economy which has two goods, silicon and zinc, and suppose that Table 6.2 gives the goods required in the production processes. For example, the entry .5 indicates that the production of 1 unit of silicon requires .5 unit of zinc.

TABLE 6.2

	Number of Units Needed to Produce 1 Unit of	
Good	**Silicon**	**Zinc**
Silicon	.6	.6
Zinc	.5	.2

Problem Find the associated technology matrix **A**, and determine whether the inverse of **I** – **A** has all positive entries.

Solution Let

$$\begin{aligned} x_1 &= \text{the number of units of silicon to be produced} \\ x_2 &= \text{the number of units of zinc to be produced} \\ d_1 &= \text{the external demand for silicon} \\ d_2 &= \text{the external demand for zinc} \end{aligned}$$

Then, using Table 6.2, we have

$$\begin{aligned} x_1 &= .6x_1 + .6x_2 + d_1 \\ x_2 &= .5x_1 + .2x_2 + d_2 \end{aligned}$$

Hence the technology matrix **A** is given by

$$\mathbf{A} = \begin{bmatrix} .6 & .6 \\ .5 & .2 \end{bmatrix} \qquad \text{and} \qquad \mathbf{I} - \mathbf{A} = \begin{bmatrix} .4 & -.6 \\ -.5 & .8 \end{bmatrix}$$

Using the techniques of Section 6.2, we determine the inverse of **I** – **A** by converting the following matrix to reduced form:

$$\left[\begin{array}{cc|cc} .4 & -.6 & 1 & 0 \\ -.5 & .8 & 0 & 1 \end{array}\right]$$

We obtain

$$\left[\begin{array}{cc|cc} 1 & 0 & 40 & 30 \\ 0 & 1 & 25 & 20 \end{array}\right]$$

Therefore, the inverse of $\mathbf{I} - \mathbf{A}$ is the matrix $\begin{bmatrix} 40 & 30 \\ 25 & 20 \end{bmatrix}$, and we see that it has all positive entries. ■

Exercises for Section 6.3

1. Using the technology matrix of Example 6.17, compute the production schedule for each of the following demand vectors.

   (*a*) $\mathbf{D} = \begin{bmatrix} 15 \\ 5 \end{bmatrix}$ (*b*) $\mathbf{D} = \begin{bmatrix} 1000 \\ 125 \end{bmatrix}$

2. Using the technology matrix of Example 6.17, find the external demand which is satisfied by each of the following production schedules.

   (*a*) $\mathbf{X} = \begin{bmatrix} 20 \\ 50 \end{bmatrix}$ (*b*) $\mathbf{X} = \begin{bmatrix} 100 \\ 240 \end{bmatrix}$

3. Using the technology matrix of Example 6.20, compute the production schedule for each of the following demand vectors.

   (*a*) $\mathbf{D} = \begin{bmatrix} 20 \\ 20 \\ 8 \end{bmatrix}$ (*b*) $\mathbf{D} = \begin{bmatrix} 100 \\ 120 \\ 50 \end{bmatrix}$

4. Using the technology matrix of Example 6.20, find the external demand which is satisfied by each of the following production schedules.

   (*a*) $\mathbf{X} = \begin{bmatrix} 9 \\ 22 \\ 20 \end{bmatrix}$ (*b*) $\mathbf{X} = \begin{bmatrix} 60 \\ 140 \\ 120 \end{bmatrix}$

5. In the setting of Example 6.20, find the production schedule which meets an external demand for 100 units of hydro-electric power and 60 units of propane. There is no external demand for titanium.
6. In the situation described in Exercise 5, how much titanium must be produced to meet the needs of the production processes?
7. An economy has two goods: good 1 is cotton and good 2 is wheat. The production of 1 unit of cotton requires .5 units of cotton and .75 units of wheat, and the production of 1 unit of wheat requires .4 units of cotton and .2 units of wheat. The external demand is 2 units of cotton and 1 unit of wheat. What is the technology matrix $\mathbf{A}$? What is $(\mathbf{I} - \mathbf{A})^{-1}$?
8. An economy has two goods: iron and copper. The production of one unit of iron requires .1 units of iron and .2 units of copper. The production of one unit of copper requires .8 units of iron and .6 units of copper. Using a Leontief model for this economy, find the production schedule that meets an external demand for 200 units of iron and 100 units of copper.

In Exercises 9 through 12, check whether the assumptions of this section hold. That is, does $(\mathbf{I} - \mathbf{A})^{-1}$ exist and have nonnegative entries?

9. $\mathbf{A} = \begin{bmatrix} .6 & .1 \\ .8 & .3 \end{bmatrix}$

10. $\mathbf{A} = \begin{bmatrix} .1 & .5 \\ .3 & .8 \end{bmatrix}$

11. $\mathbf{A} = \begin{bmatrix} .5 & .1 & .1 \\ .8 & .3 & .5 \\ 0 & .1 & .2 \end{bmatrix}$

12. $\mathbf{A} = \begin{bmatrix} .5 & .1 & .8 \\ .8 & .3 & .1 \\ .8 & .1 & .2 \end{bmatrix}$

13. Consider an economy with two goods and a technology matrix $\mathbf{A}$ as in Exercise 9.
    (*a*) Find the production schedule which meets an external demand for 24 units of good 1 and 15 units of good 2.
    (*b*) Find the production schedule which meets an external demand for 48 units of good 1 and 30 units of good 2.
    (*c*) What is the relation between the production schedules determined in (*a*) and (*b*)?
14. A Leontief input-output model for an economy with 3 goods has the technology matrix $\mathbf{A}$ and the production schedule $\mathbf{X}$. Find the *external demand* for good 2 that is satisfied by the production schedule $\mathbf{X}$.

$$\mathbf{A} = \begin{bmatrix} .2 & 0 & .6 \\ .3 & .4 & 0 \\ 0 & .2 & .3 \end{bmatrix} \qquad \mathbf{X} = \begin{bmatrix} 52 \\ 76 \\ 36 \end{bmatrix}$$

In Exercises 15 through 22, find the production schedule for the given technology matrix and demand vector.

15. $\mathbf{A} = \begin{bmatrix} .5 & .4 \\ .75 & .2 \end{bmatrix}$ $\qquad \mathbf{D} = \begin{bmatrix} 2 \\ 1 \end{bmatrix}$

16. $\mathbf{A} = \begin{bmatrix} .2 & .6 \\ .6 & .05 \end{bmatrix}$ $\qquad \mathbf{D} = \begin{bmatrix} 8 \\ 10 \end{bmatrix}$

17. $\mathbf{A} = \begin{bmatrix} .7 & .3 \\ .5 & .4 \end{bmatrix}$ $\qquad \mathbf{D} = \begin{bmatrix} 6 \\ 5 \end{bmatrix}$

18. $\mathbf{A} = \begin{bmatrix} \frac{3}{5} & \frac{3}{10} \\ \frac{1}{3} & \frac{1}{2} \end{bmatrix}$ $\qquad \mathbf{D} = \begin{bmatrix} 30 \\ 20 \end{bmatrix}$

19. $\mathbf{A} = \begin{bmatrix} .5 & 0 & .3 \\ 0 & .8 & .4 \\ 0 & .2 & .4 \end{bmatrix}$ $\qquad \mathbf{D} = \begin{bmatrix} 3 \\ 1 \\ 2 \end{bmatrix}$

20. $\mathbf{A} = \begin{bmatrix} .2 & .4 & 0 \\ 0 & .4 & .5 \\ 0 & .2 & .5 \end{bmatrix}$ $\qquad \mathbf{D} = \begin{bmatrix} 8 \\ 2 \\ 3 \end{bmatrix}$

21. $\mathbf{A} = \begin{bmatrix} .6 & .2 & 0 \\ 0 & .4 & .1 \\ .1 & .1 & .6 \end{bmatrix}$ $\qquad \mathbf{D} = \begin{bmatrix} 54 \\ 18 \\ 90 \end{bmatrix}$

22. $\mathbf{A} = \begin{bmatrix} .2 & 0 & 0 & .2 \\ 0 & .4 & 0 & .2 \\ 0 & 0 & .2 & .4 \\ 0 & 0 & .4 & .5 \end{bmatrix}$ $\qquad \mathbf{D} = \begin{bmatrix} 50 \\ 40 \\ 20 \\ 100 \end{bmatrix}$

23. An economy has two goods: aluminum and magnesium. The production of 1 unit of magnesium requires .2 unit of magnesium and .5 unit of aluminum, and the production of 1 unit of aluminum requires .6 unit of magnesium and .6 unit of aluminum. Find the production schedule which meets an external demand for 20 units of magnesium and 10 units of aluminum.

24. Consider an economy in which the goods are quinoa, coconut oil, and sesame seeds. Also suppose that the units of measurement are such that Table 6.3 describes the relationships between the units. Find the associated technology matrix, and decide whether this matrix satisfies the assumptions of this section.

TABLE 6.3

	Number of Units Needed to Produce 1 Unit of		
Good	**Quinoa**	**Coconut Oil**	**Sesame Seeds**
Quinoa	.2	.4	0
Coconut Oil	0	.4	.5
Sesame Seeds	.8	.1	.5

25. In the setting of Exercise 24, can an external demand for quinoa, coconut oil, and sesame seeds of 20, 30, and 50 units, respectively, be met? If so, what is the production schedule which meets this demand?

26. An economy has three goods: natural gas, butane, and zinc. Production of one unit of natural gas requires .9 units of natural gas. Production of 1 unit of butane requires .2 units of natural gas, .9 units of butane, and .1 units of

zinc. Production of 1 unit of zinc requires .1 units of butane and .8 units of zinc. Find the production schedule that meets the external demand **D** given that z is a number with $0 \le z \le 100$.

$$\mathbf{D} = \begin{bmatrix} 400 \\ z \\ 100 - z \end{bmatrix}$$

27. An economy has three goods: calcium, hydrogen, and sea salt. The production of 1 unit of calcium requires .4 unit of calcium, .5 unit of hydrogen, and .3 unit of sea salt. The production of 1 unit of hydrogen requires no calcium, .2 unit of hydrogen, and .6 unit of sea salt. Finally, the production of 1 unit of sea salt requires .2 unit of calcium, .5 unit of hydrogen, and .2 unit of sea salt. Find the production schedule which meets an external demand for 48 units of calcium, 24 units of hydrogen, and 18 units of sea salt.
28. In the setting of Exercise 27, what production schedules provide only hydrogen for the external market? That is, the amounts of calcium and sea salt produced are exactly the amounts used in the production process.
29. For what values of c does the technology matrix $\mathbf{A} = \begin{bmatrix} .2 & c \\ .6 & .4 \end{bmatrix}$ satisfy the assumptions of this chapter?
30. Let $\mathbf{A} = \begin{bmatrix} .5 & .5 \\ .5 & a \end{bmatrix}$. For which positive values of variable a does $\mathbf{I} - \mathbf{A}$ have an inverse with all positive entries?
31. Repeat Exercise 30 for

$$\mathbf{A} = \begin{bmatrix} .2 & a \\ .6 & .5 \end{bmatrix}$$

32. Repeat Exercise 30 for

$$\mathbf{A} = \begin{bmatrix} .2 & .4 \\ .6 & a \end{bmatrix}$$

33. Repeat Exercise 30 for

$$\mathbf{A} = \begin{bmatrix} .8 & a \\ a & .2 \end{bmatrix}$$

34. Let $\mathbf{A} = \begin{bmatrix} .5 & a \\ b & .5 \end{bmatrix}$. For which values of variables a and b does $\mathbf{I} - \mathbf{A}$ have an inverse with all positive entries?

35. An economy with two goods has the technology matrix

$$\mathbf{A} = \begin{bmatrix} .2 & k \\ .4 & .5 \end{bmatrix}$$

where k is a number, $0 < k < 1$. There is an external demand for 20 units of good 1 and 10 units of good 2.

(*a*) Find the amount of good 2 which must be produced to meet the external demand when $k = .1$.

(*b*) Repeat part *a* for $k = .2, .3, \ldots, .9$.

(*c*) Graph the amount of good 2 as a function of k. That is, on a coordinate system with k on the horizontal axis and the amount of good 2 on the vertical axis, plot the amount of good 2 for each value of k, $k = .1, .2, \ldots, .9$.

IMPORTANT TERMS AND CONCEPTS

You should be able to describe, define, or give examples of and use each of the following:

Matrix
Dimension of a matrix
The (i, j) entry in a matrix
Column vector
Row vector
Coordinates of a vector
Equality of matrices
Matrix addition
Scalar multiplication
Row-by-column multiplication
Matrix multiplication
Inverse of a matrix
Leontief model
Technology matrix
External demand vector
Production schedule

REVIEW EXERCISES

1. Find the dimensions of each of the following matrices.

(*a*) $\begin{bmatrix} 50 & -30 \\ -25 & 120 \\ 0 & 85 \\ 15 & 60 \end{bmatrix}$ (*b*) $\begin{bmatrix} 65 & 15 & 80 \\ 90 & 15 & 105 \end{bmatrix}$

(*c*) $[.2 \quad 0 \quad .2 \quad .6]$ (*d*) $\begin{bmatrix} 85 \\ 240 \\ 490 \end{bmatrix}$

2. Let **A, B, C,** and **D** be matrices with the following dimensions: **A** is 3×5, **B** is 5×3, **C** is 3×3, and **D** is 5×5. Decide which of the following matrix products are defined and, if the product is defined, determine the size of the product.

(*a*) **DAB** (*b*) **CAB** (*c*) **BAD** (*d*) **DBAC** (*e*) **DBCAB**

3. Let

$$\mathbf{A} = \begin{bmatrix} -1 & 7 \\ 0 & 15 \\ 12 & -8 \end{bmatrix} \quad \mathbf{B} = \begin{bmatrix} 5 & -1 \\ 12 & 8 \\ 5 & 2 \end{bmatrix}$$

Find $5\mathbf{A} + \mathbf{B}$ and $\mathbf{A} - 2\mathbf{B}$.

4. Let

$$\mathbf{A} = \begin{bmatrix} 10 & 3 \\ 0 & 5 \\ -2 & 4 \end{bmatrix} \quad \mathbf{X} = \begin{bmatrix} -1 \\ 5 \end{bmatrix} \quad \mathbf{B} = \begin{bmatrix} 5 \\ 25 \\ 22 \end{bmatrix}$$

Show that $\mathbf{AX} = \mathbf{B}$.

5. Using vectors $\mathbf{X} = \begin{bmatrix} -1 \\ 5 \\ -10 \end{bmatrix}$ and $\mathbf{B}$ as in Exercise 4, find vectors $\mathbf{Y}$ and $\mathbf{Z}$ such that $\mathbf{X} + 2\mathbf{Y} = \mathbf{B}$ and $2\mathbf{X} + \mathbf{Z} = \mathbf{B}$.

6. Let

$$\mathbf{A} = \begin{bmatrix} 1 & 0 & 3 \\ 1 & 1 & 1 \\ -3 & 2 & 1 \end{bmatrix} \quad \mathbf{B} = \begin{bmatrix} 2 & -1 & 1 \\ 0 & 3 & -1 \\ -2 & -1 & -3 \end{bmatrix}$$

(*a*) Find $2\mathbf{A} + 3\mathbf{B}$. (*b*) Find $\left(\frac{1}{2}\right) \cdot \mathbf{A} + \left(\frac{1}{4}\right) \cdot \mathbf{B}$.

7. Using matrices $\mathbf{A}$ and $\mathbf{B}$ of Exercise 6, find p and q such that

$$p\mathbf{A} + q\mathbf{B} = \begin{bmatrix} -3 & 1 & -4 \\ -1 & -4 & 0 \\ 5 & -1 & 2 \end{bmatrix}$$

8. Let $\mathbf{A}$ and $\mathbf{B}$ be matrices with the following dimensions: $\mathbf{A}$ is 3×2 and $\mathbf{B}$ is 2×3. Decide which of the following matrix products are defined and, if the product is defined, determine the size of the product.

(*a*) $\mathbf{AB}$ (*b*) $\mathbf{A}^2$ (*c*) $(\mathbf{AB})^2$ (*d*) $(\mathbf{ABA})^2$

9. Matrices $\mathbf{A}$, $\mathbf{B}$, $\mathbf{C}$, and $\mathbf{X}$ are defined as follows:

$$\mathbf{A} = \begin{bmatrix} 10 & 3 \\ 0 & 5 \\ -2 & 4 \end{bmatrix} \quad \mathbf{B} = \begin{bmatrix} 3 & 6 \\ 1 & 5 \end{bmatrix} \quad \mathbf{C} = \begin{bmatrix} -2 & 4 \\ 3 & 0 \\ 2 & 2 \end{bmatrix} \quad \mathbf{X} = \begin{bmatrix} 3 \\ 2 \end{bmatrix}$$

For each of the following, perform the indicated operations where possible, and express your answer as a single matrix. If the indicated operations are not defined, answer "not defined."

(*a*) $2\mathbf{B}$ (*b*) $\mathbf{A} + \mathbf{B}$ (*c*) $\mathbf{A} + \mathbf{C}$
(*d*) $\mathbf{AB}$ (*e*) $\mathbf{AC}$ (*f*) $\mathbf{AX}$

10. Matrices $\mathbf{A}$, $\mathbf{B}$, $\mathbf{C}$, and $\mathbf{X}$ are defined as follows:

$$\mathbf{A} = \begin{bmatrix} 2 & -1 \\ 3 & 1 \end{bmatrix} \quad \mathbf{B} = \begin{bmatrix} 4 & 2 \\ 1 & -1 \\ 3 & 0 \end{bmatrix} \quad \mathbf{C} = \begin{bmatrix} -1 & 0 \\ 2 & 5 \\ 3 & -2 \end{bmatrix} \quad \mathbf{X} = \begin{bmatrix} -2 \\ 3 \end{bmatrix}$$

In each of the following, perform the indicated operations where possible, and express your answer as a single matrix. If the indicated operations are not defined, answer "not defined."

(*a*) $3\mathbf{A}$ (*b*) $4\mathbf{B} - \mathbf{C}$ (*c*) $\mathbf{AB}$
(*d*) $\mathbf{BA}$ (*e*) $\mathbf{BX}$ (*f*) $\mathbf{XA}$

11. Matrices **A**, **B**, **C**, and **D** are defined as follows:

$$\mathbf{A} = \begin{bmatrix} 1 & 2 \\ -2 & 3 \end{bmatrix} \quad \mathbf{B} = \begin{bmatrix} 1 & 2 & -1 \\ 0 & -1 & 2 \end{bmatrix}$$

$$\mathbf{C} = \begin{bmatrix} 4 & 0 & 1 \\ 2 & 1 & 3 \end{bmatrix} \quad \mathbf{D} = \begin{bmatrix} 2 & 0 \\ 3 & -1 \\ -2 & 0 \end{bmatrix}$$

In each of the following, perform the indicated operations where possible, and express your answer as a single matrix. If the indicated operations are not defined, answer "not defined."

(*a*) $2\mathbf{D}$ (*b*) $2\mathbf{B} - \mathbf{C}$ (*c*) $\mathbf{CA}$
(*d*) $\mathbf{AB}$ (*e*) $\mathbf{BC}$ (*f*) $\mathbf{BD}$

12. Matrices **A**, **B**, **C**, and **Y** are defined as follows:

$$\mathbf{A} = \begin{bmatrix} -5 & -3 \\ 1 & 2 \\ 2 & -4 \end{bmatrix} \quad \mathbf{B} = \begin{bmatrix} 1 & 5 & -2 \\ 5 & -2 & 3 \end{bmatrix}$$

$$\mathbf{C} = \begin{bmatrix} 2 & -3 \\ -1 & 2 \\ 0 & 4 \end{bmatrix} \quad \mathbf{Y} = \begin{bmatrix} 1 \\ 4 \\ 5 \end{bmatrix}$$

In each of the following, perform the indicated operations where possible, and express your answer as a single matrix. If the indicated operations are not defined, answer "not defined."

(*a*) $-\mathbf{A}$ (*b*) $\mathbf{A} + \mathbf{B}$ (*c*) $\mathbf{AY}$
(*d*) $\mathbf{BY}$ (*e*) $(\mathbf{A} + \mathbf{C})\mathbf{Y}$ (*f*) $\mathbf{C} - \mathbf{AB}$

13. Let

$$\mathbf{A} = \begin{bmatrix} 2 & -1 \\ -3 & 4 \end{bmatrix} \quad \mathbf{B} = \begin{bmatrix} 4 & -2 & 0 \\ -1 & 2 & 1 \end{bmatrix}$$

Find $\mathbf{A}^2$, $\mathbf{AB}$, $\mathbf{A}(\mathbf{AB})$, and $\mathbf{A}^2\mathbf{B}$.

14. Let

$$\mathbf{A} = \begin{bmatrix} 2 & -1 \\ -2 & 2 \\ 3 & -4 \end{bmatrix} \quad \mathbf{B} = \begin{bmatrix} 4 & -2 & 1 \\ -1 & 2 & -1 \end{bmatrix}$$

Find **AB**, **BA**, and **BAB**.

15. Let

$$\mathbf{A} = \begin{bmatrix} 3 & -1 \\ -2 & 8 \end{bmatrix} \quad \mathbf{B} = \begin{bmatrix} 2 & 1 \\ 0 & 4 \end{bmatrix} \quad \mathbf{C} = \begin{bmatrix} 2 & 4 \\ 1 & 2 \end{bmatrix}$$

Find **AC** and **BC**. What do you conclude from this exercise?

16. Let **A** and **B** be as in Exercise 15. Find a matrix **D** such that $\mathbf{B} + 2\mathbf{D} = \mathbf{A}$.

17. Let $\mathbf{A} = \begin{bmatrix} 7 & 4 \\ 5 & 3 \end{bmatrix}$. Find $\mathbf{A}^{-1}$.

18. Let $\mathbf{A} = \begin{bmatrix} 1 & -2 \\ -1 & 3 \end{bmatrix}$.

(*a*) Find $\mathbf{A}^2$ (*b*) Find $\mathbf{A}^{-1}$ (*c*) Find $(\mathbf{A}^{-1})^2$ (*d*) Find $(\mathbf{A}^2)^{-1}$

19. Let $\mathbf{A} = \begin{bmatrix} 1 & 1 & 1 \\ 2 & 3 & 2 \\ 3 & 3 & 4 \end{bmatrix}$. Find $\mathbf{A}^{-1}$.

20. Let $\mathbf{A} = \begin{bmatrix} 1 & -.5 & 0 \\ 0 & 1 & -.5 \\ -.2 & -.2 & 1 \end{bmatrix}$. Find $\mathbf{A}^{-1}$.

21. Let

$$\mathbf{A} = \begin{bmatrix} 3 & 2 \\ 5 & 4 \end{bmatrix} \quad \mathbf{B} = \begin{bmatrix} -2 & 8 \\ 4 & 5 \end{bmatrix}$$

(*a*) Find a matrix **C** such that **AC** = **B**.
(*b*) Find a matrix **D** such that **DA** = **B**.

22. Decide whether the following matrix has an inverse. If it does, find it.

$$\begin{bmatrix} 1 & -1 & 2 \\ 2 & 3 & -2 \\ 3 & 2 & 0 \end{bmatrix}$$

23. For which value(s) of the constant k does the matrix shown below not have an inverse?

$$\mathbf{A} = \begin{bmatrix} 3 & k \\ -6 & 12 \end{bmatrix}$$

24. Let

$$\mathbf{A} = \begin{bmatrix} 1 & 2 & 3 \\ 2 & 4 & 7 \\ 3 & 8 & 9 \end{bmatrix} \quad \mathbf{X} = \begin{bmatrix} x_1 \\ x_2 \\ x_3 \end{bmatrix} \quad \mathbf{B} = \begin{bmatrix} 10 \\ 0 \\ -10 \end{bmatrix} \quad \text{and } \mathbf{C} = \begin{bmatrix} 2 \\ 6 \\ 6 \end{bmatrix}$$

Find $\mathbf{A}^{-1}$ and use it to solve the system **AX** = **B** and **AX** = **C**.

25. Let **A** be the matrix of Exercise 19. Solve the systems of equations

$$\mathbf{AX} = \begin{bmatrix} -1 \\ 2 \\ 3 \end{bmatrix} \quad \mathbf{AX} = \begin{bmatrix} -1 \\ 0 \\ 1 \end{bmatrix} \quad \mathbf{AX} = \begin{bmatrix} 1 \\ 2 \\ 3 \end{bmatrix}$$

26. Consider the matrices **P** and **R** shown below:

$$\mathbf{P} = \begin{bmatrix} 0 & 1 & 0 \\ 1 & 0 & 1 \\ 0 & -1 & 2 \end{bmatrix} \quad \mathbf{R} = \begin{bmatrix} 2 & 0 & 4 \\ 1 & -2 & 3 \\ 6 & -4 & 0 \end{bmatrix}$$

(*a*) Find a matrix **Q** such that $\mathbf{P} \cdot \mathbf{Q} = \mathbf{R}$.
(*b*) Find a matrix **T** such that $\mathbf{T} \cdot \mathbf{P} = \mathbf{R}$.

27. Let $\mathbf{A} = \begin{bmatrix} .2 & a \\ a & .2 \end{bmatrix}$. For which values of a does $\mathbf{I} - \mathbf{A}$ have an inverse with all positive entries?

28. Decide whether the following technology matrices **A** and **B** satisfy the assumptions of the Leontief model in Section 6.3.

$$\mathbf{A} = \begin{bmatrix} .4 & .6 \\ .6 & .4 \end{bmatrix} \quad \mathbf{B} = \begin{bmatrix} .8 & .4 \\ .2 & .8 \end{bmatrix}$$

29. Find the production vector for the following technology matrix **A** and demand vector **D**.

$$\mathbf{A} = \begin{bmatrix} .5 & .1 \\ .2 & .6 \end{bmatrix} \quad \mathbf{D} = \begin{bmatrix} 4 \\ 11 \end{bmatrix}$$

30. Given the technology matrix **A** of Exercise 29, what demand vector **D** will be met by the production schedule $\mathbf{X} = \begin{bmatrix} 30 \\ 60 \end{bmatrix}$?

31. Find the production schedule for the following technology matrix and demand vector.

$$\mathbf{A} = \begin{bmatrix} .5 & .8 & .1 \\ 0 & .2 & .4 \\ .5 & 0 & .4 \end{bmatrix} \quad \mathbf{D} = \begin{bmatrix} 3 \\ 8 \\ 2 \end{bmatrix}$$

32. Find the external demand satisfied by the technology matrix and production schedule given below.

$$\mathbf{A} = \begin{bmatrix} .2 & .4 & 0 \\ .1 & 0 & .1 \\ 0 & .1 & .2 \end{bmatrix} \quad \mathbf{X} = \begin{bmatrix} 100 \\ 150 \\ 100 \end{bmatrix}$$

33. Decide whether the following matrix **A** is such that $\mathbf{I} - \mathbf{A}$ has an inverse with all positive entries.

$$\mathbf{A} = \begin{bmatrix} .4 & .6 & .6 \\ .3 & .7 & .6 \\ .5 & .5 & .5 \end{bmatrix}$$

34. An economy has three goods—electricity, gravel, and timber—and the goods required in the production processes are specified in Table 6.4.
    (*a*) Find the technology matrix for this economy.
    (*b*) Find the production schedule which fills an external demand consisting of 45 units of electricity, 60 units of gravel, and 110 units of timber.

TABLE 6.4

	Amount Required to Produce 1 Unit of		
	Electricity	**Gravel**	**Timber**
Electricity	.20	.15	.25
Gravel	.20	.25	.30
Timber	.15	.35	.30

35. An economy with four goods has the technology matrix

$$\mathbf{A} = \begin{bmatrix} .1 & .25 & 0 & .2 \\ 0 & .2 & .2 & .3 \\ 0 & .3 & .3 & .1 \\ .15 & .25 & 0 & .3 \end{bmatrix}$$

Find the production schedule which meets the external demand

$$\mathbf{D} = \begin{bmatrix} 1200 \\ 840 \\ 660 \\ 1620 \end{bmatrix}$$

36. A production process has technology matrix and production schedule given below.

$$\mathbf{A} = \begin{bmatrix} .5 & 0 & .3 \\ 0 & .8 & .4 \\ 0 & .2 & .4 \end{bmatrix} \qquad \mathbf{X} = \begin{bmatrix} z \\ 35 \\ z \end{bmatrix}$$

If $\mathbf{X}$ is a production schedule that satisfies $\mathbf{D} = \begin{bmatrix} 3 \\ 1 \\ 2 \end{bmatrix}$, find z.

37. The economy of a small nation exports two products, wool and jade. The production of one unit of wool consumes 0.1 units of wool and 0.4 units of jade, and the production of one unit of jade consumes 0.3 units of jade and 0.2 units of wool.
   (*a*) Find the technology matrix for this economy (assume Good 1 = jade and Good 2 = wool).
   (*b*) If an order is placed for 550 units of wool and 440 units of jade, how many units of each must be produced to meet the demand?

38. An economy produces four minerals for export—aluminum, bismuth, cobalt, and dolomite. The production of one ton of aluminum consumes 0.1 tons of aluminum, no bismuth, 0.3 tons of cobalt, and 0.2 tons of dolomite. The production of one ton of bismuth consumes 0.6 tons of aluminum, 0.3 tons of bismuth, 0.1 tons of cobalt, and 0.2 tons of dolomite. The production of one ton of cobalt consumes 0.4 tons of aluminum, 0.3 tons of bismuth, no cobalt, and 0.3 tons of dolomite. Finally, the production of one ton of dolomite consumes no aluminum, 0.2 units of bismuth, 0.1 units of cobalt, and 0.5 units of dolomite. Find the technology matrix for this economy (assume Good 1 = aluminum, Good 2 = bismuth, Good 3 = cobalt, and Good 4 = dolomite).

CHAPTER 7

Linear Programming: Modeling and Graphical Solution

7.0 THE SETTING AND OVERVIEW: LINEAR OPTIMIZATION MODELS

Mathematics and physics have been tightly tied together for hundreds of years, and developments in one of these two fields often led to developments in the other. The links between mathematics and fields such as the management sciences and the social and life sciences came much later, but these links are now well established and are very important in current developments in these fields. One major use of mathematics in the management sciences and, to a lesser extent, in the life and social sciences is to formulate and solve optimization problems. In general, an optimization problem is one in which the goal is to select values of variables in such a way that some quantity that depends on the variables is as large or as small as possible. Normally, the permissible choices of the variables are restricted in some way. For example, in linear optimization problems, the quantity to be optimized and the restrictions are represented by using linear expressions, expressions such as $3x + 5y - 8z$. Linear optimization problems of the types considered in this book are referred to as *linear programming* problems.

A good case can be made that linear programming is one of the most widely applied and effective mathematical tools used in the social, life, and management sciences. The importance of linear programming became clear in the complex scheduling and resource allocation problems arising during World War II. The techniques are now routinely applied to a variety of problems arising throughout business—problems from marketing, manufacturing, finance, distribution, transportation, etc. In addition, the ideas and methods are used in both theoretical and applied economics and in unexpected ways in situations that seem far from standard business problems. For instance, the question as to whether a specific baseball team has been eliminated from contention for a playoff spot, a much more complex question than it first appears, can be answered by using linear programming.

Linear programming problems typically arise outside mathematics, and the first step in solving these problems is to formulate them correctly using linear expressions, such as those studied in Chapter 5. To illustrate this process of formulation, we use an example which has great historical importance as a setting for our modeling discussion; it is a version of one of the first problems solved by using linear programming. The problem is one of selecting foods which satisfy certain dietary requirements in a way that minimizes the cost of the food.

We make the situation specific and yet keep the discussion fairly simple by considering only two foods and two dietary requirements; the techniques developed in this chapter will enable us to handle more complicated situations. Suppose that we are to use broccoli and milk—hardly an appetizing diet, but a nutritious one—to meet dietary needs for calcium and iron and that we are to select amounts of these two foods that meet our needs at the least possible cost. The following data are available to us: The diet must contain at least .8 gram of calcium and 10 milligrams of iron. Each serving of broccoli contains .13 gram of calcium and 1.3 milligrams of iron, and each serving of milk contains .28 gram of calcium and .2 milligram of iron. Broccoli costs \$0.80 per serving, and milk costs \$0.50 per serving.

To describe a diet, we need to specify the amount of broccoli and the amount of milk. The first step in building a model consists of introducing appropriate notation. We let x denote the amount of broccoli and y denote the amount of milk to be consumed, with x and y each measured in units of servings. If there is .13 gram of calcium in one serving of broccoli, then there are $.13x$ grams in x servings; and if there are 1.3 milligrams of iron in one serving of broccoli, then there are $1.3x$ milligrams in x servings. Likewise, if there is .28 gram of calcium in one serving of milk, then there are $.28y$ grams in y servings; and if there is .2 milligram of iron in one serving of milk, then there are $.2y$ milligrams in y servings. Next, if we consume both x servings of broccoli and y servings of milk, then we have $.13x + .28y$ grams of calcium. The requirement that the diet provide at least .8 gram of calcium is, in our notation, $.13x + .28y \geq .8$.[1] A completely analogous argument leads to the inequality $1.3x + .2y \geq 10$, which represents the requirement that the diet contain at least 10 milligrams of iron.

Looking at the cost aspect of the problem, we see that since each serving of broccoli costs \$0.80, x servings should cost $\$0.80x$; and since each serving

[1]The inequality sign $\geq$ means that the quantity $.8x + .28y$ is to be *greater than or equal to* .8. If we want to restrict $.8x + .28y$ to be greater than .8, we write $.8x + .28y > .8$. The latter expression is referred to as a *strict inequality*. Similarly, the symbols $\leq$ and $<$ mean "less than or equal to" and "less than," respectively.

of milk costs \$0.50, y servings of milk cost \$0.50y. Therefore, the diet of x servings of broccoli and y servings of milk costs \$0.80x + \$0.50y. To find a least-cost diet, we should make $.80x + .50y$ as small as possible.

Although this all seems straightforward, it is important to realize that there are some unstated assumptions:

The first implicit assumption is that we actually know the calcium content of broccoli and milk. There is likely to be variation in the vitamin and mineral content of foods depending on how they are grown, processed, and stored. In some cases this variation can be quite large.

Second, we are assuming that if we get .13 gram of calcium from one serving of broccoli, then we get $.13x$ gram from x servings. This is a legitimate assumption for some values of x, but not for other values of x. As x becomes large, it is impossible for a human to extract all nutrients available in the food.

Next, we are assuming that if there is a certain amount of calcium available in the broccoli and another amount in the milk, then the sum of those two amounts is available in the combination of the two foods. This would be the case if the two foods were consumed independently; however, in some cases the presence of one food may affect the ability of the body to extract nutrients from other foods.

With regard to the cost assumptions, the statement that x servings of broccoli cost \$0.80x has the implicit assumption that there are no bulk discounts. Although the statement may be true for the amounts of broccoli that an individual normally buys, there should be some savings if the purchaser is buying broccoli by the boxcar load!

The statement that the cost of the diet is the sum of the costs of broccoli and of milk means that there are no discounts for purchasing both items. Frequently it is possible to negotiate a better price if you buy several items from one supplier.

It is clear that in formulating mathematical descriptions of situations, even fairly straightforward ones, we must be sensitive to the implications of our assumptions. The mathematical relations we develop incorporate the assumptions; and consequently, when we deduce conclusions from these relations, our conclusions will depend on the assumptions. If in some circumstances the assumptions are not completely fulfilled, then we should expect that the conclusions are not entirely valid.

This simple example illustrates the formulation of a linear programming problem and the many assumptions that underlie such a formulation. Although we will not emphasize the modeling aspect in the chapter which follows, we will formulate many mathematical problems from situations described in words. Indeed, the first section of this chapter is devoted entirely to the formulation of linear programming problems. In that discussion we will freely use the implicit assumptions that we have identified here. Remember that these are assumptions, and the reliability of the answers you obtain depends on the legitimacy of the assumptions.

7.1 FORMULATION OF LINEAR PROGRAMMING PROBLEMS

The first task in solving an optimization problem is to model the situation and to formulate a precise mathematical problem. We will model all situations discussed in this chapter as linear programming problems. The formulation phase involves taking a situation described in words and translating the information presented in words into mathematical form, i.e., into symbols and relations. The technique of translation can best be described by examples.

Example 7.1 Wilbur's Wings makes toy planes and toy drones using plastic and balsa wood. Each plane requires 4 ounces of plastic and 3 ounces of wood, while each drone requires 3 ounces of plastic and 6 ounces of wood. Each day Wilbur has 30 pounds of plastic and 45 pounds of wood to use in making toy planes and drones, and he can sell all the planes and drones he makes with these materials. His profit is \$5 per plane and \$4 per drone. Wilbur is motivated by financial goals, and he would like to know how many planes and drones he should make in order to maximize the total profit from the sale of these toys.

Problem Formulate a mathematical problem whose solution gives the numbers of planes and drones Wilbur should make to maximize his profit.

Solution Wilbur's goal is to decide how many planes and drones to make, so it is natural to introduce variables, called *decision variables*, which represent these quantities. Thus, we set

$$x = \text{number of planes to be made each day}$$

and

$$y = \text{number of drones to be made each day}$$

Next, since each plane requires 4 ounces of plastic, x planes require $4x$ ounces of plastic. Also, each drone requires 3 ounces of plastic, and y drones require $3y$ ounces of plastic. Therefore, x planes and y drones together require $4x + 3y$ ounces of plastic. Each day Wilbur has 30 pounds of plastic available, that is, $30 \cdot 16 = 480$ ounces, and the variables x and y are constrained by the requirement that at most 480 ounces of plastic can be used. Since $4x + 3y$ ounces of plastic are required to produce x planes and y drones, the mathematical constraint is

$$4x + 3y \leq 480$$

In the same way, x planes require $3x$ ounces of wood and y drones require $6y$ ounces of wood, and there are 45 pounds, or $45 \cdot 16 = 720$ ounces, of wood available. Therefore, another constraint on the number of planes and drones which can be produced is

$$3x + 6y \leq 720$$

Finally, the variables x and y cannot be negative; a negative number of planes and drones cannot be produced. Collecting all these constraints, we find that the variables x and y must satisfy the conditions

$$\begin{aligned} x \geq 0 \quad y &\geq 0 \\ 4x + 3y &\leq 480 \\ 3x + 6y &\leq 720 \end{aligned} \tag{7.1}$$

The constraints (7.1) must be satisfied by any choice of x and y that Wilbur makes. However, Wilbur's goal is to choose x and y so that his profit is a maximum. Since his profit is \$5 for each plane, it is (\$5)x when he produces x planes. Likewise, his profit for each drone is \$4, and therefore it is (\$4)y when he produces y drones. It follows that his total profit is (in dollars) $5x + 4y$ when he produces x planes and y drones. We have now formulated a mathematical problem which describes the decision Wilbur's Toys must make:

Find x and y which satisfy (7.1) and which make the profit $5x + 4y$ as large as possible [i.e., in comparison with the profit for any choice of x and y which satisfies (7.1)]. ■

Note that if Wilbur makes 10 planes and 15 drones then the constraints in (7.1) are satisfied. Indeed for $x = 10$ and $y = 15$, we have

$$\begin{aligned} 4 \cdot 10 + 3 \cdot 15 &= 85 < 480 \\ 3 \cdot 10 + 6 \cdot 15 &= 120 < 720 \end{aligned}$$

With the production of 10 planes and 15 drones, the profit is $\$5 \cdot 10 + \$4 \cdot 15 = \$110$. A profit of \$110 is unlikely to be the maximum possible profit since much of the plastic and wood that is available is not used. More planes and drones can be produced, and the question is how many should be produced?

Example 7.2 A hiker is planning her trail food, which is to include a snack mix of peanuts and raisins. Each day she wants 600 calories and 90 grams of carbohydrates from this mix. Each gram of raisins contains .8 gram of carbohydrates and 3 calories and costs 4 cents. Each gram of peanuts contains .2 gram of carbohydrates and 6 calories and costs 5 cents.

Problem Formulate a mathematical problem whose solution gives the number of grams of each food which will meet the hiker's needs at the smallest cost per day.

Solution First we identify the decision variables in the situation, i.e., the quantities which we wish to determine. Let

$$\begin{aligned} x &= \text{number of grams of raisins} \\ y &= \text{number of grams of peanuts} \end{aligned}$$

From the meaning of x and y we have the inequalities

$$x \geq 0 \qquad y \geq 0$$

Since each gram of raisins contains .8 gram of carbohydrate and each gram of peanuts contains .2 gram of carbohydrate, the total amount of carbohydrate is $.8x + .2y$; and consequently to meet the goal of the hiker regarding carbohydrate intake, we impose the constraint

$$.8x + .2y \geq 90$$

Likewise, the requirement on total calories leads to the constraint

$$3x + 6y \geq 600$$

Finally, the cost of x grams of raisins is $4x$ (in cents), and the cost of y grams of peanuts is $5y$ (in cents). Consequently, in cents,

$$\text{Total cost} = 4x + 5y$$

The mathematical problem is the following: Find the pair (or pairs) of values x and y satisfying the set of inequalities

$$\begin{aligned} x \geq 0 \quad y &\geq 0 \\ .8x + .2y &\geq 90 \\ 3x + 6y &\geq 600 \end{aligned} \tag{7.2}$$

for which $4x + 5y$ is as small as possible. ■

Some special terminology is useful in discussing linear programming problems.

Constraints, Feasible Sets, and Objective Functions

The inequalities that specify permissible values of the variables are the *constraints* of the problem. The constraints considered in this book will always be inclusive inequalities; they will be expressed with $\leq$ or $\geq$.

The set of points satisfying the constraints of the problem is known as the *feasible set* for the problem.

The function to be maximized or minimized is known as the *objective function* for the problem.

The constraints in Example 7.2 are the inequalities given in (7.2), and the feasible set is the set described by these inequalities. The objective function in Example 7.2 is the total cost, $4x + 5y$.

The formulation of a linear programming problem involves three steps:

1. Specify the variables.
2. Specify the constraints using the variables.
3. Specify the objective function using the variables.

Example 7.3 A hedge fund manager divides her time between sales and support activities. Keeping up to date on new products requires that she spend at least 5 hours each week reading trade newspapers and magazines. In addition, each hour she devotes to sales generates .1 hour of paperwork. She prefers sales, and she wants to devote at least half her time to that activity, but there is enough to do in support activities that any time not devoted to sales can be used for that purpose. She plans to devote at most 50 hours per week to her job. Finally, she estimates that the time she devotes to sales is worth \$80 per hour and that the time she devotes to support activities is worth \$40 per hour. (It would cost \$40 per hour to hire a staff person to do that work.)

Problem Formulate a mathematical problem whose solution gives the account executive an allocation of time that maximizes the value of her activities to her employer.

Solution Let x and y denote the number of hours devoted to sales and support activities, respectively. We have

$$x \geq 0 \qquad y \geq 0$$

The total number of hours worked is $x + y$, and the constraint that she work at most 50 hours per week gives

$$x + y \leq 50$$

Also, the constraint that at least half her effort be devoted to sales is

$$x \geq .5(x + y)$$

The latter inequality is equivalent to[2]

$$x \geq .5x + .5y$$

or

$$.5x - .5y \geq 0$$

[2] Here and in the remaining sections of this chapter we freely use the following properties of inequalities:

If $a \leq b$ and $c \leq d$, then $a + c \leq b + d$.
If $a \leq b$ and $\lambda > 0$, then $\lambda a \leq \lambda b$.
If $a \leq b$ and $\lambda < 0$, then $\lambda a \geq \lambda b$.

Next, each hour devoted to sales generates 0.1 hour of paperwork, and an additional 5 hours of support are required each week. Consequently, y must be at least as large as the sum of the paperwork generated by sales ($.1x$) and the normal support activities (5). We have the inequality

$$y \geq 5 + .1x$$

or

$$-.1x + y \geq 5$$

Finally, the businesswoman's contribution can be measured (in dollars) as

$$80x + 40y$$

In summary, the mathematical problem is the following:

Maximize $\qquad 80x + 40y$

subject to

$$\begin{aligned} x \geq 0 \quad y &\geq 0 \\ x + y &\leq 50 \\ .5x - .5y &\geq 0 \\ -.1x + y &\geq 5 \end{aligned}$$

■

Each of these first three examples has two unknown quantities or variables. Of course, most problems actually arising in applications have more than two variables, in some cases several hundreds or thousands of variables. We continue the formulation discussion with two examples involving more than two variables.

Example 7.4 The Plant Power Fertilizer Company makes three types of fertilizer: 20-8-8 for lawns, 4-8-4 for gardens, and 4-4-2 for general purposes. The numbers in each case refer to the percentage by weight of nitrate, phosphate, and potash, respectively, in a sack of fertilizer. The company has 6000 pounds of nitrate, 10,000 pounds of phosphate, and 4000 pounds of potash on hand. The profit is \$3 per 100 pounds of lawn fertilizer, \$8 per 100 pounds of garden fertilizer, and \$6 per 100 pounds of general-purpose fertilizer.

Problem Formulate a linear programming problem whose solution will give the number of pounds of each type of fertilizer that should be produced to yield maximum profit.

Solution Introduce the variables

x = number of hundreds of pounds of 20-8-8 fertilizer
y = number of hundreds of pounds of 4-8-4 fertilizer
z = number of hundreds of pounds of 4-4-2 fertilizer

Here the units (hundreds of pounds) are selected to simplify the equations that express the resource constraints. The equations that express the constraints on nitrate, phosphate, and potash are, respectively,

$$\begin{aligned} 20x + 4y + 4z &\leq 6{,}000 \\ 8x + 8y + 4z &\leq 10{,}000 \\ 8x + 4y + 2z &\leq 4{,}000 \end{aligned} \tag{7.3}$$

The objective function is

$$p = \text{profit} = 3x + 8y + 6z$$

It follows from the definition that each of the variables must be nonnegative.
Accordingly, the mathematical problem is:

Maximize $\quad 3x + 8y + 6z$

subject to $\quad x \geq 0 \quad y \geq 0 \quad z \geq 0$
and the inequalities (7.3) ■

Example 7.5 The office manager of an accounting firm must allocate the time of the office staff each week among three activities: auditing, business accounting, and tax accounting. Each hour billed as auditing requires 15 minutes of an accountant's time and 30 minutes of clerical time. Each hour billed as business accounting requires 20 minutes of accountant time, 60 minutes of clerical time, and 6 minutes of computer time. Each hour billed as tax accounting requires 30 minutes of accountant time, 45 minutes of clerical time, and 3 minutes of computer time. The net profit to the firm from 1 hour of auditing is \$4, and from business accounting and tax accounting the net profits are \$10 and \$6, respectively. This week the staff available can provide 80 hours of accountant time, 180 hours of clerical time, and 30 hours of computer time.

Problem Formulate a linear programming problem whose solution gives the allocation of time which provides the maximum net profit to the firm.

Solution We begin by identifying the variables. In this case, we let x, y, and z denote the number of hours billed as auditing, business accounting, and tax accounting, respectively.

In discussing the allocation of accountant, clerical, and computer time among these activities, it is convenient to express the times in minutes. The constraint resulting from the condition that accountant time not exceed 80 hours can be stated in terms of the variables x, y, and z by the equation

$$15x + 20y + 30z \leq 80(60) = 4800$$

Similarly, the constraint resulting from the limitation on clerical time is

$$30x + 60y + 45z \leq 180(60) = 10{,}800$$

and the constraint resulting from the limitation on computer time is

$$6y + 3z \leq 30(60) = 1800$$

The net profit that results from x hours billed as auditing, y hours billed as business accounting, and z hours billed as tax accounting is (in dollars)

$$4x + 10y + 6z$$

Finally, there is the nonnegativity restriction $x \geq 0, y \geq 0, z \geq 0$ which follows from the definitions of x, y, and z. Thus for the original allocation problem we have the following mathematical formulation:

Find numbers x, y, and z such that

$$p = \text{profit} = 4x + 10y + 6z$$

is a maximum for all x, y, z satisfying

$$\begin{aligned} x \geq 0 \quad\quad y \geq 0 \quad\quad z &\geq 0 \\ 15x + 20y + 30z &\leq 4{,}800 \\ 30x + 60y + 45z &\leq 10{,}800 \\ 6y + 3z &\leq 1{,}800 \end{aligned}$$

■

Exercises for Section 7.1

In each of the following exercises, formulate a linear programming problem for the situation described. Be sure to identify the variables, the constraints, and the objective function.

1. Sam's Deli makes sandwiches using bread and meat. Each small sandwich uses 6 inches of bread and 2 ounces of meat, while each large sandwich uses 10 inches of bread and 4 ounces of meat. The profit on a small sandwich is \$0.80 and on a large sandwich is \$1.20. Each day the deli has 110 feet of bread and 30 pounds of meat. How many sandwiches of each size should be made to maximize profit?
2. Lisa manages the salad preparation for a cafeteria, and each day one of her tasks is to prepare two types of fruit salads: the Salad Deluxe and the Daily Special. Each batch of Salad Deluxe requires 2.5 pounds of fresh fruit and .5 pounds of frozen fruit, and one batch of Daily Special requires 1 pound of fresh fruit and 2 pounds of frozen fruit. Each day she has 46 pounds of fresh fruit and 20 pounds of frozen fruit to use in these salads, and she has a standing order for 8 batches of Salad

Deluxe that she must fill. Her profit is $5 per batch of Salad Deluxe and $7 per batch of Daily Special salad. How many batches of each salad should she prepare to maximize her profit on these types of salads? Assume that she can sell all of these salads that she prepares.

3. The Natural Fertilizer Company produces 100-pound sacks of two types of fertilizer: 25-10-5 for lawns and 8-10-10 for gardens. The numbers in each case refer to the percentage by weight of nitrate, phosphate, and potash, respectively, in a sack of fertilizer. The company has 6 tons of nitrate, 5 tons of phosphate, and 3.5 tons of potash on hand. The profit per 100 pounds of lawn fertilizer is $7, and the profit per 100 pounds of garden fertilizer is $5. How much of each fertilizer should the company produce to maximize profit?

4. A manufacturer makes two in-line skate models, the California and the Florida. Both models require two operations in production: finishing the frame and installing and balancing the wheels. These operations require the following amounts of time (in minutes):

	Frame	Wheels
California	15	5
Florida	10	20

There are 120 hours of labor per day available for each job. The profit per California model is $15, and the profit per Florida model is $18. How should daily production be scheduled to maximize profit?

5. The New England Maple Sugar Co. of Los Angeles prepares 2 types of maple syrup from maple flavoring and water—called maple base—and sugar. One gallon of ExtraMaple syrup requires 2 gallons of maple base and 4 pounds of sugar, and each gallon of regular maple syrup requires 5 gallons of base and 2 pounds of sugar. This week the company has 10,000 gallons of maple base and 8800 pounds of sugar. Company records indicate that at most 1800 gallons of ExtraMaple syrup can be sold in a week and syrup that is not sold cannot be counted in this week's sales figures. There is a net profit of $3 per gallon of regular maple syrup and $5 per gallon of ExtraMaple syrup. How many gallons of each type should be produced to maximize net profit this week.

6. In Exercise 5, suppose that in addition to the other conditions, the manufacturing processes require that the amount of regular maple syrup produced not exceed the amount of ExtraMaple produced. Formulate the profit maximization problem in this case.

7. A company that manufactures laptop batteries purchases a portion of the material it uses from an independent supplier and a portion from a wholly owned subsidiary. The company needs 45,000 pounds of the material next month, and the subsidiary can produce at most 35,000 pounds. Antitrust regulations require that at least one third of the material needed be purchased from an independent supplier. The cost of the material is $0.80 per pound from the subsidiary and $1.00 per pound from the independent supplier. How much material should be purchased from the subsidiary and how much from the independent supplier to meet the needs at minimum cost and satisfy antitrust regulations?

8. An office furniture manufacturer has available 18 tons of sheet wood to be used to make desks and filing cabinets. It requires 50 pounds of wood and 3 hours of labor to make a filing cabinet and 75 pounds of wood and 2 hours of labor to make a desk. There are 1500 hours of labor available, but only enough tops for 400 desks. The net profit is \$20 on each desk and \$15 on each filing cabinet. How many desks and how many filing cabinets should be produced to provide maximum profit?
9. Glen and Barry's blends skim milk, sugar, and cream to make both regular and low-calorie ice cream. Each gallon of regular ice cream requires .6 gallon of skim milk, 1 pound of sugar, and .4 gallon of cream. Each gallon of low-calorie ice cream requires .7 gallon of skim milk, .3 pound of sugar, and .4 gallon of cream. Each day there are 800 gallons of skim milk, 400 pounds of sugar, and 400 gallons of cream available. The profit per gallon is \$1.00 for regular ice cream and \$1.20 for low-calorie ice cream. How many gallons of each type of ice cream should be produced to maximize profit?
10. Burt's Burgers is making regular size and kid's size cheeseburgers for a corporate cookout. A regular size cheeseburger requires 5 ounces of meat and 2 ounces of cheese. A kid's size cheeseburger requires 2 ounces of meat and 1 ounce of cheese. Burt has 15 regular size buns, 50 kid's size buns, 150 ounces of meat and 120 ounces of cheese that can be used to make the burgers. If Burt earns \$1 profit on the sale of a kid's size burger and \$3 on the sale of a regular burger, how many burgers of each size should he make in order to maximize profits?
11. A psychologist plans to conduct an experiment which involves subjects who perform activities. After data have been collected, the data are to be analyzed by a team of (highly paid) expert consultants. The psychologist has 15 subject hours available, and she will need to use at least 6 of them. She has funds for a maximum of 200 minutes of consultant time, and each hour of subject time requires at least 30 minutes of consultant time to analyze the data. Depending upon the depth of the analysis, up to 50 minutes of consultant time per subject hour can be profitably used. The information which the psychologist obtains from the experiment depends upon the number of subject hours and the amount of analysis. She estimates that, in appropriate units, 1 unit of information is obtained from each subject hour and 1 unit is obtained from each 25 minutes of consultant analysis. How should the experiment be organized (i.e., how many subject hours and how much consultant analysis) to give the maximum information?
12. River West Expeditions runs raft trips on the North Fork of the Trout River and through the Blue River Gorge. One trip on the North Fork requires 20 days of guide time and 50 hours of time from the support staff. One trip through the Blue River Gorge requires 40 days of guide time and 10 hours of time from the support staff. The company has 1680 days of guide time and 600 hours of time from the support staff. There is a commitment to have at least 25 trips down the Blue River Gorge. The profit for each trip down the North Fork is \$18,000, and the profit for each trip down the Blue River Gorge is \$3,000. How many trips of each type should be scheduled to yield maximum profit, and what is that profit?
13. The government has mobilized to inoculate the student population against sleeping sickness. There are 200 doctors and 450 nurses available. An inoculation team can consist of either 1 doctor and 3 nurses (called a *full team*) or 1 doctor and 2 nurses (called a *half team*). On average, a full team can inoculate 180 people per hour, while a half team can inoculate 100 people per hour. How many teams of each type should be formed to maximize the number of inoculations per hour?

14. The Mount Cycle Company makes two mountain bike models, Starstreak and Superstreak. Both models require three operations in production: (1) frame assembly, (2) installing the wheels, and (3) decorating. These operations require the following amounts of time (in minutes):

	Frame	Wheels	Decoration
Starstreak	20	10	14
Superstreak	10	15	18

There are 120 hours of labor available per day for frame assembly, 90 hours for attaching the wheels, and 75 for decorating. Also, each Starstreak model brings a profit of \$15 and each Superstreak model a profit of \$21. How should daily production be scheduled to maximize profit?

15. Brown Brothers Box Company produces both standard and heavy-duty shipping containers. One standard container requires 1 square foot of 100-pound test cardboard and 3 square feet of liner board. One heavy-duty container requires 5 square feet of 100-pound test cardboard and 1 square foot of liner board. Each week the company has 5000 square feet of 100-pound test cardboard and 4500 square feet of liner board available to produce shipping containers. There is a commitment to produce at least 500 standard containers each week. If the profit is \$0.30 for each standard container and \$0.40 for each heavy-duty container, how many of each type should be produced to meet the commitment and maximize profit?

16. In the situation described in Exercise 15, suppose that in addition it is required that both of the following conditions be met:
    (*a*) The number of heavy-duty containers produced does not exceed the number of standard containers.
    (*b*) There is a commitment to produce at least 200 heavy-duty containers each week.

    How many containers of each type should be produced to meet the commitments and maximize profit?

17. A toy company makes three monster dolls: Scary Harry, Horrible Harriet, and The Glob. The manufacturing of these dolls is a three-step process: (1) the body is molded from plastic, (2) clothes are put on, and (3) special monster features are added. The amounts of time and material for each step vary from doll to doll, and consequently each doll has its own production cost and associated profit. Data of the manufacturing process are shown in Table 7.1. How many dolls of each type should be manufactured each hour to maximize profit?

18. Repeat Exercise 17 for the data given in Table 7.2.

19. Is the vector which corresponds to the production of 5 Scary Harry, 5 Horrible Harriet, and 10 The Glob dolls feasible for the problem of Exercise 18? How about the vector which corresponds to 10 Scary Harry, 3 Horrible Harriet, and 2 The Glob dolls?

20. Brown Brothers Box Company recently lost a contract to produce price signs for gasoline stations, and it finds itself with excess capacity. It has 300 pounds of heavy-duty liner board, 120 pounds of finish cardboard, and 10 hours of

TABLE 7.1

Doll	Plastic, Ounces	Time for Clothes, Minutes	Time for Special Features, Minutes	Profit per Doll, $
Scary Harry	4	3	2	1.00
Horrible Harriet	3	4	4	1.25
The Glob	9	1	3	1.50
Available time or material per hour of operation	160	50	50	

TABLE 7.2

Doll	Plastic, Ounces	Time for Clothes, Minutes	Time for Special Features, Minutes	Profit per Doll, $
Scary Harry	5	2	3	1.10
Horrible Harriet	3	4	4	1.30
The Glob	10	1	6	2.00
Available time or material per hour of operation	192	55	45	

labor available each day. It can use these resources to produce shipping boxes, mailing tubes, and boxes for retail use. Each 100 shipping boxes use 150 pounds of heavy-duty liner board, 30 pounds of finish cardboard, and 2 hours of labor. Each 600 mailing tubes use 50 pounds of heavy-duty liner board and 30 pounds of finish cardboard and require 2 hours of labor. Finally, each 100 retail boxes use 60 pounds of heavy-duty liner board, 40 pounds of finish cardboard, and 5 hours of labor. The net profit is \$0.10 per retail box, \$0.01 per mailing tube, and \$0.04 per shipping box. How should the resources be allocated to produce maximum profit?

21. The Bait Shop sells three kinds of bait packages. The packages contain worms, minnows, and grasshoppers in the amounts shown in Table 7.3. The profit per package is \$1.00 for *A*, \$0.75 for *B*, and \$1.25 for *C*. There are 1000 worms available, 250 minnows, and 300 grasshoppers. How many packages of each type should be made to maximize profit?
22. University Videos, Inc., produces two types of video games, science fiction games and fantasy games. One scenario in a science fiction game requires 16 hours of

TABLE 7.3

Type	Number of Worms	Number of Minnows	Number of Grasshoppers
A	25	10	10
B	10	15	25
C	50	5	5

time from the creative staff, 14 hours of time from the technical staff, and 5 hours of editing. One scenario in a fantasy game requires 10 hours of time from the creative staff, 20 hours of time from the technical staff, and 1 hour of editing. The company has 504 hours of time from the creative staff, 756 hours of time from the technical staff, and 135 hours of editing to devote to the production of these games. The profit for each scenario for a science fiction video is $200 and the profit for each scenario for a fantasy video is $150. How many scenarios of each type should be produced to yield maximum profit?

23. Formulate the following situation as a linear programming problem. The Useful Gadget Company produces small, medium, and large gadgets with locks and small gadgets without locks. There is an assembly line with three stages: assembly, painting, and installation of locks; and there are 8 hours of assembly time, 9 hours of painting time, and 2 hours of lock installation time to be assigned. The time used (in hours) for each 100 gadgets at each stage is shown in Table 7.4. The net profit is $0.02 per gadget without lock and $0.10, $0.11, and $0.20 for small, medium, and large gadgets with locks, respectively. How should production be scheduled (i.e., how many of each type of gadget should be produced) to yield maximum net profit?

TABLE 7.4

Type of Gadget	Time for Assembly, Hours	Time for Painting, Hours	Time for Lock Installation, Hours
Small without lock	1	1	0
Small with lock	2	5	3
Medium with lock	3	4	1
Large with lock	6	8	4

24. Columbus Cruiselines offers one-week cruises using three ships: the Nina, the Pinta, and the Santa Maria. Each ship has both regular cabins and deluxe cabins. The Nina has 500 regular rooms and 200 deluxe, the Pinta has 400 regular and 400 deluxe, and the Santa Maria has 800 regular and 500 deluxe rooms. The cost to run each ship for a week is $100,000 for the Nina, $120,000 for the Pinta, and $180,000 for the Santa Maria. There is demand for 12,000 one-week cruises in regular rooms and 8000 one-week cruises in deluxe rooms. How many weeks should each ship be scheduled to meet the demand at minimum cost?

25. The California Dried Fruit Company prepares three types of dried-fruit packages for sale during the holiday season. The Deluxe Pack contains 16 ounces of dates, 24 ounces of apricots, and 12 ounces of candied fruit. The Special Pack contains 20 ounces of dates, 12 ounces of apricots, and 3 ounces of candied fruit. The Standard Pack contains 16 ounces of dates and 8 ounces of apricots. The company has 1200 ounces of dates, 900 ounces of apricots, and 360 ounces of candied fruit. If the net profit is \$3.00 for each Deluxe Pack, \$2.00 for each Special Pack, and \$1.50 for each Standard Pack, how many packages of each type should be produced to yield maximum profit?
26. Explain how the problem posed in Exercise 25 changes if both the following conditions are added:
    (*a*) The company has an order for 20 Special Packs which must be filled.
    (*b*) There are shipping cartons for only 30 Deluxe Packs.
27. A greenhouse operator plans to bid for the job of providing flowers for the city parks. He will use tulips, daffodils, and flowering shrubs in three types of layouts. A type 1 layout uses 30 tulips, 20 daffodils, and 4 flowering shrubs. A type 2 layout uses 10 tulips, 40 daffodils, and 3 flowering shrubs. A type 3 layout uses 20 tulips, 50 daffodils, and 2 flowering shrubs. The net profit is \$50 for each type 1 layout, \$30 for each type 2 layout, and \$60 for each type 3 layout. He has 1000 tulips, 800 daffodils, and 100 flowering shrubs. How many layouts of each type should be used to yield the maximum net profit?
28. Explain how the problem formulated in Exercise 27 changes if both the following constraints are imposed.
    (*a*) The number of type 1 layouts cannot exceed the number of type 2 layouts.
    (*b*) There must be at least 5 layouts of each type.
29. A timber company has forest land with trees suitable for furniture, plywood, and pulpwood. It requires 100 hours of labor and 20 hours of machine time to harvest 1 unit of timber for furniture; it requires 80 hours of labor and 30 hours of machine time to harvest 1 unit of timber for plywood; and it requires 50 hours of labor and 30 hours of machine time to harvest 1 unit of timber for pulpwood. The net profit is \$500 per unit for furniture timber, \$400 per unit for plywood timber, and \$200 per unit for pulpwood timber. The company has 1000 hours of labor, 500 hours of machine time, and ample supplies of all three types of timber. How much of each type of timber should be harvested to yield the maximum net profit?
30. Laminates Inc. produces laminated ID cards for businesses. A basic ID card requires 2 oz. laminate, .2 oz. black ink, and .1 oz. color ink. A deluxe ID card requires 2 oz. laminate, .1 oz. black ink, and .2 oz. color ink. Laminates Inc. has 2000 oz. laminate, and 190 oz. black ink, and 190 oz. color ink to use in making the ID cards. If they earn profits of \$0.73 per basic card and \$1.12 per deluxe ID card, how many cards of each type should they make in order to maximize profit?
31. Steve is a project manager at a consulting firm that includes Tommy and Pete. A study and report are due and must be written, together with a presentation about the report. One section of the necessary research study requires 3 hours of Tommy's time and one hour of Pete's time. One section of the presentation requires one hour of Tommy's time and 2 hours of Pete's time. Tommy has at most 40 hours and Pete has at most 25 hours that can be allocated to these tasks. Steve knows that the firm will profit \$500 per section of the necessary research study and \$250 per section of the presentation. How many sections of the necessary research study and

report and how many sections of the presentation should Steve ask to be produced in order to maximize the firm's profits?

32. A school cafeteria supplier mixes three types of food—foods 1, 2, and 3—for students at the school. The foods must provide at least 300 units of nutrient A, 20 units of nutrient B, and 100 units of nutrient C. The costs of the foods and the amounts of each type of nutrient that each food provides are shown in Table 7.5. How much of each type of food should be used to provide the minimum nutrient needs at the lowest cost?

TABLE 7.5

		Amount of Nutrient per Unit of Food		
Food	**Cost per Unit, $**	***A***	***B***	**C**
1	40	100	5	20
2	20	60	8	10
3	50	100	12	30

33. The Natural Fertilizer Company makes three types of fertilizer: 20-5-5 for lawns, 10-15-10 for gardens, and 5-5-5 for trees. The numbers in each case refer to the percentage by weight of nitrates, phosphates, and potash, respectively. The fertilizer is packed in 100-pound sacks. The company has the following amounts of raw materials on hand: 7 tons of nitrates, 4 tons of phosphates, and 3 tons of potash. The profit per 100-pound sack of lawn fertilizer is $6, the profit per sack of garden fertilizer is $4, and the profit per sack of tree fertilizer is $3. The company has a contract to supply at least 1 ton of garden fertilizer. How much of each fertilizer should the company produce to maximize profit?
Note: One US ton is equal to 2000 pounds.

7.2 SYSTEMS OF LINEAR INEQUALITIES IN TWO VARIABLES

The examples of Section 7.1 illustrate the way linear inequalities arise in linear programming problems. Indeed, the feasible sets for linear programming problems are defined by systems of linear inequalities, and developing a way to obtain points in feasible sets is important in the solution of linear programming problems. In Chapter 5 we developed ways to solve systems of linear equations, and we discussed the relation between algebraic expressions and the geometry of systems of linear equations. In this section we develop geometric methods to find points in sets described by systems of linear inequalities in two variables, and in Chapter 10 we develop algebraic methods for the same problem with systems of linear inequalities in any number of variables.

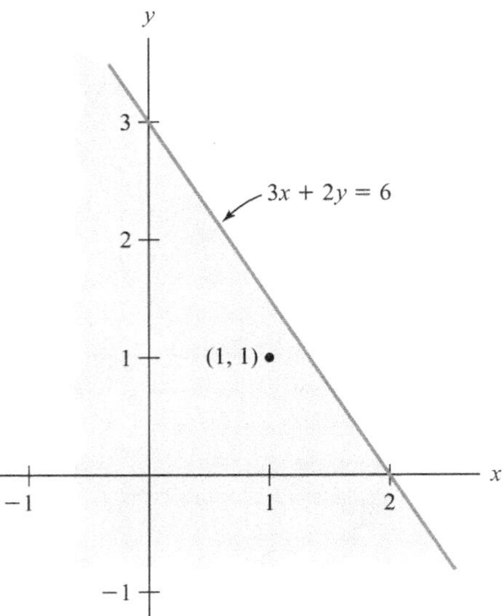

FIGURE 7.1

Example 7.6 Represent on a graph the set of points (x, y) for which $3x + 2y \leq 6$.

Solution The line specified by the equation $3x + 2y = 6$ defines two subsets, called *half planes*, of the cartesian plane. One half plane consists of the points (x, y) such that $3x + 2y \leq 6$. It is the shaded set shown in Figure 7.1 together with the set of points on the line itself. The line, i.e., the set of points which satisfy $3x + 2y = 6$, is called the *boundary* of the half plane. The other half plane consists of the points (x, y) such that $3x + 2y \geq 6$. This half plane consists of the unshaded area in Figure 7.1 together with the boundary line. We determine which of the two half planes is the one described by the given inequality $3x + 2y \leq 6$ by testing a single point not on the boundary line. For example, we can test the point (1, 1). We have $3(1) + 2(1) = 5 < 6$. Therefore, the point (1, 1) is included in the set described by the inequality $3x + 2y \leq 6$. ■

There are two points worth noting in this example.

1. The same technique can be applied to graph any set described by an inequality of the form $Ax + By \leq C$ (or $Ax + By \geq C$).
2. We used the point (1, 1) to determine which half plane was described by $3x + 2y \leq 6$ and which by $3x + 2y \geq 6$. We could have used *any* point not on the line $3x + 2y = 6$. The point (0, 0) is usually the easiest point to test, and it can be used whenever the line does not pass through the origin. Using the point (0, 0) in this example, we have $3(0) + 2(0) = 0 < 6$, so (0, 0) belongs to the half plane described by $3x + 2y \leq 6$.

Example 7.7 A hiker believes that on a long hike she will need snacks with at least 600 calories, and she plans to take chocolate and raisins. The chocolate she plans to take has 150 calories per ounce, and the raisins have 80 calories per ounce.

Problem Find a system of inequalities that describes those combinations of food which satisfy her requirements.

Solution Let x denote the number of ounces of chocolate she plans to take, and let y denote the number of ounces of raisins. This definition implies that $x \geq 0$ and $y \geq 0$. Since 1 ounce of chocolate contains 150 calories, x ounces of chocolate contain $150x$ calories. Likewise y ounces of raisins contain $80y$ calories. Also, the total calories obtained from the two foods is the sum of the number of calories from chocolate and the number of calories from raisins. That is,

$$\text{Total calories} = 150x + 80y$$

She believes that she needs at least 600 calories (the total calories must equal 600 or more). This leads to the condition

$$150x + 80y \geq 600$$

In summary, if x = number of ounces of chocolate and y = number of ounces of raisins, then her requirements are met by any (x, y) satisfying

$$\begin{gathered} x \geq 0 \qquad y \geq 0 \\ 150x + 80y \geq 600 \end{gathered} \tag{7.4}$$

■

Example 7.8 Graph the set of points (x, y) which satisfy the inequalities (7.4).

Solution This is a set of points (x, y) which satisfy three inequalities. Since these inequalities must be satisfied simultaneously, the desired set is the intersection of the three sets:

$$\begin{aligned} A &= \{(x, y): x \geq 0\} \\ B &= \{(x, y): y \geq 0\} \\ C &= \{(x, y): 150x + 80y \geq 600\} \end{aligned}$$

The set A is the half plane bounded by $x = 0$ (the y axis) and to the right of that line. The set B is the half plane bounded by $y = 0$ (the x axis) and above that line. The set C is the half plane above and to the right of the line $150x + 80y = 600$. The set $A \cap B \cap C$ is the shaded area in Figure 7.2. ■

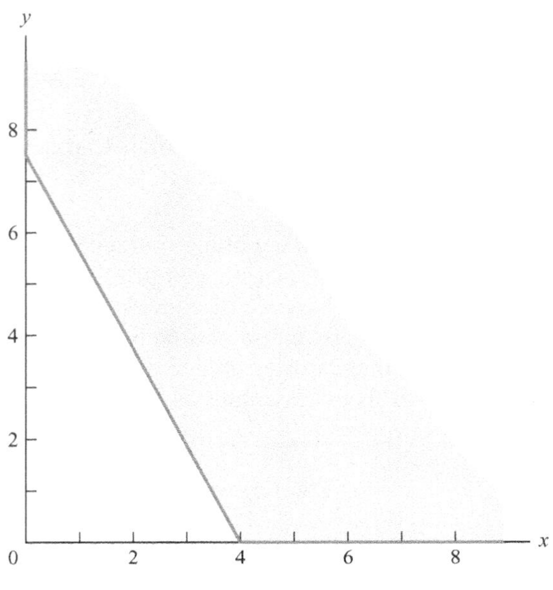

FIGURE 7.2

Examples 7.7 and 7.8 have illustrated a general technique for graphing inequalities.

Method for Finding the Set Described by Linear Inequalities

1. For each inequality, graph the boundary line and test a point not on that line to determine which half plane satisfies the inequality.
2. The desired set is the intersection of all the half planes determined in step 1.

Example 7.9 Graph the set of points which satisfy the inequalities

$$\begin{aligned} x &\geq 1 \\ x &\leq 2y \\ 3x + 4y &\leq 12 \end{aligned}$$

Solution The graph of the line whose equation is $x = 1$ is the vertical line through the point (1, 0). The half plane A described by $x \geq 1$ is the half plane to the right of this line and is shown in Figure 7.3*a*.

The graph of the line $x = 2y$ or $x - 2y = 0$ is the line through the points (0, 0) and (2, 1). The half plane B described by $x \leq 2y$ is above and to the left of this line. The half plane is shown in Figure 7.3*b*. To verify that the half plane is as shown, check that the point (1, 1) satisfies the condition $x \leq 2y$.

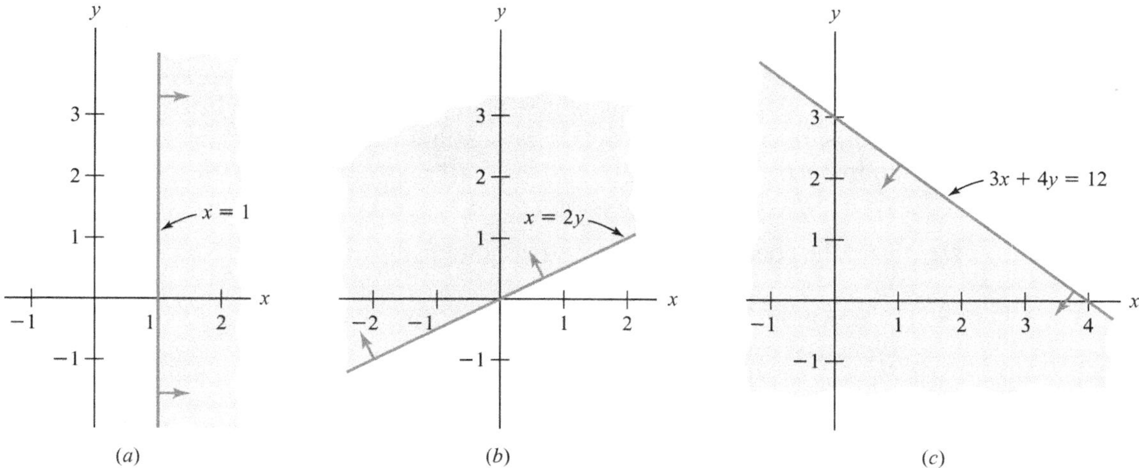

FIGURE 7.3

The graph of the line $3x + 4y = 12$ is the line through the points (4, 0) and (0, 3). The half plane C described by $3x + 4y \leq 12$ is below and to the left of this line. The half plane is shown in Figure 7.3c.

The set which we want to graph is $A \cap B \cap C$. This set is shown as the shaded area in Figure 7.4. ■

FIGURE 7.4

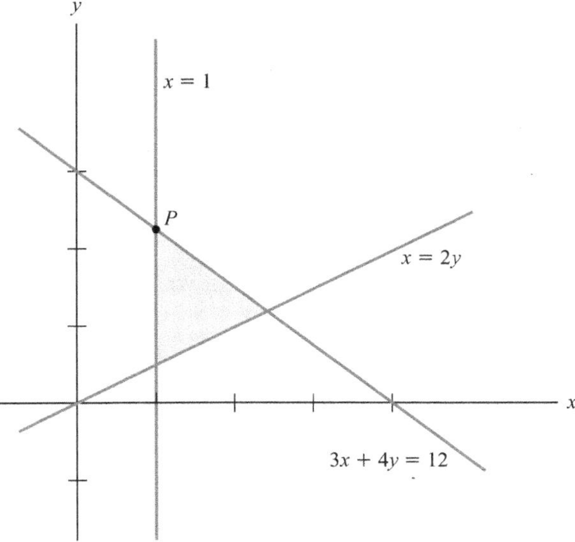

Notice that in Figure 7.3 we have shown small arrows from each boundary line directed into the half plane described by the relevant inequality. Such arrows are an alternative to shading and are frequently useful in identifying feasible sets in situations where there are several inequalities. To keep the figures in this book as simple as possible, we will not show such arrows in subsequent figures.

Example 7.10 Find the coordinates of the corner point P shown in Figure 7.4.

Solution The coordinates of the point P can be obtained by solving the system of equations

$$\begin{aligned} x &= 1 \\ 3x + 4y &= 12 \end{aligned}$$

This system is easily solved, and we find $P = (1, \frac{9}{4})$. ■

Example 7.11 Graph the set of points which satisfy the inequalities

$$\begin{aligned} x + y - 10 &\leq 0 \\ x + y + 10 &\geq 0 \\ 2x - y - 10 &\leq 0 \\ x - 3y + 15 &\geq 0 \end{aligned} \tag{7.5}$$

Solution We begin by drawing the boundary line for the first of the four half planes described by the system (7.5). The equation for the first boundary line is $x + y - 10 = 0$. The x intercept is 10, and the y intercept is 10. The boundary line is shown as the line labeled $L1$ in Figure 7.5. Since the point (0, 0) does not lie on the boundary line, it can be used to test which side of that line is described by the inequality. The point (0, 0) satisfies the inequality $x + y - 10 \leq 0$, so the half plane described by the inequality contains the origin. The boundary lines for the sets described by the remaining inequalities in the system (7.5) are shown as lines labeled $L2$, $L3$, and $L4$ in Figure 7.5. In each case the origin belongs to the set described by the inequality. The set described by the system (7.5) is shown as the shaded area in Figure 7.5. ■

Note that the point (2, 3) is in the shaded area of Figure 7.5. This means that for $x = 2$ and $y = 3$ the inequalities in (7.5) are all satisfied. We have

$$\begin{aligned} x + y - 10 &= 2 + 3 - 10 = -5 < 0 \\ x + y + 10 &= 2 + 3 + 10 = 15 > 0 \\ 2x - y - 10 &= 4 - 3 - 10 = -9 < 0 \\ x - 3y + 15 &= 2 - 9 + 15 = 8 > 0 \end{aligned}$$

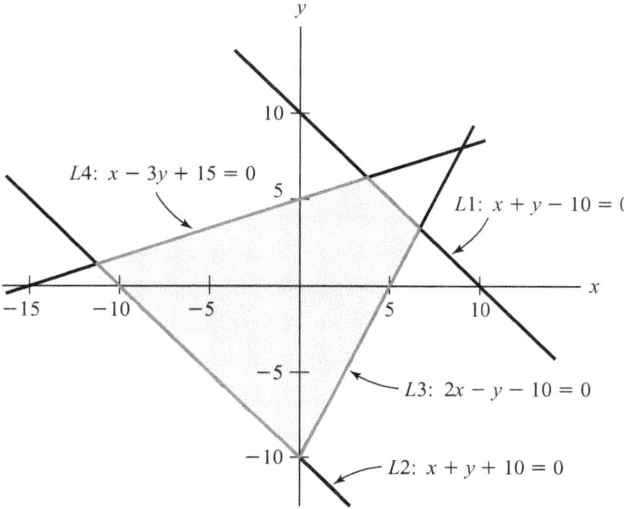

FIGURE 7.5

In fact we see that all of the inequalities in (7.5) are satisfied with a strict inequality, $<$ or $>$. This means that the point (2, 3) is inside the shaded area and not on the edge of the shaded set. The point $(0, -10)$ is an example of a point on the edge of the set since all of the inequalities are satisfied for this point and the second and third inequalities are satisfied as exact equalities. Thus, for lines $L2$ and $L3$ in Figure 7.5, we have

$$x + y + 10 = 0 + (-10) + 10 = 0$$

and

$$2x - y - 10 = 0 - (-10) - 10 = 0$$

Exercises for Section 7.2

In Exercises 1 through 10, graph and shade the set of points which satisfy the given system of inequalities.

1. $5x + 3y \le 15, \quad x - y \le 3, \quad x \ge 1$
2. $x + 3y \ge 3, \quad y \le 2, \quad x \ge 0$
3. $x \le 4, \quad -x + 4y \ge 8, \quad y - x \le 4$
4. $2x + 5y \le 10, \quad x \le 3, \quad y \ge -1$
5. $x - y \ge 0, \quad x + y \ge 2, \quad 4x + y \le 4$
6. $x + y \ge 0, \quad x - y + 2 \ge 0, \quad 5x - 2y \le 10$
7. $x - y \le 2, \quad 2x - y \ge 0, \quad 2x + y \le 6$
8. $x + y \le 2, \quad x - y \le 2, \quad -x + y \le 2, \quad -x - y \le 2$
9. $5y - 2x - 20 \le 0, \quad 4y + 3x + 24 \ge 0, \quad 6y - 7x + 21 \ge 0$
10. $3y + 2x + 12 \ge 0, \quad x + 4 \ge 0, \quad y + 2 \ge 0, \quad y - 2 \le 0$

11. Find the corner points of the set described by the inequalities in Exercise 3.
12. Find the corner points of the set described by the inequalities in Exercise 5.
13. Find the corner points of the set described by the inequalities in Exercise 7.
14. A set of points is described by the inequalities

$$\begin{aligned} x &\geq 0 \\ y &\geq 1 \\ x + 2y &\geq 4 \\ x + y &\leq 6 \end{aligned}$$

   (*a*) Graph this set of points.
   (*b*) Find the vertices of the polygon which is described by the inequalities.
15. Find the corner points of the set described by the system (7.5) in the first quadrant.
16. Suppose that in the system (7.5) the inequality $x + y - 10 \leq 0$ is replaced by the inequality $x + y - 10 \leq 10$, with all other inequalities remaining the same. Graph the set described by the inequalities, and find the corner point(s) in the first quadrant.
17. A set S is described by the inequalities

$$\begin{aligned} 3x + y &\leq 14 \\ 3x - 4y + 26 &\geq 0 \\ y &\geq 2 \end{aligned}$$

   Graph the set S and find the coordinates of the corner points for which x is positive.
18. A set S is described by the system of inequalities

$$\begin{aligned} x - y &\geq -4 \\ x - 2y &\leq -2 \\ 5x + 2y &\leq 10 \end{aligned}$$

   Graph the set S and find the coordinates of the corner points.
19. A set of points is described by the inequalities

$$\begin{aligned} x + y &\geq -2 \\ 2x + 4y &\leq 8 \\ 5x - 2y &\leq -10 \end{aligned}$$

   Graph this set of points, and find the vertices of the polygon which is described by these inequalities.
20. A set of points is described by the inequalities

$$\begin{aligned} 2y - x - 4 &\leq 0 \\ y - 1 &\geq 0 \\ 4x - y - 5 &\leq 0 \\ x &\geq 0 \end{aligned}$$

   (*a*) Graph this set of points.
   (*b*) Find the vertices of the polygon which is described by the inequalities.

21. A set of points is described by the inequalities

$$\begin{aligned} x &\geq 0 \\ x &\geq y \\ x &\leq y+2 \\ 3y+x &\leq 6 \end{aligned}$$

(*a*) Graph this set of points.
(*b*) Find the vertices of the polygon which is described by the inequalities.

22. An investor has $500,000 to invest in stocks and bonds. She determines that no more than three-fourths of the total should be invested in either type and that the amount invested in stocks should be at least as large as the amount invested in bonds. Graphically represent the set of choices available to the investor.

23. The manager of a paper-box plant is scheduling the work for one production line for a week. He can produce standard and heavy-duty boxes. Each standard box requires 2 pounds of kraft paper, and each heavy-duty box requires 4 pounds. Also it requires 8 hours of labor to produce 100 standard boxes and 3 hours of labor to produce 100 heavy-duty boxes. (The machine which produces heavy-duty boxes is more efficient.) There are 50 tons of kraft paper and 2400 hours of labor available during the week. Finally, the manager has a contract which requires him to deliver 10,000 heavy-duty boxes at the end of the week. Graphically represent the set of choices available to the manager.

24. A National Basketball Association player is about to take forced retirement (bad knee), and he has $1 million to invest for retirement income. He has decided to divide the money between a high-yield junk bond fund paying 10 percent per year and a government securities fund paying 6 percent per year. If he wants to be sure that his income is at least $75,000 per year, what allocations of funds are possible for him? Graph the set of possible investments.

25. A biologist is planning to conduct two experiments on 3 acres of a salt marsh. She plans to conduct one experiment on one portion of the 3 acres and the other experiment on all or part of the remainder. She can collect samples for the first experiment at a rate such that it would take 2 days to collect samples from 1 acre. For the second experiment, samples are much harder to collect, and it would require 8 days to collect samples from 1 acre. Laboratory work for the samples from the first experiment would take 12 hours to complete for the samples from one acre, and it would take 4 hours to complete the laboratory work for the samples collected from 1 acre for the second experiment. The biologist has 16 days to collect data from the entire 3 acres, and her budget allows for 28 hours of laboratory work. Graphically represent the set of alternatives available to the biologist.

26. The manager of a pension fund has $1 million to distribute among common stocks, bonds, and treasury notes. Guidelines for managing the fund call for no more than 60 percent of the assets to be invested in any single type of security.
(*a*) Graphically represent the set of options available to the fund manager. (*Note*: If $x =$ number of dollars allocated to stocks and $y =$ number of dollars allocated to bonds, then $1{,}000{,}000 - x - y =$ number of dollars allocated to treasury notes.)

(*b*) Suppose that stocks yield 3 percent, bonds yield 5 percent, and treasury notes yield 2 percent. If the goal of the manager is to maximize yield, find the objective function.

27. On a three-dimensional cartesian coordinate system, graph the feasible set for the following linear programming problem:

Maximize $$p = x + 2y + 3z$$

subject to $$x \geq 0 \qquad y \geq 0 \qquad z \geq 0$$
$$5x + 3y + 4z \leq 60$$

28. On a three-dimensional cartesian coordinate system, graph the feasible set for the following linear programming problem:

Maximize $$p = x + 2y + 3z$$

subject to $$x \geq 0 \qquad y \geq 0 \qquad z \geq 0$$
$$\begin{aligned} 5x + 3y + 4z &\leq 60 \\ x - y &\leq 0 \\ x - y &\geq 0 \end{aligned}$$

29. Graph the feasible set and find the corner points for the following linear programming problem:

Maximize $$p = 2x + y + 3z$$

subject to $$x \geq 0 \qquad y \geq 0 \qquad z \geq 0$$
$$\begin{aligned} 3x + 4y + 5z &\leq 60 \\ 2x + 3y &\leq 0 \\ x - y &\geq 0 \end{aligned}$$

30. Solve the linear programming problem posed in Exercise 29. In this special case the problem can be solved directly: Examine the feasible set and evaluate the objective function on this feasible set.

31. Graph the feasible set and find the corner points for the following linear programming problem:

Minimize $$p = 4x + 7y$$

subject to $$x \geq 0 \qquad y \geq 0$$
$$\begin{aligned} 4x + 4y &\geq 16 \\ 2x + 6y &\geq 12 \end{aligned}$$

Evaluate the objective function at the corner points.

32. Graph the feasible set, find the corner points, and evaluate the function p at the corner points for the following linear programming problem.

Minimize $$p = x + 2y$$

subject to
$$\begin{aligned} x + y &\geq 2 \\ y + 2 &\geq 0 \\ 3x - 2y + 6 &\geq 0 \end{aligned}$$

33. Find the corner points of the feasible set subject to the constraints: $x \leq 2, y \leq 5, y \geq -x, 4x - y \leq -5$
34. Find the corner points of the feasible set subject to the constraints: $x \leq 2, x \geq -2, x + y \geq 1, -x + y \geq 1$
35. Find the corner points of the feasible set subject to the constraints: $x \leq y, x \geq 2, x + y \geq 8$
36. Which of the feasible sets in exercises 33, 34, and 35 are unbounded and which are bounded?
37. Evaluate the following objective functions at the corner points of the feasible sets in exercise 33 and 34: $x + y, x - y, 5x + y, -5x + y$.
38. Evaluate the following objective functions at the corner points of the feasible sets in exercise 35: $x + y, x - y, 5x + y, -5x + y$.

7.3 GRAPHICAL SOLUTION OF LINEAR PROGRAMMING PROBLEMS WITH TWO VARIABLES

In this section we develop a method to solve linear programming problems with two variables similar to those formulated in Section 7.1. The method is based on the techniques of Section 7.2, namely, graphing the feasible set and finding the corner points. We begin with an example and then present the general method.

Example 7.12 (Continuation of Example 7.1) The problem formulated in Example 7.1 is to find the maximum of $5x + 4y$ for (x, y) satisfying

$$\begin{aligned} x \geq 0 \quad y &\geq 0 \\ 4x + 3y &\leq 480 \\ 3x + 6y &\leq 720 \end{aligned} \tag{7.6}$$

Recall that we are seeking x and y, where x is the number of toy planes and y is the number of toy drones that Wilbur's Wings should produce in order to maximize profit.

Problem Solve the problem posed above; i.e., find the values of x and y which maximize profit $= 5x + 4y$.

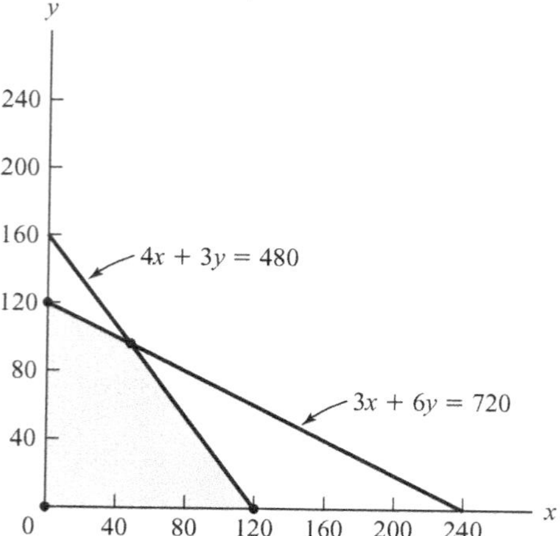

FIGURE 7.6

Solution The feasible set for the problem, the set of (x, y) satisfying the inequalities (7.6), is shown as the shaded region in Figure 7.6. Since our goal is to make $5x + 4y$ as large as possible, we begin by considering possible values for this quantity. Suppose we denote the value of $5x + 4y$ by C. Then the set of all (x, y) for which $5x + 4y = C$ is a line. For instance, the lines on which $C = 120$ and $C = 240$ are shown on Figure 7.7. For some values of C the line intersects the feasible set, for example, $C = 240$, and for some values of C the line does not intersect the feasible set, for example, $C = 700$. If for a specific value of C, say $C = C'$, the line does intersect the feasible set, then there are

FIGURE 7.7

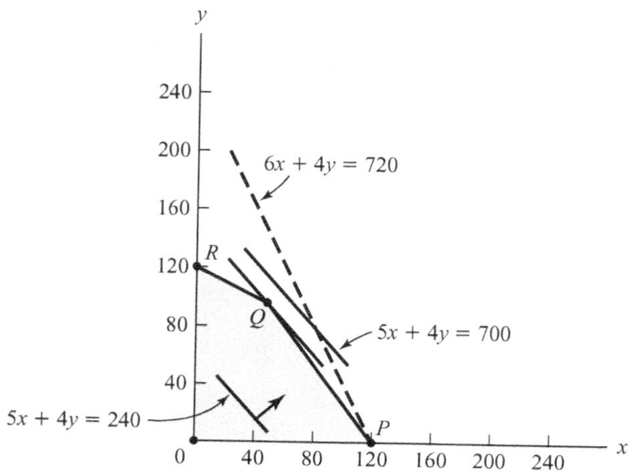

values of x and y that satisfy the inequalities (7.5) and for which $5x + 4y = C'$. Since we are interested in finding the point (x, y) in the feasible set for which $5x + 4y$ is as large as possible, we are seeking the largest value of C for which the line $5x + 4y = C$ intersects the feasible set. We denote that value of C by C^*. (It is common practice to use an asterisk to denote a maximum or a minimum value, and we use that convention in this section.)

The boundary of the feasible set is shown by the solid polygonal line in Figure 7.7 connecting points marked O, P, Q, R. Imagine a line with the equation $5x + 4y = C$ moving in the direction of the large arrow in Figure 7.7. The lines corresponding to any two values of C are parallel (they have the same slope), and the one with the larger value of C is ''farther out'' in the direction of the arrow. It is clear from Figure 7.7 that the value C^* corresponds to the line through the point labeled Q. The coordinates of the corner point Q can be obtained by solving the system of equations

$$\begin{aligned} 4x + 3y &= 480 \\ 3x + 6y &= 720 \end{aligned}$$

The solution of the system is $x = 48$, $y = 96$. Therefore,

$$C^* = 5(48) + 4(96) = 624$$

The problem posed in Example 7.1 has now been solved. The maximum value of $5x + 4y$, for (x, y) satisfying (7.6), is 624. This value is attained for $x = 48$, $y = 96$. Stated differently, for any point (x, y) satisfying (7.1), we have $5x + 4y \leq 624$, and for $(x, y) = (48, 96)$, we have $5x + 4y = 624$.

In terms of the original problem, Wilbur's Wings should make 48 toy planes and 96 toy drones to maximize profit. Notice that all the wood and all the plastic are used in the production of these toys and drones. This follows because

$$\begin{aligned} 4(48) + 3(96) &= 480 \\ 3(48) + 6(96) &= 720 \end{aligned}$$

■

The last comment in the solution of Example 7.12 touches on an important issue. Suppose we have a linear programming problem in which the goal is to allocate resources to yield maximum profit. If the solution (x, y) of the problem satisfies a constraint $Ax + By \leq D$ as an equality, that is, $Ax + By = D$, then *all* the resources which are represented by that constraint are used when production is at the level (x, y). Geometrically this means that the boundary line of the half plane defined by the resource constraint contains the point (x, y). On the other hand, if the constraint is satisfied as a strict inequality $Ax + By < D$, then *not all* the resources represented by that constraint are used when production is at the level (x, y). Geometrically, the boundary line of the half plane does not contain the point (x, y). The amount of unused resources is $D - (Ax + By)$.

Example 7.13 Suppose in Example 7.1 (solved in Example 7.12) that the profit per plane is changed from \$5 to \$6. If all other conditions remain the same, how many toy planes and drones should be produced to maximize profit? Also, are all the plastic and all the wood used in this new situation?

Solution Since only the objective function (the profit) has changed, the feasible set for this example is the same as the one in Example 7.12, namely, that shown in Figures 7.6 and 7.7. However, in this case, the profit line is $6x + 4y = C$, and we need to find the largest value of C such that this new line intersects the feasible set. Arguing as in Example 7.12, i.e., thinking of moving the line $6x + 4y = C$ by increasing the value of C, we conclude that the largest value of C for which the line meets the feasible set is $C = 720$. This line is shown as the dashed line in Figure 7.7. Since $C = 720$, the largest possible profit is \$720, and we see that this occurs at point P, where $x = 120$, $y = 0$. Thus, Wilbur's Wings should make 120 planes and no drones. Also, note that for this level of production all the wood is used, because $4(120) + 3(0) = 480$, but not all the plastic is used, because $3(120) + 6(0) = 360 < 720$. Indeed, there are $720 - 360 = 360$ ounces of plastic left over. The amount of extra plastic is called the *slack* in the constraint for plastic. ■

Notice that in both Examples 7.12 and 7.13 the maximum value of the objective function was attained at one of the corner points of the feasible set. This is true for a large class of problems which includes all linear programming problems considered in this book. Although Figure 7.7 provides some geometric intuition which supports the conclusion in the special cases of Examples 7.12 and 7.13, it is by no means obvious that the conclusion must always hold. It is in situations such as this that mathematical theorems are useful. We observed a fact in two special cases. If it were true in all cases of interest to us, it would greatly simplify the problem-solving process. Its truth under certain carefully specified hypotheses is asserted in a *theorem* and is demonstrated in a *proof*. We shall state carefully conditions under which the assertion is valid, but we omit the proof. We consider only those sets that arise as feasible sets for linear programming problems.

Bounded and Unbounded Sets

A set of points in the plane is said to be *bounded* if it is contained in some circle centered at (0, 0). Otherwise it is said to be *unbounded*.

The set shown in Figure 7.8*a* is bounded; the set in Figure 7.8*b* is unbounded.

Corner Point

A point T is a *corner point* (or an *extreme point*) of a feasible set for a linear programming problem if every line segment that is contained in the set and that contains T has T as one of its endpoints.

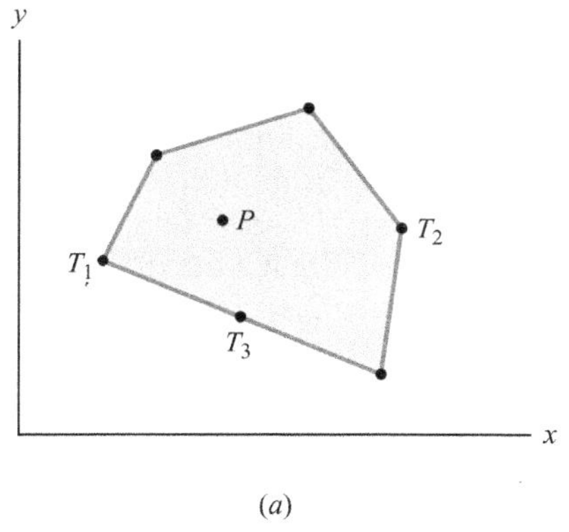

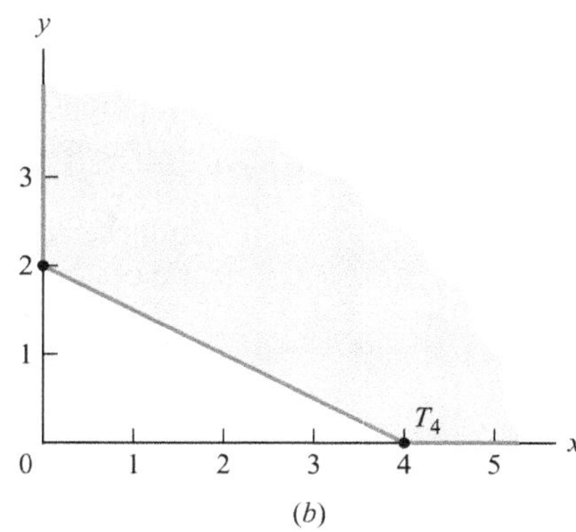

FIGURE 7.8

In Figure 7.8*a*, points T_1 and T_2 are corner points, but points P and T_3 are not. This definition makes precise the intuitive notion of a corner point used in Examples 7.12 and 7.13. As in those examples, a corner point can always be determined by solving a system of linear equations.

Using these definitions, we can state a mathematical theorem which provides the basis for the method we use to solve linear programming problems.

Theorem on Solutions of Linear Programming Problems

Let F be the feasible set for a linear programming problem, $F \neq \emptyset$, and let f be the objective function.

1. If F is bounded, then f attains its maximum value at a corner point of F and its minimum value at a corner point of F.
2. If F is unbounded and has at least one corner point, then exactly one of the following holds:
   (*a*) f attains its maximum at a corner point of F.
   (*b*) f takes arbitrarily large positive values on F.

The statement for unbounded sets and minimum values is as follows:

2′. If F is unbounded and has at least one corner point, then exactly one of the following holds:
   (*a*) f attains its minimum at a corner point of F.
   (*b*) f takes arbitrarily large negative values on F.

Stated in somewhat less formal terms, the first part of the theorem says that if the feasible set for a linear programming problem is bounded (such a set is shown shaded in Figure 7.8*a*), and if we seek to maximize the objective function, then the maximum value is attained at a corner point. Consequently, if we are to maximize the objective function in a linear programming problem and if the feasible set is bounded, then we need only examine the values of the objective function at the corner points and take the largest. This is the maximum value of the objective function on the entire feasible set. A similar statement holds for problems seeking the minimum of the objective function.

The assertions of the theorem regarding unbounded sets are necessarily phrased somewhat differently from the assertion regarding bounded sets. Indeed, for an unbounded feasible set F (e.g., the set shown in Figure 7.8*b*), the objective function need not attain a maximum or a minimum value.

For a specific instance of case 2 of the theorem, consider the problem:

Maximize $x + y$

subject to

$$x \geq 0 \quad y \geq 0$$
$$x + 2y \geq 4$$

The feasible set F is unbounded, and the objective function $x + y$ takes arbitrarily large values: Indeed at the point $x = n, y = 0$ the objective function takes the value n, and n can be any number ≥ 4. Thus, as the theorem asserts, the objective function does not attain a maximum value. See Figure 7.8*b* for the feasible set F.

The theorem justifies the use of the following method of solving linear programming problems in two variables.

Solution Method for Linear Programming Problems

1. Graph the feasible set for the problem.
2. Determine the coordinates of each of the corner points of the feasible set.
3. Evaluate the objective function at each corner point.
4. Select the largest of these values if the problem is to maximize the objective function and the smallest of these values if the problem is to minimize the objective function.
   (*a*) If the feasible set is bounded, the value selected is the solution of the problem.
   (*b*) If the feasible set is unbounded and if the problem has a solution, the value selected is the solution.

Comments on the Method

Step 1 is important because without the aid of a graph it may be difficult to determine which pairs of the constraints determine corner points.

Since each corner point is the intersection of two lines, it can be determined by solving a pair of linear equations. Thus step 2 is carried out by solving pairs of linear equations, one pair for each corner point.

The information required in step 3 is easily presented in a table with the coordinates of the corner points forming one column and the values of the objective function forming the other. (See Table 7.3 for an example.)

If the feasible set is bounded, then the selection described in step 4 solves the problem. If the feasible set is unbounded, then a separate argument is needed to determine whether the problem has a solution. Concentrate for a moment on maximum problems. Either the problem has a solution, in which case the maximum value of the objective function is attained at a corner point, or the objective function takes arbitrarily large values and the problem has no solution. Similar comments hold for minimum problems.

We illustrate the case of a bounded feasible set in Example 7.14 and the case of an unbounded feasible set in Example 7.15.

Example 7.14 Find the largest value of $x + y$ for x and y satisfying the constraints

$$\begin{aligned} x \geq 0 \quad y &\geq 0 \\ x + 2y &\geq 6 \\ x - y &\geq -4 \\ 2x + y &\leq 8 \end{aligned}$$

Solution Beginning with step 1 of our solution method, we graph the feasible set. This set is shown as the colored area in Figure 7.9. Note that the constraint $y \geq 0$ is redundant in this problem. That is, the feasible set is the same whether or not the constraint $y \geq 0$ is used to determine it.

Continuing with step 2, we determine the corner points. They are shown in Table 7.6 along with the values of the objective function $x + y$ at the corner points. We select the value $\frac{20}{3}$ as the largest value taken by the objective function at a corner point. Since the feasible set is bounded, we conclude that the maximum value of the objective function $x + y$ on the feasible set is $\frac{20}{3}$, and this value is taken at the corner point $(\frac{4}{3}, \frac{16}{3})$. ■

FIGURE 7.9

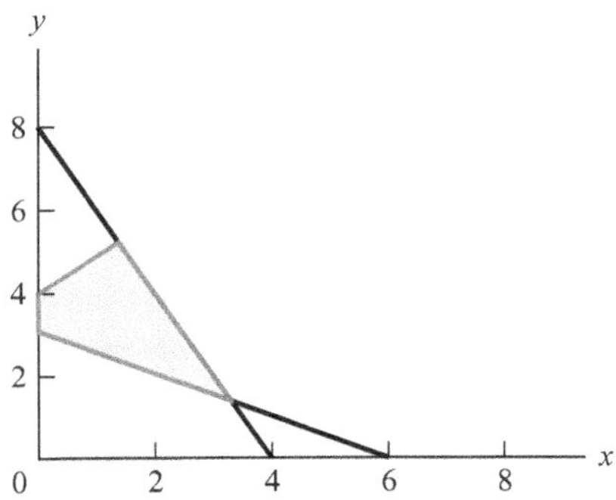

TABLE 7.6

Corner Point	Value of $x + y$
(0, 4)	4
$(\frac{4}{3}, \frac{16}{3})$	$\frac{20}{3}$
$(\frac{10}{3}, \frac{4}{3})$	$\frac{14}{3}$
(0, 3)	3

Example 7.15 Solve the linear programming problem posed in Example 7.2.

Solution The equations defining the feasible set are

$$x \geq 0 \qquad y \geq 0$$
$$.8x + .2y \geq 90$$
$$3x + 6y \geq 600$$

and we wish to minimize the objective function $3x + 5y$. The feasible set, graphed in Figure 7.10, has three corner points denoted T_1, T_2, and T_3 in that figure. The coordinates of each corner point can be determined by solving the pair of equations corresponding to the lines which intersect at the corner point. Thus to determine the coordinates of T_1, T_2, and T_3, we solve the respective equations

T_1	T_2	T_3
$x = 0$	$.8x + .2y = 90$	$y = 0$
$.8x + .2y = 90$	$3x + 6y = 600$	$3x + 6y = 600$

FIGURE 7.10

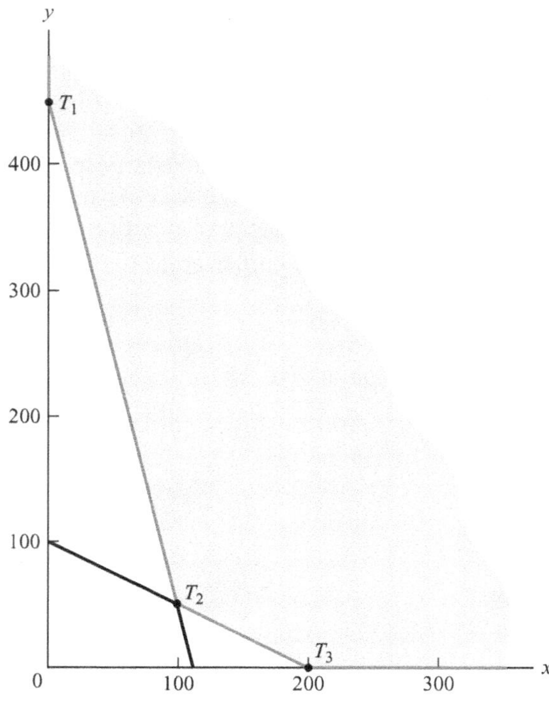

TABLE 7.7

Corner Point	Value of $3x + 5y$
(0, 450)	2250
(100, 50)	550
(200, 0)	600

We conclude that $T_1 = (0, 450)$, $T_2 = (100, 50)$, and $T_3 = (200, 0)$. Evaluating the objective function $3x + 5y$ at each corner point, we obtain the data in Table 7.7. Since the problem is to minimize the objective function (recall that the original problem was to minimize cost), we select the smallest value of the objective function. This is 550, which is attained at $T_2 = (100, 50)$. Therefore, since the feasible set is unbounded, we know that if the objective function does not attain arbitrarily large negative values, then the smallest value of the objective function is 550. In fact, this is the smallest value of the objective function on the feasible set since $3x + 5y$ takes only nonnegative values. (See 2′ of the theorem on p. 315.)

In terms of the original problem, the optimal mixture of peanuts and raisins is 100 grams of raisins and 50 grams of peanuts. The cost of this mixture is 550 cents, or \$5.50, and this is the minimum cost of a mixture meeting the conditions set in the problem. ■

As we have seen, in some cases where the feasible set is unbounded special arguments can be used to show that a problem has a solution or that it has no solution. However, it is important to have a method that can be used in all cases of unbounded feasible sets. Such a method is the following.

Solutions of Problems with Unbounded Feasible Sets

Suppose the feasible set for a linear programming problem is unbounded. Determine the corner points of the feasible set and evaluate the objective function at each corner point.

(*a*) If the problem is a maximization problem, select the corner point (or points) at which the objective function has the largest value. At each such corner point, two boundary lines of the feasible set meet. On each such boundary line, select a feasible point, not a corner point, and evaluate the objective function. If these values are all less than or equal to the largest value of the objective function attained at a corner point, then the problem has a solution, and it is the largest value attained at a corner point. Otherwise, the problem has no solution.

(*b*) If the problem is a minimum problem, select the corner point (or points) at which the objective function has the smallest value. At each such corner point, two boundary lines of the feasible set meet. On each such boundary line, select a feasible point, not a corner point, and evaluate the objective function. If these values are all greater than or equal to the smallest value of the objective function attained at a corner point, then the problem has a solution, and it is the smallest value attained at a corner point. Otherwise, the problem has no solution.

Example 7.16 Although this technique is somewhat complicated to explain, it is quite easy to apply, as the following example shows.

Minimize $5x - 3y$

subject to

$$x \geq 0 \qquad y \geq 0$$
$$.8x + .2y \geq 90$$
$$3x + 6y \geq 600$$

TABLE 7.8

Corner Point	Value of $5x - 3y$
(0, 450)	−1350
(100, 50)	350
(200, 0)	1000

Solution The constraints of this problem are the same as those of Example 7.15, and consequently the feasible sets are the same. Therefore, the feasible set for this problem is shown in Figure 7.10. The corner points and the values of the objective function at the corner points are shown in Table 7.8. The smallest value of the objective function is −1350, and it is attained at the corner point (0, 450). Following step (b) of the method, we select one point on each of the two boundary lines intersecting at (0, 450). We select (0, 500) and (25, 350). At the point (0, 500) the objective function takes the value −1500, and at (25, 350) it takes the value −925. Since −1500 is smaller than −1350, the problem has no solution. ■

The geometric method requires an additional step when the feasible set is unbounded. It would be nice to have a method in which the distinction between bounded and unbounded feasible sets is unimportant. Such a method is part of the key computational algorithm, known as the **simplex method**. This algorithm was critical for the widespread use and the great success of linear programming in solving important optimization problems. The simplex method is now available on many computer packages and is often used on problems with many thousands of variables. Examples of areas that use linear programming and the simplex method are found in manufacturing, scheduling, and network analysis.

We conclude this section, and the chapter, with an example which illustrates in a slightly different way the geometry of linear programming problems. We utilize the graphical techniques introduced in Chapter 5 to represent the feasible set in the xy plane and the value of the objective function in the direction perpendicular to that plane.

Example 7.17 A linear programming problem is defined as follows:

Maximize $3x + y$

subject to

$$x + y \geq 3$$
$$3x - y \geq -1$$
$$x \leq 2$$

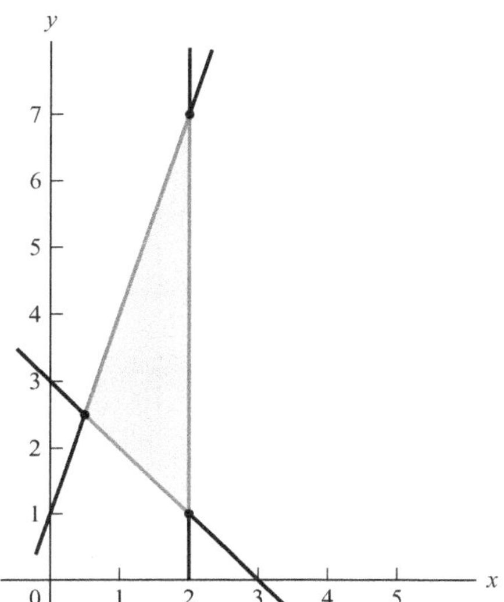

FIGURE 7.11

TABLE 7.9

Corner Point	Value of $p = 3x + y$
$(\frac{1}{2}, \frac{5}{2})$	4
(2, 1)	7
(2, 7)	13

Problem Graph the feasible set, find the value of $p = 3x + y$ for each corner point (x, y), and graph the value of p corresponding to each corner point on a three-dimensional coordinate system.

Solution The graph of the feasible set in the xy plane is shown in Figure 7.11. The values of the objective function at the corner points are shown in Table 7.9.

In Figure 7.12 the feasible set is shown as a dark-shaded area in the xy plane in a three-dimensional coordinate system. We denote the direction perpendicular to the xy plane as the p direction. For each corner point (x, y), we plot the point (x, y, p), where $p = 3x + y$. That is, for each corner point we plot the value of the objective function in the vertical direction. The relation between x, y, and p is $p = 3x + y$, or $p - 3x - y = 0$, and the graph of this linear equation is a plane in xyp space. If you consider only those points (x, y, p) on this plane for which (x, y) is in the feasible set, then you have the light-shaded area in Figure 7.12. In this example the maximum value of the objective function is 13, and this value is attained at the corner point (2, 7). It is clear from the figure that the plane $p - 3x - y = 0$ slopes in such a way that its maximum height from the xy plane is attained at the point (2, 7).

This situation prevails in general: If the feasible set is bounded, then the plane defined by

$$p - \text{objective function} = 0$$

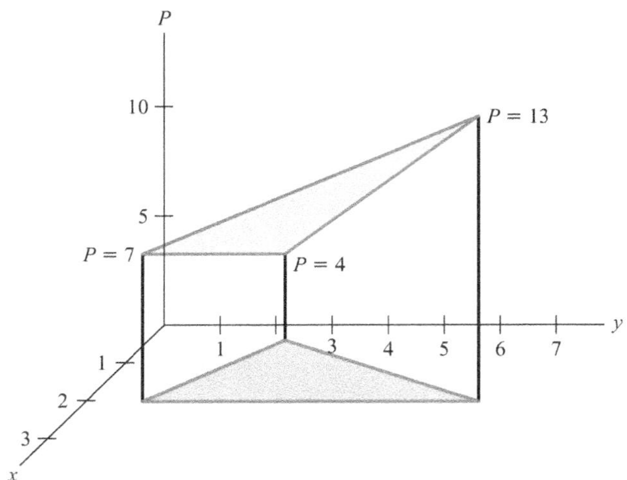

FIGURE 7.12

attains its maximum height from the xy plane at a corner point. This corner point gives the solution of the linear programming problem. ■

Exercises for Section 7.3

Each of the systems of inequalities in Exercises 1 through 5 describes a set in the xy plane. Graph that set and find the corner points. In each case decide if the set is bounded or unbounded.

1. $x - y \leq 3, \quad x + 3y \leq 3, \quad 3x + y \geq -3$
2. $x + y \leq 4, \quad x - y \leq 0, \quad x - y \geq -2$
3. $x \geq 0, y \geq 0, \quad x + y \leq 3, \quad x - y \leq 1$
4. $3x + 2y \leq 10, \quad y \leq 3, \quad x - y \leq 1, \quad x \geq 0$
5. $x - y \leq -3, \quad x - y \geq 1, \quad y \leq 3$
6. A set S in the xy plane is described by the inequalities

$$\begin{aligned} y &\geq -1 \\ x &\leq 3 \\ y &\leq 3x + 6 \\ 5y + 2x &\leq 10 \end{aligned}$$

   (*a*) Graph this set.
   (*b*) Find the corner points of the set.
   (*c*) Find the maximum value of $3x + 2y$ for $(x, y) \in S$.
7. Find the maximum value of $2x + y$ for (x, y) satisfying $x \geq 1, y \geq 1, x \leq 5, y \leq 5$, and $x + y \leq 6$. Also find the minimum value of $x - 2y$ on this set.
8. Find the minimum value of $x/2 + y$ for (x, y) satisfying $y \geq 2, x \geq 0, x \geq y$, and $x + y \leq 6$. Also find the maximum value of $-x + 2y$ on this set.

9. Find the maximum value and the minimum value of $-x + 4y$ for (x, y) satisfying $x + 2y \leq 20$, $-x + 2y \leq 10$, and $-x + 3y \geq 5$.
10. Find the maximum and minimum values of $2x - 5y$ for (x, y) satisfying $x + 3y \leq 30$, $x \geq 0$, $3x - 4y \geq -27$, and $y \geq 0$.
11. Find the minimum and maximum values of $x - 3y$ for (x, y) satisfying $x + 2y + 2 \leq 0$, $5x + 2y - 14 \leq 0$, and $x - 2y \geq 0$.
12. Find the minimum and maximum values of $-x + 4y$ for (x, y) satisfying the constraints in Exercise 10.
13. Maximize $$3x - 2y$$
subject to
$$\begin{aligned} x + y &\geq 0 \\ x - y &\leq 0 \\ -2x + 4y &\leq 5 \end{aligned}$$
14. Find the minimum of the function $3x + 2y$ on the set described by the constraints of Exercise 13.
15. Maximize $$x - 3y$$
subject to
$$\begin{aligned} x \geq 0 \quad y &\geq 0 \\ 2x - 3y &\leq 6 \\ -x + 4y &\leq 4 \end{aligned}$$
16. Let S be the set described by the inequalities $y - x \leq 1$, $2y + x \geq 5$, $y + x \leq 5$, and $x \leq 3$.
    (*a*) Find the maximum value of $y + 2x$ for $(x, y) \in S$.
    (*b*) Find the minimum value of $2y - 3x$ for $(x, y) \in S$.

Solve the linear programming problems formulated in the following exercises from Section 7.1.

17. Exercise 1
18. Exercise 2
19. Exercise 3
20. Exercise 4
21. Exercise 8
22. Exercise 9
23. Exercise 11
24. Exercise 5
25. Exercise 13
26. Exercise 14
27. Exercise 15
28. Exercise 16
29. A bakery makes two types of cakes each day: poppy seed and German chocolate. The profit to the bakery is \$2 on each poppy seed cake and \$4 on each German chocolate cake. A poppy seed cake requires 400 grams of flour, 200 grams of butter, and 100 grams of poppy seeds. A German chocolate cake requires 600 grams of flour, 100 grams of butter, and 150 grams of chocolate. There are 9600 grams of flour, 2400 grams of butter, 1500 grams of poppy seeds, and 2100 grams of chocolate.

(*a*) How many cakes of each type should be made to yield maximum profit? What is the maximum profit?
(*b*) When the baker produces cakes to yield maximum profit, does any flour remain unused at the end of the day? How much?
(*c*) Repeat (*b*) for butter.

30. In the situation described in Exercise 29, suppose the profit for each poppy seed cake is \$3 and the profit for each German chocolate cake is \$4. Answer questions (*a*), (*b*), and (*c*) of Exercise 29 for these profit levels.

31. Let F be the feasible set defined by the constraints $2x + y \geq 12$, $x + 2y \geq 12$, $-5x + 5y \leq 25$, and $5x - 5y \leq 25$.
(*a*) Find the minimum and the maximum of $x - 2y$ over the set F.
(*b*) Find the minimum and the maximum of $x + 2y$ over the set F.
(*c*) Find the minimum and the maximum of $x + 6y$ over the set F.
(*d*) Find the minimum and the maximum of $-2x + y$ over the set F.

32. Let F be the feasible set defined by the constraints $x \geq 1$, $y \geq 1$, $2x + 3y \geq 6$, and $3x - 2y \geq -6$.
(*a*) Find the minimum and the maximum of $2x - y$ over the set F.
(*b*) Find the minimum and the maximum of $-2x + 3y$ over the set F.
(*c*) Find the minimum and the maximum of $2y$ over the set F.
(*d*) Find the minimum and the maximum of $-x$ over the set F.

33. Sam's Snacks prepares packages of trail mix which contain raisins, peanuts, and dried apple slices. A box of regular mix contains 4 ounces of raisins, 8 ounces of peanuts, and 12 ounces of apple slices. A box of deluxe mix contains 6 ounces of raisins, 6 ounces of peanuts, and 8 ounces of apple slices. There are 24 pounds of raisins, 36 pounds of peanuts, and 60 pounds of apple slices available. The profit per box is \$2.00 for regular mix and \$2.50 for deluxe mix. How many boxes of each type should be prepared to maximize profit?

34. Solve the following linear programming problem:

Minimize $\qquad 3x - 2y$

subject to

$$\begin{aligned} y &\geq 0 \\ 2x + y &\geq 2 \\ 2x - y + 2 &\geq 0 \\ x - y &\leq 4. \end{aligned}$$

35. Let F be the feasible set defined by the constraints $x + y \geq 4$, $4x - y \geq 1$, and $x - 4y \leq 0$.
(*a*) Find the maximum of $2x - 10y$ for (x, y) in F.
(*b*) Find the maximum of $2x - 6y$ for (x, y) in F.
(*c*) Find the maximum of $2x - 8y$ for (x, y) in F.

36. Let F be the feasible set defined by the constraints $2x + 7y \geq 70$, $3x - 2y \geq 30$, and $x - 4y \leq 20$.
(*a*) Find the maximum of $x - 5y$ for (x, y) in F.
(*b*) Find the maximum of $x - 3y$ for (x, y) in F.
(*c*) Find the maximum of $x - y$ for (x, y) in F.

37. Let F be the feasible set defined by the constraints $3x + 2y \geq 15$, $6x - y \geq 60$, and $x + 4y \leq 10$.

(*a*) Find the minimum of $2x + y$ for (x, y) in F.
(*b*) Find the minimum of $x + y$ for (x, y) in F.
(*c*) Find the minimum of $x - y$ for (x, y) in F.

38. Let F be the feasible set defined by the inequalities $x \geq 0$, $y \geq 0$, $3x + 2y \geq 30$, $5x - 2y \geq 18$, and $x - 2y \leq 20$.
    (*a*) Find the maximum value and the minimum value of $x - y$ for (x, y) in F.
    (*b*) Find the maximum value and the minimum value of $x - 3y$ for (x, y) in F.
39. Solve the problem posed in Exercise 10 of Section 7.1.

IMPORTANT TERMS AND CONCEPTS

You should be able to describe, define, or give examples of and use each of the following:

Linear programming problem
Constraint
Feasible set
Objective function
Bounded (unbounded) set
Corner point
Graphical solution method for linear programming problems

REVIEW EXERCISES

In Exercises 1 through 8, formulate (but do not solve) each situation as a linear programming problem.

1. The Boats of Maine company manufactures and sells two types of model boats: lobster boats and tug boats. Each boat is made from a piece of pine hull material that is cut to length, mahogany cabin material, and plastic fittings. Each lobster boat uses 25 cm of pine hull material, 4 cm of mahogany cabin material, and 2 plastic fittings. Each tug boat uses 20 cm of pine hull material, 8 cm of mahogany cabin material, and 8 plastic fittings. On a particular week the company has 3000 cm pine hull material, 720 cm mahogany cabin material, and 640 plastic fittings. If the profit is \$7 per lobster boat and \$15 per tug boat, how many of each type of boat should be built to maximize profit?
2. A manufacturer of basketball shoes makes shoes using leather, nylon, rubber, and labor. The company makes two models, the Dunker and the Flyer. Each pair of Dunker shoes requires 6 ounces of leather, .6 square feet of nylon, 10 ounces of rubber, and 7 minutes of labor. Each pair of Flyer shoes requires 8 ounces of leather, .4 square foot of nylon, 12 ounces of rubber, and 9 minutes of labor. The company has 20 pounds of leather, 150 square feet of nylon, 50 pounds of rubber, and 20 hours of labor. The profit per pair is \$16 for the Dunker and \$24 for the Flyer. How many pairs of each type of shoe should the company produce to achieve maximum profit?
3. A farmer owns a 2000-acre farm and can plant any combination of two crops, *A* and *B*. Crop *A* requires 1 person-day of labor and \$90 of capital for each acre planted, while crop *B* requires 2 person-days and \$60 of capital for each acre planted. Crop *A* produces \$170 in revenue per acre, and crop *B* produces \$190

in revenue per acre. The farmer has $150,000 of capital and 3000 person-days of labor available for the year. How many acres of each crop should the farmer plant in order to maximize the total revenue?

4. White Water Rapids, Inc., offers two types of white-water adventure day trips, one using rubber rafts and one using kayaks, on the Trout and Salamander rivers. On the Trout River they can handle 50 rafts and 20 kayaks per day at a cost of $1000. On the Salamander River they can handle 60 rafts and 40 kayaks per day at a cost of $1200. During the season they have a demand for 1800 raft trips and 1000 kayak trips. How many days should they operate on each river to meet all the demand at minimum cost?

5. Students at Gigantic State University have formed a local chapter of Feathered Friends Unlimited, and they plan to raise money by making and selling birdhouses. They decide on two birdhouse types, basic and upscale, and both types are constructed from pine and cedar. The students use scrap lumber from a local contractor, which they acquire at no cost, and the wood comes in pieces of identical size. A basic birdhouse requires 4 pieces of pine and 3 pieces of cedar, and an upscale birdhouse requires 2 pieces of pine and 5 pieces of cedar. The students have 180 pieces of pine and 280 pieces of cedar. They agree to provide birdhouses to a local craft shop, and the agreement is that they will provide at least 10 basic birdhouses and at least 20 upscale birdhouses. If the net profit is $3 for a basic birdhouse and $10 for an upscale birdhouse, how many of each type should be produced to maximize net profit and meet the agreement with the craft store?

6. The Trimetal Mining Company operates two mines from which gold, silver, and copper are mined. The Alpha Mine costs $8000 per day to operate, and it yields 30 ounces of gold, 200 ounces of silver, and 400 pounds of copper each day. The Omega Mine costs $12,000 per day to operate, and it yields 40 ounces of gold, 400 ounces of silver, and 300 pounds of copper each day. The company has a contract to supply at least 300 ounces of gold, 3000 ounces of silver, and 2000 pounds of copper. How many days should each mine be operated so that the contract can be filled at minimum cost?

7. The Plant Power Fertilizer Company produces three fertilizer brands: Standard, Special, and Super. One sack (100 pounds) of each brand contains the nutrients nitrogen, phosphorus, and potash in the amounts shown below. The profit per sack is shown at the right, and the available material (in pounds) is shown at the bottom. How many sacks of each brand should be produced to maximize profit?

	Amount per Sack, Pounds			
Brand	**Nitrogen**	**Phosphorus**	**Potash**	**Profit, $**
Standard	20	5	5	10
Special	10	10	10	5
Super	5	15	10	15
Available	2000	1500	1500	

8. Ms. Li produces gadgets. For each 100 left-handed gadgets she uses 1 pound of metal and 5 pounds of fiberglass. For each 100 right-handed gadgets she uses 2 pounds of metal and 3 pounds of fiberglass. Each week Ms. Li has 65 pounds of metal and 150 pounds of fiberglass available. She makes a profit of \$2.50 on each right-handed gadget and a profit of \$2.00 on each left-handed gadget. How many gadgets of each type should Ms. Li produce each week to maximize profit?
9. Solve the problem formulated in Exercise 1. Are all the resources consumed?
10. Solve the problem formulated in Exercise 2. Are all the resources consumed?
11. Solve the problem formulated in Exercise 3. Are all the resources consumed?
12. Solve the problem formulated in Exercise 4.
13. Solve the problem formulated in Exercise 5. Are all the resources consumed?
14. Solve the problem formulated in Exercise 6.
15. Solve the problem formulated in Exercise 5, but change the profit per basic birdhouse to \$10 and the profit per upscale birdhouse to \$3. Are all the resources consumed?
16. Solve the problem formulated in Exercise 8. Are all the resources consumed?
17. In the situation described in Exercise 8, suppose that Ms. Li decides to produce only one type of widget. What type and how many should she produce to maximize profit?
18. In the situation described in Exercise 8, suppose that the production of 100 gadgets (either type) requires 10 kilowatt hours of electricity. Also suppose 350 kilowatt hours are available for this process. How many gadgets of each type should be produced each week to maximize profit?
19. A set in the plane is described by the inequalities

$$\begin{aligned} x - y &\leq 3 \\ x + 3y &\leq 0 \\ 3x + y &\geq -3 \end{aligned}$$

Graph the set and find its corner points.

20. A feasible set S is described by the inequalities

$$\begin{aligned} x + y &\geq 0 \\ x - y &\leq 2 \\ -x + 4y &\leq 4 \\ x + y &\leq 8 \end{aligned}$$

Find the x-coordinate of the corner point of S in the first quadrant.

21. A set S is defined by the inequalities

$$\begin{aligned} x - y - 4 &\leq 0 \\ x - 6 &\leq 0 \\ y - 6 &\leq 0 \\ 2x + 3y &\geq 0 \end{aligned}$$

(*a*) Graph S.
(*b*) Find the corner points of S.
(*c*) Find the maximum value of the function $2x - 5y$ on S.

22. Find the solution to the following linear programming problem:

Minimize $2x - y$

subject to

$$\begin{aligned} y + 1 &\geq 0 \\ x + 2 &\geq 0 \\ x - y + 5 &\geq 0 \\ 4x + y &\leq 15 \end{aligned}$$

23. Find the maximum and minimum values of $3x - 5y$ for (x, y) satisfying the inequalities

$$\begin{aligned} y &\leq 2 \\ x + y + 1 &\geq 0 \\ x - y &\geq 0 \end{aligned}$$

24. Find the maximum and minimum values of $5x + 3y$ for (x, y) satisfying the inequalities

$$\begin{aligned} 5x + y + 7 &\geq 0 \\ y + 7 &\geq 0 \\ x + 2y - 5 &\leq 0 \\ x - y - 10 &\leq 0 \\ x - 3 &\leq 0 \end{aligned}$$

25. A set S is defined by the inequalities

$$\begin{aligned} 2x - y &\leq 16 \\ y &\leq 6 \\ 2x + y &\geq 0 \\ x + y &\leq 14 \\ x - y + 6 &\geq 0 \end{aligned}$$

(*a*) Find the maximum and minimum values of $3x - 2y$ for (x, y) in S.
(*b*) Find the maximum and minimum values of $2x - 3y$ for (x, y) in S.

26. A feasible set S for a linear programming problem is defined by the inequalities

$$\begin{aligned} x &\geq 0 \\ y &\geq 0 \\ 2y + 4 &\geq x \\ x + y &\geq 3 \\ 2y &\leq x + 4 \end{aligned}$$

Which of the following is a true statement about the set S?
(*a*) S is unbounded and has 5 corner points.
(*b*) S is unbounded and has 3 corner points.
(*c*) S is bounded and has 3 corner points.
(*d*) S is unbounded and has 4 corner points.

27. Find the maximum and minimum values of $3x - 5y$ for (x, y) satisfying the inequalities

$$\begin{aligned} y &\le 8 \\ 10x - 14y &\le 38 \\ x - 2y + 7 &\ge 0 \\ 2x - y &\ge 4 \end{aligned}$$

28. (*a*) Graph the following system of inequalities:

$$\begin{aligned} y - 3x &\le 2 \\ 2y + 3x &\ge 12 \\ y &\le 8 \\ y + x &\le 14 \\ 2x - y &\le 16 \\ 2x - 5y &\le 8 \end{aligned}$$

(*b*) Find the corner points of the set described in (*a*).
(*c*) Find the maximum of $2x + 3y$ over this set.
(*d*) Find the minimum of $4y - 3x$ over this set.

29. A set S is defined by the inequalities:

$$\begin{aligned} x + y + 2 &\ge 0 \\ y + 1 &\ge 0 \\ x - y &\le 2 \\ 3x - y + 5 &\ge 0 \end{aligned}$$

(*a*) Find the maximum value of $x - 2y$ for $(x, y) \in S$.
(*b*) Find the minimum value of $x - 2y$ for $(x, y) \in S$.

30. Let S be the set defined in Exercise 29.
(*a*) Find the maximum value of $2x - y$ for $(x, y) \in S$.
(*b*) Find the minimum value of $2x - y$ for $(x, y) \in S$.

31. Consider the linear programming problem:

Maximize $\quad 2x - 3y$

subject to

$$\begin{aligned} x &\ge 2 \\ x - 4y &\le 4 \\ x - 2y + 4 &\ge 0. \end{aligned}$$

Which, if any, of the following statements is valid?
(*a*) The feasible set is unbounded and the problem of maximizing the objective function has no solution.
(*b*) The feasible set is bounded and the problem of maximizing the objective function has no solution.
(*c*) The feasible set is bounded and the maximum value of the objective function is 5.5.
(*d*) The feasible set is unbounded and the maximum value of the objective function is 5.5.

32. A set S is described by the inequalities

$$\begin{aligned} x - y - 3 &\geq 0 \\ x - 6y + 12 &\geq 0 \\ y + 5 &\geq 0 \\ 3x + 4y + 5 &\geq 0 \end{aligned}$$

Which of the following functions assumes a minimum value on S?
(*a*) $2x - y$ (*b*) $x - 2y$ (*c*) $x - 8y$ (*d*) $8y - x$

33. Use the inequality $x + y \geq 2$, plus two other inequalities, to describe a feasible set that is unbounded and includes the points (1, 1) and (1, 3).
34. Use the inequality $x + y \leq 10$, plus two other inequalities, to describe a feasible set that is unbounded and includes the points (1, 1) and (−1, −3).
35. Solve the problem posed in Exercise 30 of Section 7.1
36. Solve the problem posed in Exercise 31 of Section 7.1
37. Find an objective function of the form $ax + by$ that has a minimum, but that does not have a maximum on the feasible set defined by the inequalities: $x \geq -y$ and $x \geq y$

CHAPTER

8 Markov Chains

8.0 THE SETTING AND OVERVIEW

As we have illustrated in earlier chapters, multistage experiments can be used to model many situations involving uncertainty in the social, life, and management sciences. We introduced the idea of a multistage experiment in Chapter 1, including a helpful representation with tree diagrams, and we continued the study in Chapters 3 and 4. In Section 4.1 we considered the special case of experiments which can be modeled using Bernoulli trials. In this Chapter we continue our study with another special case of multistage stochastic processes, *Markov chains.*

Markov chains have several advantages as mathematical models: They are general enough to provide useful models for many situations; they have been intensively studied, and many results are known; and they are special enough to be easy to use. The diversity of application can be illustrated with a few examples: psychology—learning and memory; sociology—social mobility and demography; biology—ecological systems and nutrient flows; business—decision making under uncertainty. The ease of use is a consequence, in part, of using matrix algebra to simplify the computations.

Ideas introduced in earlier chapters play an important role in our study of Markov chains. For instance, the concepts and methods from our earlier discussions of tree diagrams, conditional probability, multistage experiments, matrices and matrix inverses, systems of equations, and the expected value of a random variable all play a role in this chapter.

8.1 STATES, TRANSITIONS, TRANSITION DIAGRAMS, AND TRANSITION MATRICES

As noted above, it is frequently useful to view a stochastic process as an experiment consisting of a number of successive steps or stages, and we introduced tree diagrams to help us study such processes. In general, the probabilities of the results at one stage depend on the results of preceding stages, and this dependence can take many forms. For example, tree diagrams for three experiments, each consisting of repetitions of a subexperiment with results labeled X and Y, are, shown in Figure 8.1. In each case the result of

FIGURE 8.1

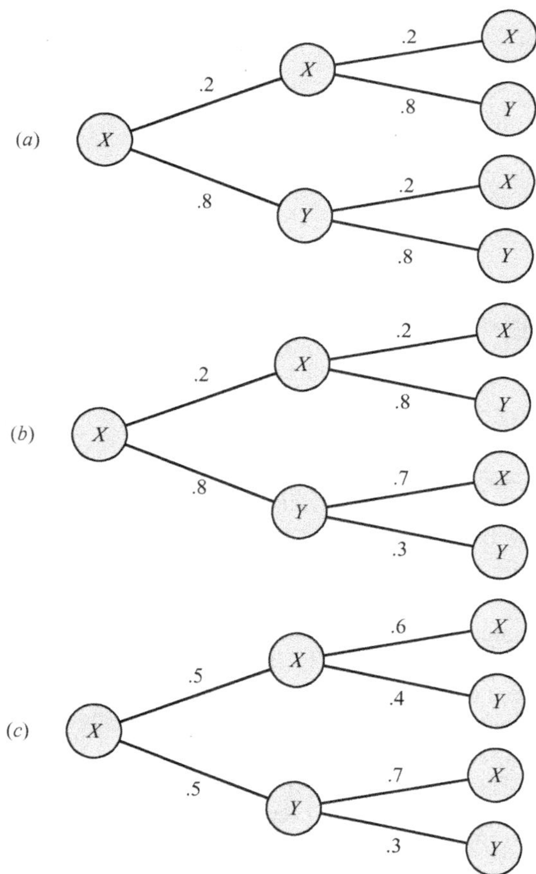

the initial observation is X. In Figure 8.1*a* the probabilities of results X and Y are .2 and .8, respectively, at every stage of the experiment and independent of the result of the preceding stage. Thus, the experiment whose tree diagram is Figure 8.1*a* is a Bernoulli trial process. Figure 8.1*b* illustrates a process in which the probabilities of results X and Y are not always the same. However, it is the case that whenever the result at one stage is X, then the probabilities of X and Y at the next stage are *always* .2 and .8, respectively; and whenever the result at one stage is Y, then the probabilities of X and Y at the next stage are *always* .7 and .3, respectively. That is, probabilities of the possible results at the next stage depend *only* on the current result. Finally, Figure 8.1*c* illustrates a process in which the probabilities of results X and Y vary with both the stage of the experiment and the result of the current stage. For instance, the tree diagram shows the result of the first stage is X and the probability of result X at the second stage is .5. But if the result is X at the second stage, then the probability of result X at the third stage is .6.

Although our basic approach to the study of multistage experiments is through the use of tree diagrams, when the experiment has many stages, such analyses become very complicated and we seek alternative methods. In Chapter 4 we developed techniques, other than tree diagrams, to study one special type of multistage experiment, Bernoulli processes. We now consider another special type, namely, processes with tree diagrams similar to Figure 8.1*b*. We distinguish among multistage experiments according to the way in which the probabilities of results at one stage depend on the results at earlier stages. For example, in a Bernoulli process the results at one stage do *not* depend at all on the results at other stages. We now distinguish another special type of multistage experiment.

Markov Chain

A *Markov chain* is a stochastic process which satisfies the conditions:

1. At each stage the result is one of a fixed number of states.
2. The conditional probability of a transition from any given state to any other state depends on only the two states.

Example 8.1 A freelance computer network consultant is employed only when she has a contract for work, and each of her contracts is for 1 week of work. Each week she is either employed (E) or unemployed (U), and her records support the following assumptions about the conditional probabilities:

(*a*) If she is employed this week, then next week she will be employed with probability .8 and unemployed with probability .2.

(*b*) If she is unemployed this week, then next week she will be employed with probability .6 and unemployed with probability .4.

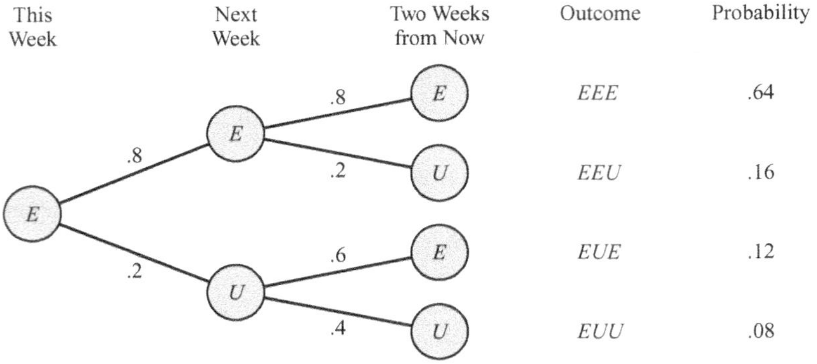

This Week	Next Week	Two Weeks from Now	Outcome	Probability
E	E (.8)	E (.8)	EEE	.64
		U (.2)	EEU	.16
	U (.2)	E (.6)	EUE	.12
		U (.4)	EUU	.08

FIGURE 8.2

Problem She is employed this week. Find the probability that she will be employed 2 weeks from now.

Solution A tree diagram for this situation is shown in Figure 8.2. Since we know that she is employed this week, the "Begin" box of the tree diagram is replaced by E. From the tree diagram we conclude that the probability that she is employed 2 weeks from now is

$$.64 + .12 = .76$$

■

The solution of this problem involved the use of techniques from Chapter 3. However, if we had asked for the probability that she will be employed in 5 weeks or in 10 weeks or "in the long run," then the techniques of Chapter 3 would be cumbersome or impossible to use. To develop techniques which will be more effective in such problems, we need to have new terminology and notation.

We will be concerned with systems which can be in any one of N possible *states*. The systems are observed successively, and *transitions* between states are noted. In Example 8.1 the system is our consultant, and the states describe her employment status: employed or unemployed. Our consultant is observed each week, and her state is noted.

The information given in Example 8.1(a) and (b) can be represented concisely in a *transition diagram* such as Figure 8.3. In Figure 8.3 we have indicated states E and U and, on arrows connecting the states, the probabilities of being in successive states on successive observations. For instance, the .2 on the arrow directed from E to U means that if the system is in state E on one observation, then it is in state U on the next observation with probability .2.

As we noted in the definition of Markov chains, the fundamental property which distinguishes a Markov chain from other sequential probabilistic processes can be described as follows:

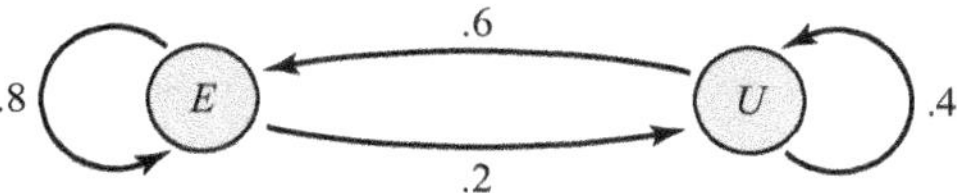

FIGURE 8.3

Markov Property

If a system is in state i on one observation, then the conditional probability that it is in state j on the next observation depends on only i and j (and not on what happened before the system reached state i or on the stage of the experiment). This probability will be denoted by p_{ij}, the probability of making a direct transition from i to j.

One way that this property can be viewed intuitively is to think of Markov chains as mathematical descriptions for systems without memories. That is, the probability that the system makes a transition from one state (say, state i) to another state (or even back into state i) depends on the two states and not on the number of transitions or the states occupied before the system reached state i.

The transition probabilities p_{ij} are the numbers on the arrows of the transition diagram. Thus, in Example 8.1, if we label state E by 1 and state U by 2, then $p_{11} = .8$ and $p_{12} = .2$.

Transition Matrix

Consider a Markov chain with N states. Let p_{ij} be the probability of making a direct transition from state i to state j, $1 \le i \le N$, $1 \le j \le N$. The matrix

$$\mathbf{P} = [p_{ij}]$$

is the *one-step transition matrix*, or simply the *transition matrix*, for the Markov chain.

Example 8.2 Find the transition matrix for the process described in Example 8.1.

Solution Let E and U be labeled as states 1 and 2, respectively. The transition probabilities are given on the transition diagram in Figure 8.2. We have

$$\mathbf{P} = \begin{bmatrix} .8 & .2 \\ .6 & .4 \end{bmatrix}$$

■

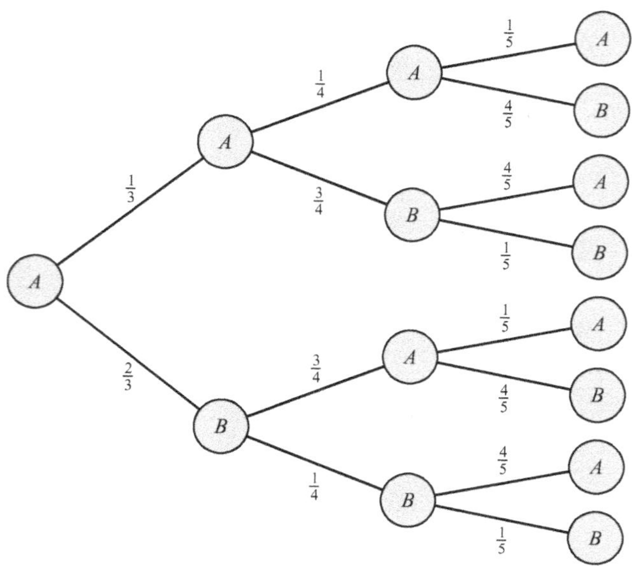

FIGURE 8.4

Note that if we had labeled the states differently, then we would have obtained a different transition matrix **P**. However, providing the identification of states with rows and columns is consistent, then all probabilities computed for the process will be the same, regardless of the transition matrix used.

Example 8.3 A tree diagram for a stochastic process with two states is shown in Figure 8.4.

Problem Determine whether this is the tree diagram of a Markov chain.

Solution The states are labeled A and B in Figure 8.4. Note that the probability of making a transition from A to A at stage 1 is $\frac{1}{3}$, the probability of making a transition from A to A at the second stage is $\frac{1}{4}$, and the probability of making a transition from A to A at the third stage is $\frac{1}{5}$. Thus, the probability of making a transition from A to A *does* depend on the stage, and consequently this is *not* the tree diagram of a Markov chain. ■

Example 8.4 The dispatcher in the office of the White Wheel Taxi Company frequently contacts a driver who is away from the office by radio with the name and address of the next customer. For reasons of efficiency the dispatcher attempts to contact a driver who is, or who will be, in the same area as the person requesting a taxi. Of course, it may not be possible to do so. One of the drivers

TABLE 8.1

Current Location of Driver	Location of Next Rider	Percentage of Messages
East	East	50
	Central	40
	West	10
Central	East	10
	Central	60
	West	30
West	East	30
	Central	60
	West	10

keeps a record of radio dispatches for a week, and the data are summarized in Table 8.1.

Problem Formulate this situation as a Markov chain; find the transition diagram and the one-step transition matrix.

Solution To formulate this as a Markov chain we must identify the states of the system. We suppose that the service area can be divided into three districts: East, Central and West. If the driver is in the East district, then we say that the system is in state 1. Similarly, the system is in states 2 or 3 when the driver is in the Central or West district, respectively. Transitions are the moves of the driver that result from calls by the dispatchers who provide locations of new customers. Using the data contained in Table 8.1, we have the transition diagram shown in Figure 8.5 and the transition matrix **P**.

$$\mathbf{P} = \begin{bmatrix} .5 & .4 & .1 \\ .1 & .6 & .3 \\ .3 & .6 & .1 \end{bmatrix}$$

■

Remark Decision problems of resource allocation and scheduling—such as the dispatching of taxis in Example 8.4—arise in many different settings and they can be studied using a variety of techniques. The approach used normally depends on the specific goals and constraints of the study (resources available, customer service expectations, cost, etc.). For instance, rather than depending only on driver location, the dispatcher may consider the priority of the customer, the type of vehicle each driver has, the experience of the driver, whether the driver's shift is about to end, and so forth.

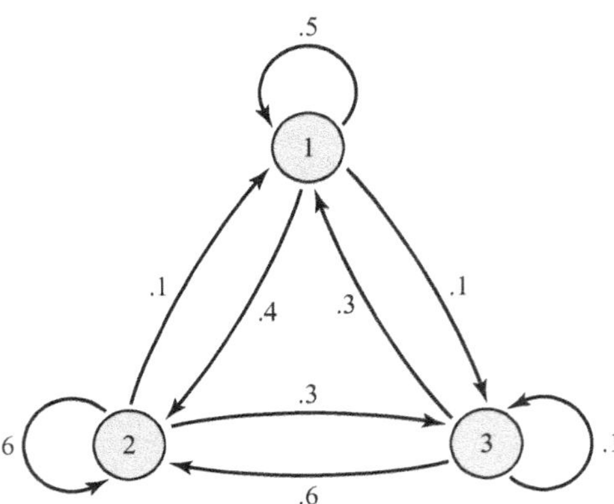

FIGURE 8.5

Exercises for Section 8.1

1. A Markov chain has the transition matrix **P** shown below. Find the transition diagram for this Markov chain.

$$\mathbf{P} = \begin{bmatrix} .6 & .4 \\ .2 & .8 \end{bmatrix}$$

2. A Markov chain has the transition matrix given in Exercise 1. On the first observation the system is in state 1.
   (*a*) Find the probability that it is in state 1 on the second observation.
   (*b*) Find the probability that it is in state 1 on the third observation.
3. A Markov chain has the transition matrix given in Exercise 1. On the first observation it is in state 2. What state is it most likely to occupy on the third observation?
4. A Markov chain has the transition matrix given in Exercise 1. Suppose that the system begins in state 1 and after three transitions it is in state 2.
   (*a*) Find the probability of the path which involves the transitions: state 1 to state 1 to state 2 to state 2.
   (*b*) Find the probability of the path which involves the transitions: state 1 to state 2 to state 1 to state 2.
5. A Markov chain has the transition matrix **P** shown below. Find the transition diagram for this Markov chain.

$$\mathbf{P} = \begin{bmatrix} .2 & .8 \\ 1 & 0 \end{bmatrix}$$

6. Each day a squirrel attacks either a bird feeder or a bed of tulip bulbs, and its target is selected at random. If it attacks the bird feeder on one day, then the next day it attacks the bird feeder with probability .3 and the tulip bulbs with probability .7. If it attacks the tulip bulbs on one day, then the next day it attacks the bird feeder

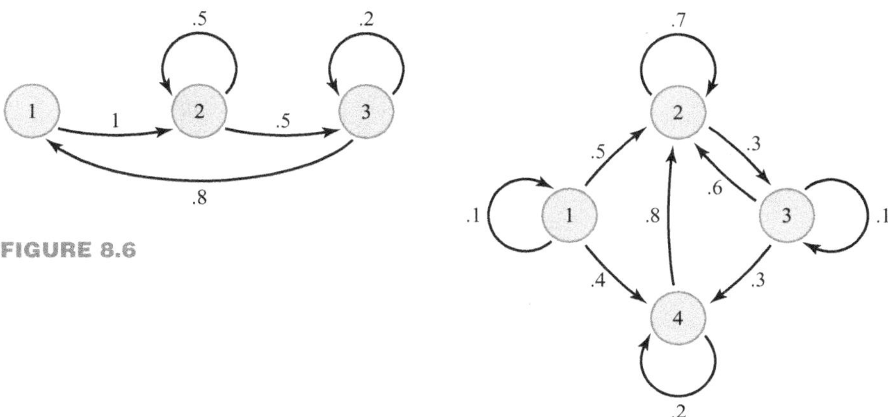

FIGURE 8.6

FIGURE 8.7

with probability .8 and the tulip bulbs with probability .2. A Markov chain model is constructed in which state 1 is a squirrel attack on the bird feeder and state 2 is a squirrel attack on the tulip bulbs. Find the transition matrix.

7. Find the transition matrix for a Markov chain whose transition diagram is shown in Figure 8.6.
8. Find the transition matrix for a Markov chain whose transition diagram is shown in Figure 8.7.
9. A Markov chain has the transition matrix $\mathbf{P}$ shown below. Find the transition diagram for this Markov chain.

$$\mathbf{P} = \begin{bmatrix} .5 & .4 & .1 \\ 0 & 0 & 1 \\ 0 & .5 & .5 \end{bmatrix}$$

10. A Markov chain has the transition matrix $\mathbf{P}$ shown below. Find the transition diagram for this Markov chain.

$$\mathbf{P} = \begin{bmatrix} .3 & .3 & .4 \\ .1 & .1 & .8 \\ .9 & .1 & 0 \end{bmatrix}$$

11. A Markov chain has the transition matrix given in Exercise 10. On the first observation it is in state 1.
    (*a*) Find the probability that it is in state 1 on the next observation.
    (*b*) What state is it most likely to occupy on the next observation?
12. A Markov chain has the transition matrix given in Exercise 10. On the first observation it is in state 3.
    (*a*) Find the probability that it is in state 3 on the third observation.
    (*b*) Find the probability that it is in state 1 on the third observation.
    (*Hint*: Use a tree diagram.)

13. A Markov chain has the transition matrix given in Exercise 9. On the first observation it is in state 1. In what state is it most likely to be on the third observation?
14. A Markov chain has the transition matrix given in Exercise 10. If it begins in state 2, find the probability that on the next four observations it successively occupies states 3, 1, 2, and 1 (in that order).
15. Profits at a brokerage firm are determined by the volume of securities sold, and this volume fluctuates from week to week. Each week volume is classified as high or low, and information collected over many weeks leads to the following assumptions:
    (*i*) If volume is high this week, then next week it will be high with probability .7 and low with probability .3.
    (*ii*) If volume is low this week, then next week it will be high or low with equal probability.

    Formulate a Markov chain model for this situation; i.e., find the states and the transition matrix.
16. In the situation described in Exercise 15, suppose that the volume is high this week.
    (*a*) Find the probability that the volume will be high two weeks from now.
    (*b*) Find the probability that volume will be high for three consecutive weeks.
17. A small animal lives in a territory that can be divided into areas described as meadow and woods, and it moves randomly from one area to another. If the animal is in the woods on one observation, then it is twice as likely to be in the woods as the meadow on the next observation. Likewise, if the animal is in the meadow on one observation, then it is twice as likely to be in the meadow as the woods on the next observation.
    (*a*) Identify appropriate states.
    (*b*) Find the transition diagram.
    (*c*) Find the transition matrix.
18. In the situation described in Exercise 17, suppose the animal is initially in the woods, and find the probability that it is in the woods on the next three observations. If it is initially in the woods, what is the probability that it is in the meadow on the next three observations?
19. People living in a small town are classified according to employment into three groups: employed in industry, employed in small business, and self-employed. Data on employment are collected for several years, and the results are summarized in Table 8.2. Formulate a Markov chain model for this situation.
    (*a*) Identify appropriate states.
    (*b*) Find the transition diagram.
    (*c*) Find the transition matrix.
20. A football player is practicing field goal kicks. He finds that if he makes a kick, then he makes the next kick 85 percent of the time, but if he misses a kick, then he makes the next kick only 60 percent of the time.
    (*a*) Identify appropriate states, and formulate this situation as a Markov chain.
    (*b*) Find the transition diagram for the Markov chain formulated in (*a*).
    (*c*) Find the transition matrix for the Markov chain formulated in (*a*).

TABLE 8.2

Employment Last Year	Employment This Year	Percentage
Industry	Industry	70
	Small business	20
	Self-employed	10
Small business	Industry	30
	Small business	50
	Self-employed	20
Self-employed	Industry	30
	Small business	30
	Self-employed	40

21. A Markov chain has the transition matrix **P** shown below. If the system is in state 3 on the initial observation, find the probability that it is in state 2 after two transitions.

$$\mathbf{P} = \begin{bmatrix} .2 & 0 & .8 \\ .1 & .5 & .4 \\ .4 & .6 & 0 \end{bmatrix}$$

22. A not-so-enthusiastic student often misses class on Friday afternoon. If he attends class on a certain Friday, then the next Friday he is twice as likely to be absent as to attend. On the other hand, if he misses on a certain Friday, then the next week he is 3 times as likely to attend as to miss class again. Formulate this situation as a Markov chain, and find the transition matrix.
23. A student eats in a restaurant every Sunday evening. Each week she chooses among Chinese, Greek, and Italian food, and she never eats the same kind of food for 2 consecutive weeks. If she eats at a Chinese restaurant one week, then she is twice as likely to have Greek as Italian food the next week. If she has Greek food one week, then she is equally likely to have Chinese and Italian food the next week. Finally, if she has Italian food one week, then she is 5 times as likely to have Chinese as Greek food the next week. Formulate this situation as a Markov chain, and find the transition matrix.
24. Using the transition matrix shown below, suppose the system is known to be in state 2 on the third observation. What is the earliest subsequent observation at which the system could be in state 4?

$$\mathbf{P} = \begin{bmatrix} .8 & 0 & 0 & .2 \\ 0 & 0 & 1 & 0 \\ 1 & 0 & 0 & 0 \\ 0 & .8 & .2 & 0 \end{bmatrix}$$

25. A nervous basketball player finds that her success at shooting a free throw depends on what happened when she last shot a free throw. If she made the last one, her

probability of making the next one is .8, while if she missed the last one, her probability of making the next one is .4. Formulate this situation as a Markov chain, and find the transition matrix.

26. A group of students has a regular pick-up basketball game once each week. Henry is a member of the group whose participation varies from week to week, and each week his participation can be described as follows: he comes and plays well, he comes and does not play well, and he does not come that week. Suppose that if he comes and plays well one week, then the next week he is equally likely to come and play well, come and not play well, or not come. If he comes and does not play well one week, then the next week he is twice as likely to come and play well as to miss, and he never comes and does not play well two consecutive weeks. If he misses one week, then he comes the following week and he is three times as likely to play well as not. Formulate this situation as a Markov chain and find the transition matrix.

27. A stock broker believes that the stock market can be described as a Markov chain. Each day she evaluates the relative strength of stocks and bonds, and she decides whether stocks are stronger than bonds, bonds are stronger than stocks, or they are equally strong. The data are summarized in Table 8.3. Formulate this situation as a Markov chain, and find the transition matrix.

TABLE 8.3

Relative Strength Last Week	Relative Strength This Week	Percentage of Weeks
Stocks stronger	Stocks stronger	60
	Bonds stronger	30
	Equally strong	10
Bonds stronger	Stocks stronger	30
	Bonds stronger	50
	Equally strong	20
Equally strong	Stocks stronger	40
	Bonds stronger	40
	Equally strong	20

28. In the setting of Exercise 26 find the probability that
    (*a*) If Henry misses the first week, then he comes and plays well for three consecutive weeks.
    (*b*) If Henry comes and plays well the first week, then either he comes and does not play well or he misses in each of the following three weeks.

29. Using the setting of Exercise 22, suppose that the student's attendance on Friday afternoon is described by a Markov chain with transition matrix

$$\begin{array}{c} \\ \text{Attends} \\ \text{Misses} \end{array} \begin{array}{c} \begin{array}{cc} \text{Attends} & \text{Misses} \end{array} \\ \begin{bmatrix} 0 & 1 \\ .5 & .5 \end{bmatrix} \end{array}$$

Also suppose that the student attends class the first Friday of the semester. Find the expected number of times the student attends class on Friday afternoon during the first 4 weeks of the semester.

30. Suppose that the basketball player of Exercise 25 has four free throws every game, and she always makes the first. What is the expected number of free throws made each game?

31. A Markov chain has the transition diagram shown below. If the system is in state 2 on the first observation, what is the most likely state it will be in on the third observation?

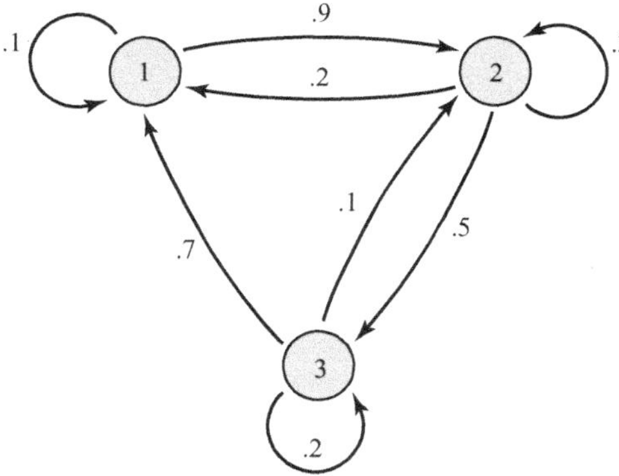

FIGURE 8.8

32. People employed in a small city are classified according to employment into three groups: employed in industry, employed in government, and self-employed. Data are collected year-by-year, and the results are summarized by the following table:

TABLE 8.4

Employment Last Year	Employment This Year	Percentage
Industry (I)	I	75
	G	15
	SE	10
Government (G)	G	60
	I	30
	SE	10
Self-employed (SE)	SE	40
	I	35
	G	25

Assuming that these transitions form a Markov chain,

(*a*) Find the transition matrix;

(*b*) If someone is self-employed now, find the most likely employment status in two years.

33. In the setting of Exercise 32, determine which job category (I, G, or SE) should be held by someone whose goal is to be self-employed two years from now.

34. Suppose that the results of a kicker on a football team can be described by a Markov chain, and the transition matrix is

$$\begin{array}{c} \\ S \\ F \end{array}\begin{array}{c} \begin{array}{cc} S & F \end{array} \\ \begin{bmatrix} .6 & .4 \\ .8 & .2 \end{bmatrix} \end{array}$$

where S denotes a successful kick and F denotes a missed kick. If the kicker attempts 4 field goals in a game and the first is a success, find the expected number of points scored (a field goal is 3 points).

35. In the setting of Exercise 34, suppose that the kicker is equally likely to make or miss his first kick. If he attempts 4 field goals in a game, find the expected number of points scored.

36. There are three boxes, labeled I, II, and III, and each box contains five balls. Box I contains 3 green and 2 blue balls; box II contains 2 green and 3 blue balls; and box III contains 1 green, 3 blue and 1 yellow ball. An experiment consists of drawing balls at random, one after another with replacement, according to the following rules:
    - The first ball is drawn from box I,
    - Each time a blue ball is drawn, the next ball is drawn from box II,
    - Each time a green ball is drawn, the next ball is drawn from box III, and
    - Each time a yellow ball is drawn, the next ball is drawn from box I.

    Formulate a Markov chain model for this situation and find the transition matrix.

8.2 BASIC PROPERTIES OF MARKOV CHAINS

We have seen that information about transitions in a Markov chain—which transitions are possible and their probabilities—can be given in a transition diagram or a transition matrix. For computational purposes, the transition matrix is often the most useful. The transition matrix for a Markov chain with N states, introduced in Section 8.1, is an $N \times N$ matrix whose (i, j) entry is the probability of a transition from state i to state j in one step. There are corresponding probabilities for transitions from one state to another in k steps; these are usually called *k-step transition probabilities*.

The conditional probability of making a transition from state i to state j in exactly k steps is denoted by $p_{ij}(k)$. The matrix whose (i, j) entry is $p_{ij}(k)$ is denoted by $\mathbf{P}(k)$ and will be called the *k-step transition matrix for a Markov chain*.

Example 8.5 The transition matrix for a two-state Markov chain is

$$\mathbf{P} = \begin{bmatrix} .8 & .2 \\ .6 & .4 \end{bmatrix}$$

Problem Use tree diagrams to find the two-step transition matrix $\mathbf{P}(2)$.

Solution To determine the first row of $\mathbf{P}(2)$, we use a tree diagram which represents a two-stage experiment in which the system is initially in state 1. Such a tree diagram is shown in Figure 8.9a. From this tree diagram we see that a transition from state 1 to state 1 in two steps can occur in either of two

FIGURE 8.9

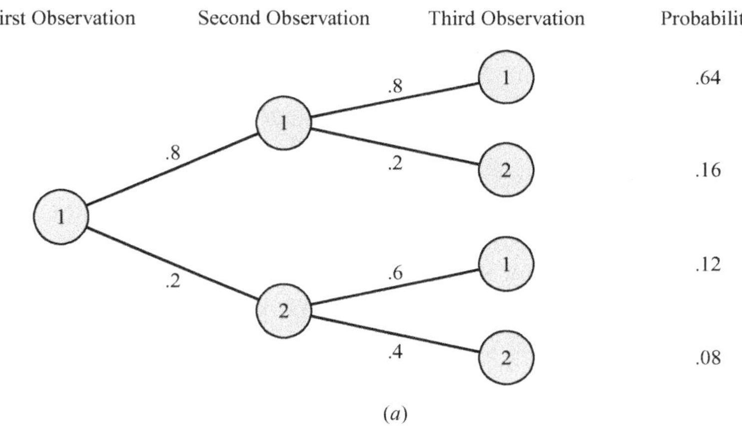

(a)

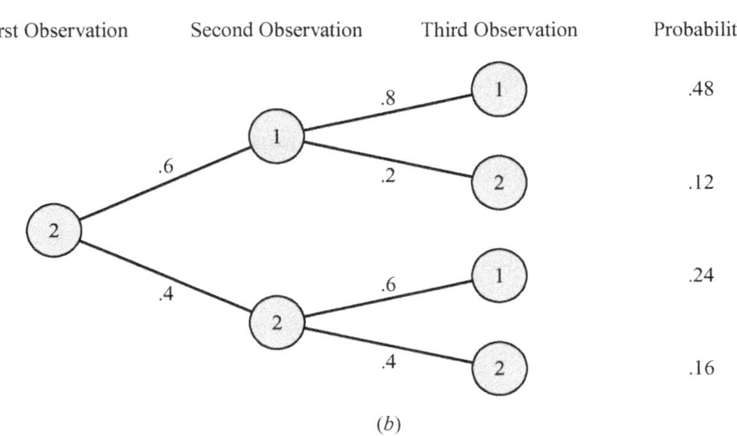

(b)

ways, and the probability $p_{11}(2)$ is the sum

$$p_{11}(2) = .64 + .12 = .76$$

Similarly,

$$p_{12}(2) = .16 + .08 = .24$$

To determine the second row of $\mathbf{P}(2)$, we use a tree diagram in which the system is initially in state 2, Figure 8.9*b* in this case. We have

$$p_{21}(2) = .48 + .24 = .72 \qquad p_{22}(2) = .12 + .16 = .28$$

Therefore,

$$\mathbf{P}(2) = \begin{bmatrix} p_{11}(2) & p_{12}(2) \\ p_{21}(2) & p_{22}(2) \end{bmatrix} = \begin{bmatrix} .76 & .24 \\ .72 & .28 \end{bmatrix}$$ ■

The technique illustrated in Example 8.5 can be used to construct $\mathbf{P}(2)$ for any Markov chain for which the transition matrix $\mathbf{P}$ can be determined. However, for large matrices the process is cumbersome, and one of the very useful properties of Markov chains is that there is a simple method of finding $\mathbf{P}(2)$ from $\mathbf{P}$ without using tree diagrams. The idea behind the method can be seen by looking more carefully at the calculation of $p_{12}(2)$ in Example 8.5. Using the tree diagram, we found

$$p_{12}(2) = .8(.2) + .2(.4) = p_{11}p_{12} + p_{12}p_{22}$$

This last expression is exactly the (1,2) entry in the matrix product $\mathbf{PP}$.

Now let us look at a similar argument in the case of a Markov chain with N states and transition matrix $\mathbf{P}$. We find an expression for $p_{ij}(2)$: the probability that if the system is in state i on one observation, then it is in state j on the second subsequent observation. The system must be in some state on the intervening observation, and consequently we have the situation depicted in Figure 8.10. The transition probabilities between the various states are shown on the lines connecting those states. The system can move from state i to state j in two steps by moving from i to 1 to j. This happens with probability $p_{i1}p_{1j}$. Recall that the probability that the system makes a transition from state 1 to state j in one step is independent of the states it occupied before state 1. Likewise, the system can move from state i to state j through any of states $2, 3, \ldots, N$. These events happen with probabilities $p_{i2}p_{2j}, p_{i3}p_{3j}, \ldots, p_{iN}p_{Nj}$, respectively. Since the system must move from state i to state j through exactly one intermediate state, we have

$$p_{ij}(2) = p_{i1}p_{1j} + p_{i2}p_{2j} + p_{i3}p_{3j} + \cdots + p_{iN}p_{Nj}$$

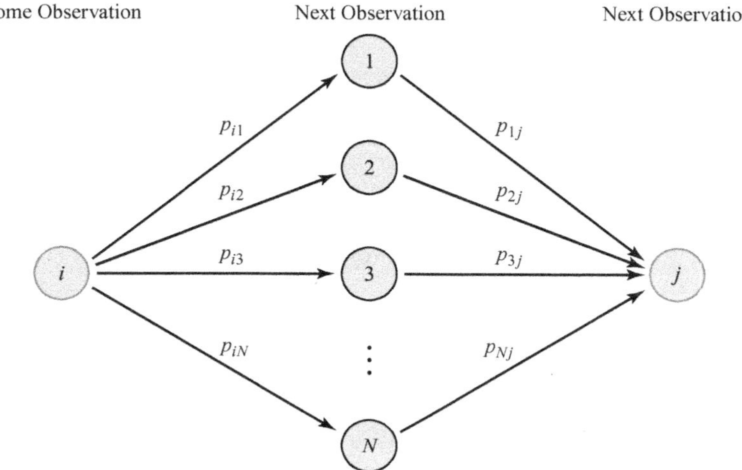

FIGURE 8.10

This expression for $p_{ij}(2)$ is exactly the (i, j) entry in the matrix product **PP**. We have the result

$$\mathbf{P}(2) = \mathbf{PP} = \mathbf{P}^2$$

This is a special case of the following more general result.

Let **P** be the (one-step) transition matrix for a Markov chain. Then the matrix $\mathbf{P}(k)$ of k-step transition probabilities is

$$\mathbf{P}(k) = \underbrace{\mathbf{PP}\cdots\mathbf{P}}_{k\text{ factors}} = \mathbf{P}^k \tag{8.1}$$

This result can be justified by using the special case $k = 2$, $\mathbf{P}(2) = \mathbf{P}^2$ (which was verified above), and mathematical induction.

Example 8.6 Use Equation (8.1) to compute $\mathbf{P}(2)$ for the Markov chain whose transition matrix is matrix **P** of Example 8.5.

Solution

$$\mathbf{P}(2) = \begin{bmatrix} .8 & .2 \\ .6 & .4 \end{bmatrix}^2 = \begin{bmatrix} .8 & .2 \\ .6 & .4 \end{bmatrix}\begin{bmatrix} .8 & .2 \\ .6 & .4 \end{bmatrix} = \begin{bmatrix} .76 & .24 \\ .72 & .28 \end{bmatrix}$$

This is the same result we obtained in Example 8.5 (as it must be). ■

Example 8.7 A Markov chain has transition matrix

$$\mathbf{P} = \begin{bmatrix} .3 & .3 & .4 \\ .5 & .5 & 0 \\ 1 & 0 & 0 \end{bmatrix}$$

Problem (*a*) Find the two-step transition matrix $\mathbf{P}(2)$.

(*b*) If the system is initially observed in state 1, what is the probability that it is in state 1 two observations later?

Solution (*a*) Applying Equation (8.1), we have

$$\mathbf{P}(2) = \mathbf{P}^2 = \begin{bmatrix} .3 & .3 & .4 \\ .5 & .5 & 0 \\ 1 & 0 & 0 \end{bmatrix}^2 = \begin{bmatrix} .64 & .24 & .12 \\ .4 & .4 & .2 \\ .3 & .3 & .4 \end{bmatrix}$$

(*b*) We are asked to find $p_{11}(2)$. This is the (1, 1) entry of $\mathbf{P}(2)$, and consequently the answer is .64. ■

Example 8.8 The transition diagram for a Markov chain is shown in Figure 8.11.

Problem Find the matrix of three-step transition probabilities for this Markov chain.

Solution Using Figure 8.11, we find that the transition matrix for this Markov chain is

$$\mathbf{P} = \begin{bmatrix} \frac{1}{4} & \frac{3}{4} & 0 \\ 0 & 0 & 1 \\ \frac{1}{2} & 0 & \frac{1}{2} \end{bmatrix}$$

FIGURE 8.11

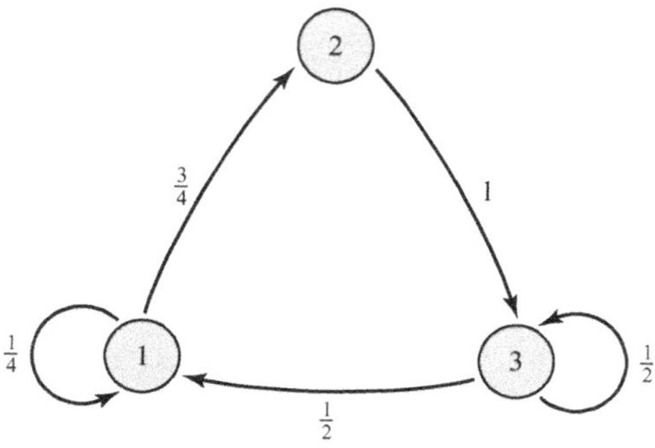

It follows from Equation (8.1) that

$$\mathbf{P}(3) = \mathbf{P}^3 = \mathbf{P}\mathbf{P}^2$$
$$= \begin{bmatrix} \frac{1}{4} & \frac{3}{4} & 0 \\ 0 & 0 & 1 \\ \frac{1}{2} & 0 & \frac{1}{2} \end{bmatrix} \begin{bmatrix} \frac{1}{16} & \frac{3}{16} & \frac{3}{4} \\ \frac{1}{2} & 0 & \frac{1}{2} \\ \frac{3}{8} & \frac{3}{8} & \frac{1}{4} \end{bmatrix}$$
$$= \begin{bmatrix} \frac{25}{64} & \frac{3}{64} & \frac{36}{64} \\ \frac{3}{8} & \frac{3}{8} & \frac{1}{4} \\ \frac{14}{64} & \frac{18}{64} & \frac{1}{2} \end{bmatrix}$$

■

In Example 8.8, notice that the 0 in the (2, 2) entry of **P** means that it is impossible to make a direct transition from state 2 to state 2. Likewise, the 0 in the (2, 2) entry of $\mathbf{P}^2$ means that it is impossible to make a transition from state 2 to state 2 in two steps. Since the (2, 2) entry of $\mathbf{P}^3$ is not zero (it is equal to $\frac{3}{8}$), it is possible to make a transition from state 2 to state 2 in three steps. In fact, beginning in state 2, there is a positive probability of making each of the transitions $2 \to 3$, $3 \to 1$, and $1 \to 2$.

Example 8.9 (Continuation of Examples 8.1 and 8.2) Suppose that the consultant is unemployed this week.

Problem Find the probability that she will be unemployed 4 weeks from now.

Solution Adopting the notation introduced in Example 8.2, that is, labeling states E and U as 1 and 2, respectively, we have the transition matrix **P**:

$$\mathbf{P} = \begin{bmatrix} .8 & .2 \\ .6 & .4 \end{bmatrix}$$

We seek $p_{22}(4)$. Using Equation (8.1), we have $\mathbf{P}(4) = \mathbf{P}^4$. Also, $\mathbf{P}^4 = \mathbf{P}^2\mathbf{P}^2$, so first we find $\mathbf{P}^2$.

$$\mathbf{P}^2 = \begin{bmatrix} .8 & .2 \\ .6 & .4 \end{bmatrix} \begin{bmatrix} .8 & .2 \\ .6 & .4 \end{bmatrix} = \begin{bmatrix} .76 & .24 \\ .72 & .28 \end{bmatrix}$$

Since we are interested in the (2, 2) entry of $\mathbf{P}(4)$, we need to compute only that entry and not the entire matrix $\mathbf{P}(4)$. That is, we need only to evaluate $[.72 \quad .28] \begin{bmatrix} .24 \\ .28 \end{bmatrix}$. We have

$$p_{22}(4) = .72(.24) + .28(.28) = .2512$$

Therefore, if the consultant is unemployed this week, then the conditional probability that she will be unemployed 4 weeks from now is .2512. ■

The entries $p_{i1}, p_{i2}, \ldots, p_{iN}$ in the ith row of the transition matrix **P** are the probabilities that the system moves from state i to states 1, 2, . . . N, respectively, in one step. Now, since at each step the system must first move from state i to some state (perhaps to i itself), it follows that the sum of the entries in the ith row of matrix **P** is 1. Vectors such as the ith row of **P** have a special name.

A *probability vector* is a vector with nonnegative coordinates for which the sum of the coordinates is 1.

Using this terminology, we have the following fact.

Each row of a transition matrix **P** of a Markov chain is a probability vector.

Likewise, for each k the rows of matrix **P**(k) are probability vectors. Indeed, the entries of the ith row of **P**(k) are the probabilities $p_{i1}(k), p_{i2}(k), \ldots, p_{iN}(k)$, and the system must move from state i to some state (perhaps i itself) in k steps. It is easily seen that each row of matrix **P** of Example 8.7 is a probability vector, that each row of matrices **P**(2) of Examples 8.6 and 8.7 is a probability vector, and that each row of matrix **P**(3) of Example 8.8 is a probability vector.

Example 8.10 Many experiments concerned with the behavior of animal subjects have been modeled by using Markov chains. We consider a very simple example of such an experiment and the behavior of a subject, say a mouse, in the setting shown in Figure 8.12. The physical apparatus consists of four compartments: a nest, a compartment containing food, a compartment containing water, and a compartment containing an exercise device known as a squirrel cage. An experiment is designed to study the mouse's moves among the compartments. The mouse is initially released in one compartment, and its movements after that time are observed.

Suppose that the behavior of the mouse can be described by a Markov chain. That is, suppose that the behavior of the mouse depends only on the compartment it currently occupies and not on where the mouse was earlier. Transitions can occur in two ways: the mouse can move to a neighboring compartment, and the mouse can stay in the same compartment for 2 minutes. In the latter case, we say that a transition into the same compartment has taken place.

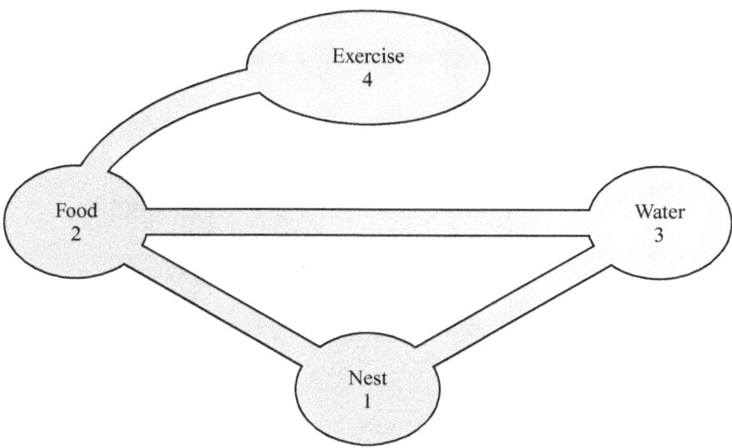

FIGURE 8.12

Problem (*a*) Find the transition matrix under the assumptions that the mouse is twice as likely to remain in the same compartment as to move and that if it moves, it is equally likely to make any of the possible moves.

(*b*) Under the assumptions of part *a*, find the probability that the mouse is in the nest after two transitions given that it began in compartment 2, the compartment with food.

Solution (*a*) Label the states as shown in Figure 8.12. Since the mouse is observed each time it moves from one compartment to another, only transitions from a compartment to itself or to an immediately adjacent compartment have nonzero probability. Consider the system when the mouse is in state 3 (the compartment with water). The mouse is twice as likely to remain in compartment 3 as to move, and if it does move, then the mouse is equally likely to move to compartments 1 and 2. Thus, using the techniques of Chapter 2, we see that the probabilities of transitions from state 3 to states 1, 2, 3, and 4 are $\frac{1}{6}$, $\frac{1}{6}$, $\frac{2}{3}$, and 0, respectively. The remaining transition probabilities are determined similarly, and the transition matrix is:

$$\mathbf{P} = \begin{bmatrix} \frac{2}{3} & \frac{1}{6} & \frac{1}{6} & 0 \\ \frac{1}{9} & \frac{2}{3} & \frac{1}{9} & \frac{1}{9} \\ \frac{1}{6} & \frac{1}{6} & \frac{2}{3} & 0 \\ 0 & \frac{1}{3} & 0 & \frac{2}{3} \end{bmatrix}$$

(*b*) If the mouse is released in compartment 2, then the probability that it is in compartment 1 after two transitions is the (2, 1) entry of the two-step transition matrix $\mathbf{P}(2) = \mathbf{P}^2$. The desired probability is $p_{21}(2) = \frac{1}{6}$. ■

Exercises for Section 8.2

1. A Markov chain has the transition matrix

$$\mathbf{P} = \begin{bmatrix} .5 & .5 \\ 1 & 0 \end{bmatrix}$$

   (*a*) Find the two-step transition matrix $\mathbf{P}(2)$.
   (*b*) Find $p_{12}(2)$ and $p_{22}(2)$.

2. A Markov chain has the transition matrix

$$\mathbf{P} = \begin{bmatrix} 0 & 1 \\ .2 & .8 \end{bmatrix}$$

   (*a*) Find the two-step transition matrix $\mathbf{P}(2)$.
   (*b*) Find $p_{11}(2)$ and $p_{22}(2)$.

3. For the transition matrix $\mathbf{P}$ of Exercise 1, find $\mathbf{P}(3)$ and $\mathbf{P}(4)$.

4. A Markov chain has the transition matrix

$$\mathbf{P} = \begin{bmatrix} .6 & .4 \\ .4 & .6 \end{bmatrix}$$

   (*a*) Find the two-step transition matrix $\mathbf{P}(2)$.
   (*b*) Find the three-step transition matrix $\mathbf{P}(3)$.

5. The transition matrix of a Markov chain is $\begin{bmatrix} .6 & .4 \\ .3 & .7 \end{bmatrix}$. If it starts in state 1, what is the probability that it will be in state 1 after 3 transitions?

6. Find the three-step transition probability $p_{13}(3)$ for the transition matrix

$$\mathbf{P} = \begin{bmatrix} .3 & .7 & 0 \\ 0 & 0 & 1 \\ .5 & 0 & .5 \end{bmatrix}$$

7. A Markov chain has the transition matrix

$$\mathbf{P} = \begin{bmatrix} 0 & 1 & 0 \\ 0 & 0 & 1 \\ 1 & 0 & 0 \end{bmatrix}$$

   (*a*) Find the two-step transition matrix $\mathbf{P}(2)$.
   (*b*) Find the three-step transition matrix $\mathbf{P}(3)$.

8. Find the four-step transition probability $p_{31}(4)$ for the transition matrix

$$\mathbf{P} = \begin{bmatrix} 0 & 1 & 0 \\ 0 & 0 & 1 \\ .5 & 0 & .5 \end{bmatrix}$$

9. A Markov chain has the transition matrix

$$\mathbf{P} = \begin{bmatrix} 0 & .8 & .2 \\ 0 & 1 & 0 \\ .5 & 0 & .5 \end{bmatrix}$$

(*a*) Find $\mathbf{P}(2)$, $\mathbf{P}(3)$, and $\mathbf{P}(4)$.
(*b*) Find $p_{22}(2)$, $p_{22}(3)$, and $p_{22}(4)$.
(*c*) What can you say about $p_{22}(k)$ for any positive integer k?

10. Let $\mathbf{P}$ be the transition matrix of Exercise 9.
(*a*) Show that the rows of $\mathbf{P}(2)$, $\mathbf{P}(3)$, and $\mathbf{P}(4)$ are probability vectors.
(*b*) What can you say about the relative sizes of $p_{12}(2)$, $p_{12}(3)$, and $p_{12}(4)$?
(*c*) What can you say about the relative sizes of $p_{32}(2)$, $p_{32}(3)$, and $p_{32}(4)$?

11. Let $\mathbf{P}$ be the transition matrix for a Markov chain where

$$\mathbf{P} = \begin{bmatrix} \frac{1}{2} & 0 & \frac{1}{2} \\ 1 & 0 & 0 \\ 0 & \frac{2}{3} & \frac{1}{3} \end{bmatrix}$$

(*a*) Suppose the system is in state 1 on an initial observation. Draw a tree diagram for a sequential experiment consisting of three observations of the system, including the initial observation.
(*b*) Determine the first row of matrix $\mathbf{P}(2)$, using the tree diagram.
(*c*) Determine matrix $\mathbf{P}(2)$, using formula (8.1).

12. Let $\mathbf{P}$ (given below) be the transition matrix for a Markov chain, and suppose that the system is initially in state 2.
(*a*) Draw the tree diagram for a sequential experiment consisting of three observations of the system, including the initial observation.
(*b*) Determine the second row of matrix $\mathbf{P}(2)$, using the tree diagram.
(*c*) Determine matrix $\mathbf{P}(2)$, using formula (8.1).

$$\mathbf{P} = \begin{bmatrix} \frac{1}{2} & 0 & \frac{1}{2} \\ 0 & \frac{1}{2} & \frac{1}{2} \\ \frac{1}{3} & \frac{1}{3} & \frac{1}{3} \end{bmatrix}$$

13. Determine $\mathbf{P}(2)$ and $\mathbf{P}(3)$ for a Markov chain with transition matrix

$$\mathbf{P} = \begin{bmatrix} .2 & .2 & .6 \\ .4 & .2 & .4 \\ .5 & 0 & .5 \end{bmatrix}$$

Verify that the rows of $\mathbf{P}(2)$ and $\mathbf{P}(3)$ are probability vectors.

14. Profits at a brokerage firm are determined by the volume of securities sold, and this volume fluctuates from week to week (see Exercise 15, Section 8.1): If volume is high this week, then next week it will be high with probability .7 and low with probability .3. If volume is low this week, then next week it will be high or low with equal probability.

(*a*) If the volume is high this week, find the probability that it will be high 4 weeks from now.

(*b*) If the volume is high this week, use the answer to part *a* to determine the probability that the volume will be low 4 weeks from now.

15. Suppose that a basketball player's success in free-throw shooting can be described with a Markov chain with transition matrix

$$\mathbf{P} = \begin{array}{c} \\ \text{Make} \\ \text{Miss} \end{array} \begin{array}{c} \begin{array}{cc} \text{Make} & \text{Miss} \end{array} \\ \begin{bmatrix} .8 & .2 \\ .4 & .6 \end{bmatrix} \end{array}$$

That is, if the player makes a free throw, then he will make the next one with probability .8, and he will miss it with probability .2. Also, if the player misses a free throw, then he will make the next one with probability .4 and miss it with probability .6.

(*a*) If the player makes his first free throw, what is the probability that he also makes the third one?

(*b*) If the player misses his first free throw, what is the probability that he makes the third?

16. A not-so-enthusiastic student tends to miss class on Friday afternoons. She is always in one of the two states, absent or present, and transitions occur according to matrix **P**, where

$$\mathbf{P} = \begin{array}{c} \\ \text{Absent} \\ \text{Present} \end{array} \begin{array}{c} \begin{array}{cc} \text{Absent} & \text{Present} \end{array} \\ \begin{bmatrix} .3 & .7 \\ .6 & .4 \end{bmatrix} \end{array}$$

If the student is absent on a given Friday afternoon, find the probability she will be present 3 weeks later.

17. An overweight student is always in one of the three states: fast, balanced diet, sweet binge. Transitions between these stages occur weekly according to the probabilities shown in matrix **P**:

$$\mathbf{P} = \begin{array}{r} \\ \text{Fast} \\ \text{Balanced diet} \\ \text{Sweet binge} \end{array} \begin{array}{c} \begin{array}{ccc} \text{Fast} & \text{Balanced diet} & \text{Sweet binge} \end{array} \\ \begin{bmatrix} .3 & .3 & .4 \\ .1 & .8 & .1 \\ .3 & .6 & .1 \end{bmatrix} \end{array}$$

Find the two-step transition matrix **P**(2) and the transition probability of going from sweet binge to sweet binge in three steps.

18. A small animal lives in a territory that can be divided into two areas described as meadow and woods, and it moves randomly from one area to another (see Exercise 17, Section 8.1). If it is in the woods on one observation, then it is twice as likely to be in the woods as the meadow on the next observation. Likewise, if it is in the meadow on one observation, then it is twice as likely to be in the meadow as the woods on the next observation. If the animal is in the woods on the first observation, find the probability that it is in the woods on the fourth observation.

19. Consider the situation described in Example 8.4. If the taxi driver is currently in the east district, what is the probability that after two more calls he will be in the west district? In what district is he most likely to be?

20. A Markov chain has the transition matrix **P** shown below. If the system begins in state 2 and makes 3 transitions, what are the probabilities of being in each of the 4 states.

$$\mathbf{P} = \begin{bmatrix} 0 & 1 & 0 & 0 \\ 0 & 0 & 1 & 0 \\ 0 & 0 & .5 & .5 \\ 1 & 0 & 0 & 0 \end{bmatrix}$$

21. Employment shifts in a certain city follow the pattern given in Table 8.5. Formulate a Markov chain model for these shifts.
    (*a*) Find the two-step transition matrix for this Markov chain.
    (*b*) Find the probability that an individual employed in industry at one time is employed in small business 2 years later.

TABLE 8.5

Employment Last Year	Employment This Year	Percentage
Industry	Industry	90
	Small business	5
	Self-employed	5
Small business	Industry	10
	Small business	80
	Self-employed	10
Self-employed	Industry	10
	Small business	30
	Self-employed	60

22. (Continuation of Exercise 21) If an individual is self-employed this year, what is her most likely employment status 2 years from now?

23. (Continuation of Exercise 22) A person would like to be self-employed 2 years from now. What current employment status gives her the greatest likelihood of achieving her goal?

24. A well-to-do anesthesiologist purchases a new car every year. Each year she chooses among Audi, BMW, and Mercedes. She is four times as likely to buy a different make from the one she last purchased as she is to buy the same make, and she is equally likely to purchase each of the other two makes. Formulate this situation as a Markov chain and find the transition matrix. If she purchases a Mercedes in 2016, find the probability that she purchases an Audi in 2018.

25. (Continuation of Exercise 24) If she purchases an Audi in 2016, what make is she most likely to purchase in 2018?

26. A Markov chain has the transition matrix **P** shown below. If the system begins in state 4, find the probability that it is in state 4 after four transitions.

$$\mathbf{P} = \begin{bmatrix} 0 & 1 & 0 & 0 \\ 0 & 0 & 1 & 0 \\ 0 & 0 & 0 & 1 \\ .5 & 0 & 0 & .5 \end{bmatrix}$$

27. Using the Markov chain of Exercise 26, suppose the system begins in state 4. In what state is it most likely to be after four transitions?
28. A Markov chain has the transition matrix

$$\mathbf{P} = \begin{bmatrix} 0 & 1 & 0 & 0 & 0 \\ 0 & 0 & 1 & 0 & 0 \\ 0 & 0 & 0 & 1 & 0 \\ 0 & 0 & 0 & 0 & 1 \\ .5 & 0 & 0 & 0 & .5 \end{bmatrix}$$

What is the smallest positive integer k for which it is possible to go between any two states in k transitions?

29. A Markov chain has the transition matrix

$$\mathbf{P} = \begin{bmatrix} .4 & .6 & 0 & 0 \\ .4 & .4 & .2 & 0 \\ 0 & 0 & 0 & 1 \\ 0 & 0 & .5 & .5 \end{bmatrix}$$

(*a*) Compute **P**(2), **P**(4), and **P**(8).
(*b*) Is it possible to go from state 3 to state 1 in 2, 4, or 8 steps?
(*c*) Is it possible to go from state 3 to state 1 in any number of steps? (*Hint*: Draw a transition diagram for this Markov chain.)

30. A Markov chain has the transition matrix **P** shown below. Without computing the powers of the matrix, give an argument to show that no power of matrix **P** has all positive entries.

$$\mathbf{P} = \begin{bmatrix} 0 & 1 & 0 & 0 \\ 0 & 0 & 1 & 0 \\ 0 & 0 & 0 & 1 \\ 1 & 0 & 0 & 0 \end{bmatrix}$$

31. A Markov chain has the transition matrix

$$\mathbf{P} = \begin{bmatrix} .6 & .4 \\ a & 1-a \end{bmatrix}$$

If $p_{11}(2) = .4$, what is a and what is $p_{22}(3)$?

32. A Markov chain has the transition matrix

$$\mathbf{P} = \begin{bmatrix} .4 & .2 & .4 \\ .2 & a & .8 - a \\ .6 & .3 & .1 \end{bmatrix}$$

If $p_{21}(2) = .36$, what is a and what is $p_{33}(2)$?

33. The transition matrix of a Markov chain with four states is shown below. If it is initially in state 4, in what state is it most likely to be after 3 transitions?

$$\mathbf{P} = \begin{bmatrix} 0 & .5 & 0 & .5 \\ 0 & 0 & 1 & 0 \\ 1 & 0 & 0 & 0 \\ .5 & .2 & 0 & .3 \end{bmatrix}$$

34. Suppose that a Markov chain with the transition matrix of Exercise 33 is observed to be in state 3 after making 4 transitions. Which initial state has the highest probability of leading to this result? Which initial state has the lowest probability of leading to this result?

35. The transition matrix for a four-state Markov chain is shown below. Find the smallest number k of transitions for which there is a positive probability of being in state 2 after k transitions independent of the initial state.

$$\mathbf{P} = \begin{bmatrix} 0 & .5 & 0 & .5 \\ 0 & 0 & 1 & 0 \\ 1 & 0 & 0 & 0 \\ .5 & 0 & 0 & .5 \end{bmatrix}$$

8.3 REGULAR MARKOV CHAINS

In the preceding sections we introduced the basic property of Markov chains, and we developed the formula $\mathbf{P}(k) = \mathbf{P}^k$, which shows that the k-step transition matrix equals the kth power of the 1-step transition matrix. In this section and the next, we continue by considering briefly two special types of Markov chains which are especially useful in applications, and we give such an application in the final section of the chapter.

Since Markov chains are stochastic processes, we do not ordinarily know what will happen at each stage, and we must describe the system in terms of probabilities.

State Vector

Consider a Markov chain with N states. A state vector for the Markov chain is a probability N vector $\mathbf{X} = [x_1 \quad x_2 \quad \cdots \quad x_N]$. The ith coordinate x_i of the state vector $\mathbf{X}$ is to be interpreted as the probability that the system is in state i. We write a state vector as a row vector, i.e., as a $1 \times N$ matrix.

Example 8.11 The Markov chain model for White Wheel Taxi Company formulated in Example 8.4 has three states. In this situation the state vector [.7 0 .3] is to be interpreted as follows: The driver is in the East district with probability .7, is not in the Central district, and is in the West district with probability .3. ■

If the system (the driver) is known to be in a specific state, then the state vector has a particularly simple form: If the system is in the ith state, the ith coordinate of the state vector is 1 and all other coordinates are 0. For instance, if in the Markov chain defined in Example 8.4 the system is in state 1 (the driver is in the East district), the associated state vector is [1 0 0].

The behavior of a Markov chain (i.e., the states it can enter and how likely it is to enter them) can be described with a sequence of state vectors. The initial state of the system can be described with a state vector which we denote by $\mathbf{X}_0$. After one transition, the system can again be described with a state vector which we call $\mathbf{X}_1$. After two transitions it can be described by another state vector which we call $\mathbf{X}_2$. In general, after k transitions the system can be described by a state vector which we call $\mathbf{X}_k$. The relation between these state vectors can be represented with vector-matrix multiplication. We summarize the facts in a theorem.

Theorem on State Vectors for a Markov Chain

If $\mathbf{X}_k$ and $\mathbf{X}_{k+1}$ denote the state vectors which describe a Markov chain after k and $k+1$ transitions, respectively, then $\mathbf{X}_{k+1} = \mathbf{X}_k\mathbf{P}$, where $\mathbf{P}$ is the transition matrix of the chain. In particular, $\mathbf{X}_1 = \mathbf{X}_0\mathbf{P}$, $\mathbf{X}_2 = \mathbf{X}_1\mathbf{P} = \mathbf{X}_0\mathbf{P}^2, \ldots,$ and in general $\mathbf{X}_k = \mathbf{X}_0\mathbf{P}^k$. That is, the state vector $\mathbf{X}_k$ which describes the system after k transitions is the product of the initial state vector and the kth power of the transition matrix.

The theorem can be verified by examining each coordinate of the product $\mathbf{X}_k\mathbf{P}$ and using the meaning of $\mathbf{X}_k$ and $\mathbf{P}$. The conclusion is that the jth coordinate of $\mathbf{X}_k\mathbf{P}$ is exactly the probability that the system is in state j after $k+1$ transitions, i.e., the jth coordinate of $\mathbf{X}_{k+1}$. Note that if the chain has N states, so that $\mathbf{X}_k$ is an N-vector and $\mathbf{P}$ is an $N \times N$ matrix, then $\mathbf{X}_k\mathbf{P}$ is also an N-vector.

Example 8.12 The Markov chain model for White Wheel Taxi Company formulated in Example 8.4 has the transition matrix $\mathbf{P}$.

$$\mathbf{P} = \begin{bmatrix} .5 & .4 & .1 \\ .1 & .6 & .3 \\ .3 & .6 & .1 \end{bmatrix}$$

Problem If the initial state vector is $\mathbf{X}_0 = [.7 \quad .0 \quad .3]$, find the state vector after one transition.

Solution Using the theorem, we find that the state vector after one transition is

$$\mathbf{X}_1 = \mathbf{X}_0\mathbf{P} = [.7 \quad 0 \quad .3]\begin{bmatrix} .5 & .4 & .1 \\ .1 & .6 & .3 \\ .3 & .6 & .1 \end{bmatrix}$$
$$= [.44 \quad .46 \quad .10]$$

■

Example 8.13 A Markov chain has the transition matrix

$$\mathbf{P} = \begin{bmatrix} .5 & .5 \\ .8 & .2 \end{bmatrix}$$

Problem If the system begins in state 2, find the state vector after two transitions.

Solution The initial state vector is $[0 \quad 1]$. According to the theorem, the state vector after two transitions is

$$\mathbf{X}_2 = \mathbf{X}_0\mathbf{P}^2 = [0 \quad 1]\begin{bmatrix} .5 & .5 \\ .8 & .2 \end{bmatrix}\begin{bmatrix} .5 & .5 \\ .8 & .2 \end{bmatrix}$$
$$= [0 \quad 1]\begin{bmatrix} .65 & .35 \\ .56 & .44 \end{bmatrix}$$
$$= [.56 \quad .44]$$

■

We now turn to the primary topic of this section. There are various ways of classifying Markov chains, and we choose one which distinguishes among chains based on their long-run behavior, i.e., on the behavior of the state vector after many transitions. As we will see in our examples, the long-run behavior of the state vector may provide important information in applications. Although the kth state vector can be determined for any k, there are practical issues in doing so. (Even using calculators, computers, or the web involves knowledge, skill, and experience.) Also, after $\mathbf{X}_k$ has been determined for some value of k, in general this does not provide much information about $\mathbf{X}_{k+1}$ or $\mathbf{X}_{k+2}$ without further computation. Thus, if you are interested in studying a stochastic process over many transitions, then it is appropriate to develop some tools for determining its long-run behavior. For instance, suppose that in Example 8.4 (White Wheel Taxi Company), the driver begins in the East district. Then we can easily determine the probabilities that future locations will be in the East district after 1, 2, or 3 transitions, that is $p_{11}, p_{11}(2)$, and $p_{11}(3)$. The task is more complex if we are interested in the corresponding probabilities after 10, 20, or 100 transitions; that is $p_{11}(10)$, $p_{11}(20)$, and $p_{11}(100)$. The long-run behavior of the probabilities $p_{11}(k)$ gives information on the likelihood that if the day begins with the driver in the East district, then late in the day (after many transitions) the driver will be again in the East district.

In the general case of a Markov chain with N states, the probability that the system is in the jth state after k trials depends upon the state in which it started. Thus $p_{1j}(k)$ is the probability that the system is in state j after k trials if it is initially in state 1. There are similar meanings attached to $p_{2j}(k), p_{3j}(k), \ldots, p_{Nj}(k)$. There is no reason to have (or expect) equality among all these probabilities. However, for some Markov chains there is a positive probability q_j associated with the jth state such that the k-step transition probabilities $p_{ij}(k)$ all become close to q_j for large k. That is, the likelihood that the system is in state j after k transitions is, for large k, nearly the same for all starting states. We study such Markov chains in some detail because they form an important special class. We begin by defining the class. The definition does not directly refer to the long-run behavior of the chain; however, the connection with that behavior will be explored below. We use our definition because it is easier to check that a chain satisfies the definition than that it has certain long-run behaviors.

Regular Markov Chain

A Markov chain with transition matrix $\mathbf{P}$ is *regular* if there is a positive integer k such that $\mathbf{P}^k$ has all positive entries.

Example 8.14 Each of the following matrices is the transition matrix for a Markov chain.

$$\mathbf{P}_1 = \begin{bmatrix} \frac{1}{2} & \frac{1}{2} \\ 1 & 0 \end{bmatrix} \qquad \mathbf{P}_2 = \begin{bmatrix} 0 & 1 \\ 1 & 0 \end{bmatrix}$$

Problem Which of the Markov chains associated with these matrices are regular?

Solution For matrix $\mathbf{P}_1$ we have

$$\mathbf{P}_1^2 = \begin{bmatrix} \frac{1}{2} & \frac{1}{2} \\ 1 & 0 \end{bmatrix} \begin{bmatrix} \frac{1}{2} & \frac{1}{2} \\ 1 & 0 \end{bmatrix} = \begin{bmatrix} \frac{3}{4} & \frac{1}{4} \\ \frac{1}{2} & \frac{1}{2} \end{bmatrix}$$

Thus, the second power of $\mathbf{P}_1$ has all positive entries, and by the definition given above, the associated Markov chain is regular.

For matrix $\mathbf{P}_2$ we have

$$\mathbf{P}_2^2 = \begin{bmatrix} 0 & 1 \\ 1 & 0 \end{bmatrix}\begin{bmatrix} 0 & 1 \\ 1 & 0 \end{bmatrix} = \begin{bmatrix} 1 & 0 \\ 0 & 1 \end{bmatrix} = \mathbf{I}$$

$$\mathbf{P}_2^3 = \mathbf{P}_2\mathbf{P}_2^2 = \begin{bmatrix} 0 & 1 \\ 1 & 0 \end{bmatrix}\begin{bmatrix} 1 & 0 \\ 0 & 1 \end{bmatrix} = \begin{bmatrix} 0 & 1 \\ 1 & 0 \end{bmatrix} = \mathbf{P}_2$$

and

$$\mathbf{P}_2^4 = \mathbf{P}_2\mathbf{P}_3^2 = \begin{bmatrix} 0 & 1 \\ 1 & 0 \end{bmatrix}\begin{bmatrix} 0 & 1 \\ 1 & 0 \end{bmatrix} = \begin{bmatrix} 1 & 0 \\ 0 & 1 \end{bmatrix} = \mathbf{I}$$

We see at this stage that $\mathbf{P}_2 = \mathbf{P}_2^3$ and $\mathbf{P}_2^2 = \mathbf{P}_2^4 = \mathbf{I}$. This means that every even power of $\mathbf{P}_2$ will be the identity matrix $\mathbf{I}$ since every even power is a power of $\mathbf{P}_2^2 = \mathbf{I}$. Also, every odd power of $\mathbf{P}_2$ will be $\mathbf{P}_2$ since it is just some power of $\mathbf{P}_2^2 = \mathbf{I}$ times $\mathbf{P}_2$. Since both $\mathbf{I}$ and $\mathbf{P}_2$ contain zeros, we see that no power of $\mathbf{P}_2$ will have all positive entries. In other words, the Markov chain for $\mathbf{P}_2$ is *not regular*. ■

It is important to connect our definition of regular with the long-run behavior of a Markov chain. The next example is a step in that direction.

Example 8.15 A Markov chain has the transition matrix

$$\mathbf{P} = \begin{bmatrix} .5 & .5 & 0 \\ 0 & .5 & .5 \\ .75 & .25 & 0 \end{bmatrix}$$

Problem (*a*) For which state i is p_{i3} largest? For which state i is it smallest?
(*b*) For which state i is $p_{i3}(2)$ largest, and for which is it smallest?
(*c*) For which state i is $p_{i3}(3)$ largest, and for which is it smallest?

Solution (*a*) The probabilities p_{i3}, $i = 1, 2, 3$, form the third column of matrix $\mathbf{P}$. Therefore, $p_{23} = .5$ is the largest, and $p_{13} = p_{33} = 0$ are the smallest. We have

$$\mathbf{P}(2) = \begin{bmatrix} .25 & .50 & .25 \\ .375 & .375 & .25 \\ .375 & .50 & .125 \end{bmatrix} \quad \text{and} \quad \mathbf{P}(3) = \begin{bmatrix} .3125 & .4375 & .2500 \\ .3750 & .4375 & .1875 \\ .28125 & .46875 & .2500 \end{bmatrix}$$

(*b*) The probabilities $p_{13}(2)$, $p_{23}(2)$, and $p_{33}(2)$ form the third column of matrix $\mathbf{P}(2)$. Therefore $p_{13}(2) = p_{23}(2) = .25$ are the largest, and $p_{33}(2) = .125$ is the smallest.

(*c*) The probabilities $p_{13}(3), p_{23}(3)$, and $p_{33}(3)$ form the third column of matrix $\mathbf{P}(3)$. Therefore, $p_{13}(3) = p_{33}(3) = .25$ are the largest, and $p_{23}(3) = .1875$ is the smallest.

Notice that the two-step transition probabilities $p_{13}(2) = .25$, $p_{23}(2) = .25$, and $p_{33}(2) = .125$ are closer together than the one-step transition probabilities. The three-step transition probabilities $p_{13}(3) = .25$, $p_{23}(3) = .1875$, and $p_{33}(3) = .25$ are still closer. Indeed, the probabilities that the system is in state 3 after three transitions given that it began in states 1, 2, and 3 differ from each other by at most .0625, whereas the differences after one transition can be as large as .5. As we shall see in a moment, the probabilities $p_{13}(k)$, $p_{23}(k)$, and $p_{33}(k)$ all approach $\frac{2}{9} = .2222$ as k becomes large. ■

The definition of a regular chain (although stated in terms of the powers of $\mathbf{P}$) has the following important consequence. For each j and for k sufficiently large, each of the transition probabilities $p_{1j}(k), p_{2j}(k), \ldots, p_{Nj}(k)$ is close to the same number, call it q_j. That is, each of the entries in the jth column of the k-step transition matrix $\mathbf{P}(k)$ is close to q_j. Another way of saying this is that for large values of k, the k-step transition matrix

$$\mathbf{P}(k) = \begin{bmatrix} p_{11}(k) & p_{12}(k) & \cdots & p_{1N}(k) \\ p_{21}(k) & p_{22}(k) & \cdots & p_{2N}(k) \\ \cdot & \cdot & & \cdot \\ \cdot & \cdot & & \cdot \\ \cdot & \cdot & & \cdot \\ p_{N1}(k) & p_{N2}(k) & \cdots & p_{NN}(k) \end{bmatrix}$$

is very close to a matrix that has all rows identical,

$$\begin{bmatrix} \mathbf{W} \\ \mathbf{W} \\ \cdot \\ \cdot \\ \cdot \\ \mathbf{W} \end{bmatrix} = \begin{bmatrix} w_1 & w_2 & \cdots & w_N \\ w_1 & w_2 & \cdots & w_N \\ \cdot & \cdot & & \cdot \\ \cdot & \cdot & & \cdot \\ \cdot & \cdot & & \cdot \\ w_1 & w_2 & \cdots & w_N \end{bmatrix}$$

where $\mathbf{W} = [w_1 \quad w_2 \quad \cdots \quad w_N]$.

Example 8.16 Consider the transition matrix $\mathbf{P}$ of Example 8.12.

$$\mathbf{P} = \begin{bmatrix} .5 & .4 & .1 \\ .1 & .6 & .3 \\ .3 & .6 & .1 \end{bmatrix}$$

A straightforward computation of the k-step transition matrices (best carried out on a computer) gives

$$\mathbf{P}(2) = \begin{bmatrix} .32 & .50 & .18 \\ .20 & .58 & .22 \\ .24 & .54 & .22 \end{bmatrix}$$

$$\mathbf{P}(4) = \begin{bmatrix} .2456 & .5472 & .2072 \\ .2328 & .5552 & .2120 \\ .2376 & .5520 & .2104 \end{bmatrix}$$

$$\mathbf{P}(8) = \begin{bmatrix} .2369 & .5526 & .2105 \\ .2368 & .5527 & .2105 \\ .2369 & .5526 & .2105 \end{bmatrix}$$

where the entries have been rounded off to the four decimal places shown. It is now clear that the rows of $\mathbf{P}(8)$ are essentially equal. This illustrates the assertion that as k increases, the k-step transition matrix $\mathbf{P}(k)$ becomes closer and closer to a matrix all of whose rows are equal to the same vector $\mathbf{W}$. ■

The rows in a transition matrix $\mathbf{P}$, and those of its powers $\mathbf{P}^k$, are all probability vectors. For regular chains the rows in $\mathbf{P}^k$ all become closer and closer to the same probability vector as k increases. This special probability vector is determined by $\mathbf{P}$ and is called a *stable vector* for $\mathbf{P}$. To be precise:

Theorem on Stable Probabilities

Let $\mathbf{P}$ be the transition matrix for a regular Markov chain. There is a unique probability vector $\mathbf{W} = [w_1 \ \ w_2 \ \ \ldots \ \ w_N]$ such that for each state j the difference $|p_{ij}(k) - w_j|$ can be made as small as we choose by selecting k sufficiently large. The vector $\mathbf{W}$ is known as a *stable* vector, and its coordinates are known as *stable probabilities* for the Markov chain.

In a regular Markov chain, the probabilities $p_{ij}(k)$ are for all large values of k nearly equal to the stable probabilities w_j. This assertion holds for each initial state i, $i = 1, 2, \ldots, N$. The stable probabilities w_j can be obtained from the vector $\mathbf{W}$, which is closely approximated by any row of $\mathbf{P}(k)$ for large values of k. However, obtaining $\mathbf{W}$ from $\mathbf{P}(k)$ usually requires computing $\mathbf{P}^k$ for several large values of k, a method that may be impractical. Fortunately there is an alternative method of obtaining the stable probabilities.

Theorem on a Method of Obtaining Stable Probabilities

Let **P** be the transition matrix of a regular Markov chain. Then there is a unique probability vector **W** which satisfies **WP** = **W**. The coordinates of this vector are the stable probabilities for the Markov chain.

This theorem (whose proof we omit) provides a direct method of obtaining the stable probabilities. Indeed, we need only solve a system of linear equations.

Example 8.17 The matrix $\mathbf{P} = \begin{bmatrix} .25 & .75 \\ .60 & .40 \end{bmatrix}$ is the transition matrix of a regular Markov chain.

Problem Determine the vector **W** of stable probabilities for this Markov chain.

Solution We make use of the theorem quoted above. That is, we find the probability vector **W** which satisfies the system of equations

$$\mathbf{WP} = \mathbf{W} \qquad \text{or equivalently} \qquad \mathbf{W}(\mathbf{P} - \mathbf{I}) = \mathbf{0}$$

If $\mathbf{W} = [w_1 \quad w_2]$, then the condition that **W** be a probability vector requires that $w_1 + w_2 = 1$, and the system $\mathbf{W}(\mathbf{P} - \mathbf{I}) = \mathbf{0}$ is

$$\begin{aligned} [w_1 \quad w_2] \begin{bmatrix} -.75 & .75 \\ .60 & -.60 \end{bmatrix} &= [0 \quad 0] \\ -.75w_1 + .60w_2 &= 0 \\ .75w_1 - .60w_2 &= 0 \end{aligned}$$

Therefore, the complete system to be solved is

$$\begin{aligned} w_1 + w_2 &= 1 \\ -.75w_1 + .60w_2 &= 0 \\ .75w_1 - .60w_2 &= 0 \end{aligned}$$

Using the techniques of Chapter 5, gaussian elimination, we find

$$w_1 = \tfrac{4}{9} \qquad \text{and} \qquad w_2 = \tfrac{5}{9}$$

The vector of stable probabilities for the Markov chain whose transition matrix is **P** is $\mathbf{W} = [\frac{4}{9} \quad \frac{5}{9}]$. ■

Example 8.18 (Continuation of Example 8.15) Find the stable probabilities for the Markov chain whose transition matrix is

$$\mathbf{P} = \begin{bmatrix} .5 & .5 & 0 \\ 0 & .5 & .5 \\ .75 & .25 & 0 \end{bmatrix}$$

Solution Since $N=3$, there are three states; $\mathbf{W}$ is a 3-vector, $\mathbf{W}=[w_1 \quad w_2 \quad w_3]$. The system of equations $\mathbf{WP}=\mathbf{W}$ or $\mathbf{W}(\mathbf{P}-\mathbf{I})=\mathbf{0}$ is

$$[w_1 \quad w_2 \quad w_3] \begin{bmatrix} -.5 & .5 & 0 \\ 0 & -.5 & .5 \\ .75 & .25 & -1 \end{bmatrix} = [0 \quad 0 \quad 0] \tag{8.2}$$

The condition that $\mathbf{W}$ be a probability vector gives

$$w_1 + w_2 + w_3 = 1$$

Therefore, the system consisting of the probability vector condition together with Equation (8.2) is

$$\begin{aligned} w_1 + \quad w_2 + \quad w_3 &= 1 \\ -.5w_1 \qquad\qquad + .75w_3 &= 0 \\ .5w_1 - .5w_2 + .25w_3 &= 0 \\ .5w_2 - \quad w_3 &= 0 \end{aligned}$$

Using the techniques of Chapter 5, we conclude that the vector of stable probabilities is $[\frac{3}{9} \quad \frac{4}{9} \quad \frac{2}{9}]$. This confirms the assertion made in Example 8.15 that as k becomes large, $p_{i3}(k)$ approaches $\frac{2}{9}$ for each initial state $i = 1, 2, 3$. ■

Note that in each of the last two examples we wrote the condition that the sum of the coordinates of $\mathbf{W}$ is 1 as the *first* equation of our system. The remaining equations came from the system $\mathbf{WP} = \mathbf{W}$. Writing the equations in this order, i.e., with the probability condition first, makes the use of the techniques of Chapter 5 somewhat easier.

Example 8.19 (Continuation of Example 8.4) The Markov chain used to describe the locations of the driver for the White Wheel Taxi Company is a regular Markov chain.

Problem Find the long-run probabilities that the driver will be in each of the three districts.

Solution We know that one of the interpretations of the stable probabilities is that they give the likelihoods that, in the long run, the system will be in each of the states. Thus we can solve the problem by determining the vector $\mathbf{W}$ of the stable probabilities. Using the fact that $\mathbf{WP} = \mathbf{W}$, we see that our task is to find a probability vector $\mathbf{W}$ which satisfies

$$\mathbf{WP} = \mathbf{W} \qquad \text{with} \qquad \mathbf{P} = \begin{bmatrix} .5 & .4 & .1 \\ .1 & .6 & .3 \\ .3 & .6 & .1 \end{bmatrix}$$

We set $\mathbf{W} = [w_1 \quad w_2 \quad w_3]$, and we write $\mathbf{WP} = \mathbf{W}$ as $\mathbf{W}(\mathbf{P} - \mathbf{I}) = \mathbf{0}$. The resulting system, including the probability condition, is

$$\begin{aligned} w_1 + \quad w_2 + \quad w_3 &= 1 \\ -.5w_1 + .1w_2 + .3w_3 &= 0 \\ .4w_1 - .4w_2 + .6w_3 &= 0 \\ .1w_1 + .3w_2 - .9w_3 &= 0 \end{aligned}$$

Using the techniques of Chapter 5, we find that

$$\mathbf{W} = \begin{bmatrix} \frac{9}{38} & \frac{21}{38} & \frac{8}{38} \end{bmatrix}$$

Thus, in the long run the driver will be in the East district with probability $\frac{9}{38}$, in the Central district with probability $\frac{21}{38}$, and in the West district with probability $\frac{8}{38}$. ■

We now have a means of computing the vector of stable probabilities for any regular Markov chain. To show that a Markov chain is regular, we must be able to show that some power of the transition matrix has all positive entries. It is important to note that we do not need to know the actual entries of the power of the matrix. We only need to know that the entries are all positive.

Example 8.20 Show that the matrix $\mathbf{P}$ given below is the transition matrix of a regular Markov chain.

$$\mathbf{P} = \begin{bmatrix} \frac{1}{3} & \frac{2}{3} & 0 & 0 \\ \frac{1}{4} & \frac{1}{4} & \frac{1}{2} & 0 \\ 0 & \frac{1}{4} & \frac{1}{4} & \frac{1}{2} \\ 0 & 0 & \frac{1}{2} & \frac{1}{2} \end{bmatrix}$$

Solution Since we are only interested in knowing which entries are positive and which ones are zero, we adopt the convention that $+$ and 0 denote positive and zero entries, respectively, in $\mathbf{P}^k$. For $k = 1$, we have

$$\mathbf{P} = \begin{bmatrix} + & + & 0 & 0 \\ + & + & + & 0 \\ 0 & + & + & + \\ 0 & 0 & + & + \end{bmatrix}$$

For $k = 2$ and $k = 3$, we have

$$\mathbf{P}(2) = \mathbf{P}^2 = \begin{bmatrix} + & + & + & 0 \\ + & + & + & + \\ + & + & + & + \\ 0 & + & + & + \end{bmatrix} \quad \text{and} \quad \mathbf{P}(3) = \mathbf{P}^3 = \begin{bmatrix} + & + & + & + \\ + & + & + & + \\ + & + & + & + \\ + & + & + & + \end{bmatrix}$$

We conclude that $\mathbf{P}(3)$ contains only positive entries, and therefore $\mathbf{P}$ is the transition matrix of a regular Markov chain. ■

We comment that the techniques of using pluses and zeros as described in Example 8.20 is useful only when we are dealing with nonnegative matrices.

How many $\mathbf{P}^k$ might you be required to test to determine whether a Markov chain is regular? The answer depends upon the size of matrix $\mathbf{P}$. If $\mathbf{P}$ is the transition matrix for a regular Markov chain with N states, then one of the first $(N-1)^2 + 1$ powers of $\mathbf{P}$ contains only positive entries. [In most regular chains one has to test fewer than $(N-1)^2 + 1$ powers to find one with only positive entries.] Thus, if each of the first $(N-1)^2 + 1$ powers of the transition matrix contains at least one zero entry, the Markov chain is not regular.

In general, it is not efficient to compute $\mathbf{P}^2$, then $\mathbf{P}^3$, then $\mathbf{P}^4$, etc. Instead it is preferable to compute $\mathbf{P}^2$, then multiply $\mathbf{P}^2$ by $\mathbf{P}^2$ to obtain $\mathbf{P}^4$, then multiply $\mathbf{P}^4$ by $\mathbf{P}^4$ to obtain $\mathbf{P}^8$, and so on. This method enables you to determine whether $\mathbf{P}^8$ has only positive entries with only three matrix multiplications. We do not have to worry about ''missing'' a power which had all positive entries, say, $\mathbf{P}^7$, because any time one power has only positive entries, all higher powers also have only positive entries. A zero can never return after all zeros are gone.

Exercises for Section 8.3

1. Which of the following are probability vectors?
   (*a*) [.3 0 0 .2 .5] (*b*) [.1 .2 0 0 .6]
   (*c*) [.1 .4 .5 0 .1] (*d*) [0 .1 0 .1 .8]
2. In each case find a value of the number x for which the vector is a probability vector.
   (*a*) $[.2 \quad x \quad 0 \quad 0 \quad .5]$ (*b*) $[x \quad 0 \quad x \quad 0 \quad .2]$
   (*c*) $[x \quad x \quad x \quad 0 \quad x]$ (*d*) $[2x \quad 3x \quad 3x \quad 2x \quad x]$

3. A state vector **X** for a three-state Markov chain is described as follows: The system is equally likely to be in states 1 and 2, and it is twice as likely to be in state 3 as in state 1. Find the state vector **X**.
4. A state vector **X** for a four-state Markov chain is described as follows: The system is twice as likely to be in state 1 as in state 3, it is never in state 4, and it is in state 2 with probability .4. Find the state vector **X**.
5. (Continuation of Exercise 15, Section 8.1) Profits at a brokerage firm are determined by the volume of securities sold, and this volume fluctuates from week to week. Each week volume is classified as high or low, and information collected over many weeks leads to the following assumptions:
   (*i*) If volume is high this week, then next week it will be high with probability .7 and low with probability .3.
   (*ii*) If volume is low this week, then next week it will be high or low with equal probability.

   The manager estimates that volume is twice as likely to be high as low this week.
   (*a*) Find the state vector which represents the manager's estimate.
   (*b*) Using the estimate as an initial state vector, find the probability of high volume 2 weeks from now.
   (*c*) Repeat (*b*) for 3 weeks from now.
6. In the situation described in Exercise 5, the volume this week is low. How many weeks must pass before a week comes along in which the probability of high volume is at least .6?
7. (Continuation of Exercise 17, Section 8.1) A small animal lives in a territory that can be divided into areas described as meadow and woods, and it moves randomly from one area to another. If it is in the woods on one observation, then the animal is twice as likely to be in the woods as the meadow on the next observation. Likewise, if it is in the meadow on one observation, then it is twice as likely to be in the meadow as the woods on the next.
   (*a*) If the animal is 3 times as likely to be in the meadow as the woods, find the state vector which represents this fact.
   (*b*) Using the state vector determined in (*a*) as an initial state vector, find the probability that the animal is in the meadow after three transitions.
8. Consider the situation described in Exercise 7. If the probability that the animal is in the meadow is .1 at a specific time, how many subsequent observations must be made before the probability that it is in the meadow exceeds .3?
9. Find the vector of stable probabilities for the situation described in Exercise 5.
10. The matrix $\mathbf{P} = \begin{bmatrix} 0 & 1 \\ .4 & .6 \end{bmatrix}$ is the transition matrix of a regular Markov chain. Determine $\mathbf{P}^2$, $\mathbf{P}^4$, and $\mathbf{P}^8$. Use this information to estimate the vector of stable probabilities.
11. Find the vector of stable probabilities for the Markov chain whose transition matrix is

$$\begin{bmatrix} \frac{1}{2} & \frac{1}{2} \\ \frac{2}{3} & \frac{1}{3} \end{bmatrix}$$

12. Suppose $\mathbf{P}$ is the transition matrix of a regular Markov chain:

$$\mathbf{P} = \begin{bmatrix} 0 & .5 & .5 \\ 0 & 0 & 1 \\ 1 & 0 & 0 \end{bmatrix}.$$

What is the second coordinate of the stable vector for this Markov chain?

For Exercises 13 through 17, decide whether the Markov chain with the transition matrix shown is regular. If it is, determine the vector of stable probabilities.

13. $\begin{bmatrix} 0 & 1 \\ \frac{1}{3} & \frac{2}{3} \end{bmatrix}$

14. $\begin{bmatrix} 0 & 1 & 0 \\ 0 & \frac{1}{2} & \frac{1}{2} \\ \frac{1}{3} & 0 & \frac{2}{3} \end{bmatrix}$

15. $\begin{bmatrix} 1 & 0 & 0 \\ \frac{1}{2} & \frac{1}{2} & 0 \\ 0 & \frac{2}{3} & \frac{1}{3} \end{bmatrix}$

16. $\begin{bmatrix} 0 & 1 & 0 & 0 \\ 0 & 0 & 1 & 0 \\ 0 & 0 & 0 & 1 \\ .1 & .1 & 0 & .8 \end{bmatrix}$

17. $\begin{bmatrix} .6 & .4 & 0 & 0 \\ 0 & .5 & .5 & 0 \\ 0 & 0 & .6 & .4 \\ .5 & 0 & .5 & 0 \end{bmatrix}$

18. Consider a Markov chain whose transition matrix is

$$\begin{bmatrix} 0 & .5 & .5 & 0 \\ 0 & 0 & .5 & .5 \\ 0 & .5 & 0 & .5 \\ 1 & 0 & 0 & 0 \end{bmatrix}$$

In which state is the system most likely to be in the long run?

19. Find the long-run free-throw shooting probabilities for a basketball player who has the properties that if she makes a shot, then she makes the next one with probability .85, but if she misses a shot, then she makes the next one with probability .6.

20. A fisherman has either good luck or poor luck each time he goes fishing. He notices that if he has good luck one time, then he has good luck the next time with probability .6 and if he has poor luck one time, then he has good luck the next time with probability .8. What fraction of the time in the long run does the fisherman have good luck?

21. How often (in the long run) does our not-so-enthusiastic student attend class on Friday afternoon? Use the transition matrix

$$\mathbf{P} = \begin{matrix} \text{Absent} \\ \text{Present} \end{matrix} \overset{\begin{matrix} \text{Absent} & \text{Present} \end{matrix}}{\begin{bmatrix} .3 & .7 \\ .6 & .4 \end{bmatrix}}$$

22. The matrices shown below are transition matrices for various Markov chains. Two of the chains are regular. Which ones are regular?

$$(a)\ \begin{bmatrix} .2 & 0 & .8 \\ .1 & .5 & .4 \\ .4 & .6 & 0 \end{bmatrix} \quad (b)\ \begin{bmatrix} .2 & 0 & .8 \\ .1 & .5 & .4 \\ .4 & 0 & .6 \end{bmatrix} \quad (c)\ \begin{bmatrix} 0 & 0 & 1 \\ .1 & .4 & .5 \\ .4 & .6 & 0 \end{bmatrix} \quad (d)\ \begin{bmatrix} .1 & .5 & .4 \\ 0 & 1 & 0 \\ .4 & .6 & 0 \end{bmatrix}$$

23. Consider the situation described in Example 8.10.
   (*a*) Determine $\mathbf{P}^4$ and $\mathbf{P}^8$.
   (*b*) What is the largest difference between elements of the first column of $\mathbf{P}^4$? Of $\mathbf{P}^8$?
   (*c*) Find the vector of stable probabilities for this situation.
   (*d*) In which state is the mouse most likely to be in the long run?
24. Consider a mouse moving in a set of compartments connected as shown in Figure 8.13. Suppose that the movements of the mouse can be modeled as a Markov chain. Assume that the mouse is twice as likely to move as not and that if it moves, then it is equally likely to move to any adjacent compartment. (See also Example 8.10.) In what compartment is the mouse most likely to be in the long run, and what is the probability that the mouse is in that compartment?
25. Two four-state Markov chains have the transition matrices shown below.

$$\mathbf{P}_1 = \begin{bmatrix} 0 & 1 & 0 & 0 \\ 0 & 0 & 1 & 0 \\ 0 & 0 & 0 & 1 \\ .5 & .5 & 0 & 0 \end{bmatrix} \quad \mathbf{P}_2 = \begin{bmatrix} 0 & 1 & 0 & 0 \\ 0 & 0 & 1 & 0 \\ 0 & 0 & 0 & 1 \\ .5 & 0 & 0 & .5 \end{bmatrix}$$

   (*a*) Find the transition diagram for each Markov chain.
   (*b*) In each case find the smallest integer *k* for which the *k*th power of the transition matrix has only positive entries.

FIGURE 8.13

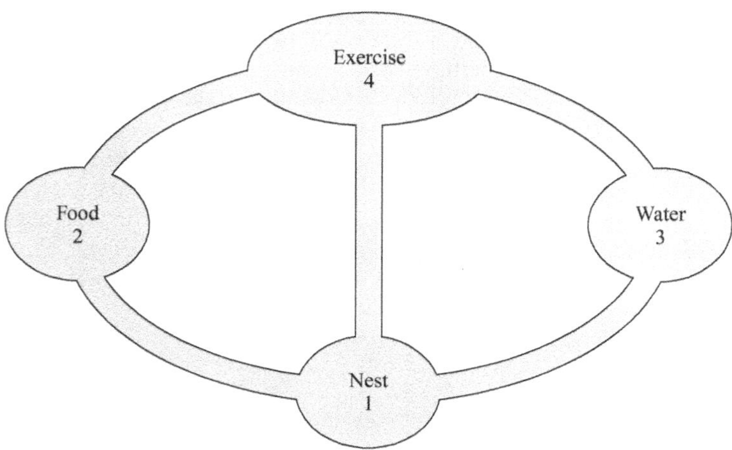

26. A four-state Markov chain has the transition matrix

$$\mathbf{P} = \begin{bmatrix} 0 & 1 & 0 & 0 \\ 0 & 0 & 1 & 0 \\ 0 & 0 & 0 & 1 \\ .5 & 0 & .5 & 0 \end{bmatrix}$$

(*a*) Find the transition diagram for this Markov chain.
(*b*) Show that there is a positive probability of making a transition from state 1 to state 3 in two steps, in four steps, in six steps, in eight steps, etc.
(*c*) Show that it is impossible to go from state 1 to state 3 in any odd number of steps.

27. A five-state Markov chain has the transition matrix **P**.

$$\mathbf{P} = \begin{bmatrix} 0 & 1 & 0 & 0 & 0 \\ 0 & 0 & 1 & 0 & 0 \\ 0 & 0 & 0 & 1 & 0 \\ 0 & 0 & 0 & 0 & 1 \\ x & y & 0 & z & 0 \end{bmatrix}$$

Show that for any nonnegative values of x, y, and z the eight-step transition matrix $\mathbf{P}(8) = \mathbf{P}^8$ has at least one zero entry.

28. With the transition matrix **P** of Exercise 27, find values of x, y, and z for which the 16th power of the matrix **P** has at least one zero and the 17th power contains only positive entries. (*Hint*: Work Exercises 25 and 26 first.)

29. Let the transition matrix for a regular Markov chain be

$$\mathbf{P} = \begin{bmatrix} a & 1-a \\ b & 1-b \end{bmatrix}$$

where $0 < a < 1$ and $0 < b < 1$. Show that the vector of stable probabilities is

$$\begin{bmatrix} \dfrac{b}{1+b-a} & \dfrac{1-a}{1+b-a} \end{bmatrix}$$

30. Use the result of Exercise 29 to compute the stable probabilities for the matrix

$$\mathbf{P} = \begin{bmatrix} \frac{3}{4} & \frac{1}{4} \\ \frac{1}{3} & \frac{2}{3} \end{bmatrix}$$

31. Find the vector of stable probabilities for the Markov chain with the transition matrix

$$\mathbf{P} = \begin{bmatrix} 0 & 1 \\ b & 1-b \end{bmatrix} \qquad 0 < b < 1$$

32. Find the vector of stable probabilities for the Markov chain with transition matrix

$$\mathbf{P} = \begin{bmatrix} 0 & 1 & 0 \\ 0 & 0 & 1 \\ a & b & 1-a-b \end{bmatrix}$$

where $0 < a < 1$, $0 < b < 1$, and $a + b < 1$.

33. A Markov chain has the transition matrix $\mathbf{P}$ and the initial vector $\mathbf{X}_0$ shown below. If $\mathbf{X}_2 = [.416 \quad .484 \quad .1]$, find a.

$$\mathbf{P} = \begin{bmatrix} 0 & .8 & .2 \\ .8 & .2 & 0 \\ 1 & 0 & 0 \end{bmatrix} \qquad \mathbf{X}_0 = [.4 \quad a \quad .6 - a]$$

34. A successful anesthesiologist purchases a new car every year, and for many years she has chosen among Audi, BMW, and Mercedes. If she chooses an Audi one year, then the next year she never chooses a BMW and she is 3 times as likely to choose another Audi as to choose a Mercedes. If she chooses a BMW one year, then she never chooses a Mercedes the next year and she is equally likely to choose another BMW as an Audi, and if she chooses a Mercedes one year, then she never chooses an Audi the next year and is three times as likely to choose another Mercedes as a BMW. Assuming that her choices can be modeled as a Markov chain, find the long-run probability that she drives a BMW.

35. A regular Markov chain has the transition matrix $\mathbf{P}$ shown below.

$$\mathbf{P} = \begin{bmatrix} 0 & .6 & .4 \\ .2 & .4 & .4 \\ 0 & .4 & .6 \end{bmatrix}$$

(*a*) Find the stable vector for $\mathbf{P}$.

(*b*) Suppose state 2 is the initial state and find the smallest number k of transitions for which the state vector is within 4 percent of the stable vector for $\mathbf{P}$. That is, each coordinate of the state vector is within 4 percent of the corresponding coordinate of the stable vector. (If w is a coordinate of the stable vector, then the corresponding coordinate of the state vector after k transitions is in the interval $(.96w,\ 1.04w)$.)

36. Consider a situation similar to that of Exercise 24. In this case assume that the mouse is twice as likely to remain in the same compartment as to move, and if it moves, then it is equally likely to move to any adjacent compartment. Determine the long-run behavior of the state vectors.

8.4 ABSORBING MARKOV CHAINS

The behavior of a Markov chain which is not regular can differ from that of a regular chain in several ways. For a regular chain, some power of the transition matrix contains only positive entries, and consequently it is possible to make transitions between *any* two states in some number of steps. One way in which this can fail is for there to be a state, or a subset of states, from which transitions are impossible. This is illustrated in the next example.

Example 8.21 Consider the arrangement of connected compartments introduced in Example 8.10 (and shown in Figure 8.12), and suppose that the mouse can enter compartment 3 but cannot leave it. This can be accomplished, e.g., by making one-way doors into compartment 3.

Problem If the transitions are governed by the assumptions of Example 8.10, find the transition matrix of the resulting Markov chain.

Solution Since the transitions from compartments 1, 2, and 4 are unaffected by making it impossible to leave compartment 3, rows 1, 2, and 4 of the transition matrix **P** are as in Example 8.10. The third row must be changed to represent the fact that the only possible transition from state 3 is back to state 3. We have

$$\mathbf{P} = \begin{bmatrix} \frac{2}{3} & \frac{1}{6} & \frac{1}{6} & 0 \\ \frac{1}{9} & \frac{2}{3} & \frac{1}{9} & \frac{1}{9} \\ 0 & 0 & 1 & 0 \\ 0 & \frac{1}{3} & 0 & \frac{2}{3} \end{bmatrix}$$

■

The situation illustrated in Example 8.21 is typical of a type of Markov chain called an *absorbing Markov chain*. To define absorbing Markov chains, we introduce the notion of an *absorbing state*. Heuristically, an absorbing state is a state which it is impossible to leave. We give a precise definition using the concept of a unit vector.

The *i*th unit vector is a probability vector with a 1 as the *i*th coordinate.

Absorbing States

The *i*th state of a Markov chain is said to be an *absorbing state* if $p_{ii} = 1$ and $p_{ij} = 0$ for $j \neq i$. That is, state *i* is absorbing if the *i*th row of the transition matrix is the *i*th unit vector.

In the Markov chain whose transition matrix is shown below, the second state is absorbing. Note, however, that the fifth state is not absorbing. Even though the fifth row contains a single 1, it is not in the fifth column, so the fifth row is not the fifth unit vector.

$$\begin{bmatrix} \frac{1}{3} & 0 & \frac{1}{3} & 0 & \frac{1}{3} \\ 0 & 1 & 0 & 0 & 0 \\ \frac{1}{2} & 0 & \frac{1}{2} & 0 & 0 \\ \frac{1}{10} & \frac{2}{10} & \frac{3}{10} & \frac{4}{10} & 0 \\ 0 & 0 & 0 & 1 & 0 \end{bmatrix} \tag{8.3}$$

Absorbing chains must have absorbing states, but that is not enough. It must also be possible to go from nonabsorbing states to absorbing states.

Absorbing Markov Chain

A Markov chain is said to be *absorbing* if

(*a*) There is at least one absorbing state, and

(*b*) For every nonabsorbing state i there is some absorbing state j and a positive integer k such that the probability of a transition from state i to state j in k steps is positive.

Notice that there are two parts to the definition of an absorbing chain. For a chain to be absorbing, *both* conditions must hold. For example, the transition matrix (8.3) is the transition matrix of an absorbing chain. Indeed, condition (*a*) is satisfied since the second state is absorbing, and condition (*b*) is satisfied since transitions can occur from each of the other states to state 2; that is,

$$p_{12}(3) > 0 \qquad p_{32}(4) > 0 \qquad p_{42} > 0 \qquad p_{52}(2) > 0$$

To verify this, it is convenient to use the technique introduced at the end of Section 8.3 or the transition diagram for the chain.

A chain is not absorbing if *either* of the conditions of the definition fails to hold. For instance, the transition matrix shown below is not the transition matrix for an absorbing Markov chain since condition (*b*) fails to hold for states 3 and 4. State 2 is the only absorbing state, and the probability of a transition in any number of steps from either state 3 or state 4 to state 2 is zero.

$$\begin{bmatrix} \frac{1}{2} & \frac{1}{2} & 0 & 0 \\ 0 & 1 & 0 & 0 \\ 0 & 0 & \frac{1}{3} & \frac{2}{3} \\ 0 & 0 & \frac{3}{5} & \frac{2}{5} \end{bmatrix}$$

The analysis of situations modeled by absorbing Markov chains will be easier if the transition matrices are written in a particular form. Since the absorbing states play a special role, it is conventional to collect them together and to label them as states 1 through k—we suppose that there are k absorbing states. The remaining states are labeled $k+1$ through N. In relabeling states, it is important to note that both the rows and columns of the transition matrix are altered. A transition matrix with the states labeled in this way is said to be in *canonical form*. A technique for writing a transition matrix in canonical form is illustrated in the next example.

Example 8.22 Matrix $\mathbf{P}$ is the transition matrix of a Markov chain.

$$\mathbf{P} = \begin{bmatrix} \frac{1}{3} & 0 & \frac{2}{3} \\ 0 & 1 & 0 \\ 0 & \frac{1}{2} & \frac{1}{2} \end{bmatrix}$$

Problem Show that this is the transition matrix of an absorbing chain, and write the matrix in canonical form.

Solution State 2 is an absorbing state, so condition (a) of the definition of an absorbing Markov chain is satisfied. Also $p_{32} > 0$ and $p_{12}(2) > 0$, so condition (b) is satisfied. Therefore, $\mathbf{P}$ is the transition matrix of an absorbing Markov chain.

To write the transition matrix in canonical form, we relabel the states so that absorbing states are listed first. In this example the only absorbing state is state 2. We relabel the states so that the original state 2 is relabeled as state 1. The labels assigned to the remaining states are not important. We relabel the states as follows:

Old label	1	2	3
New label	2	1	3

After the states are relabeled, the transition matrix changes to reflect the new labels. For instance, the old (1, 3) entry $p_{13} = \frac{2}{3}$ becomes the new (2, 3) entry; the old (2, 2) entry $p_{22} = 1$ becomes the new (1, 1) entry, and so on. The transition matrix written in canonical form is

$$\begin{array}{c} \\ 2 \\ 1 \\ 3 \end{array} \begin{array}{c} \begin{array}{ccc} 2 & 1 & 3 \end{array} \\ \begin{bmatrix} 1 & 0 & 0 \\ 0 & \frac{1}{3} & \frac{2}{3} \\ \frac{1}{2} & 0 & \frac{1}{2} \end{bmatrix} \end{array}$$

The labels beside the rows and above the columns are the old state labels. Thus the first row corresponds to the relabeled state 1, which is state 2 in terms of the original transition matrix. ■

In Example 8.22 we noted the original state labels along the rows and columns of the canonical form. These labels are useful both in forming the canonical form and in answering questions by using the canonical form. Consequently, we frequently use such labels in the pages that follow.

Example 8.23 Show that a transition matrix may have more than one canonical form by using different relabelings to find two canonical forms for the matrix in Example 8.21.

Solution The transition matrix of Example 8.21 is

$$\mathbf{P} = \begin{bmatrix} \frac{2}{3} & \frac{1}{6} & \frac{1}{6} & 0 \\ \frac{1}{9} & \frac{2}{3} & \frac{1}{9} & \frac{1}{9} \\ 0 & 0 & 1 & 0 \\ 0 & \frac{1}{3} & 0 & \frac{2}{3} \end{bmatrix}$$

The state relabeling

Old label	1	2	3	4
New label	3	2	1	4

results in the canonical form

$$\begin{array}{c} \\ 3 \\ 2 \\ 1 \\ 4 \end{array} \begin{array}{c} \begin{array}{cccc} 3 & 2 & 1 & 4 \end{array} \\ \begin{bmatrix} 1 & 0 & 0 & 0 \\ \frac{1}{9} & \frac{2}{3} & \frac{1}{9} & \frac{1}{9} \\ \frac{1}{6} & \frac{1}{6} & \frac{2}{3} & 0 \\ 0 & \frac{1}{3} & 0 & \frac{2}{3} \end{bmatrix} \end{array}$$

On the other hand, the state relabeling

Old label	1	2	3	4
New label	4	3	1	2

results in the canonical form

$$\begin{array}{c} \\ 3 \\ 4 \\ 2 \\ 1 \end{array} \begin{array}{c} \begin{array}{cccc} 3 & 4 & 2 & 1 \end{array} \\ \begin{bmatrix} 1 & 0 & 0 & 0 \\ 0 & \frac{2}{3} & \frac{1}{3} & 0 \\ \frac{1}{9} & \frac{1}{9} & \frac{2}{3} & \frac{1}{9} \\ \frac{1}{6} & 0 & \frac{1}{6} & \frac{2}{3} \end{bmatrix} \end{array} \tag{8.4}$$

■

We conclude from Example 8.23 that the entries in a canonical form are not necessarily uniquely defined. However, the form of the matrix is unique. In particular, when written in canonical form, the transition matrix of an absorbing chain has a $k \times k$ identity matrix in the upper left-hand corner. Also the submatrix in the upper right-hand corer consists of all zeros. It is conventional to identify the submatrices in $\mathbf{P}$ as follows:

$$\mathbf{P} = \begin{bmatrix} \mathbf{I} & \mathbf{O} \\ \mathbf{R} & \mathbf{Q} \end{bmatrix} \tag{8.5}$$

Here $\mathbf{I}$ is a $k \times k$ identity matrix, $\mathbf{O}$ is a matrix with all zeros, and $\mathbf{R}$ and $\mathbf{Q}$ consist of transition probabilities which correspond to transitions which lead directly to absorption, $\mathbf{R}$, and transitions which do not lead directly to absorption, $\mathbf{Q}$.

In Example 8.23 matrix (8.4) is in the form shown in (8.5), with a 1×1 identity matrix $\mathbf{I} = [1]$ and with

$$\mathbf{R} = \begin{bmatrix} 0 \\ \frac{1}{9} \\ \frac{1}{6} \end{bmatrix} \quad \text{and} \quad \mathbf{Q} = \begin{matrix} & \begin{matrix} 4 & 2 & 1 \end{matrix} \\ \begin{matrix} 4 \\ 2 \\ 1 \end{matrix} & \begin{bmatrix} \frac{2}{3} & \frac{1}{3} & 0 \\ \frac{1}{9} & \frac{2}{3} & \frac{1}{9} \\ 0 & \frac{1}{6} & \frac{2}{3} \end{bmatrix} \end{matrix} \tag{8.6}$$

In this example $N - k = 4 - 1 = 3$.

The matrix $\mathbf{Q}$ is always square, and in fact, for an identity matrix $\mathbf{I}$ the same size as $\mathbf{Q}$, the matrix $\mathbf{I} - \mathbf{Q}$ is invertible.

Fundamental Matrix

Consider an absorbing Markov chain whose transition matrix is written in canonical form as (8.5). The matrix $\mathbf{N} = (\mathbf{I} - \mathbf{Q})^{-1}$ is called the *fundamental matrix* for the absorbing Markov chain. It is understood that since $\mathbf{Q}$ is $(N - k) \times (N - k)$, the identity matrix in the expression $\mathbf{I} - \mathbf{Q}$ must be the same size, and so is $\mathbf{N}$.

The computation of $\mathbf{N}$ is illustrated in the next example.

Example 8.24 An absorbing Markov chain has the transition matrix

$$\begin{bmatrix} 1 & 0 & 0 & 0 \\ 0 & 1 & 0 & 0 \\ \frac{1}{3} & 0 & \frac{2}{3} & 0 \\ 0 & \frac{1}{5} & \frac{2}{5} & \frac{2}{5} \end{bmatrix} \tag{8.7}$$

Problem Find the fundamental matrix.

Solution The transition matrix is already written in canonical form. The matrix $\mathbf{Q}$ is

$$\mathbf{Q} = \begin{bmatrix} \frac{2}{3} & 0 \\ \frac{2}{5} & \frac{2}{5} \end{bmatrix}$$

and therefore

$$\mathbf{I} - \mathbf{Q} = \begin{bmatrix} 1 & 0 \\ 0 & 1 \end{bmatrix} - \begin{bmatrix} \frac{2}{3} & 0 \\ \frac{2}{5} & \frac{2}{5} \end{bmatrix} = \begin{bmatrix} \frac{1}{3} & 0 \\ -\frac{2}{5} & \frac{3}{5} \end{bmatrix}$$

We determine $(\mathbf{I} - \mathbf{Q})^{-1} = \mathbf{N}$ by using the techniques introduced in Chapter 6. We have

$$\mathbf{N} = \begin{bmatrix} 3 & 0 \\ 2 & \frac{5}{3} \end{bmatrix}$$

■

Example 8.25 Find the fundamental matrix for the absorbing Markov chain defined in Example 8.21.

Solution The transition matrix for Example 8.21 is written in canonical form in (8.4). The matrix $\mathbf{Q}$ was determined in (8.6) to be

$$\mathbf{Q} = \begin{bmatrix} \frac{2}{3} & \frac{1}{3} & 0 \\ \frac{1}{9} & \frac{2}{3} & \frac{1}{9} \\ 0 & \frac{1}{6} & \frac{2}{3} \end{bmatrix}$$

Therefore,

$$\mathbf{I} - \mathbf{Q} = \begin{bmatrix} 1 & 0 & 0 \\ 0 & 1 & 0 \\ 0 & 0 & 1 \end{bmatrix} - \begin{bmatrix} \frac{2}{3} & \frac{1}{3} & 0 \\ \frac{1}{9} & \frac{2}{3} & \frac{1}{9} \\ 0 & \frac{1}{6} & \frac{2}{3} \end{bmatrix} = \begin{bmatrix} \frac{1}{3} & -\frac{1}{3} & 0 \\ -\frac{1}{9} & \frac{1}{3} & -\frac{1}{9} \\ 0 & -\frac{1}{6} & \frac{1}{3} \end{bmatrix}$$

We use the techniques of Chapter 6 to find

$$\mathbf{N} = (\mathbf{I} - \mathbf{Q})^{-1} = \begin{bmatrix} 5 & 6 & 2 \\ 2 & 6 & 2 \\ 1 & 3 & 4 \end{bmatrix}$$

■

Let us now consider the long-run behavior of an absorbing Markov chain. Since there is a positive probability that the system moves from each nonabsorbing state to some absorbing state in some number of transitions, we expect that sooner or later it reaches an absorbing state. Of course, once the system reaches an absorbing state, it does not leave it. However, this is a stochastic process, and we do not know exactly when the system will reach an absorbing state. As usual, in such circumstances we turn to the notion of expected value to help us describe the behavior of the process. It turns out that the fundamental matrix is very useful in this respect. In fact, it fully deserves its name!

Assume for the moment that we are given an absorbing Markov chain whose transition matrix $\mathbf{P}$ is written in canonical form (8.5), with absorbing states numbered 1 through k and nonabsorbing states numbered $k+1$ through N. We refer to state $k+1$ as the first nonabsorbing state, state $k+2$ as the second nonabsorbing state, etc. The rows and columns of $\mathbf{Q}$ are identified with nonabsorbing states in order. This identification carries over to the fundamental matrix $\mathbf{N}$.

Our results are contained in the following theorem, stated here without proof.

Theorem on the Interpretation of the Fundamental Matrix

The (i, j) entry in the fundamental matrix $\mathbf{N}$ gives the expected number of times that a system which begins in the ith nonabsorbing state will be in the jth nonabsorbing state before it reaches an absorbing state. The sum of the entries in the ith row of $\mathbf{N}$ gives the expected number of transitions of a system which begins in the ith nonabsorbing state and continues until it first reaches an absorbing state.

Example 8.26 (Continuation of Example 8.24) An absorbing Markov chain whose transition matrix is (8.7) is initially in state 3, the first nonabsorbing state.

Problem Find the expected number of transitions before the system first reaches an absorbing state.

Solution The fundamental matrix is $\mathbf{N} = \begin{bmatrix} 3 & 0 \\ 2 & \frac{5}{3} \end{bmatrix}$. The expected number of times the system is in state 3 (the first nonabsorbing state) before absorption is 3, and the expected number of times it is in state 4 (the second nonabsorbing state) is 0. Therefore, the expected number of transitions before the system reaches an absorbing state is $3 + 0 = 3$. ■

If we are given an absorbing Markov chain whose transition matrix is not in canonical form, the methods described above can still be applied. It is only necessary to relabel the states, so that the transition matrix is in canonical form, and then to consistently attach original state labels to the appropriate rows and columns of **Q** and **N**. We illustrate this technique in the following examples.

Example 8.27 (Continuation of Example 8.21) An arrangement of connected compartments is described in Example 8.21. A mouse is released in compartment 2.

Problem Find the expected number of transitions before the mouse first reaches compartment 3, the compartment with the one-way doors.

Solution We relabel the states as follows:

Old label	1	2	3	4
New label	4	3	1	2

The resulting fundamental matrix (computed in Example 8.25) is

$$\mathbf{N} = \begin{bmatrix} 5 & 6 & 2 \\ 2 & 6 & 2 \\ 1 & 3 & 4 \end{bmatrix}$$

Attaching the original state labels to the appropriate rows and columns of **N** [see labeling in (8.6)], we have

$$\mathbf{N} = \begin{array}{c} \\ 4 \\ 2 \\ 1 \end{array} \begin{array}{c} \begin{array}{ccc} 4 & 2 & 1 \end{array} \\ \begin{bmatrix} 5 & 6 & 2 \\ 2 & 6 & 2 \\ 1 & 3 & 4 \end{bmatrix} \end{array}$$

Since the mouse was released in compartment 2, we look for old state label 2. We see that it is attached to the second row of **N**. Thus, if the system is initially in old state 2, then the expected number of times the mouse occupies the first nonabsorbing state (old state 4) before reaching an absorbing state is 2. The expected numbers of times the mouse occupies the second and third nonabsorbing states (old states 2 and 1) are 6 and 2, respectively. Therefore, the expected total number of transitions before the mouse first reaches an absorbing state is

$$2 + 6 + 2 = 10$$

Thus, in terms of the original situation, if the mouse begins in compartment 2, then the expected number of transitions before the mouse first reaches compartment 3, the one with the one-way doors, is 10. Naturally, in any specific case, the number of transitions may be more or less than 10. This number is simply an average over many repetitions of the experiment. ■

The method of Example 8.27 can also be used to answer this question: If the mouse begins in compartment 2 of the original maze (no one-way doors), what is the expected number of transitions before the mouse *first reaches compartment 3*? We simply imagine the original maze to be altered to one with a oneway door on compartment 3. The resulting system is an absorbing Markov chain (as in Example 8.21), and the expected number of transitions before absorption, given that the mouse began in compartment 2, provides an answer to the question.

The fundamental matrix can also be used to obtain other types of information about the system. For example, if the system has a single absorbing state, then the system will eventually reach that state, but if there is more than one absorbing state, then it may in general be absorbed in any one of them. Given the state in which the system begins, the likelihood that it will be absorbed in various absorbing states can be computed by using the fundamental matrix. A method to carry out the computation is described in Exercise 25.

Exercises for Section 8.4

1. A transition matrix of a Markov chain is given as

$$\begin{bmatrix} 0 & .5 & .5 \\ 0 & 1 & 0 \\ .8 & 0 & .2 \end{bmatrix}$$

   (*a*) Determine whether it is the transition matrix of an absorbing Markov chain.
   (*b*) If not, which condition of the definition of an absorbing Markov chain is violated?
   (*c*) If so, determine for each nonabsorbing state the *minimum* number of transitions necessary to reach some absorbing state.

For Exercises 2 through 6, repeat Exercise 1 with the given transition matrix.

2. $\begin{bmatrix} .5 & 0 & .5 \\ 0 & 1 & 0 \\ .8 & 0 & .2 \end{bmatrix}$

3. $\begin{bmatrix} 1 & 0 & 0 & 0 \\ 0 & .2 & .2 & .6 \\ 0 & 0 & 1 & 0 \\ 0 & .5 & 0 & .5 \end{bmatrix}$

4. $\begin{bmatrix} 0 & .5 & .5 & 0 \\ 0 & 1 & 0 & 0 \\ 0 & 0 & 1 & 0 \\ 0 & 0 & 0 & 1 \end{bmatrix}$

5. $\begin{bmatrix} 1 & 0 & 0 & 0 \\ 0 & 1 & 0 & 0 \\ 0 & 0 & .8 & .2 \\ 0 & 0 & 1 & 0 \end{bmatrix}$

6. $\begin{bmatrix} 1 & 0 & 0 & 0 \\ \frac{1}{3} & 0 & \frac{2}{3} & 0 \\ 0 & 1 & 0 & 0 \\ 0 & 0 & 1 & 0 \end{bmatrix}$

7. For the transition matrix of Example 8.21, find the canonical form which corresponds to this relabeling:

Old label	1	2	3	4
New label	2	3	1	4

8. For the transition matrix of Example 8.21, find the canonical form which corresponds to this relabeling:

Old label	1	2	3	4
New label	2	4	1	3

9. Find the canonical form for the transition matrix (8.3) which corresponds to this relabeling:

Old label	1	2	3	4	5
New label	2	1	3	4	5

10. Repeat Exercise 9 for this relabeling:

Old label	1	2	3	4	5
New label	5	1	2	3	4

11. Write the transition matrix

$$\begin{bmatrix} 0 & \frac{1}{2} & \frac{1}{2} \\ 0 & 1 & 0 \\ \frac{1}{3} & \frac{1}{3} & \frac{1}{3} \end{bmatrix}$$

in canonical form, and find the associated fundamental matrix.

For Exercises 12 through 16, repeat Exercise 11 for the given transition matrix.

12. $\begin{bmatrix} 0 & 1 & 0 \\ 0 & 1 & 0 \\ .4 & 0 & .6 \end{bmatrix}$

13. $\begin{bmatrix} 0 & \frac{1}{2} & 0 & \frac{1}{2} \\ 0 & 1 & 0 & 0 \\ \frac{1}{4} & 0 & \frac{1}{2} & \frac{1}{4} \\ 0 & 0 & 0 & 1 \end{bmatrix}$

14. $\begin{bmatrix} \frac{1}{3} & \frac{2}{3} & 0 & 0 \\ 0 & \frac{1}{2} & \frac{1}{2} & 0 \\ 0 & 0 & 1 & 0 \\ 1 & 0 & 0 & 0 \end{bmatrix}$

15. $\begin{bmatrix} \frac{1}{2} & 0 & \frac{1}{4} & \frac{1}{4} \\ 1 & 0 & 0 & 0 \\ 0 & 1 & 0 & 0 \\ 0 & 0 & 0 & 1 \end{bmatrix}$

16. $\begin{bmatrix} .4 & 0 & .4 & .2 \\ 0 & 0 & 0 & 1 \\ 0 & 0 & 0 & 1 \\ 0 & 0 & 0 & 1 \end{bmatrix}$

17. Suppose that the absorbing Markov chain whose transition matrix is (8.7) is initially in state 4. Find the expected number of transitions before it reaches an absorbing state. (*Hint*: Use Example 8.24.)

18. In the situation described in Example 8.21, suppose the mouse begins in compartment 1.
    (*a*) Find the expected number of times the mouse is in compartment 2 before it first reaches compartment 3.
    (*b*) Find the expected total number of transitions before the mouse first reaches compartment 3.

19. Consider the arrangement of compartments introduced in Example 8.10. If the mouse begins in the nest, find the expected number of transitions before the mouse first reaches the compartment with the exercise device.

20. Consider the employment classification situation described in Exercise 19, Section 8.1. If a person is self-employed now, what is the expected number of years before she is first employed in small business?

21. A successful anesthesiologist purchases a new car every year, and for many years she has chosen among Audi, BMW, and Mercedes. If she chooses an Audi one year, then the next year she never chooses a Mercedes and she is equally likely to choose another Audi as to choose a BMW. If she chooses a BMW one year, then she is twice as likely to choose another BMW as each of the other makes, and if she chooses a Mercedes one year, then she is twice as likely to choose another Mercedes as each of the other makes. Assuming that her choices can be modeled as a Markov chain, if she chooses an Audi one year, find the expected number of years before she first purchases a Mercedes.

22. A game is played on the board pictured in Figure 8.14. On each play a marker either remains in place or moves to an adjacent space on the board. On each

FIGURE 8.14

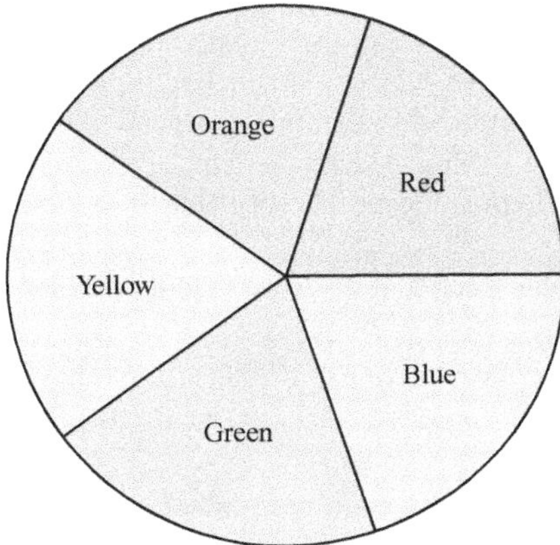

play the marker is twice as likely to move as to remain in place, and if it moves, it is twice as likely to move clockwise as counterclockwise. If the marker is initially in the red space, find the expected number of plays before the marker first reaches the green space.

23. An absorbing Markov chain has the transition matrix shown below. If the system is initially in state 3, find the expected number of transitions before it first reaches an absorbing state.

$$\begin{bmatrix} .5 & 0 & 0 & 0 & .5 & 0 \\ 0 & 1 & 0 & 0 & 0 & 0 \\ .2 & 0 & .2 & .2 & .2 & .2 \\ 0 & .4 & .2 & .2 & 0 & .2 \\ 0 & 0 & 0 & 0 & 1 & 0 \\ 1 & 0 & 0 & 0 & 0 & 0 \end{bmatrix}$$

24. A Markov chain has the transition matrix shown below. If it begins in state 5, find the expected number of transitions before it first reaches state 3.

$$\begin{bmatrix} 0 & 1 & 0 & 0 & 0 & 0 \\ 0 & 0 & 1 & 0 & 0 & 0 \\ 0 & 0 & 0 & 1 & 0 & 0 \\ 0 & 0 & 0 & 0 & 1 & 0 \\ 0 & 0 & 0 & 0 & 0 & 1 \\ .5 & 0 & 0 & 0 & .5 & 0 \end{bmatrix}$$

25. The matrix $\mathbf{R}$ in the canonical form $\begin{bmatrix} \mathbf{I} & \mathbf{O} \\ \mathbf{R} & \mathbf{Q} \end{bmatrix}$ is an $(N-k) \times k$ matrix. Thus, the matrix product $\mathbf{NR}$ is also $(N-k) \times k$. Each row of $\mathbf{NR}$ is associated with a nonabsorbing state, and each column is associated with an absorbing state. Each row of $\mathbf{NR}$ is a probability vector. The (i, j) entry of $\mathbf{NR}$ is the probability that if the system begins in the ith nonabsorbing state, it will be absorbed in the jth absorbing state.
   (*a*) Suppose that the Markov chain with transition matrix (8.7) begins in the first nonabsorbing state. What is the probability that it is absorbed in the first absorbing state?
   (*b*) Suppose that this Markov chain begins in the second nonabsorbing state. What is the probability that it is absorbed in the first absorbing state?

26. Consider the absorbing Markov chain of Exercise 23. If the system is initially in state 3, find the probability that it is absorbed in state 2. (*Hint*: Use Exercise 25.)

27. Let a be a number such that $0 < a < 1$, and consider the transition matrix

$$\mathbf{P} = \begin{bmatrix} 1 & 0 \\ a & 1-a \end{bmatrix}$$

Show that if the Markov chain with transition matrix $\mathbf{P}$ starts in state 2, then the expected number of times it is in state 2 before it is absorbed is $1/a$.

28. Let a and b be positive numbers such that $0 < a+b < 1$, and consider the transition matrix

$$\mathbf{P} = \begin{bmatrix} 1 & 0 & 0 \\ 0 & 1 & 0 \\ a & b & 1-a-b \end{bmatrix}$$

Suppose the Markov chain with transition matrix **P** starts in state 3. Find the expected number of moves before it is absorbed, and find the probability it is absorbed in state 1.

29. A regular Markov chain has the transition matrix shown below. If the system is initially in state 2,
    (*a*) find the expected number of visits to state 1 before it first reaches state 3
    (*b*) find the expected number of transitions before it first reaches state 3

$$\begin{bmatrix} 0 & 1 & 0 \\ .50 & 0 & .50 \\ .25 & .25 & .50 \end{bmatrix}$$

30. A regular Markov chain has the transition matrix shown below. If the system is initially in state 3,
    (*a*) find the expected number of visits to state 1 before it first reaches state 2
    (*b*) find the expected number of transitions before it first reaches state 2

$$\begin{bmatrix} .50 & .50 & 0 \\ .20 & .50 & .30 \\ .40 & .20 & .40 \end{bmatrix}$$

31. A regular Markov chain has the transition matrix shown below. If the system is initially in state 2,
    (*a*) find the expected number of visits to state 3 before it first reaches state 4
    (*b*) find the expected number of transitions before it first reaches state 4

$$\begin{bmatrix} .25 & .25 & .50 & 0 \\ 0 & .25 & .50 & .25 \\ .25 & .25 & .50 & 0 \\ .25 & 0 & .50 & .25 \end{bmatrix}$$

32. For the Markov chain of Exercise 31, if the system is initially in state 3, find the probability that it is in state 1 before first reaching state 4.
    (*Hint:* Use Exercise 25.)

8.5 A MARKOV CHAIN MODEL FOR PLANT SUCCESSION

In many areas in temperate climates there is a natural progression of vegetation as time passes: from open meadow grasslands through brush and shrubs to young forests and eventually to mature forests. Even in the absence of interference by humans, there are events which significantly alter, and sometimes reverse, this progression. Such an event, and a very important one, is fire. Fires arise naturally through lightning strikes and are an important contributor to the perpetuation of grasslands. The natural progression of vegetation, and especially the occurrence of fires, is influenced by random events and therefore can be modeled by using stochastic processes. In addition to fires, other random events influencing vegetation include the introduction of seeds of plants not currently represented, the amount and timing of rainfall, the feeding habits of wildlife, and similar natural events. Under certain circumstances, Markov chains are appropriate as models for such situations.

To construct a Markov chain model for plant succession, we focus on a single area which we suppose is small enough that it can be classified into exactly one of four states. The state is determined by the dominant vegetation form: grassland (G), brush and shrubs (B), young forest (YF), and mature forest (MF). We suppose that the area is observed every decade and that the state or character of the area is noted at each observation. For the moment we consider the progression from state to state in the absence of fire. We assume that the period between observations is such that progression proceeds at most one step between successive observations. That is, if the area is grassland at one observation, then at the next observation it is either grassland or brush and shrubs, and so on for other plant types. We also assume that once an area becomes a mature forest, it remains so throughout the time of observation.

Continuing to consider the situation in the absence of fires, suppose the data support the assumption that one-step (10-year) transition probabilities are as follows:

$$\begin{aligned}
&\Pr[G \mid G] = .7 \text{ and } \Pr[B \mid G] = .3\\
&\Pr[B \mid B] = .8 \text{ and } \Pr[YF \mid B] = .2\\
&\Pr[YF \mid YF] = .5 \text{ and } \Pr[MF \mid YF] = .5\\
&\Pr[MF \mid MF] = 1
\end{aligned}$$

Next, we turn to what happens when there is a fire. We consider only fires which are severe enough to cause an area to revert to grassland. Fires which have no effect on the state of the system or which cause the system to revert to a state other than grassland are not considered in this model. Suppose that in any decade a fire which reverts the area to grassland occurs with probability .1. We note that if the occurrence of such fires can be viewed as a Bernoulli process, then this assumption leads to the conclusion that the expected number of such fires is one per century. It follows that, in each decade, with probability .9 the area does not have a fire which affects the state of the system.

Combining our assumptions about the occurrence of fires and what happens in the two situations (no fire and fire), we find that between two successive observations we have the following:

Probability of transition from grassland to grassland

$$\begin{aligned}
&= \Pr[G \mid G \text{ and no fire}] \cdot \Pr[\text{no fire}] + \Pr[G \mid G \text{ and fire}] \cdot \Pr[\text{fire}]\\
&= .7(.9) + 1(.1) = .73
\end{aligned}$$

This approach also yields transition probabilities for the other possible transitions. For example,

Probability of transition from grassland to brush
$$= \Pr[B \mid G \text{ and no fire}] \cdot \Pr[\text{no fire}] + \Pr[B \mid G \text{ and fire}] \cdot \Pr[\text{fire}]$$
$$= .3(.9) + 0(.1) = .27$$

Probability of transition from brush to grassland
$$= \Pr[G \mid B \text{ and no fire}] \cdot \Pr[\text{no fire}] + \Pr[G \mid B \text{ and fire}] \cdot \Pr[\text{fire}]$$
$$= 0(.9) + 1(.1) = .1$$

Probability of transition from brush to brush
$$= \Pr[B \mid B \text{ and no fire}] \cdot \Pr[\text{no fire}] + \Pr[B \mid B \text{ and fire}] \cdot \Pr[\text{fire}]$$
$$= .8(.9) + 0(.1) = .72$$

Probability of transition from brush to young forest
$$= \Pr[YF \mid B \text{ and no fire}] \cdot \Pr[\text{no fire}] + \Pr[YF \mid B \text{ and fire}] \cdot \Pr[\text{fire}]$$
$$= .2(.9) + 0(.1) = .18$$

We now have the entries in the first two rows of the transition matrix for this Markov chain. Entries in the last two rows can be determined by using the same approach. We collect all this information in a transition matrix which describes the plant succession, including the possibility of fire. The transition matrix **P**, with states as the types of vegetation which dominate the area, is

$$\mathbf{P} = \begin{array}{c} \\ G \\ B \\ YF \\ MF \end{array} \begin{array}{c} \begin{array}{cccc} G & B & YF & MF \end{array} \\ \begin{bmatrix} .73 & .27 & 0 & 0 \\ .1 & .72 & .18 & 0 \\ .1 & 0 & .45 & .45 \\ .1 & 0 & 0 & .9 \end{bmatrix} \end{array} \tag{8.8}$$

Suppose that the succession of vegetation is described by this model and that the area is observed over many decades. What is the probability that over the long run it is grassland? Since a power of the matrix **P** has all positive entries, this is a regular Markov chain, and we can answer the question by determining the stable vector for the chain. That is, we find the unique probability vector **W** which satisfies the equation **WP** = **W**. The system of equations **WP** = **W** is

$$[w_1 \quad w_2 \quad w_3 \quad w_4] \begin{bmatrix} .73 & .27 & 0 & 0 \\ .1 & .72 & .18 & 0 \\ .1 & 0 & .45 & .45 \\ .1 & 0 & 0 & .9 \end{bmatrix} = [w_1 \quad w_2 \quad w_3 \quad w_4]$$

or

$$\begin{aligned} .27w_1 - .1w_2 - .1w_3 - .1w_4 &= 0 \\ .27w_1 - .28w_2 \qquad\qquad\qquad &= 0 \\ .18w_2 - .55w_3 \qquad\quad &= 0 \\ .45w_3 - .1w_4 &= 0 \end{aligned}$$

The solution of this system which satisfies the additional condition $w_1 + w_2 + w_3 + w_4 = 1$ is

$$\mathbf{W} = [w_1 \quad w_2 \quad w_3 \quad w_4] = [.270 \quad .261 \quad .085 \quad .384]$$

From this we conclude that over the long term we would expect the area to be grassland about 27 percent of the time, brush about 26.1 percent of the time, young forest about 8.5 percent of the time, and mature forest about 38.4 percent of the time.

Next, suppose that through intervention it is possible to control fires if a decision is made to do so. Also suppose it is social policy to control fires in mature forests, and therefore once the area reaches a mature forest, it remains in that state. In this situation the transition matrix becomes

$$\begin{array}{c} \\ G \\ B \\ YF \\ MF \end{array} \begin{array}{c} \begin{array}{cccc} G & B & YF & MF \end{array} \\ \begin{bmatrix} .73 & .27 & 0 & 0 \\ .1 & .72 & .18 & 0 \\ .1 & 0 & .45 & .45 \\ 0 & 0 & 0 & 1 \end{bmatrix} \end{array}$$

This is the transition matrix of an absorbing Markov chain.

Suppose that the area is initially a grassland. How many years before it becomes a mature forest?

To answer the question, we determine the expected number of transitions required for the system to first reach state MF, given that it began in state G. Labeling nonabsorbing states in the order G, B, YF, the matrices $\mathbf{Q}$ and $\mathbf{N}$ (as defined in Section 8.4) are

$$\mathbf{Q} = \begin{bmatrix} .73 & .27 & 0 \\ .1 & .72 & .18 \\ .1 & 0 & .45 \end{bmatrix}$$

$$\mathbf{N} = \begin{bmatrix} 7.04 & 6.79 & 2.22 \\ 3.34 & 6.79 & 2.22 \\ 1.28 & 1.23 & 2.22 \end{bmatrix}$$

From this we conclude that if the system is initially in state 1 (grassland), then the expected number of transitions until the system first reaches state 4 (mature forest) is $7.04 + 6.79 + 2.22 = 16.05$, and consequently the expected number of years is about 160.

Exercises for Section 8.5

1. Suppose the area is now grassland. Using the model developed in this section which includes the possibility of fire, the model with transition matrix $\mathbf{P}$, find the probability that it is a young forest in 40 years. Find the probability that it is grassland after 80 years.

2. As in Exercise 1, suppose the area is now grassland. Find the probability that it is a young forest in 40 years and grassland in 80 years. Find the probability that it is a young forest in 40 years and either grassland or a young forest in 80 years.
3. Suppose that a change in rainfall results in a decrease in the probability of a transition from a young forest to a mature forest. In particular, suppose that, in the absence of fire, the transition from young forest to mature forest is .4. If all other conditions remain the same as discussed in the text, find the stable vector for this model. In the long run, what percentage of the time will the area be mature forest?
4. Suppose that an increase in pollution results in a decrease in the probability of a transition from grassland to brush. In this case suppose that, in the absence of fire, the transition from grassland to brush is .2. If all other conditions remain the same as discussed in the text, find the stable vector for this model. In the long run, what percentage of the time will the area be mature forest?
5. Suppose that both the changes in rainfall and pollution described in Exercises 3 and 4 hold, but otherwise the situation is as described in the text. Find the new stable vector. What percentage of the time, in the long run, will the area be mature forest?
6. Show that the Markov chain with transition matrix **P** is a regular Markov chain.
7. Consider a situation similar to that described in this section except that the probability of a fire in any decade is .2. Find the stable probability vector in this case, and interpret each of the entries.
8. In the situation described in this section, suppose the area is initially a young forest. Find the expected number of observations before it first becomes a mature forest.
9. Suppose that there are two types of fires, minor and major. In a minor fire, mature forest remains mature forest, and young forest and brush revert to grassland. Suppose a minor fire occurs each decade with probability .05 and a major fire with probability .1. Construct a Markov chain model for this situation, and find the stable vector. Assume that the probabilities for succession in the absence of fire are as given in this section.
10. Consider the situation described in Exercise 9. If the area is initially grassland, find the expected number of years before it first becomes a mature forest.

IMPORTANT TERMS AND CONCEPTS

You should be able to describe, define, or give examples of and use each of the following:

State
Transition
Transition diagram
Transition matrix
Markov chain
State vector
Regular Markov chain
Long-run behavior
Stable probabilities
Absorbing state
Absorbing Markov chain
Canonical form
Fundamental matrix
Unit vector

REVIEW EXERCISES

1. A Markov chain has the transition matrix

$$\begin{bmatrix} .5 & .5 \\ .8 & .2 \end{bmatrix}$$

   (*a*) Find the transition diagram of this Markov chain.
   (*b*) If the system is initially in state 2, find the probability that it is in state 2 after two transitions.

2. A Markov chain has the transition matrix shown below.

$$\begin{bmatrix} 0 & 0 & 1 \\ .1 & .1 & .8 \\ .5 & .5 & 0 \end{bmatrix}$$

   (*a*) Find the transition diagram of this Markov chain.
   (*b*) If the system is initially in state 1, find the probability that it is in state 2 after two transitions. After four transitions.

3. A Markov chain has the transition diagram shown in Figure 8.15.
   (*a*) Find the transition matrix for this Markov chain.
   (*b*) If the system is initially in state 1, find the probability that it is in state 2 after two transitions.

4. A Markov chain has the transition matrix

$$\begin{bmatrix} .9 & .1 \\ .2 & .8 \end{bmatrix}$$

   (*a*) If the initial state vector is $[.3 \quad .7]$, in what state is the system most likely to be after three transitions?
   (*b*) Find the vector of stable probabilities.

5. A Markov chain has the transition matrix

$$\mathbf{P} = \begin{bmatrix} 0 & 0 & 1 \\ 1 & 0 & 0 \\ 0 & .4 & .6 \end{bmatrix}$$

   (*a*) Find the matrix $\mathbf{P}(2)$ of two-step transition probabilities.
   (*b*) If the initial state vector is $[.3 \quad 0 \quad .7]$, find the state vector after two transitions.

FIGURE 8.15

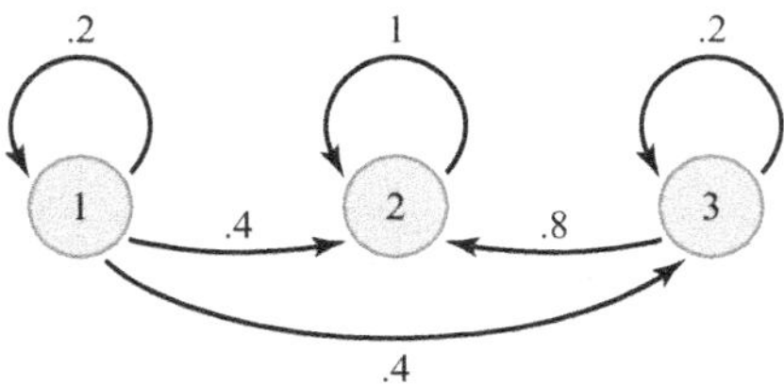

6. A Markov chain has the transition matrix

$$\begin{bmatrix} 0 & .3 & .7 \\ .7 & 0 & .3 \\ .5 & .5 & 0 \end{bmatrix}$$

(*a*) Find the transition diagram for this Markov chain.
(*b*) Find the matrix of two-step transition probabilities.
(*c*) If the initial state vector is $[\frac{3}{5} \quad \frac{1}{5} \quad \frac{1}{5}]$, what is the state vector after one transition?

7. The transition matrix of a Markov chain is

$$\begin{bmatrix} .5 & .1 & .4 \\ .2 & .8 & 0 \\ .2 & .6 & .2 \end{bmatrix}$$

On the first observation the Markov chain is in state 2. What is the probability that on both of the following two observations it is in state 1?

8. A Markov chain has the transition matrix

$$\mathbf{P} = \begin{bmatrix} .5 & .5 \\ .2 & .8 \end{bmatrix}$$

(*a*) Find $\mathbf{P}(2)$ and $\mathbf{P}(4)$.
(*b*) Find the vector $\mathbf{W}$ of stable probabilities.
(*c*) How close are the rows of $\mathbf{P}(4)$ to the vector obtained in part (*b*)? That is, what is the largest entry in $\mathbf{P}(4) - \mathbf{WI}$?

9. A Markov chain has the transition matrix

$$\mathbf{P} = \begin{bmatrix} 0 & 0 & 1 \\ .6 & 0 & .4 \\ 0 & 1 & 0 \end{bmatrix}$$

(*a*) Determine whether this Markov chain is regular.
(*b*) If it is regular, find the vector of stable probabilities.

10. A Markov chain has the transition matrix

$$\begin{bmatrix} 0 & .5 & .5 & 0 \\ 0 & 0 & 1 & 0 \\ .5 & 0 & .5 & 0 \\ 0 & .5 & 0 & .5 \end{bmatrix}$$

(*a*) Determine whether this Markov chain is regular.
(*b*) If it is regular, find the vector of stable probabilities.
(*c*) If it is regular, in which state is the system most likely to be in the long run?

11. A Markov chain has the transition matrix

$$\begin{bmatrix} 0 & 1 & 0 & 0 \\ 0 & 0 & 0 & 1 \\ .5 & .5 & 0 & 0 \\ 0 & 0 & .5 & .5 \end{bmatrix}$$

(*a*) Determine whether this Markov chain is regular.
(*b*) If it is regular, find the vector of stable probabilities.
(*c*) If it is regular, in which state is the system most likely to be in the long run?

12. A Markov chain has the transition matrix

$$\begin{bmatrix} .5 & .5 & 0 & 0 \\ 0 & 0 & 1 & 0 \\ 0 & 0 & .5 & .5 \\ 1 & 0 & 0 & 0 \end{bmatrix}$$

(*a*) Determine whether this Markov chain is regular.
(*b*) If it is regular, find the vector of stable probabilities.
(*c*) If it is regular, in which state is the system most likely to be in the long run?

13. A simplified model for forest succession is formulated as a Markov chain with the transition matrix given below.

	Blackgum	Red maple	Beech
Blackgum	.55	.25	.20
Red maple	.15	.55	.30
Beech	0	.05	.95

Suppose that a transition represents the evolution of the forest over 50 years. The forest now consists of 50 percent blackgum and 50 percent red maple.
(*a*) Find a state vector which describes the current composition of the forest.
(*b*) Find the composition of the forest in 100 years.
(*c*) Find the long-run composition of the forest.

14. The transition matrix of a Markov chain is

$$\begin{bmatrix} 1 & 0 & 0 & 0 \\ \frac{1}{2} & \frac{1}{2} & 0 & 0 \\ 0 & 0 & 1 & 0 \\ 0 & 0 & \frac{2}{3} & \frac{1}{3} \end{bmatrix}$$

(*a*) Verify that it is the transition matrix of an absorbing Markov chain.
(*b*) Determine the expected number of transitions to absorption for each initial state.

15. A Markov chain has the transition matrix

$$\begin{bmatrix} \frac{1}{4} & 0 & \frac{1}{4} & \frac{1}{2} \\ 0 & 1 & 0 & 0 \\ \frac{1}{3} & \frac{1}{3} & \frac{1}{3} & 0 \\ 0 & 0 & 0 & 1 \end{bmatrix}$$

(*a*) Verify that this is the transition matrix of an absorbing Markov chain.
(*b*) If the system is initially in state 3, determine the expected number of transitions before it reaches an absorbing state.

16. Consider the arrangement of compartments introduced in Example 8.10. If the mouse begins in the nest, find the expected number of times the mouse is in the compartment with the exercise device before it first reaches the compartment with the water.

17. A game is played on the board pictured in Figure 8.14. On each play a marker either remains in place or moves to an adjacent space on the board. On each play the marker is twice as likely to move as to remain in place, and if it moves, it is equally likely to move clockwise and counterclockwise. If the marker is initially in the red space, find the expected number of times it is in the yellow space before it first reaches the green space.

18. Suppose that the Markov chain with the transition matrix given in Exercise 10 is initially in state 3. Find the expected number of transitions before it first reaches state 1.

19. An absorbing Markov chain has the transition diagram shown in Figure 8.16.
(*a*) If the system begins in state 2, find the expected number of transitions before it reaches an absorbing state.
(*b*) If the system begins in state 3, find the expected number of visits to state 2 before it reaches an absorbing state.

20. The employment shifts of people living in a small town are described in Exercise 19, Section 8.1. Using a Markov chain model, find the expected number of years before a person who is now self-employed is first employed in industry.

21. The Sunday evening eating habits of a student are described in Exercise 23, Section 8.1. If she eats this week in a Chinese restaurant, use a Markov chain model to find the expected number of weeks before she first eats in an Italian restaurant.

FIGURE 8.16

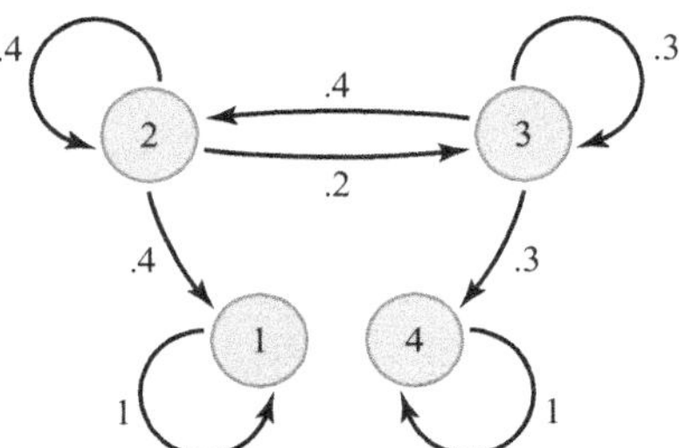

22. A consumer organization surveyed 1000 individuals immediately after each had purchased a headache remedy. Four brands were considered, A, B, C, and X, and purchase probabilities were determined. In particular, part of the data obtained in the survey can be summarized as follows:

PURCHASE PROBABILITIES

Previous Purchase	This Purchase A	B	C	X
A	.2	.3	.2	.3
B	0	.5	.2	.3
C	.1	0	.8	.1
X	.2	0	0	.8

Assume that this situation can be modeled as a Markov chain.

(*a*) Determine the probability that an individual who buys brand A this time will buy brand X on the second subsequent purchase.

(*b*) Which users (A, B, or C) will become brand X users in the smallest expected number of purchases?

(*c*) Determine the anticipated long-run distribution of users.

23. In the situation described in Exercise 22, a person is currently using brand X. Find the expected number of purchases before brand A is first used.

24. A mouse moves at random in the maze shown in Figure 8.17. In particular, suppose that the mouse moves in such a way that

(1) It is twice as likely to change compartments as to remain where it is.

(2) If it changes compartments, then the mouse is equally likely to make any of the possible moves.

Observations are made every 5 minutes and every time the mouse changes compartments.

(*a*) Model this as a Markov chain, and find the transition matrix.

(*b*) Find the stable probability vector for this situation.

25. In the situation described in Exercise 24, suppose that the mouse begins in the dark compartment. Find the expected number of observations before the mouse first reaches the bright compartment.

26. Consider the situation described in Exercise 24. Suppose that (1) remains valid and that (2) is replaced by the following: If the mouse changes compartments and has a choice, then the mouse is twice as likely to move toward a darker compartment as a lighter one. Answer (*a*) and (*b*) in this situation.

FIGURE 8.17

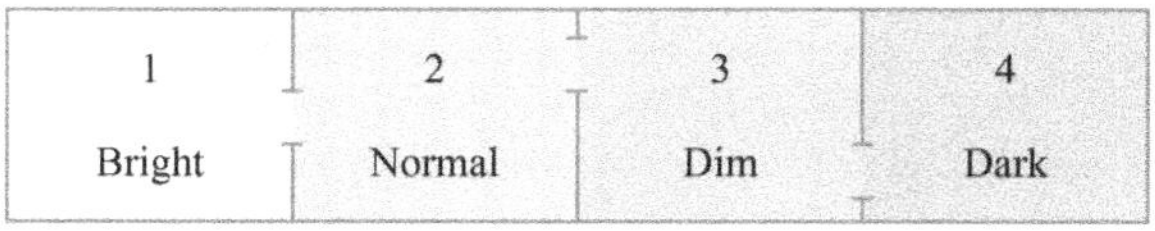

1	2	3	4
Bright	Normal	Dim	Dark

27. An absorbing Markov chain has the transition matrix

$$\begin{bmatrix} .2 & .2 & .2 & .2 & .2 \\ 0 & 1 & 0 & 0 & 0 \\ .5 & 0 & .5 & 0 & 0 \\ 0 & 0 & 0 & 1 & 0 \\ 0 & 0 & 0 & 0 & 1 \end{bmatrix}$$

(*a*) Find the fundamental matrix for this absorbing chain.
(*b*) If the system begins in state 3, find the expected number of transitions before it reaches an absorbing state.

28. An absorbing Markov chain has the transition matrix

$$\begin{bmatrix} 0 & .5 & 0 & .5 & 0 \\ 0 & 1 & 0 & 0 & 0 \\ 0 & 0 & 1 & 0 & 0 \\ .2 & 0 & .4 & 0 & .4 \\ 0 & .3 & 0 & .3 & .4 \end{bmatrix}$$

(*a*) Find the fundamental matrix for this absorbing chain.
(*b*) If the system begins in state 1, find the expected number of visits to state 5 before it reaches an absorbing state.

29. Suppose a is a number such that $0 < a < 1$. Show that the Markov chain with the transition matrix $\mathbf{P}$ is regular, where

$$\mathbf{P} = \begin{bmatrix} 0 & 1 & 0 \\ 0 & 0 & 1 \\ a & 0 & 1-a \end{bmatrix}$$

30. Find the vector of stable probabilities for matrix $\mathbf{P}$ of Exercise 29.

31. Profits at a retail brokerage firm are determined by the volume of securities (stocks and bonds) sold, and this volume fluctuates from month to month. Each month volume is classified as low, average or high and information collected over many months leads to the following description of volume patterns:
   - If volume is low this month, then next month it will be high with probability .2 and equally likely to be low and average.
   - If volume is average this month, then next month it will be low with probability .2 and equally likely to be average and high.
   - If volume is high this month, then next month it will be average or high, each with probability .5

(*a*) Formulate a Markov chain model for this situation
(*b*) Determine the long-run probabilities for volume of securities sold.

32. Consider the situation of Exercise 31. If volume is average this month, find the expected number of months before volume is high for the first time.

33. A faculty member at a large urban university prefers to live in a rural setting, and as a result she has a rather long commute each time she drives from home to campus. To help pass the time, she began to pay attention to the patterns of green and red in the many traffic lights she encountered during each trip, and she quickly

accumulated a large amount of data. Based on the data, she felt comfortable in assuming that:

- If the current light is green, then the next will be green with probability .6 and red with probability .4.
- If the current light is red, then the next will be green with probability .3 and red with probability .7.

(*a*) Formulate this situation as a Markov chain and find the transition matrix.

(*b*) If the first light is equally likely to be green or red, find the probability that the third light is green.

34. In the situation described in Exercise 33, find the long run frequency of red and green lights that she encounters on a commute.

35. Suppose you have two boxes, Box I and Box II. Box I contains one red and three blue balls, and Box II contains three red and two blue balls. An experiment consists of successively drawing balls from the boxes and replacing each ball in the box from which it was drawn.
    - The experiment begins by drawing a ball at random from Box I, noting its color and replacing it. Subsequent draws are made according to the following rules.
    - If at any stage a blue ball is drawn, the next ball is drawn from the same box and its color is noted.
    - If at any stage a red ball is drawn, the next ball is drawn from the other box and its color is noted.

    (*a*) Formulate this experiment as a Markov chain and find the transition matrix.

    (*b*) Find the probability that the third ball drawn is red.

36. In the experiment of Exercise 35, find the long-run probability that a blue ball is drawn.

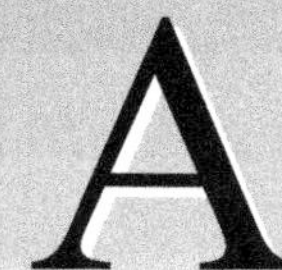

APPENDIX A Sample Examinations

This Appendix includes two sample midterm examinations and two sample final examinations. The midterm examinations are designed as 90 minute tests over Chapters 1–3 and Sections 4.1–4.2. The final examinations are designed as 2 hour tests over the entire course: the material included in the midterm plus Chapters 5 and 7, Sections 6.1–6.2, and 8.1–8.3.

MIDTERM—VERSION 1

This is a 90 minute test.

1. Suppose that a student selects all his answers to this test entirely at random among choices (A) through (E), never choosing (F). If indeed, "none of these" is not the correct answer to any of the questions, and the correct answers are positioned entirely at random, what is the expected score for this student? Recall that this test consists of 25 problems and each problem is worth 4 points.
(A) 16 (B) 20 (C) 24 (D) 28 (E) 32 (F) none of these
2. Identify the shaded set in the following Venn diagram.

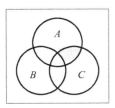

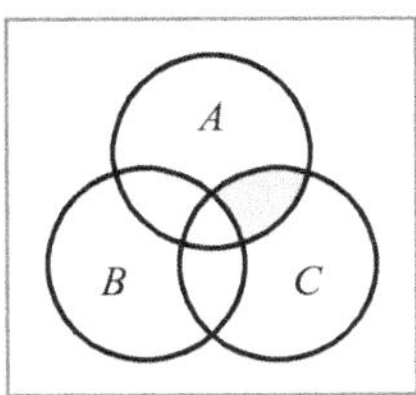

(A) $(A' \cap B) \cup C$ (B) $A' \cap B \cap C$ (C) $A \cap B \cap C'$
(D) $(A' \cup B) \cap C$ (E) $A \cap B' \cap C$ (F) none of these

3. Let $A = \{a, b\}$, $B = \{1, 2, 3\}$, $C = \{1, 2\}$ and the universal set $U = A \times B$. Find $(A \times C)'$.
(A) $\{(a, 1), (b, 2)\}$ (B) $\{(a, 3), (b, 3)\}$ (C) $\{(a, 3), (b, 2)\}$
(D) $\{(1, a), (2, b)\}$ (E) $\{(3, a), (2, b)\}$ (F) none of these

4. An unfair coin for which Pr[heads] = .48 and Pr[tails] = .52 is tossed 8 times. Find the probability that heads will occur at most twice.
(A) $(.52)^8 + 8(.48)(.52)^7 + 28(.48)^2(.52)^6$ (B) $(.48)^8 + 8(.52)(.48)^7 + 28(.52)^2(.48)^6$
(C) $(.52)^8 + 8(.48)(.52)^7$ (D) $8(.48)(.52)^7 + 28(.48)^2(.52)^6$
(E) $(.52)^8 + 8(.52)(.48)^7 + 28(.52)^2(.48)^6$ (F) none of these

5. A store can order jeans in 3 styles; flared, relaxed-fit, or regular fit. Each style comes in 2 colors, black and blue, and with 2 options on the fly, either zipper or buttons. Determine how many different types of jeans the store can order.
(A) 8 (B) 10 (C) 12 (D) 14 (E) 16 (F) none of these

6. Let A and B be events in a sample space with $\Pr[A] = .5$, $\Pr[B] = .4$, and $\Pr[A \cup B] = .7$. Find $\Pr[A|B]$.
(A) .4 (B) .45 (C) .50 (D) .55 (E) .60 (F) none of these

7. Events E and F are independent in a sample space S with $\Pr[E] = .3$ and $\Pr[F] = .4$. Find $\Pr[E' \cap F]$.
(A) .24 (B) .28 (C) .30 (D) .32 (E) .36 (F) none of these

8. It is found that by the fourth year of ownership, 27% of all Joltmobile cars develop transmission problems, 11% develop steering problems, and 23% start to leak oil. Furthermore 5% develop both transmission and steering problems, 10% both develop transmission problems and start to leak oil, but strangely enough, no car is found to both develop steering problems and leak oil. Find the total percentage of Joltmobile cars which suffer from at least one of these three conditions during the first four years of ownership.
(A) 37% (B) 41% (C) 46% (D) 47% (E) 52% (F) none of these

9. How many subsets with exactly 8 elements are there for a set of 11 elements?
(A) 125 (B) 165 (C) 256 (D) 720 (E) 7920 (F) none of these

10. An experiment with equally likely outcomes has a sample space S and an event E, with $\Pr[E] = .5$ and $n(E) = 45$. We also know that for another event F in S, $\Pr[F] = .4$. Find $n(F)$, the number of outcomes in F.
(A) 36 (B) 35 (C) 34 (D) 33 (E) 32 (F) none of these

11. A club is made up of 5 women and 4 men. Find the number of ways a president, vice-president and treasurer can be selected, if these positions are to be filled by two women and one man.
(A) 150 (B) 180 (C) 200 (D) 240 (D) 260 (F) none of these

12. You and 8 others completely fill a shuttle van to the Indianapolis airport. Among the others are 4 students. If you sit in the middle of the last row, so that you have a passenger on either side, what is the probability that you are sitting next to at least one student.
(A) $\frac{3}{8}$ (B) $\frac{5}{8}$ (C) $\frac{3}{7}$ (D) $\frac{9}{7}$ (E) $\frac{11}{14}$ (F) none of these

13. Suppose an experiment has a sample space of outcomes $S = \{\mathcal{O}_1, \mathcal{O}_2, \mathcal{O}_3, \mathcal{O}_4, \mathcal{O}_5\}$ with associated weights (probabilities) $w_1 = .20$, $w_2 = .15$, $w_3 = .25$, $w_4 = .30$, and $w_5 = .10$. If $E_1 = \{\mathcal{O}_1, \mathcal{O}_2, \mathcal{O}_3\}$, $E_2 = \{\mathcal{O}_2, \mathcal{O}_4\}$, find $\Pr[E_1 \cap E_2']$.
(A) .25 (B) .30 (C) .35 (D) .45 (E) .50 (F) none of these

14. A five-person subcommittee is to be selected from among 5 Republicans and 4 Democrats. Find the number of ways in which the committee can be formed if it must include at least two members of each party.
(A) 100 (B) 84 (C) 81 (D) 72 (E) 63 (F) none of these

15. In a certain large city 50% of the eligible voters actually voted in the last election. If 5 eligible voters are selected at random, what is the probability that at least 2 of them voted in the last election? Assume that the

population of the city is so large that the probability of voting is $\frac{1}{2}$ for each eligible voter selected.

(A) $\frac{1}{2}$ (B) $\frac{25}{32}$ (C) $\frac{13}{16}$ (D) $\frac{17}{32}$ (E) $\frac{5}{8}$ (F) none of these

16. There are 12 apples in bag. Four of them have worms in them. If two apples are pulled from the bag at random, find the probability that neither has a worm in it.

(A) $\frac{7}{33}$ (B) $\frac{14}{33}$ (C) $\frac{3}{11}$ (D) $\frac{10}{33}$ (E) $\frac{1}{3}$ (F) none of these

17. For $4 you can have a chance to roll a single fair die, and receive back the dollar amount equal to the number on the die. What is your expected gain or loss on each play?

(A) lose $1 (B) lose 50 cents (C) lose 25 cents
(D) gain 25 cents (E) gain $1 (F) none of these

18. A company car pool consists of 40% Fords, 20% Chryslers and 40% Hondas. While each Honda has a passenger side airbag, only 50% of the Fords and 60% of the Chryslers do. A car is selected at random from the car pool. Determine the probability that it has a passenger side airbag.

(A) .54 (B) .56 (C) .63 (D) .64 (E) .72 (F) none of these

19. Suppose that on any given day a student oversleeps with probability .3, finishes his daily assignments with probability .8, and does both with probability .2. Determine the probability that on a given day the student wakes up on time, but fails to complete his assignment.

(A) .05 (B) .10 (C) .15 (D) .20 (E) .25 (F) none of these

20. An experiment consists of rolling two *fair* dice and noting the *product* of the numbers on top. Determine the probability of getting a product *greater* than 2.

(A) $\frac{29}{36}$ (B) $\frac{17}{36}$ (C) $\frac{31}{36}$ (D) $\frac{17}{18}$ (E) $\frac{11}{12}$ (F) none of these

21. A box contains 1 red, 2 white and 4 blue balls. Two balls are drawn without replacement, noting the color of each. If the first two balls drawn are white and blue in either order, then one more ball is drawn, and its color noted. Determine the number of elements in the sample space for this experiment. (*Hint*: Draw a tree diagram.)

(A) 8 (B) 9 (C) 10 (D) 11 (E) 12 (F) none of these

22. From the tree diagram below, determine $\Pr[Y \mid A]$.

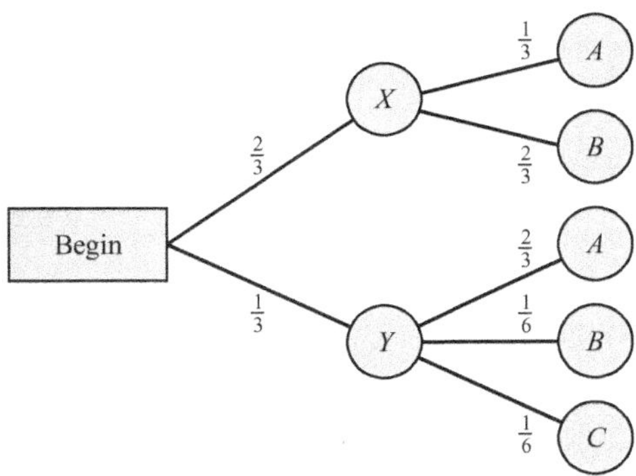

(A) $\frac{2}{9}$ (B) $\frac{1}{3}$ (C) $\frac{4}{9}$ (D) $\frac{1}{2}$ (E) $\frac{3}{5}$ (F) none of these

23. A customer survey at a local coffee shop revealed the following preferences.

45% like cappuccino
50% like café au lait
20% like espresso

35% like both cappuccino and café au lait
10% like both cappuccino and espresso
7% like both café au lait and espresso
3% like all three.

Find the percentage of those surveyed who like cappuccino but neither espresso, nor café au lait.
(A) 3% (B) 6% (C) 7% (D) 8% (E) 11% (F) none of these

24. In the state of Indiana 1% of the population is infected with a strange new disease called purduecosis. A new blood test for the early detection of purduecosis is being developed. If a person who is known to have the disease is tested, the result is positive 99% of the time, and if a person without the disease is tested, the result is negative 98% of the time. If the test is applied to someone for whom it is not known whether or not they have purduecosis, and it comes up positive, determine the probability that the person actually has the disease.
(A) $\frac{3}{10}$ (B) $\frac{1}{3}$ (C) $\frac{9}{10}$ (D) $\frac{98}{100}$ (E) $\frac{99}{100}$ (F) none of these

25. A basketball team with 4 boys and 5 girls has made it to the championship game. The coach must decide which five players will start the game, and the *particular order* in which they are to be introduced. If the players are all equally talented, so the coach makes the choice entirely at random, determine the probability that two girls will be introduced as starters, followed by three boys.
(A) $\frac{1}{21}$ (B) $\frac{3}{29}$ (C) $\frac{2}{63}$ (D) $\frac{4}{35}$ (E) $\frac{6}{35}$ (F) none of these

MIDTERM—VERSION 2

This is a 90 minute test.

1. A set X with $n(X) = 50$ is partitioned into three subsets X_1, X_2 and X_3. If $n(X_2) = 3n(X_1)$ and $n(X_3) = 2n(X_2)$, find the number of elements in subset X_2.
(A) 5 (B) 10 (C) 15 (D) 20 (E) 30 (F) 35

2. 52 people are interviewed about their food preferences. 20 of them like Mexican food, 30 like Italian food, and 10 like neither Mexican nor Italian food. How many like both Mexican and Italian food?
(A) 8 (B) 10 (C) 12 (D) 22 (E) 32 (F) 16

3. An experiment consists of rolling a red die and a blue die and noting the result of each roll. Find the probability that the sum is 7.
(A) $\frac{1}{6}$ (B) $\frac{5}{36}$ (C) $\frac{1}{4}$ (D) 0 (E) $\frac{1}{2}$ (F) none of the above

4. A bag contains 5 red balls and 6 yellow balls. If 4 balls are drawn at random what is the probability that 2 are red and 2 are yellow?
(A) $\frac{4}{11}$ (B) $\frac{5}{11}$ (C) $\frac{1}{5}$ (D) $\frac{2}{3}$ (E) $\frac{1}{2}$ (F) $\frac{1}{3}$

5. Suppose A and B are two events with $\Pr[A] = .4$ and $\Pr[B] = .2$. If $\Pr[A|B] = .6$, find $\Pr[B|A]$.
(A) .12 (B) .40 (C) .3 (D) .52 (E) $\frac{1}{3}$ (F) .5

6. An experiment has the sample space $S = \{O_1, O_2, O_3\}$, and it is known that $w_1 = \frac{1}{2}$, $w_2 = \frac{1}{6}$ (recall $w_i = \Pr[O_i]$). If $E = \{O_2, O_3\}$, what is $\Pr[E]$?
(A) $\frac{1}{8}$ (B) $\frac{1}{6}$ (C) $\frac{1}{2}$ (D) $\frac{2}{3}$ (E) $\frac{3}{4}$ (F) $\frac{6}{7}$

7. A Senate committee contains 4 Democrats, 3 Republicans, and one Independent. How many ways can a subcommittee of 4 be chosen, if the subcommittee must contain at least three Democrats?
(A) 36 (B) 53 (C) 52 (D) 17 (E) 100 (F) none of the above

8. A box contains 2 right gloves and 3 left gloves. A glove is drawn at random. If it is a left glove, it is returned to the box and another glove is randomly drawn. If it is a right glove, then it is kept out of the box and another

glove is randomly drawn. What is the probability that the second draw will result in a left glove?
(A) $\frac{6}{25}$ (B) $\frac{1}{3}$ (C) $\frac{33}{147}$ (D) $\frac{33}{50}$ (E) $\frac{14}{25}$ (F) none of the above

9. A fair coin is flipped 4 times. What is the probability of getting exactly 2 heads, given that at least one head came up?
(A) $\frac{2}{5}$ (B) $1-(\frac{1}{2})^4$ (C) $6(\frac{1}{2})^4$ (D) $\frac{3}{5}$ (E) $\frac{1}{16}$ (F) $\frac{1}{2}$

10. In today's business world, computer viruses can be lethal to the operations of a company. Suppose a local business has 50 laptop computers and, unknown to the company, three of these are infected with the deadly OUCH disease. The CEO of the company is making a big presentation to a major client and has randomly selected two of the laptops to use during the presentation. Find the probability that at least one of the computers is infected with the OUCH virus.
(A) $\frac{2162}{2450}$ (B) $\frac{282}{2450}$ (C) $\frac{288}{2450}$ (D) $\frac{2228}{1450}$ (E) $\frac{6}{2450}$ (F) none of the above

11. How many 4-letter words can be formed with the letters in the word "good"?
(A) 120 (B) 24 (C) 4 (D) $C(4, 2)$ (E) 99 (F) 12

12. Consider a town in which there are two plumbers, whom we call A and B. On a certain day, four residents of the town telephone for a plumber. If each resident selects a plumber at random from the telephone directory, what is the probability that two residents will call A and two residents will call B?
(A) $\frac{1}{8}$ (B) $\frac{1}{4}$ (C) $\frac{3}{8}$ (D) $\frac{1}{2}$ (E) $\frac{1}{3}$ (F) none of the above

13. If you have a $\frac{1}{10}$ probability of gaining \$200, a $\frac{3}{10}$ probability of losing \$300, and a $\frac{6}{10}$ probability of breaking even, what is your expected value?
(A) −\$40 (B) −\$50 (C) −\$60 (D) −\$70 (E) \$40 (F) none of the above

14. The table shown below gives the values of a random variable X and the density function of X. Suppose that $E[X] = 1$. Find the missing value x and the missing probability p.

Value of *X*	**Probability**
−4	.10
−3	p
x	.50
3	.15
4	.10

(A) $x = 1, p = .30$ (B) $x = 2, p = .15$ (C) $x = 3, p = .15$
(D) $x = 2, p = .30$ (E) $x = -3, p = .15$ (F) $x = 4, p = .50$

15. Suppose in a survey concerning the reading habits of students it is found that:

60 per cent read magazine A.
50 per cent read magazine B.
50 per cent read magazine C.
30 per cent read magazines A and B.
20 per cent read magazines B and C.
30 per cent read magazines A and C.
10 per cent read all three magazines.

What percent read exactly two magazines?
(A) 50 (B) 45 (C) 40 (D) 35 (E) 30 (F) none of the above

16. Let A and B be disjoint subsets of U with $n(U) = 45$, $n(A) = 15$, and $n(B') = 20$. Find $n(A' \cap B)$.
(A) 15 (B) 20 (C) 25 (D) 30 (E) 35 (F) none of the above

17. In the experiment described by the tree diagram below, find $\Pr[a \mid X]$.
(A) .1 (B) .2 (C) .3 (D) .4 (E) .8 (F) .6

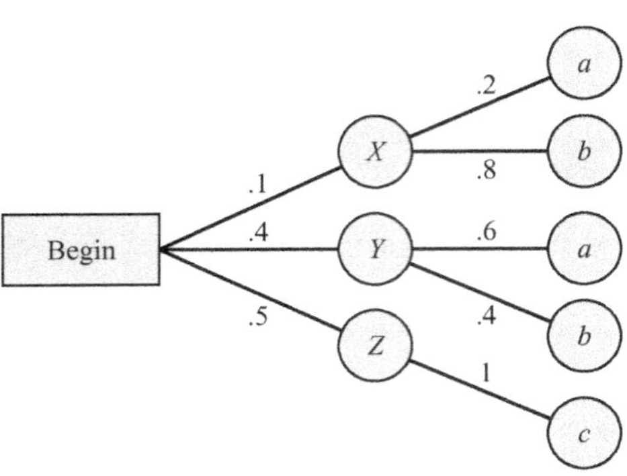

18. In the experiment described by the tree diagram above, find $\Pr[Y \mid b]$.
(A) $\frac{2}{3}$ (B) .16 (C) $\frac{1}{3}$ (D) .5 (E) .4 (F) .24

19. How many lunches consisting of a soup, a sandwich, a dessert, and a drink are possible if we can select from 4 soups, 3 kinds of sandwiches, 5 desserts and 4 drinks?
(A) 120 (B) 32 (C) 16 (D) 95 (E) 240 (F) none of the above

20. If there are nine horses in a race, in how many different ways can they finish first, second and third?
(A) $C(8, 3)$ (B) 504 (C) 120 (D) 403 (E) 240 (F) none of the above

21. The probability that Paula passes Mathematics is $\frac{2}{3}$, and the probability that she passes English is $\frac{1}{2}$. If the probability of passing both courses is $\frac{1}{4}$, what is the probability that Paula will pass at least one of these courses?
(A) $\frac{7}{12}$ (B) $\frac{3}{4}$ (C) $\frac{1}{12}$ (D) $\frac{5}{12}$ (E) $\frac{11}{12}$ (F) none of the above

22. Suppose the probability that a man aged 60 will live to be 70 is 0.5. If 4 sixty-year-old men are chosen randomly, what is the probability that at least 3 will live to be 70?
(A) .62523 (B) .52546 (C) .42876 (D) .12453 (E) .22768 (F) .31250

23. Let A and B be subsets of a universal set U. Which relation below is always true?
(A) $A' \cap B \subset A$ (B) $A \cup B \subset A \cap B$ (C) $U \cap A \subset A'$
(D) $A \cup B \subset A' \cap B'$ (E) $A \cup B \subset A \cap B'$ (F) $A' \cap B' \subset (A \cap B)'$

24. Let $U = \{x, y, z, 1, 2, 3\}$, $A = \{y, z, 2\}$, $B = \{y, z, 1\}$, and $C = \{x, y, z, 1\}$. List the elements in $(A \cup B) \cap C'$.
(A) $\{2, 3\}$ (B) $\{1, 2\}$ (C) $\{1, 2, 3\}$ (D) $\{2\}$ (E) $\{z, 3\}$ (F) none of the above

25. Suppose $A \times B = \{(a, b), (a, 1), (b, b), (b, 1)\}$. Find $A \cap B$.
(A) $\{a\}$ (B) $\{b\}$ (C) $\{1\}$ (D) The empty set $\emptyset$ (E) $\{a, b\}$ (F) $\{b, 1\}$

FINAL—VERSION 1

This is a 120 minute test.

1. Bob and Carol make two sizes of kites out of paper and wood strips. Each small kite uses 4 square feet of paper and 2 feet of wood strips, and each large kite uses 8 square feet of paper and 3 feet of wood strips. There are 160 square feet of paper and 70 feet of wood strips available. If all of the paper and all of the wood strips are used to make small and large kites, how many large kites will be made?
(A) 100 (B) 200 (C) 10 (D) 20 (E) 50 (F) none of the above

2. At a large university, 30 percent of the students have taken chemistry in high school. Of those who have taken chemistry in high school, 70 percent plan to major in science. Of those who have not taken chemistry in high school, 20 percent plan to major in science. What is the probability that a randomly selected student will plan to major in science?
(A) .21 (B) .09 (C) .14 (D) .35 (E) .30 (F) none of the above
3. A certain 3×3 matrix A has as its inverse the matrix

$$\mathbf{A}^{-1} = \begin{bmatrix} 0 & -1 & 1 \\ 1 & 5 & 4 \\ 1 & 2 & -2 \end{bmatrix}.$$

If

$$\mathbf{A}\begin{bmatrix} x \\ y \\ z \end{bmatrix} = \begin{bmatrix} 1 \\ 0 \\ 2 \end{bmatrix},$$

then what is the value of x?
(A) 2 (B) -3 (C) 9 (D) 0 (E) -4 (F) none of the above
4. Let $A = \{a, b, c\}$ and $B = \{a, b, d\}$. How many elements does $(A \times B) \cap (B \times A)$ have?
(A) 81 (B) 12 (C) 9 (D) 4 (E) 2 (F) 1
5. For which of the following matrices are the corresponding Markov chains regular?
(1) $\begin{bmatrix} 0 & 1 \\ .2 & .8 \end{bmatrix}$ (2) $\begin{bmatrix} 1 & 0 \\ .3 & .7 \end{bmatrix}$ (3) $\begin{bmatrix} .8 & .2 \\ 1 & 0 \end{bmatrix}$ (4) $\begin{bmatrix} 0 & 1 \\ 1 & 0 \end{bmatrix}$
(A) (1) and (2) (B) (2) and (4) (C) (1) and (4)
(D) (2) and (3) (E) (1) and (3) (F) none of the above

For each of the augmented matrices in the next three problems, determine which of the following statements is true about the associated system of linear equations:

(A) The system has no solution.
(B) The system has a unique solution.
(C) The system has exactly two solutions.
(D) The system has infinitely many solutions in which one variable can be selected arbitrarily.
(E) The system has infinitely many solutions in which two variables can be selected arbitrarily.
(F) none of the above

6. $\left[\begin{array}{cc|c} 1 & 2 & 5 \\ 1 & 1 & 9 \\ 2 & 2 & 8 \\ 1 & 3 & 6 \end{array}\right]$

7. $\left[\begin{array}{ccc|c} 1 & 2 & -1 & 5 \\ 0 & 1 & 1 & 2 \\ 0 & -1 & -1 & -2 \end{array}\right]$

8. $\left[\begin{array}{ccc|c} 1 & 1 & 1 & 0 \\ 1 & 1 & 0 & -2 \\ 0 & -1 & -1 & 1 \end{array}\right]$

9. From three red, four green, and five yellow apples, how many selections consisting of six apples are possible if two of each color are to be selected?
(A) 60 (B) 360 (C) 480 (D) 180 (E) 36 (F) none of the above

10. Find the entry in the second row and third column of $\mathbf{A}^{-1}$ for

$$\mathbf{A} = \begin{bmatrix} 1 & 0 & 0 \\ 0 & 2 & 1 \\ 0 & 2 & 0 \end{bmatrix}$$

(A) -1 (B) 0 (C) $\frac{1}{2}$ (D) 1 (E) $\frac{3}{2}$ (F) none of the above

11. A regular Markov chain has the transition matrix

$$\mathbf{P} = \begin{bmatrix} \frac{1}{2} & \frac{1}{2} \\ \frac{2}{3} & \frac{1}{3} \end{bmatrix}$$

What is the second entry of its stable vector?
(A) $\frac{5}{7}$ (B) $\frac{4}{7}$ (C) $\frac{3}{7}$ (D) $\frac{2}{7}$ (E) $\frac{1}{7}$ (F) none of the above

12. A Markov chain has the transition matrix

$$\mathbf{P} = \begin{bmatrix} .2 & .8 \\ .3 & .7 \end{bmatrix}$$

Find $p_{21}(2)$.
(A) .28 (B) .72 (C) .27 (D) .73 (E) .5 (F) none of the above

13. A regular Markov chain has the transition matrix

$$\mathbf{P} = \begin{bmatrix} 0 & 1 \\ a & 1-a \end{bmatrix}.$$

Find a if the vector of stable probabilities is $\left[\frac{1}{4}\ \frac{3}{4}\right]$.
(A) $\frac{1}{3}$ (B) $\frac{2}{3}$ (C) $\frac{1}{4}$ (D) $\frac{1}{2}$ (E) $\frac{3}{4}$ (F) none of the above

14. A Markov chain has the transition matrix **P** shown below. On the first observation it is in state 3. What state is it most likely to occupy on the next observation?

$$\mathbf{P} = \begin{bmatrix} \frac{2}{3} & \frac{1}{6} & \frac{1}{12} & 0 & \frac{1}{12} \\ \frac{1}{18} & \frac{2}{3} & \frac{1}{9} & \frac{1}{9} & \frac{1}{18} \\ \frac{1}{6} & \frac{1}{6} & \frac{1}{4} & \frac{1}{12} & \frac{1}{3} \\ \frac{1}{6} & \frac{1}{6} & \frac{2}{3} & 0 & 0 \\ 0 & \frac{1}{6} & 0 & \frac{2}{3} & \frac{1}{6} \end{bmatrix}$$

(A) 1 (B) 2 (C) 3 (D) 4 (E) 5 (F) none of the above

15. Which of the following matrices are in reduced form?

(1) $\begin{bmatrix} 1 & 2 & 2 & 0 \\ 0 & 1 & 3 & 0 \\ 0 & 0 & 0 & 1 \end{bmatrix}$ (2) $\begin{bmatrix} 1 & 2 & 0 & 0 \\ 0 & 0 & 1 & 0 \\ 0 & 0 & 0 & 1 \end{bmatrix}$ (3) $\begin{bmatrix} 1 & 0 & 0 & 0 \\ 0 & 0 & 1 & 3 \\ 0 & 1 & 0 & 0 \end{bmatrix}$

(4) $\begin{bmatrix} 1 & 0 & 0 & 2 \\ 0 & 1 & 0 & -1 \\ 0 & 0 & 1 & 3 \end{bmatrix}$ (5) $\begin{bmatrix} 1 & 0 & 0 & 4 \\ 0 & 3 & 0 & 1 \\ 0 & 0 & 1 & 2 \\ 0 & 0 & 0 & 0 \end{bmatrix}$

(A) (1) and (2) (B) (2) and (4) (C) (1) and (4)
(D) (2) only (E) (1) and (5) (F) none of the above

16. Which of the following points is on the line through the points (0, 3) and (1, 5)?
(1) (3, 9) (2) (2, 8) (3) (−1, 1)
(A) (1) and (2) (B) (1) only (C) (1) and (3)
(D) (2) only (E) (2) and (3) (F) none of the above

17. A Leontief input-output model has two goods, lumber and steel. The production processes are such that 0.8 units of lumber and 0.1 units of steel are required to produce 1 unit of lumber, and 0.4 units of lumber and 0.5 units of steel are required to produce 1 unit of steel. Find the number of units of steel in the production schedule that meets an external demand for 30 units of lumber and 45 units of steel.
(A) 525 (B) 350 (C) 200 (D) 550 (E) 325 (F) none of the above

18. An investment club has at most \$30,000 to invest in junk and premium-quality bonds. Each type of bond costs \$1000 apiece. The junk bonds have an average yield of 12% and the premium-quality bonds 7%. The policy of the club is to invest at least twice the amount in premium-quality bonds as in junk bonds. How many of each type bond should the club buy to maximize its investment return? Let

$$x = \text{number of junk bonds the club buys},$$
$$y = \text{number of premium bonds the club buys}.$$

Formulate a linear programming problem whose solution gives the number of each type of bond the club should buy in order to maximize its investment return?
(A) Maximize $70x + 120y$ subject to $x \geq 0,\ y \geq 2x,\ x + y \leq 30$
(B) Maximize $120x + 70y$ subject to $x \geq 0,\ y \geq 0,\ y \geq 2x,\ x + y \leq 30$
(C) Maximize $.12x + .70y$ subject to $x \geq 0,\ y \geq 2x,\ 2x + y \leq 30$
(D) Maximize $.12x + .70y$ subject to $x \geq 0,\ y \geq 0,\ y \geq 2x,\ x + y \leq 30$
(E) Maximize $120x + 70y$ subject to $2y \geq x,\ x + y \leq 30$
(F) none of the above

19. A set S is defined by the inequalities.

$$x \geq 0, \quad x \leq 1, \quad y \leq 1, \quad x - y - 1 \leq 0$$

Find the corner points of S
(A) (0, −1), (0, 1), (1, 2), (1, 0), (2, 1)
(B) (0, 0), (0, 1), (1, 2), (2, 1)
(C) (0, 1), (1, 2), (1, 0), (2, 1)
(D) (0, −1), (0, 1), (1, 1), (1, 0)
(E) (0, 0), (0, −1), (0, 1), (1, 2), (1, 0), (2, 1)
(F) none of the above

20. Two grains, barley and corn, are to be mixed for animal food. Barley contains 1 unit of fat per pound, and corn contains two units of fat per pound. The total amount of fat in the mixture are not to exceed 12 units. No more than 6 pounds of barley and no more than 5 pounds of corn are to be used in the mixture. If barley and corn each contain 1 unit of protein per pound, how many pounds of each grain should be used to maximize the number of units of protein in the mixture.
(A) 3 pounds of barley and 2 pounds of corn
(B) 4 pounds of barley and 3 pounds of corn
(C) 5 pounds of barley and 3 pounds of corn
(D) 5 pounds of barley and 4 pounds of corn
(E) 6 pounds of barley and 3 pounds of corn
(F) none of the above

21. A Markov chain has the transition matrix

$$\mathbf{A} = \begin{bmatrix} \frac{1}{8} & \frac{7}{8} \\ \frac{1}{2} & \frac{1}{2} \end{bmatrix}$$

If the system begins in state 2, find the state vector after 2 transitions.

(A) $\begin{bmatrix} \frac{1}{8} & \frac{7}{8} \end{bmatrix}$ (B) $\begin{bmatrix} \frac{1}{2} & \frac{1}{2} \end{bmatrix}$ (C) $\begin{bmatrix} \frac{5}{16} & \frac{11}{16} \end{bmatrix}$
(D) $\begin{bmatrix} \frac{5}{8} & \frac{3}{8} \end{bmatrix}$ (E) $\begin{bmatrix} \frac{1}{3} & \frac{2}{3} \end{bmatrix}$ (F) none of the above

22. An experiment has the sample space $S = \{\mathcal{O}_1, \mathcal{O}_2, \mathcal{O}_3\}$, and it is known that $\Pr[\{\mathcal{O}_1, \mathcal{O}_2\}] = \frac{5}{6}$, $\Pr[\{\mathcal{O}_1, \mathcal{O}_3\}] = \frac{2}{3}$. What is $\Pr[\mathcal{O}_1]$?
(A) $\frac{1}{2}$ (B) $\frac{1}{3}$ (C) $\frac{1}{4}$ (D) $\frac{1}{5}$ (E) $\frac{1}{6}$ (F) none of the above

23. In a particular city, 80 households were asked these two questions:
Q1: Do you own a Chevrolet?
Q2: Do you own at least two cars?
Twenty five households answered "yes" to Question 1, 52 answered "yes" to Question 2, and 18 answered "yes" to both questions. How many of these households answered "no" to both questions?
(A) 59 (B) 41 (C) 21 (D) 7 (E) 14 (F) none of the above

24. A thousand dragons have been terrorizing the village. Suppose that 60 of them breathe fire and have bad breath, while 300 have at least one of these bad habits. Suppose too that 20 dragons only breathe fire. How many dragons breathe fire or have had bad breath but not both?
(A) 220 (B) 260 (C) 240 (D) 40 (E) 100 (F) none of the above

25. Suppose A and B are subsets of a universal U. Which of the following statements is always true?
(A) $n(A \cap B) = n(A) \cdot n(B)$ (B) $n(A \cup B) = n(A) \cdot n(B)$
(C) $n(A \cup B) = n(A) + n(B)$ (D) $n(A' \cup B') = n(A) + n(B)$
(E) $n(A \times B) = n(A) \cdot n(B)$ (F) none of the above

26. The basic Post Office Zip Code in New England consists of five digits. Each of the five digits can be any of the ten integers 0, 1, 2, . . . , 9, for example, 01021 is a Zip Code. How many different Zip Codes are possible with this system?
(A) 100,000 (B) $C(10, 5)$ (C) $P(10, 5)$ (D) 5! (E) 10!5! (F) none of the above

27. What is the probability of a couple having at least four girls if they have six children (assuming equally likely outcomes for both sexes)?
(A) $\frac{1}{7}$ (B) $\frac{11}{64}$ (C) $\frac{7}{32}$ (D) $\frac{15}{64}$ (E) $\frac{11}{32}$ (F) none of the above

28. Let A and B be disjoint events for which $\Pr[A] = 0.21$ and $\Pr[B] = 0.33$, find $\Pr[A' \cap B]$.
(A) .5 (B) .79 (C) .64 (D) .21 (E) .33 (F) none of the above

29. In the game of Parcheesi each player rolls a pair of six-sided dice on each turn. In order to begin the game, you must roll a five on at least one die, or a sum of five. Find the probability that a player begins the game on his or her first roll.
(A) $\frac{15}{36}$ (B) $\frac{13}{36}$ (C) $\frac{16}{36}$ (D) $\frac{10}{36}$ (E) $\frac{6}{36}$ (F) none of the above

30. A drawer contains 2 pennies and 8 nickels. One coin is randomly selected from the drawer. What is the expected value of the coin selected?
(A) \$0.010 (B) \$0.050 (C) \$0.210 (D) \$0.042 (E) \$0.630 (F) none of the above

31. Six people are about to enter a cage in a single file. In how many ways could they arrange themselves in a row to go through the entrance.
(A) $C(6, 1)$ (B) 15 (C) 360 (D) 2^6 (E) 720 (F) none of the above

32. Consider a Bernoulli process consisting of $n = 1000$ trials with success probability p. Suppose the expected value of the number of successes is 200, find the value of p.
(A) .8 (B) .2 (C) .5 (D) .9 (E) .1 (F) none of the above

33. A diagnostic test for a certain disease is said to be 90% accurate in that, if a person has the disease, the test will detect it with probability 0.9. Also, if the person does not have the disease, the test will report that he or she doesn't have it with probability .9. Only 10% of the population has the disease in question. If a person

is chosen at random from the population and the diagnostic test reports him to have the disease, what is the conditional probability that he does, in fact, have the disease?
(A) 0.2500 (B) 0.1875 (C) 0.5000 (D) 0.1233 (E) 0.6000 (F) none of the above

FINAL—VERSION 2

1. We have a universal set U with $n(U) = 25$, and a subset A of U with $n(A) = 8$. Find $n(A')$.
   (A) Not enough information is given. (B) 10 (C) 15
   (D) 17 (E) 8 (F) none of these
2. A used car dealer has 120 cars in his lot. Of these cars, 45 are missing the steering wheel, 95 are missing the windshield, and 25 are missing both. How many cars are missing neither windshield, nor steering wheel?
   (A) Not enough information is given. (B) 5 (C) 20
   (D) 45 (E) 115 (F) none of these
3. In a yard there are 420 abandoned cars. Each car has either two or three wheels, a total of 1000 wheels. How many of these cars have two wheels?
   (A) 60 (B) 160 (C) 260 (D) 360 (E) 460 (F) none of these
4. Professor Umbuggio has found in an old notebook three matrices A, B, C, and he knows that $AB = C$. Unfortunately, some of the entries are not written clearly; we will indicate these entries by x and y. Help Umbuggio by finding the value of x. Here are the matrices: $A = \begin{bmatrix} 2 & 1 \\ 3 & x \end{bmatrix}$, $B = \begin{bmatrix} 1 & 2 \\ x & 2 \end{bmatrix}$, $C = \begin{bmatrix} y & y \\ 19 & 14 \end{bmatrix}$
   (A) 0 (B) 2 (C) 4 (D) 6 (E) 8 (F) none of these
5. The transition matrix for a Markov chain is given as $P = \begin{bmatrix} x & y & .7 \\ 2y & .3 & 3x \\ 0 & .4 & .6 \end{bmatrix}$.
   Find the value of x.
   (A) .1 (B) .2 (C) .3 (D) .4 (E) .5 (F) none of these
6. A vase contains 5 roses and 4 carnations. Three flowers are selected at random. What is the probability that at least two roses were selected, given that at least one carnation was selected?
   (A) 3/8 (B) 5/9 (C) 10/14 (D) 20/37 (E) 1/2 (F) none of these
7. Matrices A, B, and C are known to satisfy the equation $AB - C = \begin{bmatrix} 1 & 2 & -1 \\ 4 & 0 & 9 \end{bmatrix}$. Exactly one of the following must be true.
   (A) A has two rows (B) A has three rows (C) B has four columns
   (D) B has two columns (E) C has two columns (F) none of these
8. A fair die is rolled independently 4 times. What is the probability that a six came up exactly twice?
   (A) 1/36 (B) 1/216 (C) 25/216 (D) 25/1296 (E) 1/2 (F) none of these
9. For two events A and B in a sample space S it is known that $\Pr[A] = 1/2$, $\Pr[B] = 2/3$, and $\Pr[A \cap B] = 1/5$. Find $\Pr[A \mid B]$.
   (A) 1/2 (B) 2/5 (C) 3/10 (D) 1/3 (E) 2/3 (F) none of these
10. A bag contains 6 green balls, 1 yellow ball, and 2 red balls. An experiment consists of picking three balls, one after another without replacement, and noting only their colors as they are selected. How many outcomes are there?
    (A) 19 (B) 84 (C) 93 (D) 504 (E) 729 (F) none of these
11. A bag contains four blue balls and three red balls. Two balls are selected at random. What is the probability they have the same color?
    (A) 17/42 (B) 3/7 (C) 13/21 (D) 1/2 (E) 25/49 (F) none of these
12. For two events A, B in a sample space it is known that $\Pr[A|B] = 1/2$ and $\Pr[B'] = 1/4$. Find $\Pr[A \cap B]$.
    (A) 2/3 (B) 3/8 (C) 1/2 (D) 1/4 (E) 1/8 (F) none of these

13. The transition matrix of a Markov chain is $\begin{bmatrix} .3 & .6 & .1 \\ .4 & .6 & 0 \\ .2 & .2 & .6 \end{bmatrix}$. On the first observation the Markov chain is in state 1. What is the probability that on both of the following two observations it will be in state 3?
(A) .08 (B) .04 (C) .12 (D) .18 (E) .06 (F) none of these

14. The transition matrix of a Markov chain is $\begin{bmatrix} .3 & .7 \\ .4 & .6 \end{bmatrix}$. On the first observation the chain is in state 2. What is the probability that two observations later it will be in state 1?
(A) .36 (B) .37 (C) .63 (D) .64 (E) .25 (F) none of these

15. A Markov chain has transition matrix $\begin{bmatrix} .2 & .8 \\ 1 & 0 \end{bmatrix}$ What is the long run probability of the chain being in state 2?
(A) 4/9 (B) 5/9 (C) 5/8 (D) 3/8 (E) 1/2 (F) none of these

16. A feasible set is given by the following inequalities:

$$\begin{aligned} x &\geq 0 \\ y &\geq 0 \\ x + y &\leq 3 \\ x + 2y &\leq 4 \end{aligned}$$

Which of the following points belongs to this feasible set?
(A) (0, 3) (B) (1, 1) (C) (4, 0) (D) (2, 2) (E) (−1, 3) (F) none of these

17. Find the maximum value of $x - 9y$ subject to the following constraints:

$$\begin{aligned} x &\geq 1 \\ 2y - x &\geq 1 \\ -x - y &\geq -8 \end{aligned}$$

(A) −3 (B) −5 (C) −8 (D) −62 (E) −22 (F) none of these

18. What is the slope of the line passing through the points (1, 2) and (3, −1)?
(A) −1/2 (B) 1/2 (C) 3/2 (D) −3/2 (E) 0 (F) none of these

19. A Markov chain has transition matrix

$$\begin{bmatrix} 0 & 0 & 1 \\ 0 & .5 & .5 \\ .4 & .3 & .3 \end{bmatrix}.$$

Find the vector of stable probabilities for this chain.
(A) [.4, .1, .5] (B) [.3, .5, .2] (C) [.3, .3, .5] (D) [.5, .2, .3] (E) [.2, .3, .5] (F) none of these

20. Find the entry in the second row, first column of the matrix $AB - C$, where

$$A = \begin{bmatrix} 1 & 2 & -1 \\ 4 & 0 & 5 \end{bmatrix}, \quad B = \begin{bmatrix} 4 & 6 \\ -2 & -1 \\ 2 & 6 \end{bmatrix}, \quad \text{and} \quad C = \begin{bmatrix} 7 & 7 \\ 8 & -9 \end{bmatrix}.$$

(A) 63 (B) 18 (C) 0 (D) −9 (E) −13 (F) none of these

21. A random variable X takes only the values 1 and 2, and it has expected value 1.3. Find the probability that $X = 1$.
(A) .3 (B) .4 (C) .5 (D) .6 (E) .7 (F) none of these

22. 20% of the seats in a classroom are red, and the remaining 80% are blue. 10% of the red ones are broken, while 30% of the blue ones are broken. A student is assigned a seat at random, and it turns out the seat is

broken. What is the probability that the assigned seat was red?
(A) 1/5 (B) 4/5 (C) 12/13 (D) 1/13 (E) 6/11 (F) none of these

23. Erin needs to buy two sweaters and two hats. The store has five sweaters and six hats which would fit Erin. How many choices does Erin have?
(A) 25 (B) 55 (C) 150 (D) 330 (E) 600 (F) none of these

24. An experiment consists in picking at random one of the digits {0, 1, 2, 3, 4, 5, 6, 7, 8, 9}. The experiment is performed independently seven times and the results are recorded in the order in which they were obtained. What is the probability that the seven digits form your telephone number? (If you do not have a telephone then you may consider that your number is 855-5236.)
(A) $7!/7^{10}$ (B) $7!/10^7$ (C) $1/7!$ (D) $1/C(10, 7)$ (E) $1/10^7$ (F) none of these

25. A final exam consists of 100 multiple choice questions. Each question has five answers, exactly one of which is correct. A student chooses the answer to each question at random, and the 100 choices are independent. What is the expected number of incorrect answers the student will obtain?
(A) 75 (B) 80 (C) 90 (D) 85 (E) 100 (F) none of these

26. The Finite Cookie Co. makes three kinds of cookies. The A cookie requires 2 oz. flour, 1 oz. oatmeal, and 10 chocolate chips. The B cookie requires 1 oz. flour, 1/2 oz. sugar, and 5 chocolate chips. The C cookie requires 1 oz. oatmeal, 1 oz. sugar, and 7 chocolate chips. A system of equations is set up in order to determine how many cookies of each kind must be baked in order to use the entire supply of 600 oz. flour, 600 oz. oatmeal, 300 oz. sugar, and 1200 chocolate chips. Exactly one of the following statements is true.
(A) The system has 3 equations and 3 unknowns.
(B) The system has 4 equations and 3 unknowns.
(C) The system has 3 equations and 4 unknowns.
(D) The system has exactly two solutions.
(E) None of these.

27. The augmented matrices below correspond to certain systems of linear equations. Of these systems, exactly two have no solutions. Which are they?

(1) $\left[\begin{array}{cccc|c} 2 & 6 & 4 & 2 & 5 \\ 1 & 3 & 3 & 1 & \frac{5}{2} \end{array}\right]$ (2) $\left[\begin{array}{cccc|c} 2 & 6 & 4 & 2 & 5 \\ 1 & 3 & 2 & 1 & 5 \end{array}\right]$

(3) $\left[\begin{array}{ccc|c} 1 & 2 & 4 & 9 \\ 2 & 5 & 9 & 3 \\ 1 & 2 & 6 & -3 \end{array}\right]$ (4) $\left[\begin{array}{cccc|c} 1 & 2 & -3 & 4 & 0 \\ 2 & 4 & 6 & -9 & 3 \\ 5 & 10 & -3 & 3 & 4 \end{array}\right]$

(A) (1) and (2) (B) (1) and (3) (C) (1) and (4)
(D) (2) and (3) (E) (2) and (4) (F) (3) and (4) (G) none of these

28. The sets A, B, and C partition a universal set containing 63 elements. It is known that $n(A) = 2n(B)$ and $n(C) = 3n(A)$. Find $n(A)$.
(A) 7 (B) 9 (C) 14 (D) 18 (E) 21 (F) none of these

29. A mouse living in a two room apartment is observed at regular intervals. It is noted that, if the mouse is in one of the rooms on a given observation, then on the next observation it is twice as likely to be in the same room as it is to be in the other room. The observations of the mouse are described by a Markov chain. Find the transition matrix for this chain.

(A) $\begin{bmatrix} \frac{2}{3} & \frac{1}{3} \\ \frac{1}{3} & \frac{2}{3} \end{bmatrix}$ (B) $\begin{bmatrix} \frac{1}{3} & \frac{2}{3} \\ \frac{2}{3} & \frac{1}{3} \end{bmatrix}$

(C) $\begin{bmatrix} \frac{1}{3} & \frac{2}{3} \\ \frac{1}{3} & \frac{2}{3} \end{bmatrix}$ (D) $\begin{bmatrix} \frac{2}{3} & \frac{1}{3} \\ \frac{2}{3} & \frac{1}{3} \end{bmatrix}$ (E) none of the above

30. The matrices below are transition matrices for various Markov chains. Two of them are regular. Which ones?

(1) $\begin{bmatrix} 0 & 0 & 1 \\ .2 & .3 & .5 \\ .1 & .2 & .7 \end{bmatrix}$ (2) $\begin{bmatrix} 1 & 0 & 0 \\ .2 & .3 & .5 \\ .1 & .2 & .7 \end{bmatrix}$

(3) $\begin{bmatrix} .2 & .3 & .5 \\ 0 & 1 & 0 \\ .1 & .2 & .7 \end{bmatrix}$ (4) $\begin{bmatrix} .5 & .5 & 0 \\ .5 & 0 & .5 \\ 0 & .5 & .5 \end{bmatrix}$

(A) (1) and (2) (B) (1) and (3) (C) (1) and (4)
(D) (2) and (3) (E) (2) and (4) (F) (3) and (4) (G) none of these

ANSWER KEYS

Midterm—Version 1 Key

1. B
2. E
3. B
4. A
5. C
6. C
7. B
8. C
9. B
10. A
11. D
12. E
13. D
14. A
15. C
16. B
17. B
18. E
19. B
20. E
21. E
22. D
23. A
24. B
25. C

Midterm—Version 2 Key

1. C
2. A
3. A
4. B
5. C
6. C
7. D
8. D
9. A
10. C
11. F
12. C
13. D
14. B
15. A
16. C
17. B
18. A
19. E
20. B
21. E
22. F
23. F
24. D
25. B

Final—Version 1 Key

1. C
2. D
3. A
4. D
5. E
6. A
7. D
8. B
9. D
10. C
11. C
12. C
13. A
14. E
15. B
16. C
17. C
18. B
19. D
20. E
21. C
22. A
23. C
24. C
25. E
26. A
27. E
28. E
29. A
30. D
31. E
32. B
33. C

Final—Version 2 Key

1. D
2. B
3. C
4. C
5. A
6. D
7. A
8. C
9. C
10. A
11. B
12. B
13. E
14. A
15. A
16. B
17. C
18. D
19. E
20. B
21. E
22. D
23. C
24. E
25. B
26. B
27. E
28. C
29. A
30. C

APPENDIX

B Success Probabilities For Bernoulli Processes

The probability of obtaining exactly r successes in a Bernoulli process consisting of n trials with success probability p is $C(n, r)p^r(1-p)^{n-r}$. These probabilities are given for $n = 4$ through 10 and selected values of p in Table B.1. The probabilities for $n = 1$, 2, and 3 can easily be obtained by direct calculation. Success probabilities for $p = .55, .60, \ldots, .95$ can be obtained from Table B.1 by using the following fact:

Probability of r successes in n trials with success probability p
$=$ probability of $n - r$ successes in n trials with success probability $1 - p$

TABLE B.1 Success Probabilities for Bernoulli Processes

		p									
n	r	.05	.10	.15	.20	.25	.30	.35	.40	.45	.50
4	0	.8145	.6561	.5220	.4096	.3164	.2401	.1785	.1296	.0915	.0625
	1	.1715	.2916	.3685	.4096	.4219	.4116	.3845	.3456	.2995	.2500
	2	.0135	.0486	.0975	.1536	.2109	.2646	.3105	.3456	.3675	.3750
	3	.0005	.0036	.0115	.0256	.0469	.0756	.1115	.1536	.2005	.2500
	4	.0000	.0001	.0005	.0016	.0039	.0081	.0150	.0256	.0410	.0625
5	0	.7783	.5905	.4437	.3277	.2373	.1681	.1160	.0778	.0503	.0313
	1	.2036	.3280	.3915	.4096	.3955	.3601	.3124	.2592	.2059	.1563
	2	.0214	.0729	.1382	.2048	.2637	.3087	.3364	.3456	.3369	.3125
	3	.0011	.0081	.0244	.0512	.0879	.1323	.1811	.2304	.2757	.3125
	4	.0000	.0005	.0022	.0064	.0146	.0284	.0488	.0768	.1128	.1563
	5	.0000	.0000	.0001	.0003	.0010	.0024	.0053	.0102	.0185	.0313

TABLE B.1 (continued)

n	r	p .05	.10	.15	.20	.25	.30	.35	.40	.45	.50
6	0	.7351	.5314	.3771	.2621	.1780	.1176	.0754	.0467	.0277	.0156
	1	.2321	.3543	.3993	.3932	.3560	.3025	.2437	.1866	.1359	.0938
	2	.0305	.0984	.1762	.2458	.2966	.3241	.3280	.3110	.2780	.2344
	3	.0021	.0146	.0415	.0819	.1318	.1852	.2355	.2765	.3032	.3125
	4	.0001	.0012	.0055	.0154	.0330	.0595	.0951	.1382	.1861	.2344
	5	.0000	.0001	.0004	.0015	.0044	.0102	.0205	.0369	.0609	.0938
	6	.0000	.0000	.0000	.0001	.0002	.0007	.0018	.0041	.0083	.0156
7	0	.6983	.4783	.3206	.2097	.1335	.0824	.0490	.0280	.0152	.0078
	1	.2573	.3720	.3960	.3670	.3115	.2471	.1848	.1306	.0872	.0547
	2	.0406	.1240	.2097	.2753	.3115	.3177	.2985	.2613	.2140	.1641
	3	.0036	.0230	.0617	.1147	.1730	.2269	.2679	.2903	.2918	.2734
	4	.0002	.0026	.0109	.0287	.0577	.0972	.1442	.1935	.2388	.2734
	5	.0000	.0002	.0012	.0043	.0115	.0250	.0466	.0774	.1172	.1641
	6	.0000	.0000	.0001	.0004	.0013	.0036	.0084	.0172	.0320	.0547
	7	.0000	.0000	.0000	.0000	.0001	.0002	.0006	.0016	.0037	.0078
8	0	.6634	.4305	.2725	.1678	.1001	.0576	.0319	.0168	.0084	.0039
	1	.2793	.3826	.3847	.3355	.2670	.1977	.1373	.0896	.0548	.0313
	2	.0515	.1488	.2376	.2936	.3115	.2965	.2587	.2090	.1569	.1094
	3	.0054	.0331	.0839	.1468	.2076	.2541	.2786	.2787	.2568	.2188
	4	.0004	.0046	.0185	.0459	.0865	.1361	.1875	.2322	.2627	.2734
	5	.0000	.0004	.0026	.0092	.0231	.0467	.0808	.1239	.1719	.2188
	6	.0000	.0000	.0002	.0011	.0038	.0100	.0217	.0413	.0703	.1094
	7	.0000	.0000	.0000	.0001	.0004	.0012	.0033	.0079	.0164	.0313
	8	.0000	.0000	.0000	.0000	.0000	.0001	.0002	.0007	.0017	.0039
9	0	.6302	.3874	.2316	.1342	.0751	.0404	.0207	.0101	.0046	.0020
	1	.2985	.3874	.3679	.3020	.2253	.1556	.1004	.0605	.0339	.0176
	2	.0629	.1722	.2597	.3020	.3003	.2668	.2162	.1612	.1110	.0703
	3	.0077	.0446	.1069	.1762	.2336	.2668	.2716	.2508	.2119	.1641
	4	.0006	.0074	.0283	.0661	.1168	.1715	.2194	.2508	.2600	.2461
	5	.0000	.0008	.0050	.0165	.0389	.0735	.1181	.1672	.2128	.2461
	6	.0000	.0001	.0006	.0028	.0087	.0210	.0424	.0743	.1160	.1641
	7	.0000	.0000	.0000	.0003	.0012	.0039	.0098	.0212	.0407	.0703
	8	.0000	.0000	.0000	.0000	.0001	.0004	.0013	.0035	.0083	.0176
	9	.0000	.0000	.0000	.0000	.0000	.0000	.0001	.0003	.0008	.0020
10	0	.5987	.3487	.1969	.1074	.0563	.0282	.0135	.0060	.0025	.0010
	1	.3151	.3874	.3474	.2684	.1877	.1211	.0725	.0403	.0207	.0098
	2	.0746	.1937	.2759	.3020	.2816	.2335	.1757	.1209	.0763	.0439
	3	.0105	.0574	.1298	.2013	.2503	.2668	.2522	.2150	.1665	.1172
	4	.0010	.0112	.0401	.0881	.1460	.2001	.2377	.2508	.2384	.2051
	5	.0001	.0015	.0085	.0264	.0584	.1029	.1536	.2007	.2340	.2461
	6	.0000	.0001	.0012	.0055	.0162	.0368	.0689	.1115	.1596	.2051
	7	.0000	.0000	.0001	.0008	.0031	.0090	.0212	.0425	.0746	.1172
	8	.0000	.0000	.0000	.0001	.0004	.0014	.0043	.0106	.0229	.0439
	9	.0000	.0000	.0000	.0000	.0000	.0001	.0005	.0016	.0042	.0098
	10	.0000	.0000	.0000	.0000	.0000	.0000	.0000	.0001	.0003	.0010

APPENDIX C

Answers to Odd-Numbered Exercises

CHAPTER 1

Section 1.1

1. (*a*) False (*b*) false (*c*) true
3. $(R \cup S) \cap T = \{a, b, c\}$
5. $B = \{p\}$, $C = \{q, r\}$; $B = \{q\}$, $C = \{p, r\}$; $B = \{r\}$, $C = \{p, q\}$; also $B = \{q, r\}$, $C = \{p\}$; $B = \{p, r\}$, $C = \{q\}$; $B = \{p, q\}$, $C = \{r\}$
7. (*a*) True (*b*) false (*c*) true (*d*) false (*e*) false (*f*) true
9. (*a*) $\{u, v, x, 1, 3\}$ (*b*) $\{u, v, x, y, z, 2, 3\}$ (*c*) $\{u, z\}$
11. (*a*) $A \cup B = \{a, b, c, 2, 3\}$ (*b*) $B \cap C = \{2, 3\}$ (*c*) $(A \cup B) \cap (B \cup C) = \{a, 2, 3\}$ (*d*) $A' = \{1, 2, 3\}$ (*e*) $A \cap B' = \{b, c\}$ (*f*) $A \cup C' = \{a, b, c\}$
13. (*a*) $A \cap B = \{x : x$ owns a GM car *and* x works for GM$\}$
    (*b*) $B \cap A' = \{x : x$ works for GM and x does not own a GM car$\}$
    (*c*) $(A \cup B) \cap D = \{x : x$ owns stock in GM and also x owns a GM car or x works for GM$\}$
    (*d*) $C \cap A = \{x : x$ owns a GM car and x is the president of GM$\}$
15. (*a*) No (*b*) yes (*c*) yes (*d*) no
17. (*a*) Yes (*b*) no (*c*) yes
19. $A = X \cap Y, B = X \cap Z', C = Y \cup Z$
21. (*a*) $\varnothing, \{x\}$ (*b*) $\varnothing, \{x\}, \{y\}, \{x, y\}$
    (*c*) $\varnothing, \{x\}, \{y\}, \{z\}, \{x, y\}, \{y, z\}, \{x, z\}, \{x, y, z\}$
23. $Z = \{b, 4, 6\}$ $(Z' = \{a, c, 2\})$, $Y = \{b, 2, 4\}$ $(Y' = \{a, c, 6\})$, $X = \{b, c, 2, 4, 6\}$
    or
    $Z = \{b, 4, 6\}$ $(Z' = \{a, c, z\})$, $Y = \{b, 2, 4, 6\}$ $(Y' = \{a, c\})$, $X = \{b, c, 2, 4\}$
25. (*a*) $A \times B = \{(a, a), (a, b), (a, d), (b, a), (b, b), (b, d), (c, a), (c, b), (c, d)\}$
    (*b*) $(A \times B) \cap (B \times A) = \{(a, a), (a, b), (b, a), (b, b)\}$

27. $A = \{a, b\}$, $B = \{1, 2, 3\}$
29. (*a*) Yes (*b*) yes (*c*) no (*d*) no
31. $C \times A = \{(d, 1), (d, 2), (e, 1), (e, 2)\}$
33. 23
35. There are 16 subsets of S which do not include a or b. There are 16 subsets of S which include a, but not b.

Section 1.2

1. Figure C1.1
3. (*a*) v, x, y, z (*b*) y (*c*) v, w, x, y, z (*d*) v, y
5. (*a*) False (*b*) true (*c*) false (*d*) true
7. (*a*) $(B \cap C) \cap A'$ (*b*) $[B \cap (A \cup C)'] \cup [C \cap (A \cup B)']$
(*c*) $(A \cup B \cup C)' \cup (B \cap C)$
9. (*c*) and (*f*)
11. 5
13. 60
15. (*b*), (*d*)
17. $A \times B = \{(1, v), (1, w), (2, v), (2, w), (3, v), (3, w)\}$, $A \times \{v\} = \{(1, v), (2, v), (3, v)\}$, and $A \times \{w\} = \{(1, w), (2, w), (3, w)\}$; clearly, $A \times \{v\} \cup A \times \{w\} = A \times B$ and $A \times \{v\} \cap A \times \{w\} = \emptyset$. Hence, these sets form a partition of $A \times B$.
19. (*a*) $n(A \times B) = 5 \cdot 2 = 10$ (*b*) $n(B \times B \times B) = 2 \cdot 2 \cdot 2 = 8$
21. 15
23. If $n(B) = 4$, there are 4 ways because B must contain $A[n(A) = 3]$ so you must choose one element from the four left in $C \cap A'$. If $n(B) = 5$, there are 6 ways: if $C = \{1, 2, 3, 4, 5, 6, 7\}$ and $A = \{1, 2, 3\}$, then you may choose:

$B = \{1, 2, 3, 4, 5\}$ $B = \{1, 2, 3, 4, 6\}$ $B = \{1, 2, 3, 4, 7\}$
$B = \{1, 2, 3, 5, 6\}$ $B = \{1, 2, 3, 5, 7\}$ $B = \{1, 2, 3, 6, 7\}$

FIGURE C1.1

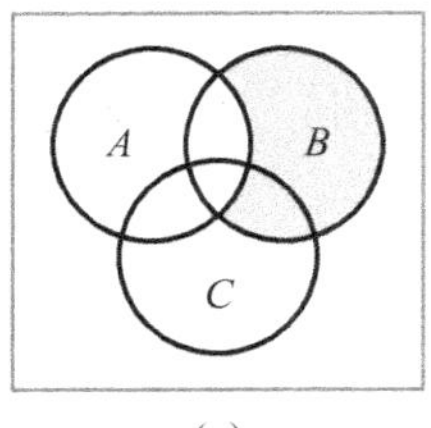

(*a*)

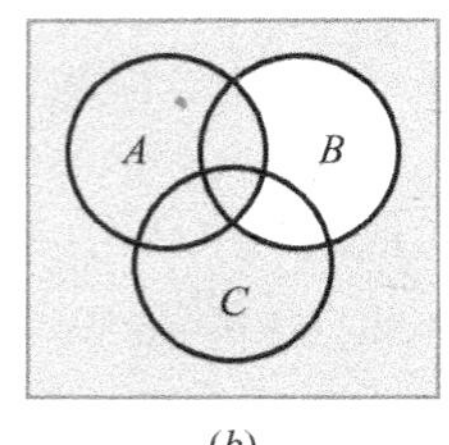

(*b*)

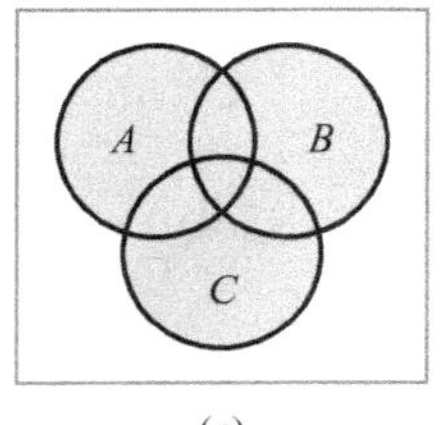

(*c*)

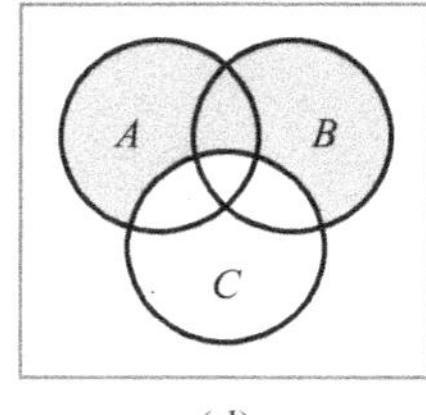

(*d*)

25. $n(X_1) = 4, n(X_2) = 9, n(X_3) = 6$
27. $n(X_1) = 10, n(X_2) = 5, n(X_3) = 25$
29. $n(X_1) = 16$
31. 25
33. $n((A \cup B \cup C) \cap D) = 80$

Section 1.3

1. (*a*) 21 (*b*) 31 (*c*) 7
3. 55
5. 110
7. 23
9. 10
11. 36
13. 7 types of phones have improved both reliability and durability.
15. 37
17. 4
19. 10
21. 32
23. 15
25. 8
27. (*a*) 50 (*b*) 0 (*c*) 30
29. There is not enough information to determine the exact number of students who like canoeing and exactly one of hiking or camping; however, it is known that this number is at most 30.
31. 9
33. 1400
35. 4 people owned only a laptop.

Section 1.4

1. $\{HHH, HHT, HTH, HTT, THH, THT, TTH, TTT\}$
3. 120
5. $S = \{0, 1, 2, 3, 4\}$
7. Each outcome is an ordered pair taken from $A = \{0, 2, 4, 6\}$. $S = A \times A$, $n(S) = 16$.
9. 84
11. 36
13. 243
15. $U =$ untrained, $T =$ trained, $S = \{UTU, UUT, UUU, TUU\}$ (see Figure C1.2)
17. (*a*) $5^4 = 625$ (*b*) $4^4 = 256$ (*c*) $4^4 = 256$
19. (*a*) Figure C1.3 (*b*) Figure C1.4
21. 2460
23. 16
25. 7
27. 19
29. $1 \times 4 + 1 \times 2 = 6$
31. $5 \times 9^3 = 3645$
33. 14
35. 72 ways

FIGURE C1.2

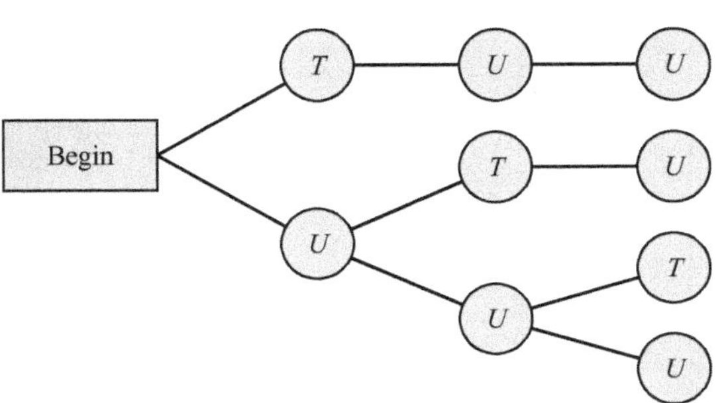

FIGURE C1.3

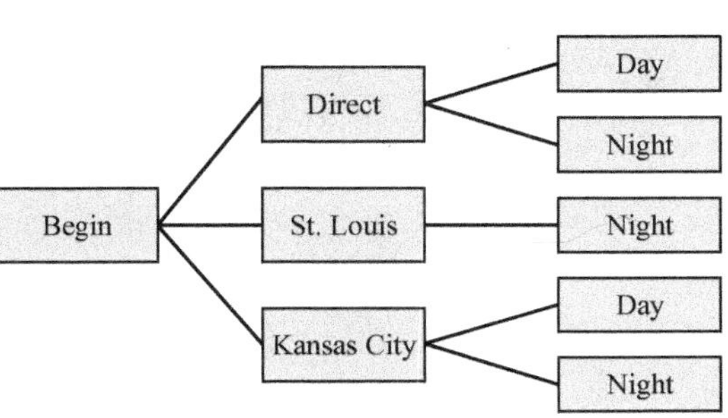

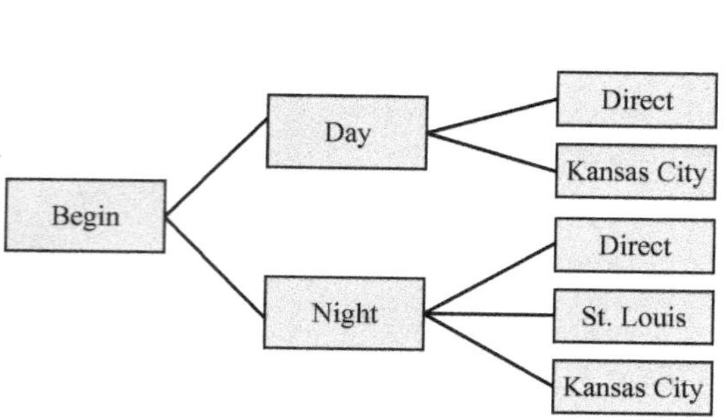

FIGURE C1.4

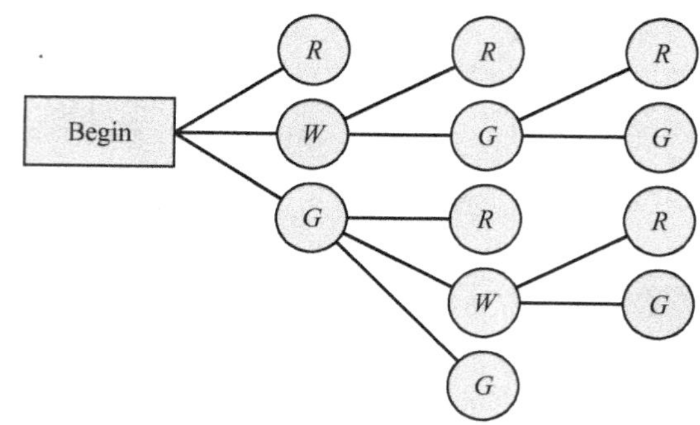

FIGURE C1.5

Review Exercises

1. (*a*) $A \cap B = \{2, x\}$ (*b*) $A \cup B = \{1, 2, 3, 4, u, v, x, y, z\}$ (*c*) $(A \cap B) \cup C = \{2, 3, x, z\}$
3. (*a*) $\{m, p, s\}$ (*b*) $\{k, m, p, r, s, y\}$
5. $(A \times B) \cap (B \times A) = \{(1, 1), (1, y), (y, 1), (y, y)\}$
7. 240
9. (*a*) Cannot be determined (*b*) can be determined, 8
11. 147
13. $65 - 10 = 55$
15. 139
17. Figure C1.5 $S = \{R, WR, WGR, WGG, GR, GWR, GWG, GG\}$
19. Figure C1.6 $S = \{RW, RG, WR, WW, WG, GR, GW, GG\}$
21. 210
23. $3 \times 4 \times 5 = 60$
25. 15
27. 24
29. Figure C1.7 R = report, S = market survey.
    The set of work schedules = $\{SS, SRR, RSR, RRS, RRRR\}$

FIGURE C1.6

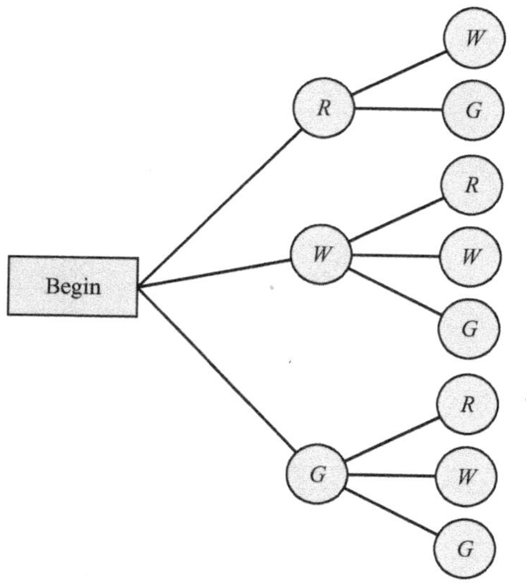

FIGURE C1.7

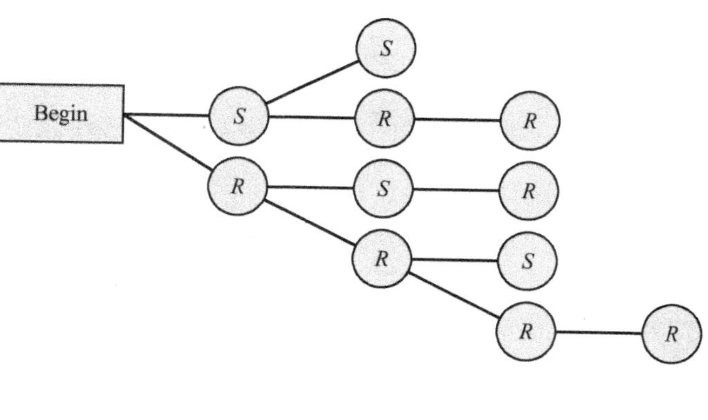

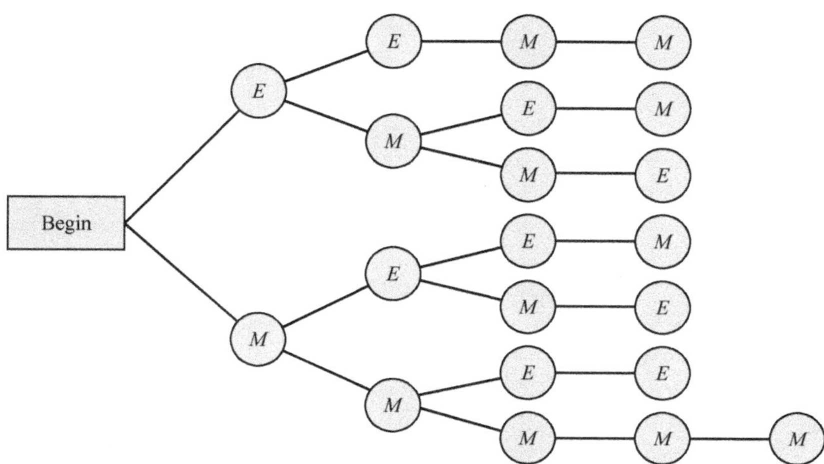

FIGURE C1.8

31. 6
33. Figure C1.8 $S = \{EEMM, EMEM, EMME, MEEM, MEME, MMEE, MMMMM\}$
35. $X = \{2, 3, 4, 8, 9, 10, 14, 15, 16, 20\}$
37. (*a*) 10 (*b*) 29

CHAPTER 2

Section 2.1

1. Let S denote sale; N, no sale.
   $S = \{SS, SNS, SNN, NSS, NSN, NN\}$
3. .3
5. $E = \{(3, 1), (3, 2), (3, 4), (3, 5), (3, 6), (1, 3), (2, 3), (4, 3), (5, 3), (6, 3)\}$
   $F = E \cup \{(3, 3)\}$
   $G = \{(1, 2), (1, 4), (1, 6), (2, 1), (2, 3), (2, 5), (3, 2), (3, 4), (3, 6), (4, 1), (4, 3), (4, 5), (5, 2), (5, 4), (5, 6), (6, 1), (6, 3), (6, 5)\}$
   $H = \{(1, 1), (1, 2), (1, 3), (1, 4), (1, 5), (1, 6), (2, 1), (2, 2), (2, 3), (2, 4), (2, 5), (3, 1), (3, 2), (3, 3), (3, 4), (4, 1), (4, 2), (4, 3), (5, 1), (5, 2), (6, 1)\}$
7. $S = \{QQ, QD, QN, DQ, DN, DDQ, DDN, DDDQ, DDDN, N\}$
9. 26
11. .15
13. $\frac{1}{12}$
15. $w_1 = w_2 = \frac{3}{10}, w_3 = w_4 = w_5 = w_6 = \frac{1}{10}$
17. $a = 6$
19. $\frac{5}{9}$
21. $\Pr[E] = \frac{3}{10}, \Pr[F'] = 1 - \Pr[F] = \frac{7}{10}$
23. Pr[Pass the course] = Pr[A, B, C, or D] $= \frac{255}{300} = \frac{17}{20} = 0.85$
    Pr[Withdraw or Fail] = Pr[W or F] $= \frac{45}{300} = \frac{3}{20} = 0.15$

25. Pr[win 10] = .01, Pr[win 1000] = .0002, Pr[win 10,000] = .00001, Pr[lose] = .98979

27. (a) $4 \times 3 \times 3 = 36$ (b) $\frac{1}{36}$ (c) $\frac{1}{4}$

29. (a) 20 (b) $\frac{1}{20}$ (c) $\frac{9}{10}$

31. 8, $\frac{1}{8}$

33. 677

35. 6

37. 72

39. (a) $\{S, WS, NS, WWS, WNS, NWS, NNS\}$
(b) $\{WS, WNS, WNN, WNW, WWS, WWN, WWW, NWS, NWN, NWW, NNW\}$
(c) $\{WS, WNS, WNN, NWS, NWN, NNW\}$

Section 2.2

1. (a) 5040 (b) 56 (c) 504 (d) 2,598,960
3. $P(6, 4) = 360$
5. $P(5, 5) = 120$
7. $22 \times 22 = 484$
9. 60 numbers can be formed, 24 of which are less than 500.
11. $P(8, 2) = 56$
13. 720, $5 \times P(5, 4) = 600$
15. $P(9, 3) = 504$
17. $P(11, 7) = 1{,}663{,}200$
19. (a) $P(6, 4) = 360$ (b) $P(5, 3) = 60$
21. $P(5, 3) = 60$
23. (a) $P(10, 3) = 720$ (b) $3 \cdot P(9, 2) = 216$ (c) $P(9, 2) = 72$
25. 336
27. (a) $P(7, 4) = 840$ (b) 816
29. 3240
31. 30
33. 120
35. 2520
37. 72

Section 2.3

1. $C(5, 3) = 10$, $C(7, 4) = 35$, $C(8, 5) = 56$, $C(9, 2) \cdot C(9, 7) = 1296$
3. 252
5. 20 subsets have exactly 3 elements, 30 subsets have either 2 or 4 (15 subsets have 2 and 15 have 4).
7. (a) $C(8, 2) = 28$ (b) $C(8, 2) - C(3, 2) = 25$
9. (a) $C(5, 2) = 10$ (b) $C(3, 2) = 3$ (c) $3 \cdot 2 = 6$ (d) $C(5, 2) - C(2, 2) = 9$
11. 17
13. (a) $C(9, 3) = 84$ (b) $C(9, 3) - C(3, 3) - C(4, 3) = 79$
15. (a) $C(3, 2) \cdot C(5, 2) = 30$ (b) $C(3, 2) + C(5, 2) = 13$ (c) $C(13, 2) = 78$
17. $C(5, 2) \cdot C(4, 2) = 60$
19. (a) $C(6, 3) \cdot C(4, 2) = 120$ (b) $120 + C(6, 4) \cdot C(4, 1) = 180$
21. $3 \cdot C(6, 4) = 45$
23. (a) $C(14, 5) = 2002$ (b) $C(14, 5) - C(6, 5) - C(8, 5) = 1940$
25. $C(10, 2) - C(6, 2) - C(4, 2) = 24$
27. (a) $C(13, 3) \cdot C(39, 2) = 211{,}926$ (b) $4 \cdot 211{,}926 = 847{,}704$ (c) 685,464
29. $P(6, 3) - P(4, 3) - P(3, 3) = 90$
31. 35

33. $$\begin{aligned} C(n,2)+C(n,3) &= \frac{n!}{(n-2)!2!}+\frac{n!}{(n-3)!3!} \\ &= \frac{n(n-1)}{2}+\frac{n(n-1)(n-2)}{3\cdot 2} \\ &= \frac{n(n-1)}{2}\frac{3+n-2}{3}=\frac{n(n-1)}{2}\frac{n+1}{3} \\ &= \frac{(n+1)(n)(n-1)}{3\cdot 2}=\frac{(n+1)!}{(n-2)!3!}=C(n+1,3) \end{aligned}$$

35. $n = 1, 2, 3, 4, 5$

Section 2.4

1. $\dfrac{C(3,2)}{C(5,2)}=\dfrac{3}{10}$

3. $\dfrac{C(13,3)}{C(52,3)}=\dfrac{286}{22{,}100}=\dfrac{143}{11{,}050}=\dfrac{11}{850}$

5. $\dfrac{C(4,3)}{C(7,3)}=\dfrac{4}{35}$

7. $\frac{1}{216}$

9. Pr[both hired] $= \frac{3}{10}$, Pr[one, but not both] $= \frac{3}{5}$

11. $\dfrac{1}{C(8,2)}=\dfrac{1}{28}$

13. $\frac{125}{126}$

15. $\dfrac{C(5,2)C(5,2)}{C(10,4)}=\dfrac{100}{210}=\dfrac{10}{21}$

17. $\frac{1}{7}$

19. $\dfrac{C(4,2)C(5,3)+C(4,3)C(5,2)+C(4,4)(5,1)}{C(9,5)}=\dfrac{105}{126}$

21. (*a*) $\dfrac{P(9,2)}{P(10,3)}=\dfrac{1}{10}$ (*b*) $\dfrac{C(9,2)}{C(10,3)}=\dfrac{3}{10}$

23. $\frac{5}{8}$

27. $\frac{8}{32}=\frac{1}{4}$

29. (*a*) $\dfrac{C(4,1)\cdot C(5,2)}{C(9,3)}=\dfrac{10}{21}$ (*b*) $\dfrac{C(8,2)}{C(9,3)}=\dfrac{1}{3}$

31. $\dfrac{C(14,7)-C(8,7)-C(8,6)\cdot C(6,1)-C(8,1)\cdot C(6,6)}{C(14,7)}=\dfrac{3248}{3432}$

33. (*a*) 41580 (*b*) $\frac{3}{11}$

35. $n > 6$

37. $1 < n \leq 9$

Review Exercises

1. $S = \{(R,R,R), (R,R,B), (R,B,R), (R,B,B), (B,R,R), (B,R,B), (B,B,R)\}$. The event that at least one blue ball is drawn is $\{(R,R,B), (R,B,R), (R,B,B), (B,R,R), (B,R,B), (B,B,R)\}$

3. (*a*) $P(5,3) = 60$ (*b*) $C(5,3) = 10$

5. $\Pr[1] = \Pr[2] = \Pr[5] = \frac{1}{12}$, $\Pr[3] = \Pr[4] = \Pr[6] = \frac{1}{4}$

7. 1728

9. (*a*) $3 \times 14 \times 14 = 588$ (*b*) $3 \times 14 \times 13 = 546$

11. $\frac{5}{12}$

13. 24

15. .0001

17. $\frac{14}{36}=\frac{7}{18}$

19. $\frac{25}{28}$

21. 2510

23. $\frac{1}{5}$

25. (*a*) $C(24, 3) = 2024$ (*b*) $C(6, 3) = 20$
(*c*) $C(18, 3) = 816$ (*d*) $816 + C(18, 2) \cdot 6 = 1734$

27. (*a*) $\dfrac{48}{C(52, 5)}$ (*b*) $\dfrac{13 \cdot 48}{C(52, 5)}$ (*c*) $\dfrac{4 \cdot 10}{C(52, 5)}$

29. 80262

31. (*a*) $\dfrac{C(3, 2)}{C(6, 2)} = \dfrac{1}{5}$ (*b*) $\dfrac{C(6, 2) - C(3, 2)}{C(6, 2)} = \dfrac{4}{5}$ (*c*) $\frac{4}{15}$

33. $\frac{1}{24}$

35. (*a*) $P(6, 2) \cdot 3 \cdot 2 = 180$ (*b*) 90 (*c*) $\frac{1}{6}$

37. $1 \leq n \leq 9$

39. $\frac{4}{9}$

CHAPTER 3

Section 3.1

1. (*a*) .2 (*b*) .5 (*c*) .05
3. (*a*) .35 (*b*) .50 (*c*) 1.0
5. (*a*) .55 (*b*) .25 (*c*) .4
7. (*a*) .9 (*b*) .2 (*c*) .3
9. (*a*) .3 (*b*) .4 (*c*) .1
11. (*a*) .35 (*b*) 1 (*c*) .8 (*d*) .9 (*e*) .25 (*f*) 0
13. .2
15. .6
17. $\frac{5}{9}$
19. .86
21. $.6 + .7 - .5 = .8$
23. .25
25. (*a*) .6 (*b*) .4
27. .1
29. .88
31. Yes. Using a computer we find that K is approximately 0.1928.
33. $\frac{26}{45}$

Section 3.2

1. $\Pr[A \mid B] = \frac{2}{5}$, $\Pr[B \mid A] = \frac{1}{2}$
3. $\Pr[F \mid E] = \Pr[E \mid F] = 0$
5. $\Pr[B \mid A] = \frac{3}{8}$, $\Pr[B \mid A'] = \frac{1}{8}$
7. $\Pr[E \mid F] = .32$, $\Pr[E' \mid F] = .68$
9. (*a*) .5 (*b*) .2
11. $\frac{1}{2} = \Pr[A \mid B] = \dfrac{\Pr[A \cap B]}{\Pr[B]}$ so that $\Pr[B] = \frac{2}{5}$

    $\frac{1}{3} = \Pr[B \mid A] = \dfrac{\Pr[A \cap B]}{\Pr[A]}$ so that $\Pr[A] = \frac{3}{5}$

    Consequently, $\Pr[A] \times \Pr[B] = \frac{6}{25} \neq \frac{1}{5} = \Pr[A \cap B]$; so A and B are *not* independent.
13. Not independent
15. $\frac{3}{4}$
17. (*a*) $\frac{2}{5}$ (*b*) $\frac{1}{5}$ (*c*) $\frac{2}{11}$
19. .6
21. $\frac{2}{3}$
23. $\frac{11}{18}$
25. $\frac{2}{11}$

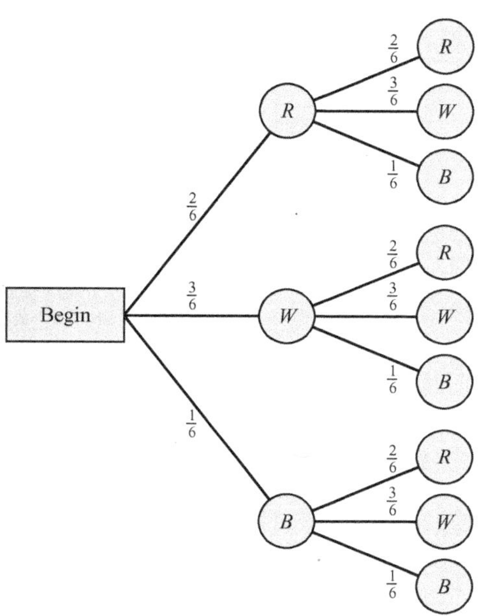

FIGURE C3.1

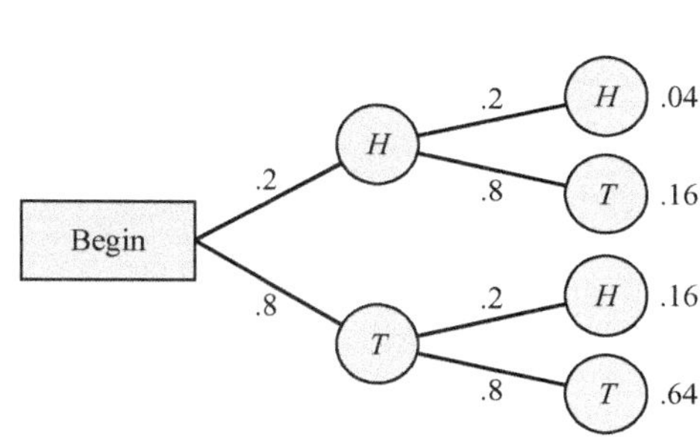

FIGURE C3.2

27. (a) $\dfrac{\frac{1}{66}}{\frac{10}{66}} = \dfrac{1}{10}$ (b) $\dfrac{\frac{2\cdot 3}{66}}{\frac{10}{66}} = \dfrac{6}{10}$

29. .6

31. Figure C3.1

33. .2 (for seat A103), .3 (for seat A102)

35. 3 cards in a run

Section 3.3

1. Figure C3.2
3. (a) Figure C3.3 (b) .44
5. Figure C3.4: Let G denote a green ball, NG a ball which is not green, R a red ball, and NR a ball which is not red
7. (a) $\frac{5}{9}$ (b) $\frac{5}{6}$
9. $\frac{19}{30}$
11. (a) .67 (b) .845
13. (a) $\frac{4}{7}$ (b) $\frac{3}{5}$
15. .64
17. Figure C3.5
19. .4096
21. Figure C3.6: Pr[2 red balls] $= \frac{1}{3}$, Pr[2 red | first is red] $= \frac{1}{2}$
23. $\frac{13}{24}$
25. Pr[exactly 2 profitable years in first 3 years] $= (.2)(.6)(.4) + (.2)(.4)(.4) + (.8)(.4)(.6) = .272$
27. .305
29. $\frac{27}{98}$
31. .002852
33. $\frac{1}{3}$

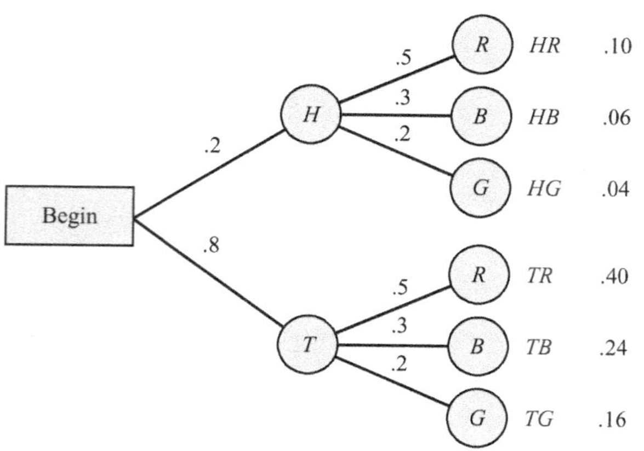

FIGURE C3.3

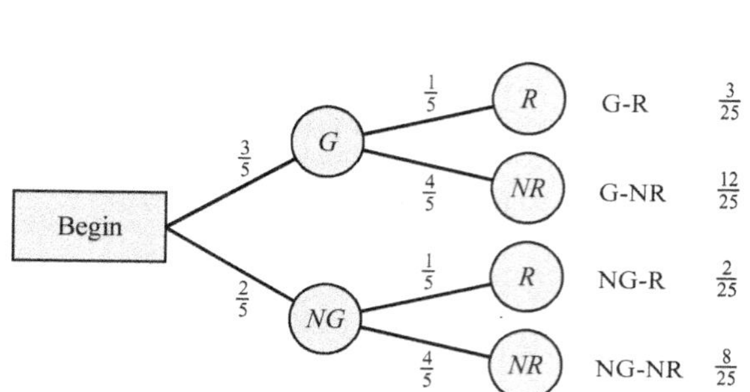

FIGURE C3.4

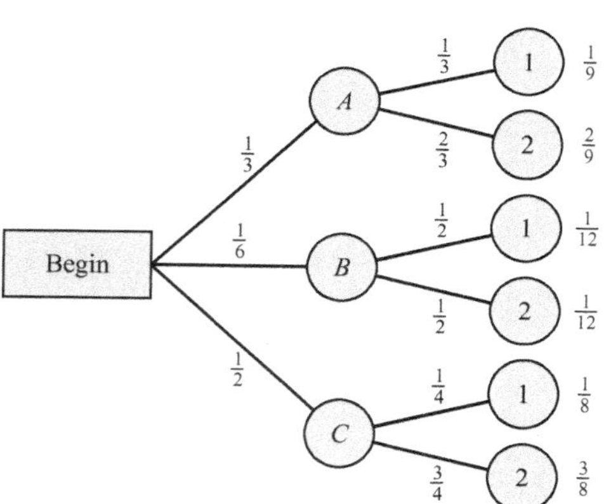

FIGURE C3.5

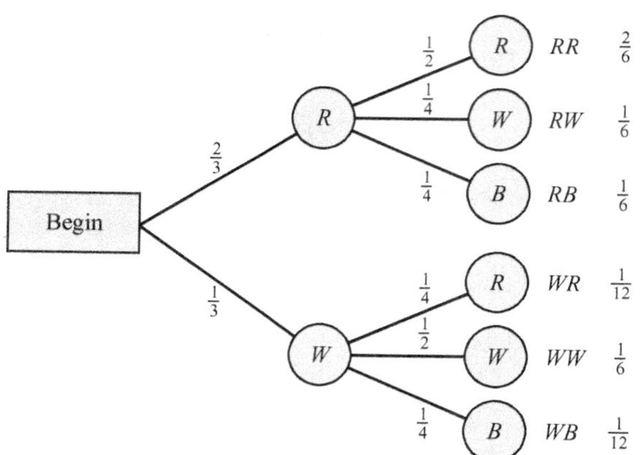

FIGURE C3.6

Section 3.4

1. (*a*) $\frac{1}{2}$ (*b*) $\frac{17}{24}$ (*c*) $\frac{2}{3}$ (*d*) $\frac{8}{17}$

3. $\frac{3}{4}$

5. (*a*) $\frac{1}{5}$ (*b*) $\frac{1}{5}$

7. $\Pr[X|B] = \frac{1}{2}$, $\Pr[Y|B \text{ or } W] = \frac{1}{4}$

9. $\Pr[\text{first } B \mid \text{second } R] = \dfrac{\frac{3}{6} \cdot \frac{2}{5}}{\frac{2}{6} \cdot \frac{1}{5} + \frac{1}{6} \cdot \frac{2}{5} + \frac{3}{6} \cdot \frac{2}{5}} = \dfrac{3}{5}$

11. $\frac{25}{61}$

13. $\frac{3}{5}$

15. $\dfrac{.6(.5)}{.6(.5) + .2(.75) + .2(.6)} = \dfrac{.30}{.57} = \dfrac{10}{19}$

17. $\frac{1}{3}$

19. $\frac{67}{94}$

21. .5

23. $\frac{6}{11}$

25. $\frac{.6(.3)}{.6(.3)+.3(.4)+.1(.7)} = \frac{.18}{.37} = \frac{18}{37}$

27. $\frac{2}{5}$

29. (*a*) $\frac{2}{3}$ (*b*) $\frac{4}{9}$

31. Pr[Best Air] $= \frac{10}{58}$, Pr[East-West] $= \frac{28}{58}$, Pr[Bi-Coastal] $= \frac{20}{58}$

33. Undergraduate degree

35. Senior (Pr[Senior | not a state resident] = .3075)

Review Exercises

1. (*a*) .54 (*b*) 1.0 (*c*) .23 (*d*) .27

3. (*a*) .7 (*b*) .65 (*c*) .05 (*d*) .35

5. $\frac{1}{3}$

7. (*a*) .6 (*b*) .5 (*c*) .6

9. .44

11. $\frac{5}{12}$

13. $\frac{3}{7}$

15. 1.0 (if exactly one mouse is gray, the other must be white, therefore male)

17. Pr[exactly one evaluated favorably] = .03 + .16 + .06 = .25

19. $\frac{18}{67}$

21. $\frac{625}{648}$

23. Figure C3.7

25. $\frac{2}{3}$

27. (*a*) $\frac{3}{5}$ (*b*) $\frac{3}{5}$ (*c*) $\frac{7}{12}$ (*d*) $\frac{7}{12}$

29. (*a*) $\frac{1}{2}$ (*b*) $\frac{1}{3}$

31. $\Pr[E \mid F] = \frac{1}{4}$, $\Pr[F \mid E] = \frac{1}{4}$

33. .15

35. $\Pr[F'] = .4$, $\Pr[E \cap F] = .2$

37. (*a*) .45 (*b*) .50 (*c*) .625

FIGURE C3.7

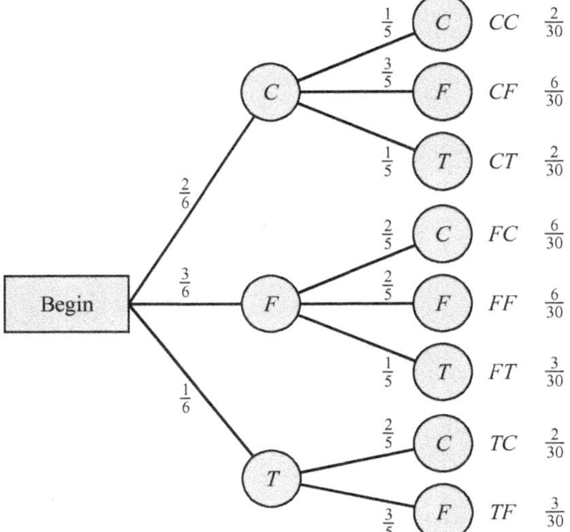

CHAPTER 4

Section 4.1

1. (*a*) $C(3, 1)(.4)^1(.6)^2 = .432$ (*b*) $C(5, 1)(.2)^1(.8)^4 = .4096$ (*c*) $C(5, 3)(\frac{1}{3})^3(\frac{2}{3})^2 = \dfrac{40}{243}$
3. (*a*) $C(6, 4)(.6)^4(.4)^2 = .31104$ (*b*) $C(5, 3)(.4)^3(.6)^2 = .2304$
5. (*a*) $1 - C(6, 0)(.8)^6 - C(6, 1)(.2)^1(.8)^5 - C(6, 2)(.2)^2(.8)^4 = .09888$
   (*b*) $C(5, 2)(.8)^2(.2)^3 + C(5, 1)(.8)^1(.2)^4 + C(5, 0)(.2)^5 = .05792.$
7. $1 - C(5, 5)(\frac{2}{5})^5 - C(5, 0)(\frac{3}{5})^5 = .912$
9. $C(5, 2)(.4)^2(.6)^3 + C(5, 3)(.4)^3(.6)^2 = .576$
11. $1 - (\frac{2}{3})^4 - (\frac{1}{3})^4 = \frac{64}{81}$
13. (*a*) $5(.6)(.4)^4 = .0768$ (*b*) $(.6)^5 = .07776$
    (*c*) $(.4)^5 + 5(.6)(.4)^4 = .08704$
15. $C(20, 18)(\frac{1}{2})^{20}$
17. $C(8, 2)(\frac{1}{4})^2(\frac{3}{4})^6$
19. $1 - C(3, 0)(\frac{1}{10})^0(\frac{9}{10})^3 = .271$
21.

Number of Lines	Probability of Catching at Least 4 Fish
4	$C(4, 4)(.7)^4 = (.7)^4 = .2401$
5	$C(5, 4)(.6)^4(.4) + C(5, 5)(.6)^5 = 5(.6)^4(.4) + 1(.6)^5 = .3370$
6	$C(6, 4)(.5)^4(.5)^2 + C(6, 5)(.5)^5(.5) + C(6, 6)(.5)^6 = 15(.5)^6 + 6(.5)^6 + (.5)^6 = .3438$

Therefore, the fisherman's chance of catching at least 4 fish is best with 6 lines.

23. 3
25. 29
27. $\frac{11}{64}$
29. $\frac{47}{128}$
31. $[210(\frac{1}{5})^4(\frac{4}{5})^6]^2 = .00776$
33. .2500
35. .6080
37. $C(8, 5) \times \left(\frac{4}{9}\right)^5 \times \left(\frac{5}{9}\right)^3$ (which is 0.1665, correct to four decimal places)

Section 4.2

1. (*a*) {3, 4, 5, 6}
1. (*b*)

Value of X	Probability
3	.064
4	.288
5	.432
6	.216

3. 0.3
5.

Value of X	Probability
0	$\frac{1}{15}$
1	$\frac{8}{15}$
2	$\frac{6}{15}$

7. $\frac{15}{28}$
9.

Value of X	Probability
0	.008
1	.096
2	.384
3	.512

11.

Value of X	Probability
4	$\frac{1}{3}$
6	$\frac{1}{3}$
8	$\frac{1}{3}$

13.

Value of X	Probability
1	$\frac{1}{5}$
2	$\frac{1}{5}$
3	$\frac{3}{5}$

15.

Value of X	Probability
0	.36
1	.54
2	.10

17.

Value of X	Probability
0	$\frac{4}{35}$
1	$\frac{18}{35}$
2	$\frac{12}{35}$
3	$\frac{1}{35}$

19.

Value of X	Probability
0	$C(48, 5)/C(52, 5)$
1	$C(48, 4)C(4, 1)/C(52, 5)$
2	$C(48, 3)C(4, 2)/C(52, 5)$
3	$C(48, 2)C(4, 3)/C(52, 5)$
4	$C(48, 1)C(4, 4)/C(52, 5)$

21.

Value of X	Probability
0	.48
1	.48
2	.04

23.

Value of X	Probability
0	$\frac{1}{56}$
1	$\frac{15}{56}$
2	$\frac{30}{56}$
3	$\frac{10}{56}$

25.

Value of X	Probability
1	$\frac{18}{36} = .50000$
2	$\frac{15}{36} = .41667$
3	$\frac{17}{216} = .07870$
4	$\frac{1}{216} = .00463$

27.

Value of X	Probability
0	.32768
1	.40960
2	.20480
3	.05120
4	.00640
5	.00032

29.

Value of X	Probability
0	$\frac{13}{72}$
1	$\frac{34}{72}$
2	$\frac{25}{72}$

31.

Value of X	Probability
−1	.9999
500	.0001

33.

Value of X	Probability
1	.19333
2	.45756
3	.28375
4	.06125
5	.00412

Note: Probabilities do not sum to 1 because of rounding to 5 decimal places.

35.

Value of X	Probability
1	$\frac{1}{27}$
2	$\frac{14}{27}$
3	$\frac{12}{27}$

Section 4.3

1. 3.5
3. $\frac{91}{21}$
5. -1.1
7.

Value of X	Probability	Product
-1	.3	$-.3$
-2	.2	$-.4$
1.5	.2	.3
2	.3	.6

$E[X] = .2$

9. \$0.15
11. $\frac{4}{7}$
13. 4
15. $\frac{7}{6}$
17. 1.624
19. $-\$9.30$, a loss of \$9.30
21. \$18.00
23. Expected value $= 12$, standard deviation $= \sqrt{97.6} \approx 9.879$
25. 1.4
27. 84.788
29. -2
31. $\frac{11}{9}$
33. $E[X] = 2.4$, $\sigma[X] = 0.8$
35. 50
37. $\text{Var}[X] = 12.69$, $\sigma[X] = 3.5623$ (accurate to 4 decimal places)

Review Exercises

1.

Value of X	Probability
-1	$\frac{1}{6}$
2	$\frac{1}{3}$
5	$\frac{1}{2}$

3.

Value of X	Probability
0	$\frac{1}{10}$
1	$\frac{6}{10}$
2	$\frac{3}{10}$

5. $\Pr[X = 3] = \frac{1}{6}$

7.

Value of X	Probability
$-.4$	$\frac{10}{56}$
$-.1$	$\frac{30}{56}$
.2	$\frac{15}{56}$
.5	$\frac{1}{56}$

9. \$2.40

11. (*a*)

Value of Y	Probability
350	$\frac{2}{35}$
400	$\frac{5}{35}$
450	$\frac{12}{35}$
500	$\frac{9}{35}$
550	$\frac{6}{35}$
600	$\frac{1}{35}$

(*b*) $E[Y] = \dfrac{3300}{7}$

(*c*) $\sigma[Y] = 58.90$

13. (*a*) $\mu = .4(365) = 146$
(*b*) $\sigma = \sqrt{87.6} = 9.36$

15.

Value of X	Probability
1	$\frac{1}{6}$
2	$\frac{1}{6}$
3	$\frac{4}{6}$

17. (*a*) The mean of X is $np = 100(.6)$. The mean of Y is $150p$. If the two means are equal, then $150p = 60$ and the value of p for Y must be $p = \frac{60}{150} = .4$.
(*b*) The variance for X is $100(.6)(.4) = 24$, and the variance for Y is $150(.4)(.6) = 36$. The variance for Y is larger.

19. $p = \frac{5}{11}$

21. (*a*) .0729 (*b*) .01

23. .729

25. .0466

27. (*a*) 0 (*b*) .0044

29. Expected income from bonuses = \$76.56; Standard deviation of income from bonuses = \$80.51

31.

Value of $X + Y$	Probability	Product
0	$\frac{6}{60}$	0
1	$\frac{24}{60}$	.4
2	$\frac{6}{60}$	.2
6	$\frac{12}{60}$	1.2
7	$\frac{12}{60}$	1.4

$E[X + Y] = 3.2$

33. $E[X] = \$72$

35. Expected gain to the state is \$764,012.91

CHAPTER 5

Section 5.1

1. (*a*) (Figure C5.1) (*b*) (Figure C5.2)
3. (*a*) x intercept $= 2$, y intercept $= -4$ (Figure C5.3)
(*b*) no x intercept, y intercept $= 5$ (Figure C5.4)
(*c*) x intercept $= -9$, y intercept $= 3$ (Figure C5.5)
(*d*) x intercept $= -2$, no y intercept (Figure C5.6)
5. (*a*) $Y = -4$ (*b*) $3x - y = 4$
7. (*a*) $\frac{5}{3}$ (*b*) 2
9. slope $= \frac{1}{4}$, x intercept $= -6$, y intercept $= \frac{3}{2}$
11. (Figure C5.7); (*a*) $y = (-\frac{2}{3})x + \frac{11}{3}$ (*b*) (Figure C5.8); $y = x + 2$
13. 110 tons

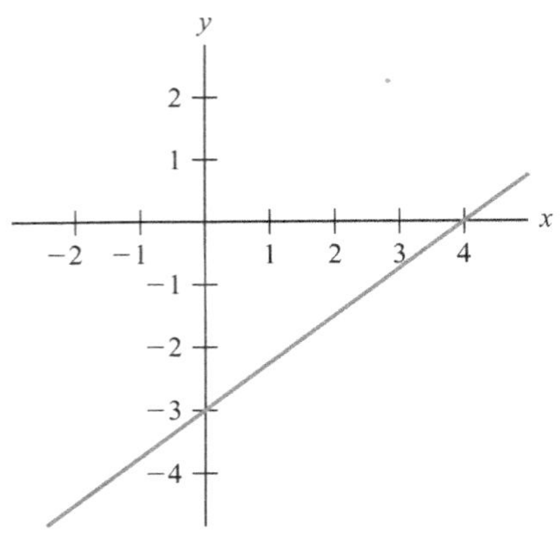

FIGURE C5.1

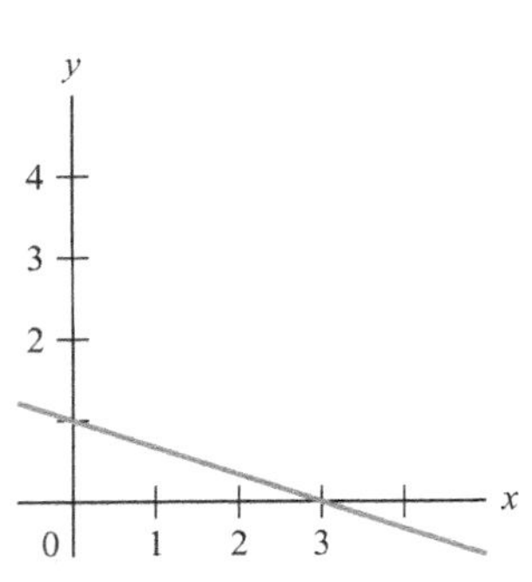

FIGURE C5.2

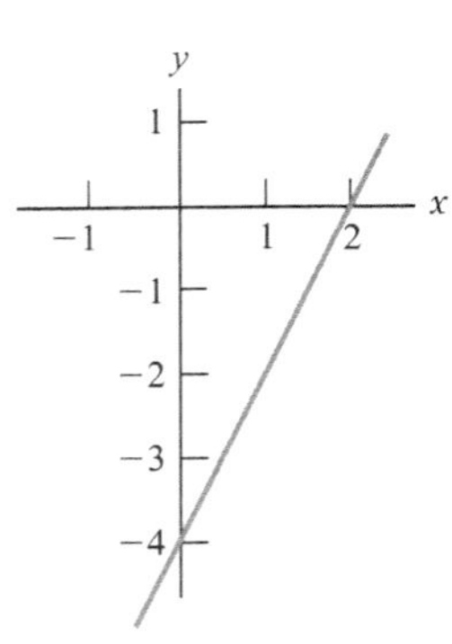

FIGURE C5.3

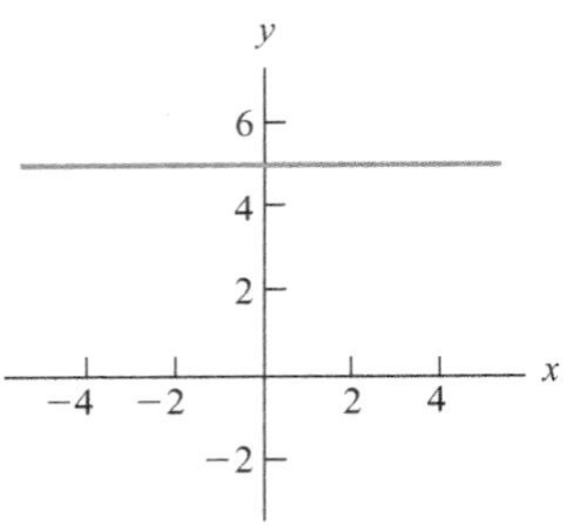

FIGURE C5.4

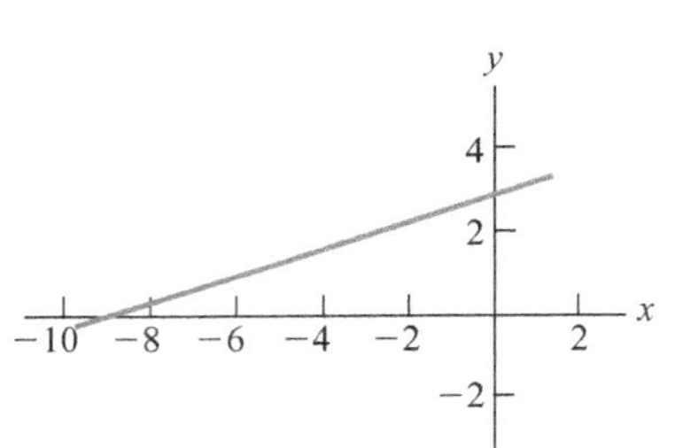

FIGURE C5.5

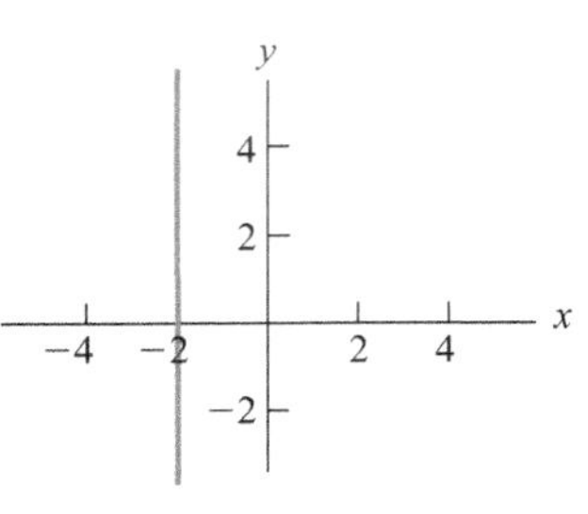

FIGURE C5.6

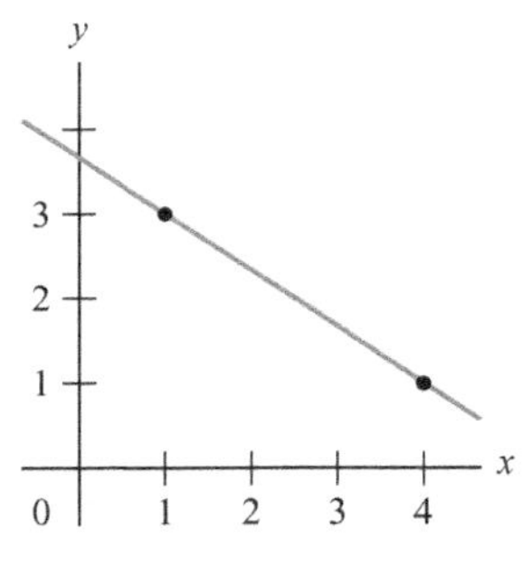

FIGURE C5.7

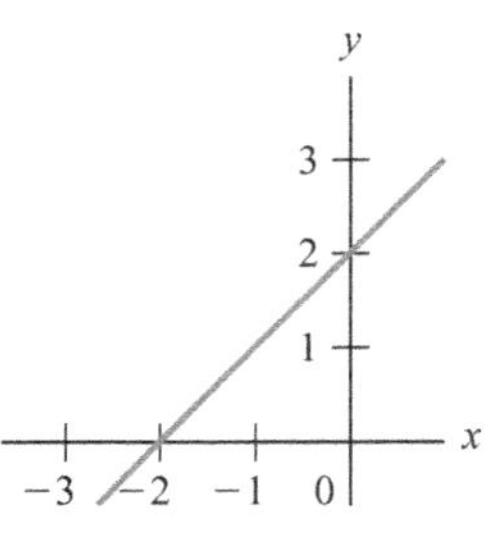

FIGURE C5.8

15. (Figure C5.9); $y = -x - 3$
17. (*a*) 18 defective balls will be produced
    (*b*) 675 balls should be produced

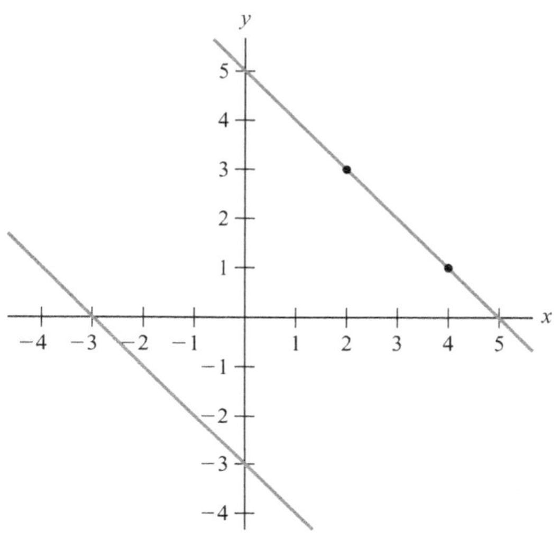

FIGURE C5.9

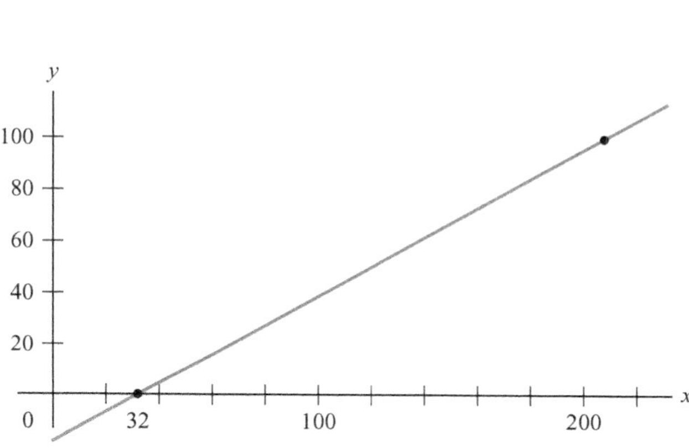

FIGURE C5.10

19. (Figure C5.10); $y = (\frac{5}{9})(x - 32)$; slope $= \frac{5}{9}$
x-axis is degrees fahrenheit
y-axis is degrees celsius

21. (*a*) $y_A = 40 + .3x$ and $y_B = 30 + .5x$
(*b*) Plan B is less expensive.
(*c*) Plan A is less expensive.
(*d*) 50 miles at a cost of \$55 for each plan.

25. cost (in dollars) $= 4x, \quad x \leq 300$
$= 12 + 5.5(x - 3000), \quad x > 3000$

where x is the number of gallons of water used

27. (*a*) Cost of wi-fi service $= .25x, \quad$ for $0 \leq x \leq 10$
$= 2.50 + 0.5(x - 10), \quad$ for $10 < x \leq 20$
$= 7.50 + 1.0(x - 20), \quad$ for $20 < x \leq 30$
$= 17.50 + 2.0(x - 30), \quad$ for $30 < x \leq 40$
(*b*) cost of 37 minutes of service = \$31.50

29. $Ax_1 + By_1 = C$ and $Ax_2 + By_2 = C$
Subtract to obtain:
$Ax_1 + By_1 - (Ax_2 + By_2) = 0$
$A(x_1 - x_2) + B(y_1 - y_2) = 0$
Proof by contradiction:
Suppose $x_1 = x_2$; then $x_1 - x_2 = 0$.
By the above equation: $B(y_1 - y_2) = 0$, and since $B \neq 0$ we conclude $y_1 - y_2 = 0$ or $y_1 = y_2$.
So $x_1 = x_2$ and $y_1 = y_2$ and therefore the points are not distinct.

Section 5.2

1. l = length; w = width; $l = 1.3w$; $l + w = 115$
3. x = number of adventure games produced
   y = number of fantasy games produced

$$\begin{aligned} 200x + 400y &= 16{,}800 \quad \text{(time from creative staff)} \\ 500x + 100y &= 6{,}000 \quad \text{(time from technical staff)} \end{aligned}$$

5. x = number of packages of Hiker's Mix prepared
   y = number of packages of Mountain Mix prepared

$$\begin{aligned} 40x + 20y &= 1{,}200 \quad \text{(peanuts)} \\ 20x + 60y &= 1{,}800 \quad \text{(raisins)} \\ 6x + 5y &= 2{,}700 \quad \text{(sunflower seeds)} \end{aligned}$$

7. (*a*) No solution (Figure C5.11) (*b*) $x = 0, y = -\frac{1}{2}$ (Figure C5.12)
9. (*a*) $x = 2 - \frac{1}{2}y$, y arbitrary. (The two lines are the same; solution set is the entire line.) (Figure C5.13)
   (*b*) $x = -1, y = 6$ (Figure C5.14)
11. Width = 50; length = 65
13. No solution. Using the solution to the first two equations, the third equation gives:
    $x + (\frac{1}{3})y = 70 + (\frac{1}{3})20 = 77.67 \neq 75$
15. $50{,}000 + 7500x = 1{,}000{,}000 - 125{,}000x$ gives $x = 7.17$ years.
17. (*a*) \$400,000 in utility bonds and \$600,000 in savings
    (*b*) \$250,000 in utility bonds and \$750,000 in savings
    (*c*) \$450,000 in utility bonds and \$550,000 in savings
19. 12 camp dinners and 10 water bottles.
21. \$30,000 = amount invested in stock X, \$70,000 = amount invested in stock Y
23. \$2,500,000 in bonds; \$5,000,000 in stocks; \$2,500,000 in real estate
25. $a = \frac{1}{2}$; $b = \frac{5}{2}$

FIGURE C5.11

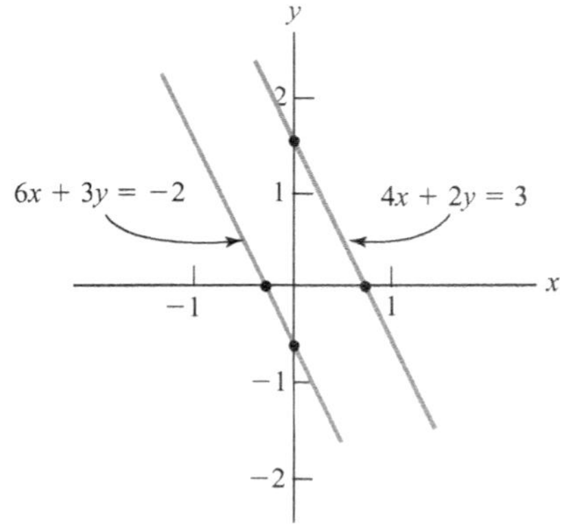

FIGURE C5.12

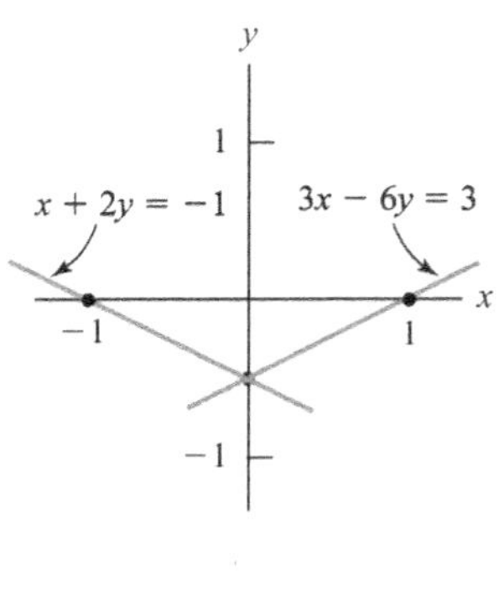

FIGURE C5.13

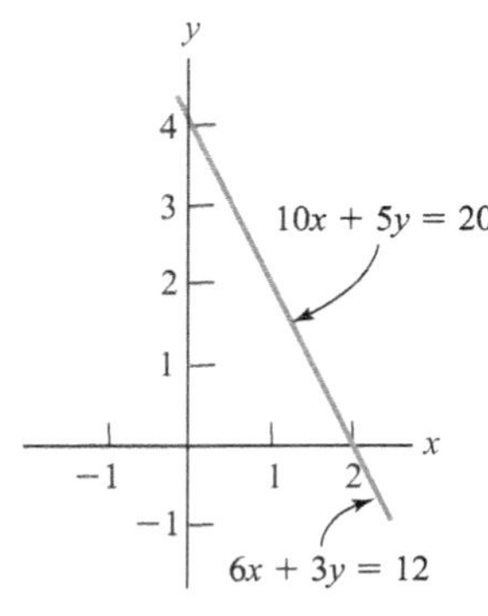

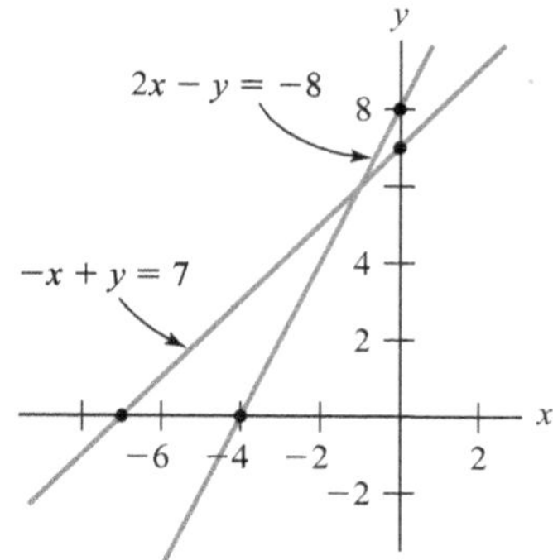

FIGURE C5.14

27. Tom is lying. His figures are not compatible with either Dick's or Harry's. In each case, the resulting system of equations does not have a solution with nonnegative prices. However, the claims by Dick and Harry are compatible. They are satisfied if each apple costs 35 cents and each orange costs 30 cents.
29. No, with only 25 ounces of raisins, all dough and apples cannot be used. He should make 50 large and no small muffins to use all raisins and apples.
31. No. The only schedule that uses all the time available is 4 trips down the North Fork and 40 trips through the Blue River Gorge.

Section 5.3

1. $x =$ number of airplanes; $y =$ number of boats; $z =$ number of cars

$$\begin{aligned} 100x + 50y + 50z &= 10{,}500 \\ 10x + 100y &= 1{,}500 \\ 200x + 50y + 150z &= 25{,}500 \end{aligned}$$

3. $x =$ number of packages of Hiker's Mix prepared
$y =$ number of packages of Biker's Mix prepared
$z =$ number of packages of Mike's Special mix prepared

$$\begin{aligned} 60x + 40y + 30z &= 18{,}000 && \text{(raisins)} \\ 20x + 40y + 30z &= 14{,}000 && \text{(peanuts)} \\ 10x + 20y + 30z &= 7{,}000 && \text{(chocolate chips)} \end{aligned}$$

5. (*a*) Not reduced: does not satisfy *A*, *B*, or *C* (*b*) reduced (*c*) not reduced: does not satisfy *B*.

7. (*a*) $\left[\begin{array}{rrr|r} 2 & -1 & -1 & 2 \\ 1 & 1 & 2 & 4 \end{array}\right]$ (*b*) $\left[\begin{array}{rr|r} 3 & -2 & 4 \\ 1 & 3 & -1 \end{array}\right]$

9. (*a*) $\left[\begin{array}{rrr|r} 3 & -1 & 6 & 8 \\ 2 & 1 & 4 & 7 \end{array}\right]$

(*b*) $3(-1) - 1(1) + 6(2) = -3 - 1 + 12 = 8$
$2(-1) + 1(1) + 4(2) = -2 + 1 + 8 = 7$

(c) If $x_2 = 0$, then x_1 and x_3 must satisfy

$$\begin{aligned} 3x_1 + 6x_3 &= 8 \\ 2x_1 + 4x_3 &= 7 \end{aligned}$$

and this system of equations has no solutions.

11. $x = 2, y = 0, z = \frac{1}{2}$
13. $x = 2 - (\frac{3}{2})z, y = -\frac{3}{4} - (\frac{1}{2})z$, z arbitrary
15. $x = 3 - z, y = -(\frac{1}{2})z$, z arbitrary
17. $x = 2, y = -2, z = -1$.
19. $x = 3, y = 1, z = -2$
21. $x = 9 - 5z, y = -4 + 2z$, z arbitrary
23. 50 airplanes, 10 boats, 100 cars
25. The system of equations in Exercise 3 does not have a solution with all nonnegative values, so the goals cannot be achieved with nonnegative returns. If we allow negative returns, then the goals can be achieved with returns of 18% on stocks, −2% on bonds, and 2% on money market funds.
27. (a) $x =$ time for old clients, $y =$ time for new clients, $z =$ time for office man., $w =$ time for long range planning

$$\begin{aligned} 2(x + y) &= x + y + z + w \\ x &= 2y \\ y &= 2w \\ x + y + z + w &= 40 \end{aligned} \qquad \text{or} \qquad \begin{aligned} x + y &= 20 \\ x - 2y &= 0 \\ y - 2w &= 0 \\ x + y + z + w &= 40 \end{aligned}$$

(b) $\frac{40}{3}$ hours for old clients; $\frac{20}{3}$ hours for new clients; $\frac{50}{3}$ hours for office management; $\frac{10}{3}$ hours for long range planning
29. (a) $x_1 = \frac{7}{4} - (\frac{7}{8})x_4, x_2 = (\frac{1}{2})x_3 - (\frac{5}{16})x_4 - \frac{3}{8}$, x_3 arbitrary, x_4 arbitrary

(b) Setting $x_1 = 0$, we obtain $x_2 = -1 + (\frac{1}{2})x_3$, x_3 arbitrary, $x_4 = 2$
31. No solution, this is an inconsistent system.
33. (a) $x = 1 + \left(\frac{1}{5}\right) z, y = 3 - \left(\frac{3}{5}\right) z$, z is arbitrary

(b) $\left(\frac{3}{2}, \frac{3}{2}, \frac{5}{2}\right)$
35. (a) $x = 100, y = 250, z = \frac{200}{3}$ (Notation as in Exercise 3)

(b) Solution has $z < 0$, so not meaningful. (Solution is $x = 100, y = 350, z = \frac{-200}{3}$)

(c) 2000 grams
37. (a) $(5 - 2y + z, -2 + y - z, y, z)$ where y and z are arbitrary.

(b) $y = 3$

(c) $z = -2$

Review Exercises

1. 2.5 years
3. 33 pages
5. $x = 2, y = 3$
7. $x = 2, y = -\frac{5}{2}$
9. Flo catches up to Shirley after $t = 3$ hours. At this time, Mary will have walked $3(3) = 9$ miles.
11. 9 years
13. (a)

$$\begin{aligned} 1(4) + 1(3) + 0(-1) + 3(-1) &= 4 + 3 - 3 = 4 \\ 0(4) + 1(3) - 1(-1) + 0(-1) &= 3 + 1 \qquad = 4 \\ 1(4) + 0(3) + 1(-1) - 2(-1) &= 4 - 1 + 2 = 5 \end{aligned}$$

(b)

$$\begin{aligned} 1(4) + 0(2) + 1(-1) &= 4 - 1 = 3 \\ 1(4) - 1(2) + 0(-1) &= 4 - 2 = 2 \\ 0(4) + 1(2) - 1(-1) &= 2 + 1 = 3 \end{aligned}$$

15. $x_1 = \frac{8}{5}, x_2 = \frac{6}{5}$
17. $x = 5 - 5z, y = 2 - 2z$, z arbitrary
19. $x_1 = 0, x_2 = -1, x_3 = -2$
21. $x_1 = \frac{2}{5}x_2 + 3$, x_2 arbitrary, $x_3 = 1 - \frac{1}{2}x_4$, x_4 arbitrary
23. 20 violins, 10 banjos, and 12 guitars.
25. b
27. a
29. c
31. (a) $x_1 = \frac{1}{2},\ x_2 = \frac{3}{2},\ x_3 = \frac{1}{2}$ (b) No solutions (c) $x_1 = 1 - x_3,\ x_2 = 1 + x_3,\ x_3$ arbitrary
33. There are 20 small, 12 medium, 10 large, and 4 extra-large boxes on the truck.

CHAPTER 6

Section 6.1

1. (a) 3×3 (b) 3×2 (c) 3×1, column vector
3. $A + B = \begin{bmatrix} 6 & 6 \\ 3 & 3 \end{bmatrix}$ $A - B = \begin{bmatrix} 4 & -2 \\ -1 & -3 \end{bmatrix}$
5. $3A + 2B = \begin{bmatrix} 7 & 1 & 7 \\ 4 & 4 & 3 \\ 12 & -14 & 0 \end{bmatrix}$

   $2A - B = \begin{bmatrix} 7 & -4 & 7 \\ -2 & 5 & 2 \\ 8 & 0 & -7 \end{bmatrix}$
7. (a) Not defined

   (b) $AB = \begin{bmatrix} -4 & 3 \\ 1 & 12 \end{bmatrix}$

   (c) $BC = \begin{bmatrix} 5 & -4 & 1 & 5 \\ 0 & -2 & -2 & 5 \\ 1 & -4 & -3 & 9 \end{bmatrix}$

   (d) $ABC = \begin{bmatrix} 10 & -6 & 4 & 5 \\ 23 & -24 & -1 & 37 \end{bmatrix}$

   (e) $(B + D)C = \begin{bmatrix} 0 & -2 & -2 & 5 \\ 8 & -10 & -2 & 17 \\ 8 & -10 & -2 & 17 \end{bmatrix}$
9. $\begin{bmatrix} -14 & 12 \\ 2 & -4 \\ -11 & 5 \end{bmatrix}$
11. Elisa wins the Epée with a score of 39, Arianna wins the Foil with a score of 24, and Arianna wins the Saber with a score of 43.
13. (a) $2B = \begin{bmatrix} 6 & 2 \\ -2 & 0 \\ 8 & 4 \end{bmatrix}$ (b) $BA = \begin{bmatrix} 9 & 7 \\ -2 & -2 \\ 14 & 10 \end{bmatrix}$ (c) $CBA = \begin{bmatrix} 50 & 38 \\ 39 & 29 \\ 39 & 29 \end{bmatrix}$
15. (a) $3A - B = \begin{bmatrix} 7 & -2 & -9 \\ 2 & 8 & 15 \end{bmatrix}$ (b) $CA = \begin{bmatrix} 7 & 4 & -3 \\ 4 & 0 & -6 \end{bmatrix}$

    (c) $(A - 2B)C$ is undefined (d) ABC is undefined

17. $AB = \begin{bmatrix} 1 & c-3 \\ 0 & c-2 \end{bmatrix}$ so if $AB = I$, then $c = 3$

19. (*a*) $2A + C = B$ is equivalent to $C = B - 2A = \begin{bmatrix} -6 & 5 \\ -9 & 2 \end{bmatrix}$

(*b*) $A + B + D = I$ is equivalent to $D = I - A - B = \begin{bmatrix} 1 & -2 \\ -3 & -1 \end{bmatrix}$

21. There are many possible answers. For example,

Set $A = \begin{bmatrix} 1 & -1 \\ 1 & -1 \end{bmatrix}, B = \begin{bmatrix} 2 & -2 \\ 2 & -2 \end{bmatrix}, C = \begin{bmatrix} 2 & 3 \\ 2 & 3 \end{bmatrix}$

23. $A^2 = \begin{bmatrix} 5 & 2 \\ 2 & 1 \end{bmatrix} \qquad A^3 = \begin{bmatrix} 12 & 5 \\ 5 & 2 \end{bmatrix}$

25. $[2 \quad 1] \begin{bmatrix} \frac{1}{2} & \frac{1}{2} \\ 1 & 0 \end{bmatrix} = [2 \quad 1]$, so

$XP^2 = (XP)P = XP = X$

27. $P^2 = \begin{bmatrix} 0 & 1 & 0 \\ 0 & 0 & 1 \\ \frac{2}{3} & 0 & \frac{1}{3} \end{bmatrix} \begin{bmatrix} 0 & 1 & 0 \\ 0 & 0 & 1 \\ \frac{2}{3} & 0 & \frac{1}{3} \end{bmatrix} = \begin{bmatrix} 0 & 0 & 1 \\ \frac{2}{3} & 0 & \frac{1}{3} \\ \frac{2}{9} & \frac{2}{3} & \frac{1}{9} \end{bmatrix}$

$P^4 = \begin{bmatrix} 0 & 0 & 1 \\ \frac{2}{3} & 0 & \frac{1}{3} \\ \frac{2}{9} & \frac{2}{3} & \frac{1}{9} \end{bmatrix} \begin{bmatrix} 0 & 0 & 1 \\ \frac{2}{3} & 0 & \frac{1}{3} \\ \frac{2}{9} & \frac{2}{3} & \frac{1}{9} \end{bmatrix} = \begin{bmatrix} \frac{2}{9} & \frac{2}{3} & \frac{1}{9} \\ \frac{2}{27} & \frac{2}{9} & \frac{19}{27} \\ \frac{38}{81} & \frac{2}{27} & \frac{37}{81} \end{bmatrix}$

29. (*a*) If $XP = X$, then $k(XP) = kX$ or $(kX)P = kX$; that is, if $Y = kX$, then $YP = Y$;
(*b*) let $Y = (\frac{2}{7})[1 \quad 1 \quad \frac{3}{2}] = [\frac{2}{7} \quad \frac{2}{7} \quad \frac{3}{7}]$

31. $X = [1 \quad 2 \quad 4]$ is one such vector and another is $[\frac{1}{4} \quad \frac{1}{2} \quad 1]$.

33. $AX = \begin{bmatrix} 1 & 2 & 1 \\ 2 & 3 & 1 \\ -2 & 4 & 6 \end{bmatrix} \begin{bmatrix} 2+t \\ 1-t \\ t \end{bmatrix} = \begin{bmatrix} 1(2+t) + 2(1-t) + t \\ 2(2+t) + 3(1-t) + t \\ -2(2+t) + 4(1-t) + 6t \end{bmatrix} = \begin{bmatrix} 4 \\ 7 \\ 0 \end{bmatrix}$

35. Solve $\begin{bmatrix} 1 & -2 \\ -3 & 4 \end{bmatrix} \begin{bmatrix} x_{11} & x_{12} \\ x_{21} & x_{22} \end{bmatrix} = \begin{bmatrix} x_{11} - 2x_{21} & x_{12} - 2x_{22} \\ -3x_{11} + 4x_{21} & 3x_{12} + 4x_{22} \end{bmatrix} = \begin{bmatrix} 10 & -7 \\ -22 & 15 \end{bmatrix}$

to obtain $x_{11} = 2, x_{12} = -1, x_{21} = -4, x_{22} = 3$. Therefore, $B = \begin{bmatrix} 2 & -1 \\ -4 & 3 \end{bmatrix}$

37. $x = 2, y = 5, z = 3$.

Section 6.2

1. Yes, $B = A^{-1}$

3. $y = 5$

5. $AA^{-1} = \begin{bmatrix} 3 & 2 \\ 4 & 3 \end{bmatrix} \begin{bmatrix} 3 & -2 \\ -4 & 3 \end{bmatrix} = \begin{bmatrix} 1 & 0 \\ 0 & 1 \end{bmatrix}$

7. $C^{-1} = \begin{bmatrix} \frac{3}{5} & \frac{1}{5} \\ -\frac{2}{5} & \frac{1}{5} \end{bmatrix} \qquad D^{-1} = \begin{bmatrix} 20 & -10 \\ -\frac{25}{2} & \frac{15}{2} \end{bmatrix}$

9. $A^{-1} = \begin{bmatrix} \frac{1}{2} & 0 \\ -\frac{3}{2} & 1 \end{bmatrix}$

If $AX = \begin{bmatrix} 1 \\ 0 \end{bmatrix}$, then $X = \begin{bmatrix} \frac{1}{2} \\ -\frac{3}{2} \end{bmatrix}$

If $AX = \begin{bmatrix} 1 \\ -1 \end{bmatrix}$, then $X = \begin{bmatrix} \frac{1}{2} \\ -\frac{5}{2} \end{bmatrix}$

11. No inverse

13. $A^{-1} = \begin{bmatrix} 0 & \frac{1}{2} & -\frac{1}{2} \\ 1 & 0 & -1 \\ 0 & 0 & 1 \end{bmatrix}$

15. (*a*) $\begin{bmatrix} 2 & 4 \\ 1 & 3 \end{bmatrix} \begin{bmatrix} x_1 \\ x_2 \end{bmatrix} = \begin{bmatrix} -2 \\ 4 \end{bmatrix}$

(*b*) $A^{-1} = \begin{bmatrix} \frac{3}{2} & -2 \\ -\frac{1}{2} & 1 \end{bmatrix}$ $\quad X = A^{-1} \begin{bmatrix} -2 \\ 4 \end{bmatrix} = \begin{bmatrix} -11 \\ 5 \end{bmatrix}$

17. $x = 3$

19. $A^{-1}B^{-1} = \begin{bmatrix} 1 & -2 \\ -2 & 5 \end{bmatrix} \begin{bmatrix} -5 & 3 \\ 2 & -1 \end{bmatrix} = \begin{bmatrix} -9 & 5 \\ 20 & -11 \end{bmatrix} = (BA)^{-1}$

$B^{-1}A^{-1} = \begin{bmatrix} -5 & 3 \\ 2 & -1 \end{bmatrix} \begin{bmatrix} 1 & -2 \\ -2 & 5 \end{bmatrix} = \begin{bmatrix} -11 & 25 \\ 4 & -9 \end{bmatrix} = (AB)^{-1}$

21. (*a*) $A^{-1} = \begin{bmatrix} -10 & 0 & -15 \\ -8 & 2 & -8 \\ -5 & 0 & -5 \end{bmatrix}$ $\quad$ (*b*) $AA^{-1}A = A$

23. (*a*) $x = -2$ $\quad$ (*b*) $\frac{1}{2}$

25. $A^{-1} = \begin{bmatrix} \frac{2}{5} & -\frac{1}{5} & \frac{1}{5} \\ \frac{1}{5} & \frac{2}{5} & -\frac{2}{5} \\ \frac{1}{5} & \frac{2}{5} & \frac{3}{5} \end{bmatrix}$ $\quad AX = \begin{bmatrix} 1 \\ 3 \\ 1 \end{bmatrix}$ has solution $X = A^{-1} \begin{bmatrix} 1 \\ 3 \\ 1 \end{bmatrix} = \begin{bmatrix} 0 \\ 1 \\ 2 \end{bmatrix}$.

$AX = \begin{bmatrix} 2 \\ 1 \\ 0 \end{bmatrix}$ has solution $X = A^{-1} \begin{bmatrix} 2 \\ 1 \\ 0 \end{bmatrix} = \begin{bmatrix} \frac{3}{5} \\ \frac{4}{5} \\ \frac{4}{5} \end{bmatrix}$

27. Each of the systems has the same coefficient matrix, call it A. Then A^{-1} exists and

$A^{-1} = \begin{bmatrix} -1 & 1 & 2 \\ 1 & 0 & -1 \\ 1 & -1 & -1 \end{bmatrix}$

(*a*) The system has solution $X = A^{-1} \begin{bmatrix} 15 \\ 1 \\ 10 \end{bmatrix} = \begin{bmatrix} 6 \\ 5 \\ 4 \end{bmatrix}$, therefore $x = 6, y = 5, z = 4$

(*b*) $x = 3, y = 3, z = 3$; $\quad$ (*c*) $x = 1, y = 0, z = -1$

29. $A^2 = \begin{bmatrix} 4 & 18 \\ 6 & 28 \end{bmatrix}$, $A^{-1} = \begin{bmatrix} \frac{5}{2} & -\frac{3}{2} \\ -\frac{1}{2} & \frac{1}{2} \end{bmatrix}$, $(A^{-1})(A^{-1}) = \begin{vmatrix} 7 & -\frac{9}{2} \\ -\frac{3}{2} & 1 \end{vmatrix}$,

$(AA)^{-1} = (A^2)^{-1} = \begin{bmatrix} 7 & -\frac{9}{2} \\ -\frac{3}{2} & 1 \end{bmatrix}$. Yes, $(A^{-1})(A^{-1}) = (AA)^{-1}$.

31. $A^{-1} = \begin{bmatrix} 1 & -b \\ 0 & 1 \end{bmatrix}$

33. $A^{-1} = \begin{bmatrix} \dfrac{d}{ad-bc} & -\dfrac{b}{ad-bc} \\ -\dfrac{c}{ad-bc} & \dfrac{a}{ad-bc} \end{bmatrix}$, $ad \neq bc$

35. $A^{-1} = \begin{bmatrix} 1 & -a & ac-b \\ 0 & 1 & -c \\ 0 & 0 & 1 \end{bmatrix}$

37. Yes. Letting $x = 3$ and $y = -2$ will make the statement true.

39. $A^{-1} = \begin{bmatrix} 1 & 0 & -1 & 1 & -1 \\ 0 & 1 & 0 & -2 & 2 \\ 0 & 0 & 0 & 1 & -1 \\ 0 & 0 & 0 & 1 & 0 \\ 0 & 0 & 1 & -1 & 1 \end{bmatrix}$

Section 6.3

1. $A = \begin{bmatrix} .1 & .3 \\ 2 & 0 \end{bmatrix}$ $\quad (I - A)^{-1} = \begin{bmatrix} \frac{10}{3} & 1 \\ \frac{20}{3} & 3 \end{bmatrix}$

(a) $\begin{bmatrix} \frac{10}{3} & 1 \\ \frac{20}{3} & 3 \end{bmatrix} \begin{bmatrix} 15 \\ 5 \end{bmatrix} = \begin{bmatrix} 55 \\ 115 \end{bmatrix}$

(b) $\begin{bmatrix} \frac{10}{3} & 1 \\ \frac{20}{3} & 3 \end{bmatrix} \begin{bmatrix} 1000 \\ 125 \end{bmatrix} = \begin{bmatrix} \frac{10,375}{3} \\ \frac{21,125}{3} \end{bmatrix}$

3. (a) $X = \begin{bmatrix} 7.6 & 4 & 2 \\ 16 & 15 & 5 \\ 14 & 10 & 5 \end{bmatrix} \begin{bmatrix} 20 \\ 20 \\ 8 \end{bmatrix} = \begin{bmatrix} 248 \\ 660 \\ 520 \end{bmatrix}$

(b) $\begin{bmatrix} 7.6 & 4 & 2 \\ 16 & 15 & 5 \\ 14 & 10 & 5 \end{bmatrix} \begin{bmatrix} 100 \\ 120 \\ 50 \end{bmatrix} = \begin{bmatrix} 1340 \\ 3650 \\ 2850 \end{bmatrix}$

5. $X = \begin{bmatrix} 7.6 & 4 & 2 \\ 16 & 15 & 5 \\ 14 & 10 & 5 \end{bmatrix} \begin{bmatrix} 100 \\ 60 \\ 0 \end{bmatrix} = \begin{bmatrix} 1000 \\ 2500 \\ 2000 \end{bmatrix}$

7. $A = \begin{bmatrix} 0.5 & 0.4 \\ 0.75 & 0.2 \end{bmatrix}$ $\quad (I - A)^{-1} = \begin{bmatrix} 8 & 4 \\ 7.5 & 5 \end{bmatrix}$

9. Yes, $(I - A)^{-1} = \begin{bmatrix} \frac{7}{2} & \frac{1}{2} \\ 4 & 2 \end{bmatrix}$

11. Yes, $(I - A)^{-1} = \begin{bmatrix} \frac{510}{183} & \frac{90}{183} & \frac{120}{183} \\ \frac{640}{183} & \frac{400}{183} & \frac{330}{183} \\ \frac{80}{183} & \frac{50}{183} & \frac{270}{183} \end{bmatrix}$

13. (a) $\begin{bmatrix} 74 \\ 102 \end{bmatrix}$ (b) $\begin{bmatrix} 158 \\ 204 \end{bmatrix}$ (c) If D is doubled, then the production schedule X must be doubled.

15. $(I - A)^{-1} = \begin{bmatrix} 8 & 4 \\ 7.5 & 5 \end{bmatrix}$ and $X = \begin{bmatrix} 20 \\ 20 \end{bmatrix}$

17. $(I - A)^{-1} = \begin{bmatrix} 20 & 10 \\ \frac{50}{3} & 10 \end{bmatrix}$ and $X = \begin{bmatrix} 170 \\ 150 \end{bmatrix}$

19. $(I - A)^{-1} = \begin{bmatrix} 2 & 3 & 3 \\ 0 & 15 & 10 \\ 0 & 5 & 5 \end{bmatrix}$ and $X = \begin{bmatrix} 15 \\ 35 \\ 15 \end{bmatrix}$

21. $(I-A)^{-1} = \begin{bmatrix} \frac{23}{9} & \frac{8}{9} & \frac{2}{9} \\ \frac{1}{9} & \frac{16}{9} & \frac{4}{9} \\ \frac{2}{3} & \frac{2}{3} & \frac{8}{3} \end{bmatrix}$ and $X = \begin{bmatrix} 174 \\ 78 \\ 288 \end{bmatrix}$

23. x_1 = amount of magnesium and x_2 = amount of aluminum produced.

$$A = \begin{bmatrix} .2 & .6 \\ .5 & .6 \end{bmatrix} \qquad (I-A)^{-1} = \begin{bmatrix} 20 & 30 \\ 25 & 40 \end{bmatrix} \qquad \text{and} \qquad X = (I-A)^{-1}\begin{bmatrix} 20 \\ 10 \end{bmatrix}$$

Required production is 700 units of magnesium and 900 units of aluminum.

25. Yes, the production schedule is 525 units of quinoa, 1000 units of coconut oil, and 1140 units of sesame seeds.

27. Let x_1 = number of units of calcium
x_2 = number of units of hydrogen
x_3 = number of units of sea salt

Then $A = \begin{bmatrix} .4 & 0 & .2 \\ .5 & .2 & .5 \\ .3 & .6 & .2 \end{bmatrix}$ $\qquad (I-A)^{-1} = \begin{bmatrix} 3.5417 & 1.250 & 1.667 \\ 5.7292 & 4.375 & 4.167 \\ 5.625 & 3.750 & 5.000 \end{bmatrix}$

and the required production scheduled is $x_1 = 230$, $x_2 = 455$, and $x_3 = 450$.

29. $A = \begin{bmatrix} .2 & c \\ .6 & .4 \end{bmatrix}$ and $(I-A)^{-1} = \begin{bmatrix} \frac{5}{4-5c} & \frac{25c}{3(4-5c)} \\ \frac{5}{4-5c} & \frac{20}{3(4-5c)} \end{bmatrix}$

Thus, both A and $(I-A)^{-1}$ have nonnegative entries for c satisfying $0 \le c < .8$.

31. $0 < a < \frac{2}{3}$

33. $0 < a < .4$

35. The matrix $(1-A)^{-1}$ is

$$\begin{bmatrix} 1.25/(1-k) & 2.5k/(1-k) \\ 1/(1-k) & 2/(1-k) \end{bmatrix}$$

Thus, for $0 < k < 1$, the assumptions of the Leontief model are satisfied.

(*a*) If $k = .1$ and $D = \begin{bmatrix} 20 \\ 10 \end{bmatrix}$, then $X = \begin{bmatrix} 275/9 \\ 400/9 \end{bmatrix}$.

(*b*)

k	Amount of good 2
.1	44.44
.2	50.00
.3	57.14
.4	66.67
.5	80.00
.6	100.00
.7	133.33
.8	200.00
.9	400.00

(*c*) (Figure C6.1)

FIGURE C6.1

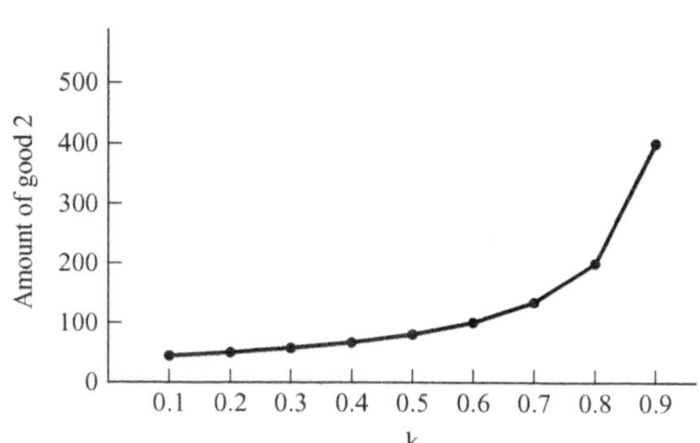

Review Exercises

1. (*a*) 4×2 (*b*) 2×3 (*c*) 1×4 (*d*) 3×1

3. $5A + B = \begin{bmatrix} 0 & 34 \\ 12 & 83 \\ 65 & -38 \end{bmatrix}$ $A - 2B = \begin{bmatrix} -11 & 9 \\ -24 & -1 \\ 2 & -12 \end{bmatrix}$

5. $Y = \begin{bmatrix} 3 \\ 10 \\ 16 \end{bmatrix}$ $Z = \begin{bmatrix} 7 \\ 15 \\ 42 \end{bmatrix}$

7. $p = -1, q = -1$

9. (*a*) $\begin{bmatrix} 6 & 12 \\ 2 & 10 \end{bmatrix}$ (*b*) Not defined (*c*) $\begin{bmatrix} 8 & 7 \\ 3 & 5 \\ 0 & 6 \end{bmatrix}$

(*d*) $\begin{bmatrix} 33 & 75 \\ 5 & 25 \\ -2 & 8 \end{bmatrix}$ (*e*) Not defined (*f*) $\begin{bmatrix} 36 \\ 10 \\ 2 \end{bmatrix}$

11. (*a*) $\begin{bmatrix} 4 & 0 \\ 6 & -2 \\ -4 & 0 \end{bmatrix}$ (*b*) $\begin{bmatrix} -2 & 4 & -3 \\ -2 & -3 & 1 \end{bmatrix}$ (*c*) Not defined

(*d*) $\begin{bmatrix} 1 & 0 & 3 \\ -2 & -7 & 8 \end{bmatrix}$ (*e*) Not defined (*f*) $\begin{bmatrix} 10 & -2 \\ -7 & 1 \end{bmatrix}$

13. $A^2 = \begin{bmatrix} 7 & -6 \\ -18 & 19 \end{bmatrix}$

$AB = \begin{bmatrix} 9 & -6 & -1 \\ -16 & 14 & 4 \end{bmatrix}$

$A(AB) = A^2B = \begin{bmatrix} 34 & -26 & -6 \\ -91 & 74 & 19 \end{bmatrix}$

15. $AC = \begin{bmatrix} 5 & 10 \\ 4 & 8 \end{bmatrix}$ $BC = \begin{bmatrix} 5 & 10 \\ 4 & 8 \end{bmatrix}$

One conclusion is that there are matrices A, B, and C such that $AC = BC$ but $A \neq B$. That is, the fact "for numbers a, b, and $c \neq 0$, if $ac = bc$, then $a = b$" does not carry over to matrices.

17. $A^{-1} = \begin{bmatrix} 3 & -4 \\ -5 & 7 \end{bmatrix}$

19. $A^{-1} = \begin{bmatrix} 6 & -1 & -1 \\ -2 & 1 & 0 \\ -3 & 0 & 1 \end{bmatrix}$

21. (*a*) $\begin{bmatrix} -8 & 11 \\ 11 & -\frac{25}{2} \end{bmatrix}$ (*b*) $\begin{bmatrix} -24 & 14 \\ -\frac{9}{2} & \frac{7}{2} \end{bmatrix}$

23. $k = -6$

25. $X = \begin{bmatrix} -11 \\ 4 \\ 6 \end{bmatrix}$, $X = \begin{bmatrix} -7 \\ 2 \\ 4 \end{bmatrix}$, $X = \begin{bmatrix} 1 \\ 0 \\ 0 \end{bmatrix}$

27. $0 < a < .8$

29. $\begin{bmatrix} 15 \\ 35 \end{bmatrix}$

31. $\begin{bmatrix} 152 \\ 75 \\ 130 \end{bmatrix}$

33. $(I - A)^{-1}$ exists, but has negative entries.

35. $\begin{bmatrix} 3205.6 \\ 3375.0 \\ 2990.2 \\ 4206.6 \end{bmatrix}$

37. (*a*) $A = \begin{bmatrix} 0.3 & 0.4 \\ 0.2 & 0.1 \end{bmatrix}$

(*b*) $(I - A)^{-1} = \begin{bmatrix} \frac{18}{11} & \frac{8}{11} \\ \frac{4}{11} & \frac{14}{11} \end{bmatrix}$ and $X = \begin{bmatrix} 1120 \\ 860 \end{bmatrix}$

CHAPTER 7

Section 7.1

1. Let x = number of regular sandwiches
   y = number of large sandwiches

   Maximize: $.8x + 1.2y$

   Subject to:
   $$\begin{aligned} x \geq 0, y &\geq 0 \\ 6x + 10y &\leq 1320 \quad \text{(bread)} \\ 2x + 4y &\leq 480 \quad \text{(meat)} \end{aligned}$$

3. Let x = number of sacks of 25-10-5
   y = number of sacks of 8-10-10

   Maximize: $7x + 5y$

   Subject to:
   $$\begin{aligned} x \geq 0, y &\geq 0 \\ 25x + 8y &\leq 12000 \quad \text{(nitrate)} \\ 10x + 10y &\leq 10000 \quad \text{(phosphate)} \\ 5x + 10y &\leq 7000 \quad \text{(potash)} \end{aligned}$$

5. Let x = number of gallons of ExtraMaple syrup
   y = number of gallons of regular maple syrup

   Maximize: $5x + 3y$

   Subject to:
   $$\begin{aligned} x \geq 0, y &\geq 0 \\ 2x + 5y &\leq 10{,}000 \quad \text{(maple base)} \\ 4x + 2y &\leq 8{,}800 \quad \text{(sugar)} \\ x &\leq 1{,}800 \quad \text{(constraint on sales)} \end{aligned}$$

7. Let x = number of pounds of material purchased from subsidiary
   y = number of pounds of material purchased from independent supplier

Minimize: $.80x + 1.00y$

Subject to:
$$x \geq 0, y \geq 0$$
$$x + y \geq 45{,}000 \quad \text{(amount required)}$$
$$x \leq 35{,}000 \quad \text{(constraint on amount from subsidiary)}$$
$$\tfrac{1}{3}(x + y) \leq y \quad \text{(antitrust condition)}$$

9. Let x = gallons of regular ice cream
   y = gallons of low-calorie ice cream

   Maximize: $x + 1.2y$

   Subject to:
$$x \geq 0, y \geq 0$$
$$.6x + .7y \leq 800 \quad \text{(skim milk)}$$
$$x + .3y \leq 400 \quad \text{(sugar)}$$
$$.4x + .4y \leq 400 \quad \text{(cream)}$$

11. Let x = number of subject hours
    y = number of consultant minutes

    Maximize: $x + .04y$

    Subject to:
$$x \geq 0, y \geq 0$$
$$x \leq 15$$
$$x \geq 6$$
$$y \leq 200$$
$$y \geq 30x$$
$$y \leq 50x$$

13. Let x = number of full teams
    y = number of half teams

    Maximize: $180x + 100y$

    Subject to:
$$x \geq 0, y \geq 0$$
$$x + y \leq 200 \quad \text{(doctors)}$$
$$3x + 2y \leq 450 \quad \text{(nurses)}$$

15. Let x = number of standard boxes produced each week
    y = number of heavy duty boxes produced each week

    Maximize: $3x + 4y$

    Subject to:
$$x \geq, y \geq 0$$
$$x + 5y \leq 5000 \quad \text{(100-pound test)}$$
$$3x + y \leq 4500 \quad \text{(liner)}$$
$$x \geq 500$$

17. Let x = number of Scary Harry
    y = number of Horrible Harriet
    z = number of The Glob

    Maximize: $x + 1.25y + 1.5z$

    Subject to:
$$x \geq 0, y \geq 0, z \geq 0$$
$$4x + 3y + 9z \leq 160 \quad \text{(plastic)}$$
$$3x + 4y + z \leq 50 \quad \text{(clothes)}$$
$$2x + 4y + 3z \leq 50 \quad \text{(features)}$$

19. [5 5 10] is not feasible because the time constraint for features is violated; [10 3 2] is not feasible because the time constraint for features is violated.

21. Let x = number of type A
y = number of type B
z = number of type C

Maximize: $x + .75y + 1.25z$

Subject to:

$$\begin{aligned} x \geq 0, y \geq 0, z \geq 0 & \\ 25x + 10y + 50z \leq 1000 & \quad \text{(worms)} \\ 10x + 15y + 5z \leq 250 & \quad \text{(minnows)} \\ 10x + 25y + 5z \leq 300 & \quad \text{(grasshoppers)} \end{aligned}$$

23. Let x = number of hundreds of small widgets without locks
y = number of hundreds of small widgets with locks
z = number of hundreds of medium widgets with locks
w = number of hundreds of large widgets with locks

Maximize: $2x + 10y + 11z + 20w$

Subject to:

$$\begin{aligned} x \geq 0, y \geq 0, z \geq 0, w \geq 0 & \\ x + 2y + 3z + 6w \leq 8 & \quad \text{(assembly)} \\ x + 5y + 4z + 8w \leq 9 & \quad \text{(painting)} \\ 3y + z + 4w \leq 2 & \quad \text{(installation)} \end{aligned}$$

25. Let x = number of Deluxe Packs
y = number of Special Packs
z = number of Standard Packs

Maximize: $3x + 2y + 1.5z$

Subject to:

$$\begin{aligned} x \geq 0, y \geq 0, z \geq 0 & \\ 16x + 20y + 16z \leq 1200 & \quad \text{(dates)} \\ 24x + 12y + 8z \leq 900 & \quad \text{(apricots)} \\ 12x + 3y \leq 360 & \quad \text{(candied fruit)} \end{aligned}$$

27. Let x = number of type 1 layouts,
y = number of type 2 layouts,
z = number of type 3 layouts,

Maximize: $50x + 30y + 60z$

Subject to:

$$\begin{aligned} x \geq 0, y \geq 0, z \geq 0 & \\ 30x + 10y + 20z \leq 1000 & \quad \text{(tulips)} \\ 20x + 40y + 50z \leq 800 & \quad \text{(daffodils)} \\ 4x + 3y + 2z \leq 100 & \quad \text{(flowering shrubs)} \end{aligned}$$

29. Let x = units of furniture timber
y = units of plywood timber
z = units of pulpwood timber

Maximize: $500x + 400y + 200z$

Subject to:

$$\begin{aligned} x \geq 0,\ y \geq 0,\ z \geq 0& \\ 100x + 80y + 50z \leq 1000 &\quad \text{(labor)} \\ 20x + 30y + 30z \leq 500 &\quad \text{(machine time)} \end{aligned}$$

31. Let x = number of sections of research study
 y = number of sections of presentation

Maximize: $500x + 250y$

Subject to:

$$\begin{aligned} x \geq 0,\ y \geq 0& \\ 3x + y \leq 40 &\quad \text{(Tommy)} \\ x + 2y \leq 25 &\quad \text{(Pete)} \end{aligned}$$

33. Let x = number of sacks of 20-5-5 (for lawns)
 y = number of sacks of 10-15-10 (for gardens)
 z = number of sacks of 5-5-5 (for trees)

Maximize: $6x + 4y + 3z$

Subject to:

$$\begin{aligned} x \geq 0,\ y \geq 0,\ z \geq 0& \\ 20x + 10y + 5z \leq 14,000 &\quad \text{(nitrates)} \\ 5x + 15y + 5z \leq 8,000 &\quad \text{(phosphates)} \\ 5x + 10y + 5z \leq 6,000 &\quad \text{(potash)} \\ y \geq 2,000& \end{aligned}$$

Section 7.2

1. (Figure C7.1)
3. (Figure C7.2)
5. (Figure C7.3)
7. (Figure C7.4)

FIGURE C7.1

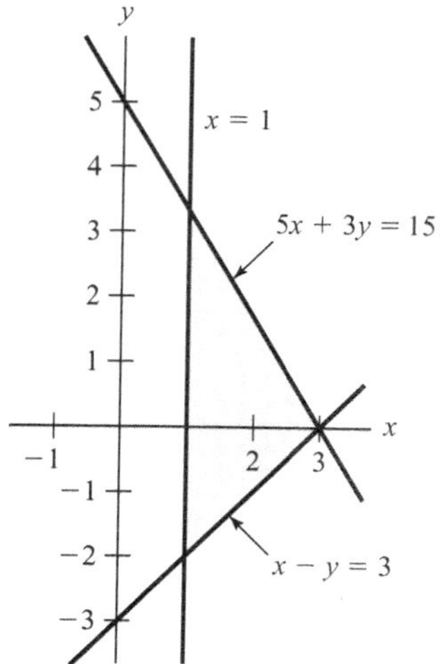

FIGURE C7.2

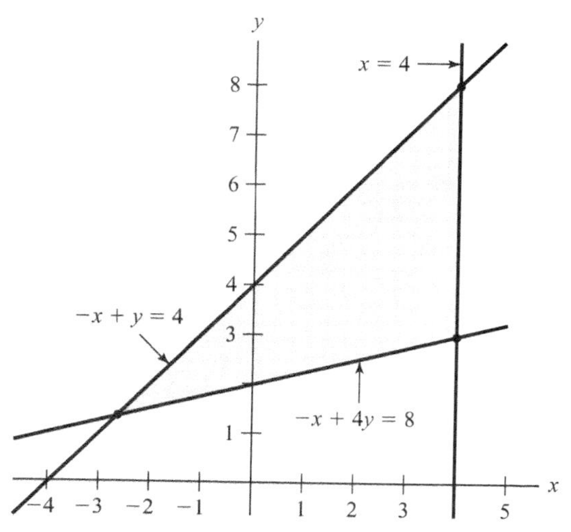

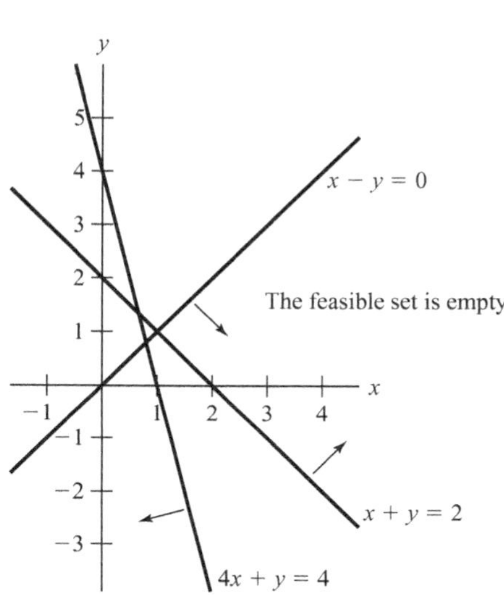

FIGURE C7.3

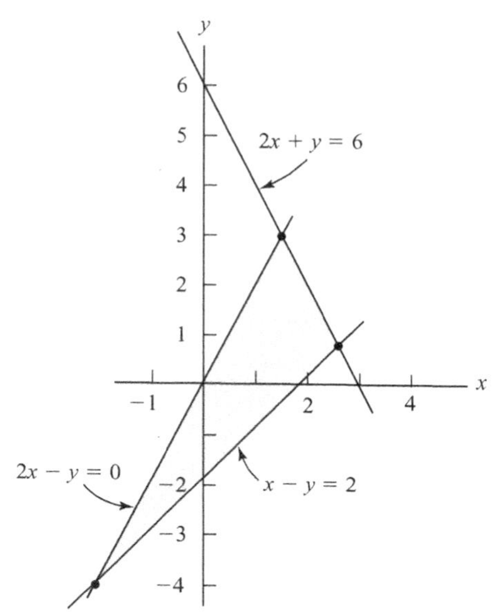

FIGURE C7.4

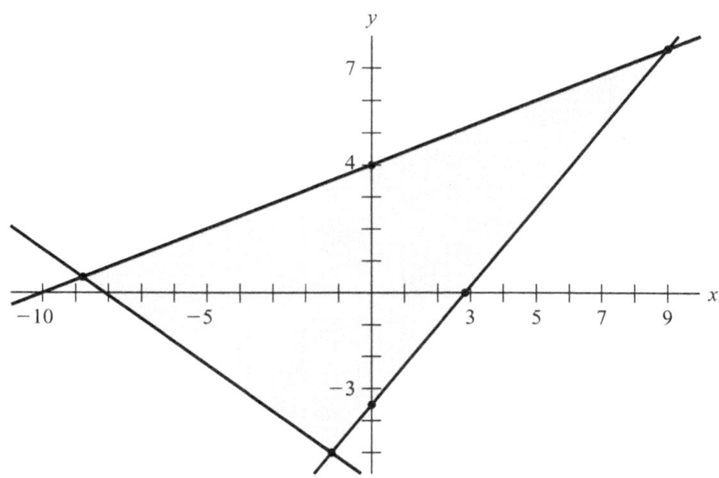

FIGURE C7.5

9. (Figure C7.5) 11. $(4, 8), (4, 3), (-\frac{8}{3}, \frac{4}{3})$ 13. $(\frac{5}{2}, \frac{7}{2}), (\frac{3}{5}, \frac{8}{5}), (12, -6)$ 15. $(\frac{20}{3}, \frac{10}{3}), (\frac{15}{4}, \frac{25}{4})$

17. Corner points with x positive: $P = (2, 8)$ and $Q = (4, 2)$; (Figure C7.6)

19. (Figure C7.7); Corner points: $(-8, 6), (-2, 0), (-1, \frac{5}{2})$

21. (Figure C7.8); Corner points: $(0, 0), (0, -2), (\frac{3}{2}, \frac{3}{2}), (3, 1)$

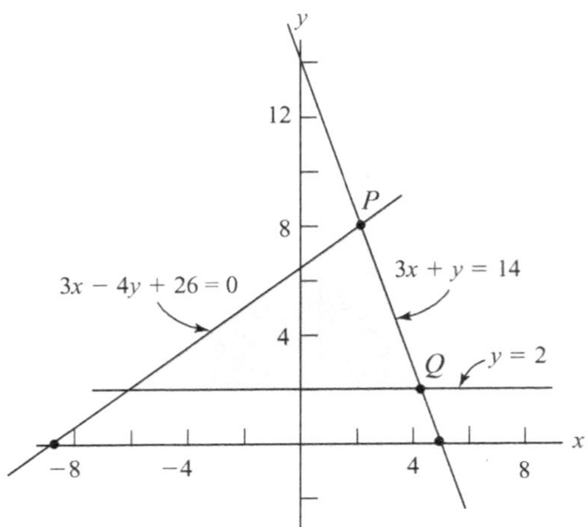

FIGURE C7.6

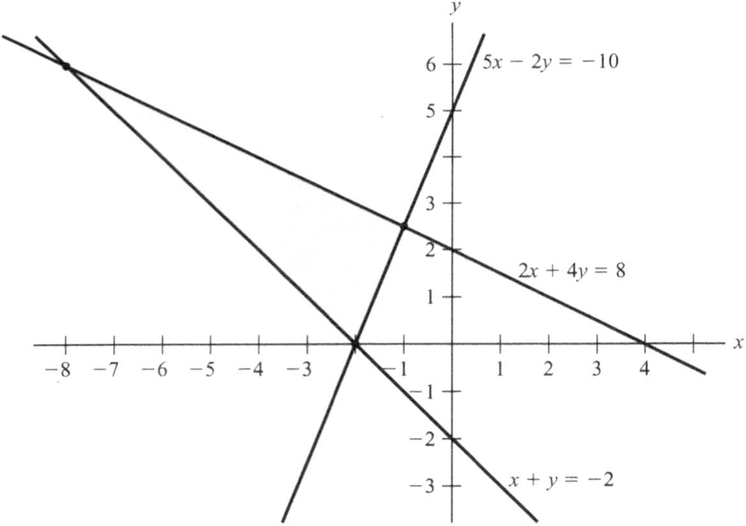

FIGURE C7.7

23. (Figure C7.9)
Let x = number of standard boxes, hundreds
y = number of heavy duty boxes, hundreds

$$\begin{aligned} x \geq 0 \; y &\geq 0 \\ 200x + 400y &\leq 100{,}000 \\ 8x + \;\; 3y &\leq 2400 \\ y &\geq 100 \end{aligned}$$

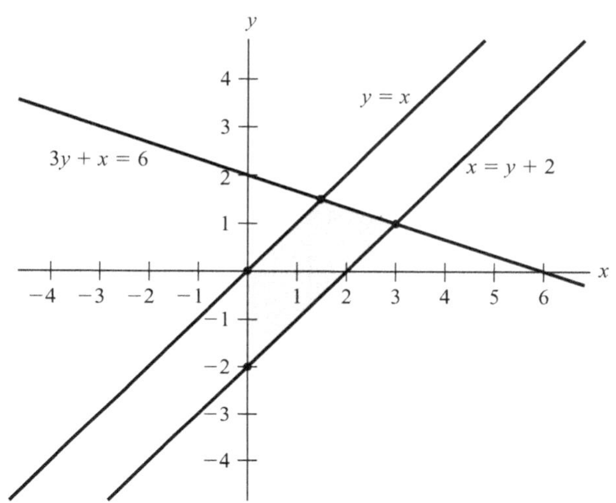

FIGURE C7.8

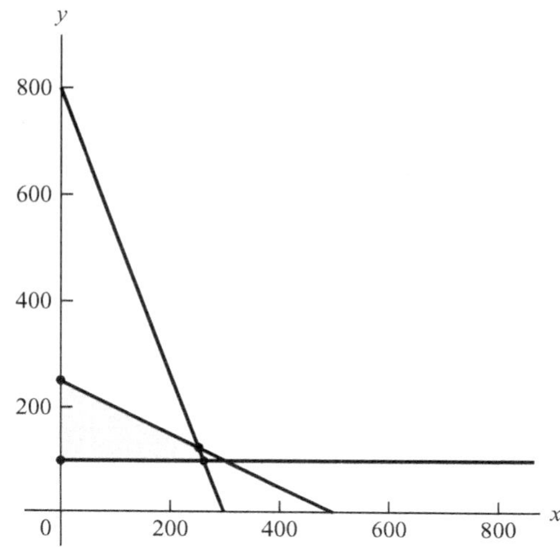

FIGURE C7.9

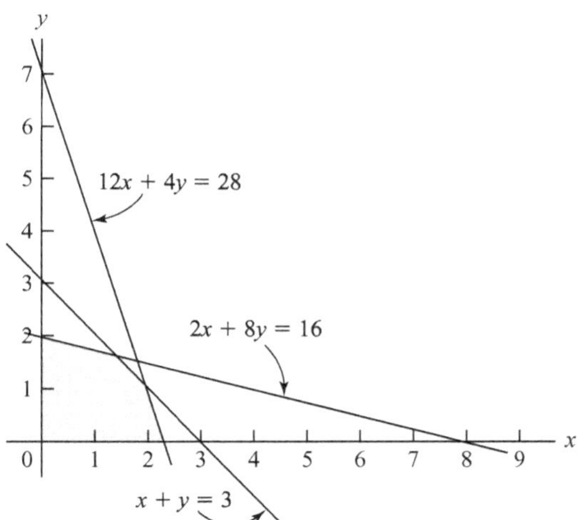

FIGURE C7.10

25. (Figure C7.10)
    Let x = number of acres used on first experiment
    y = number of acres used on second experiment

$$\begin{array}{rl} x \geq 0 \; y \geq 0 & \\ x + y \leq 3 & \text{(acres available)} \\ 2x + 8y \leq 16 & \text{(days to collect data)} \\ 12x + 4y \leq 28 & \text{(hours for laboratory work)} \end{array}$$

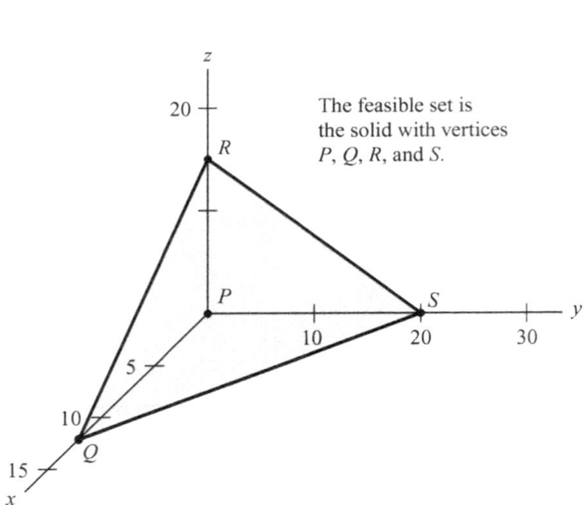

FIGURE C7.11

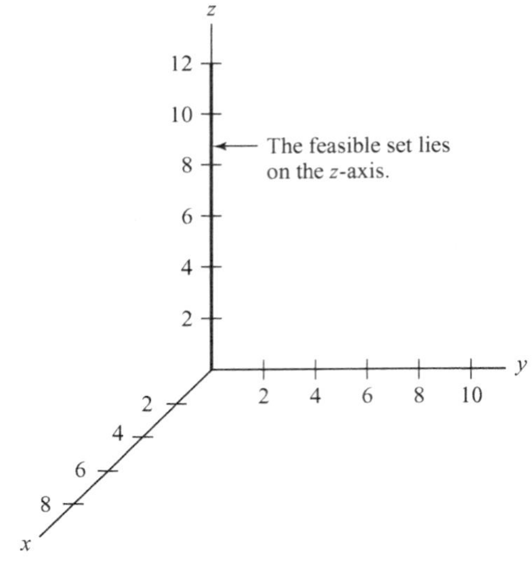

FIGURE C7.12

27. (Figure C7.11)

29. (Figure C7.12)
The feasible set lies on the z axis

31. (Figure C7.13)
At $(0, 4)$, $p = 28$
At $(6, 0)$, $p = 24$
At $(3, 1)$, $p = 19$

33. $(0, 5), (-5, 5), (-1, 1)$

35. $(2, 6), (4, 4)$

37.

Exercise	Point	$x+y$	$x-y$	$5x+y$	$-5x+y$
33	(0, 5)	5	−5	5	5
33	(−5, 5)	0	−10	−20	30
33	(−1, 1)	0	−2	−4	6
34	(−2, 3)	1	−5	−7	13
34	(2, 3)	5	−1	13	7
34	(0, 1)	1	−1	1	1

Section 7.3

1. (Figure C7.14); Bounded — Corner points: $(0, 3), (3, 0), (-\frac{3}{2}, \frac{3}{2})$
3. (Figure C7.15); Bounded — Corner points: $(1, 0), (0, 0), (0, 3), (2, 1)$

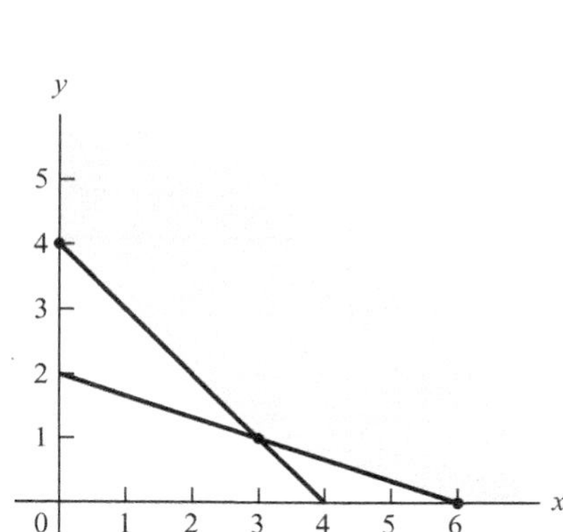

FIGURE C7.13

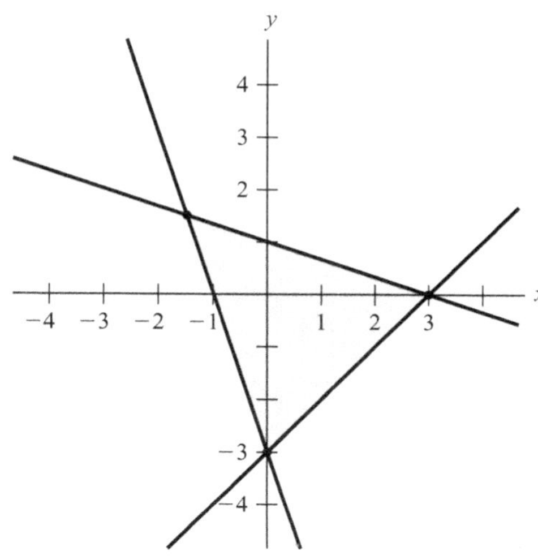

FIGURE C7.14

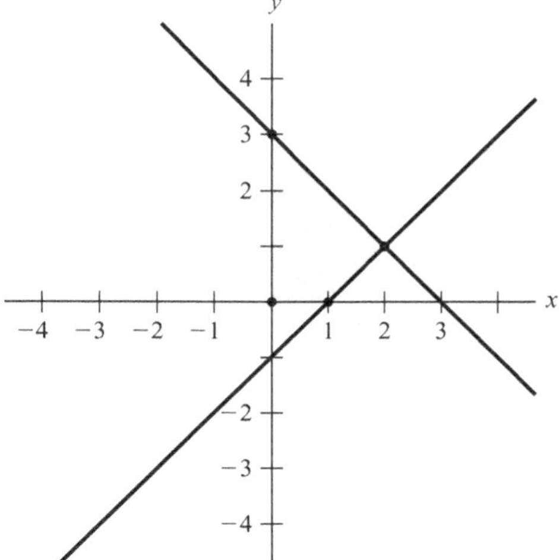

FIGURE C7.15

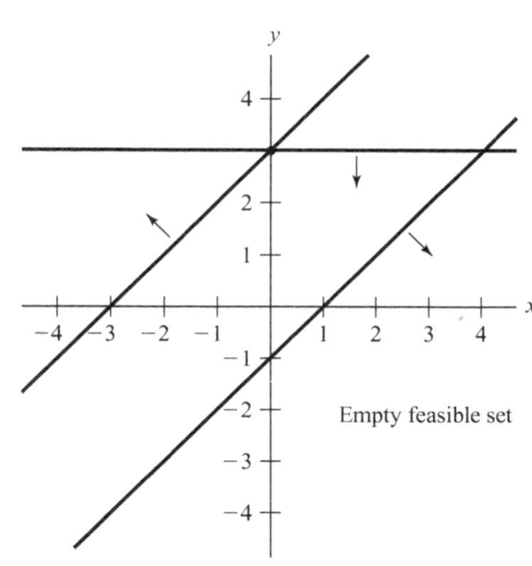

FIGURE C7.16

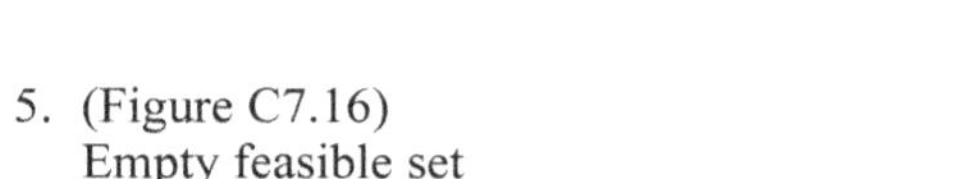

5. (Figure C7.16)
   Empty feasible set
7. Maximum of $2x + y$ is 11 at (5, 1); minimum of $x - 2y$ is -9 at (1, 5)

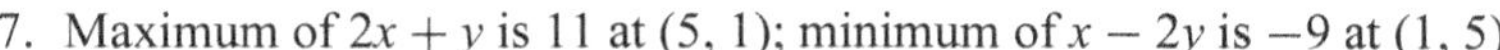

9. Maximum of $-x + 4y$ is 25 at (5, 7.5); minimum is 0 at $(-20, -5)$.
11. No maximum value; minimum of $x - 3y$ is $\frac{1}{2}$ at $(-1, -\frac{1}{2})$

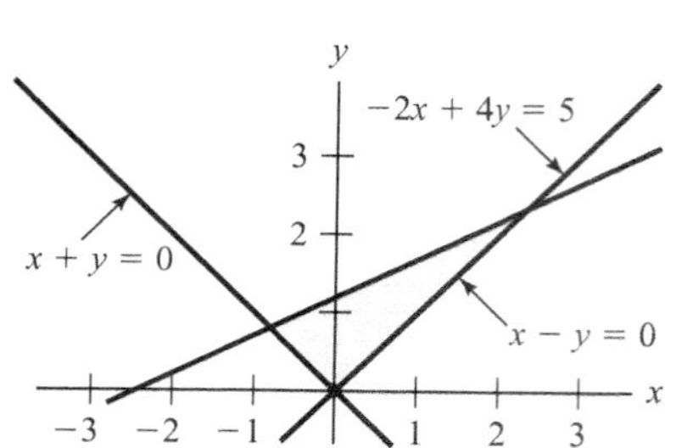

FIGURE C7.17

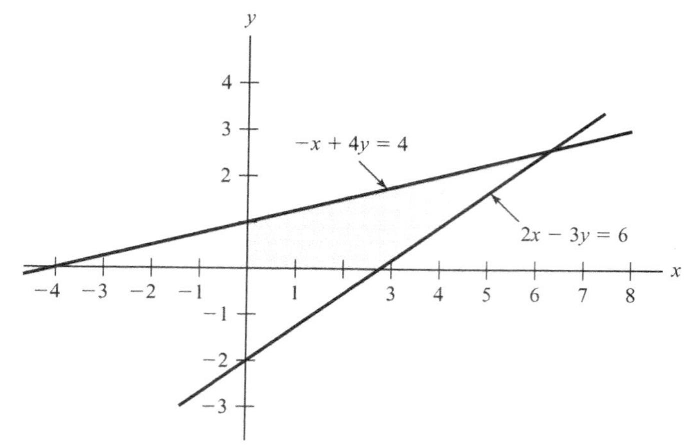

FIGURE C7.18

13. see Figure C7.17

Corner point	Value of $3x - 2y$
(0,0)	0
$(-\frac{5}{6}, \frac{5}{6})$	$-\frac{25}{6}$
$(\frac{5}{2}, \frac{5}{2})$	$\frac{5}{2}$ ← maximum

15. see Figure C7.18

Corner point	Value of $x - 3y$
(0,0)	0
(0, 1)	−3
$(\frac{36}{5}, \frac{14}{5})$	$-\frac{6}{5}$
(3, 0)	3 ← maximum

17. Maximum of \$176 for 220 regular sandwiches and no large sandwiches
19. Maximum of $\$\frac{34,100}{7}$ for $\frac{6400}{21}$ sacks of 25-10-5 and 11, 500/21 sacks of 8-10-10
21. Maximum of \$10,140 for 264 desks and 324 file cabinets.
23. Maximum of $\frac{44}{3}$ for $\frac{20}{3}$ subject hours and 200 consultant minutes.
25. Maximum of 2700 at $x = 150$ and $y = 0$.
27. Maximum of 675 at $x = 1250$ and $y = 750$.
29. (*a*) 3 poppy seed and 14 German chocolate for a profit of \$62; (*b*) no; (*c*) yes, 400 grams
31. (*a*) Maximum of $\frac{8}{3}$ at $(\frac{22}{3}, \frac{7}{3})$; minimum does not exist
    (*b*) Maximum does not exist; minimum of 12 at $(\frac{22}{3}, \frac{7}{3})$. Minimum is not unique
    (*c*) Maximum does not exist; minimum of $\frac{64}{3}$ at $(\frac{22}{3}, \frac{7}{3})$; minimum is unique
    (*d*) Maximum of $\frac{8}{3}$ at $(\frac{7}{3}, \frac{22}{3})$; maximum is unique; minimum does not exist
33. 48 boxes of regular mix and 32 boxes of deluxe mix for a profit of \$176
35. (*a*) Maximum of $-\frac{8}{5}$ at $(\frac{16}{5}, \frac{4}{5})$
    (*b*) No maximum
    (*c*) Maximum of 0 attained at $(\frac{16}{5}, \frac{4}{5})$ and at other points too
37. Minimum does not exist
39. The best corner point is 15 regular burgers and 37.5 kid's burgers with profit \$82.50. However, Burt may not want to make 1/2 of a burger, so he will likely make 15 regular and 37 kid's burgers for a profit of \$82.

Review Exercises

1. Let x = number of lobster boats built, y = number of tug boats built

Maximize: $7x + 15y$

subject to:

$$\begin{aligned} x \geq 0, y &\geq 0 \\ 25x + 20y &\leq 3000 \quad \text{(hull material)} \\ 4x + 8y &\leq 720 \quad \text{(cabin material)} \\ 2x + 8y &\leq 640 \quad \text{(plastic fittings)} \end{aligned}$$

3. Let x = number of acres of crop A, y = number of acres of crop B

Maximize: $170x + 190y$

subject to:

$$\begin{aligned} x \geq 0, y &\geq 0 \\ x + 2y &\leq 3000 \quad \text{(labor)} \\ 90x + 60y &\leq 150{,}000 \quad \text{(capital)} \\ x + y &\leq 2000 \quad \text{(land)} \end{aligned}$$

5. Let x = number of basic birdhouses, y = number of upscale birdhouses

Maximize: $3x + 10y$

subject to:

$$\begin{aligned} x \geq 0, y &\geq 0 \\ 4x + 2y &\leq 180 \quad \text{(pine)} \\ 3x + 5y &\leq 280 \quad \text{(cedar)} \\ x &\geq 10 \quad \text{(craftshop agreement)} \\ y &\geq 20 \quad \text{(craftshop agreement)} \end{aligned}$$

7. Let x = number of sacks of Standard, y = number of sacks of Special, z = number of sacks of Super

Maximize: $10x + 5y + 15z$

Subject to:

$$\begin{aligned} x \geq 0, y \geq 0, z &\geq 0 \\ 20x + 10y + 5z &\leq 2000 \quad \text{(nitrogen)} \\ 5x + 10y + 15z &\leq 1500 \quad \text{(phosphorus)} \\ 5x + 10y + 10z &\leq 1500 \quad \text{(potash)} \end{aligned}$$

9. Maximum profit of \$1,330 is attained for 40 lobster boats and 70 tug boats. All cabin material and plastic fittings are used; 600 cm of pine hull material remain unused.
11. Maximum of 360,000 at (1000, 1000). Yes, all resources are consumed.
13. Maximum net profit of \$530 is attained for 10 basic birdhouses and 50 upscale birdhouses. All cedar is used, but 40 pieces of pine remain unused.
15. Make 35 basic birdhouses and 20 upscale birdhouses. The pine pieces are all used, but there are extra cedar pieces.
17. She should produce only right-hand widgets. She should make 32.5 sets of 100, i.e., 3250 of them.
19. (Figure C7.19); corner points at $(0, -3)$, $(\frac{9}{4}, -\frac{3}{4})$, $(-\frac{9}{8}, \frac{3}{8})$
21. (*a*) (Figure C7.20) (*b*) $(6, 2)$, $(6,6)$, $(-9,6)$, $(\frac{12}{5}, -\frac{8}{5})$ (*c*) $\frac{64}{4}$
23. Maximum does not exist; minimum of -4 at $(2, 2)$
25. (*a*) Maximum of 28 at $(4, -8)$; minimum of -14 at $(-2, 4)$
(*b*) Maximum of 32 at $(4, -8)$; minimum of -18 at $(0, 6)$

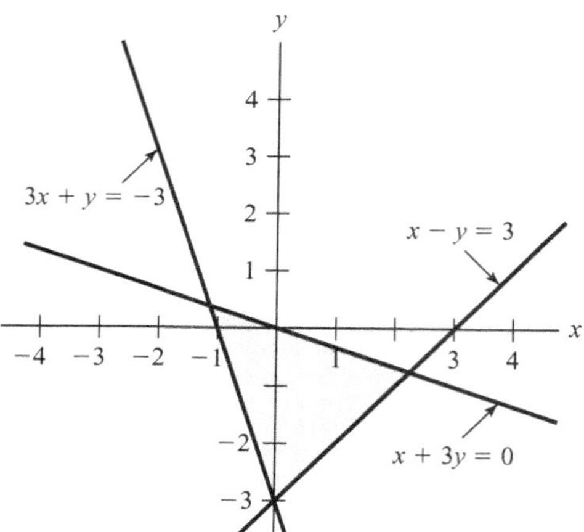

FIGURE C7.19

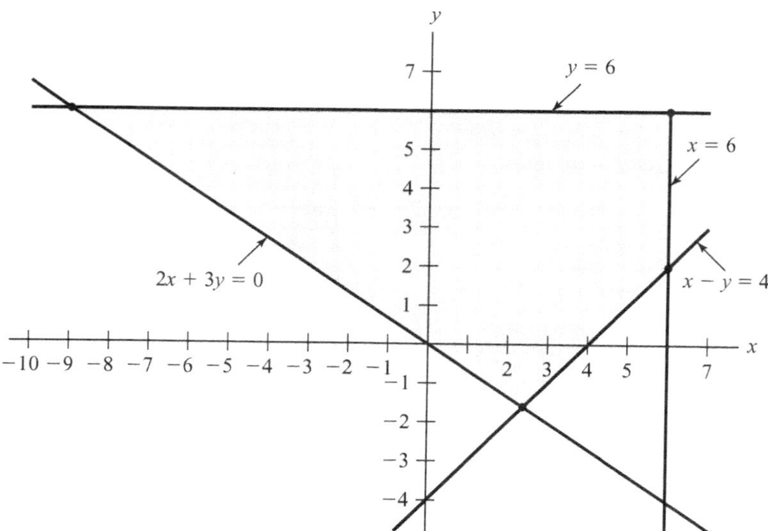

FIGURE C7.20

27. Maximum of 13 at $(1, -2)$; minimum of -15 at $(5, 6)$
29. (*a*) Maximum of 3 at $(1, -1)$ (*b*) There is no minimum.
31. (*a*)
33. One solution is $x \geq 1, y \geq 0$
35. 100 basic ID cards, 900 deluxe ID cards
37. One solution is the objective function x

CHAPTER 8

Section 8.1

1. (Figure C8.1)
3. State 2
5. (Figure C8.2)
7. $\begin{bmatrix} 0 & 1 & 0 \\ 0 & .5 & .5 \\ .8 & 0 & .2 \end{bmatrix}$
9. (Figure C8.3)
11. (*a*) .3 (*b*) State 3
13. State 3
15. The states are high volume and low volume. If state 1 is high volume and state 2 is low volume, then the transition matrix is

$$\begin{bmatrix} .7 & .3 \\ .5 & .5 \end{bmatrix}$$

17. (*a*) System is in state 1 if the small animal is in the meadow and in state 2 if it is in the woods.
    (*b*) (Figure C8.4)
    (*c*) $\begin{bmatrix} \frac{2}{3} & \frac{1}{3} \\ \frac{1}{3} & \frac{2}{3} \end{bmatrix}$

FIGURE C8.1

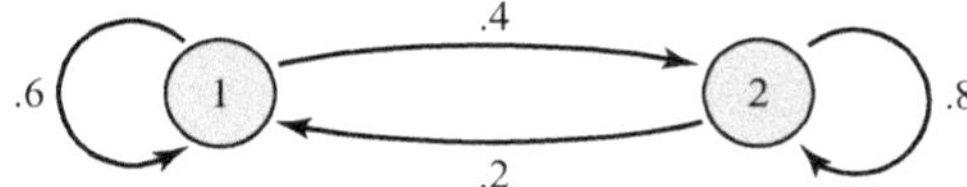

FIGURE C8.2

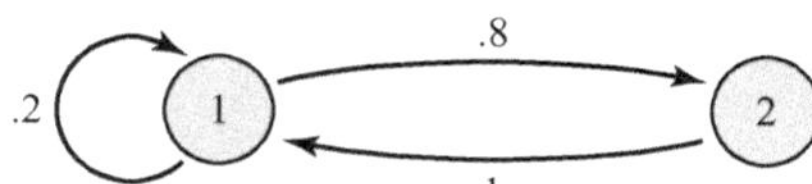

FIGURE C8.3

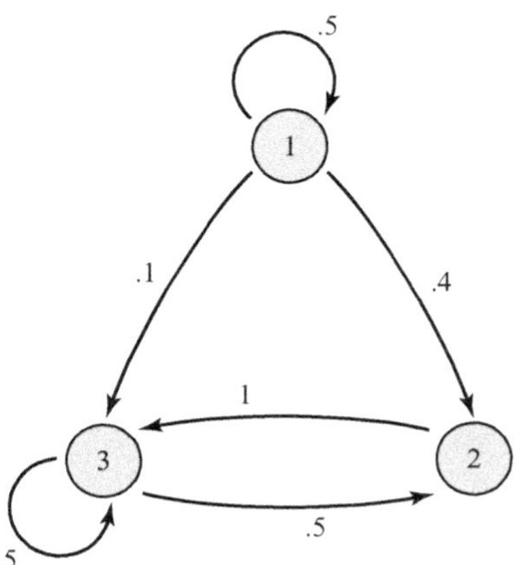

FIGURE C8.4

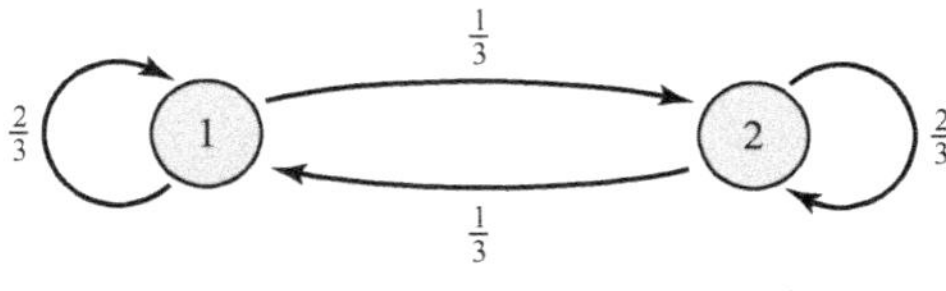

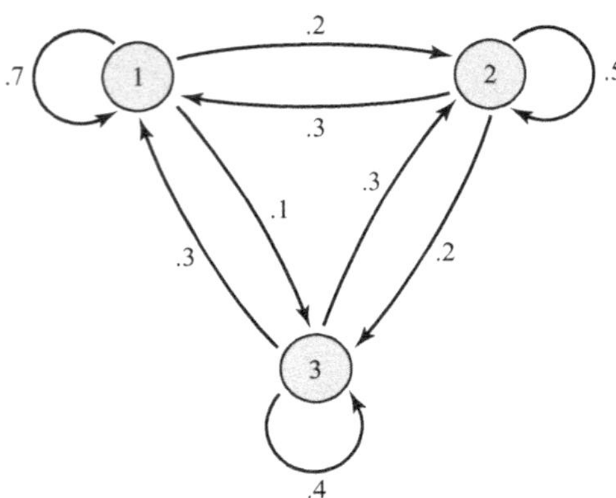

FIGURE C8.5

19. (*a*) The states are the three employment groups: industry, small business, and self-employed. Identify these states as 1, 2, and 3, respectively.

    (*b*) (Figure C8.5) (*c*) $\begin{bmatrix} .70 & .20 & .10 \\ .30 & .50 & .20 \\ .30 & .30 & .40 \end{bmatrix}$

21. .30

23. The states are: 1, she eats Chinese food; 2, she eats Greek food; and 3, she eats Italian food. The transition matrix is

$$\begin{bmatrix} 0 & \frac{2}{3} & \frac{1}{3} \\ \frac{1}{2} & 0 & \frac{1}{2} \\ \frac{5}{6} & \frac{1}{6} & 0 \end{bmatrix}$$

25. State 1 is make a free throw, state 2 is miss. The transition matrix is $\begin{bmatrix} .8 & .2 \\ .4 & .6 \end{bmatrix}$.

27. The states are: 1, if stocks are stronger; 2, if bonds are stronger; and 3, if both are equally strong. Transition matrix is

$$\begin{bmatrix} .6 & .3 & .1 \\ .3 & .5 & .2 \\ .4 & .4 & .2 \end{bmatrix}$$

29. Let X be a random variable which associates with each attendance schedule for the first 4 weeks the number of times the student attends class.

Values of X	**Probabilities**
1	$\frac{1}{4}$
2	$\frac{3}{4}$

$[X] = 1(\frac{1}{4}) + 2(\frac{3}{4}) = \frac{7}{4}$

31. State 1

33. Self-employed

35. 7.584 points

Section 8.2

1. (a) $\mathbf{P}(2) = \begin{bmatrix} .75 & .25 \\ .5 & .5 \end{bmatrix}$ (b) $p_{12}(2) = .25, \quad p_{21}(2) = .5$

3. $\mathbf{P}(3) = \begin{bmatrix} .625 & .375 \\ .75 & .25 \end{bmatrix}$ $\mathbf{P}(4) = \begin{bmatrix} .6875 & .3125 \\ .625 & .375 \end{bmatrix}$

5. .444

7. (a) $\mathbf{P}(2) = \begin{bmatrix} 0 & 0 & 1 \\ 1 & 0 & 0 \\ 0 & 1 & 0 \end{bmatrix}$ (b) $\mathbf{P}(3) = \begin{bmatrix} 1 & 0 & 0 \\ 0 & 1 & 0 \\ 0 & 0 & 1 \end{bmatrix}$

9. (a) $\mathbf{P}(2) = \begin{bmatrix} .1 & .8 & .1 \\ 0 & 1 & 0 \\ .25 & .40 & .35 \end{bmatrix}$ $\mathbf{P}(3) = \begin{bmatrix} .05 & .88 & .07 \\ 0 & 1 & 0 \\ .175 & .600 & .225 \end{bmatrix}$ $\mathbf{P}(4) = \begin{bmatrix} .035 & .920 & .045 \\ 0 & 1 & 0 \\ .1125 & .7400 & .1475 \end{bmatrix}$

   (b) $p_{22}(2) = 1, \; p_{22}(3) = 1, \; p_{22}(4) = 1$ (c) $p_{22}(k) = 1$ for all k

11. (a) Figure C8.6 (b) $\begin{bmatrix} \frac{1}{4} & \frac{1}{3} & \frac{5}{12} \end{bmatrix}$ (c) $\mathbf{P}(2) = \begin{bmatrix} \frac{1}{4} & \frac{1}{3} & \frac{5}{12} \\ \frac{1}{2} & 0 & \frac{1}{2} \\ \frac{2}{3} & \frac{2}{9} & \frac{1}{9} \end{bmatrix}$

13. $\mathbf{P}(2) = \begin{bmatrix} .42 & .08 & .50 \\ .36 & .12 & .52 \\ .35 & .10 & .55 \end{bmatrix}$

    $\mathbf{P}(3) = \begin{bmatrix} .366 & .100 & .534 \\ .380 & .096 & .524 \\ .385 & .090 & .525 \end{bmatrix}$

    For $\mathbf{P}(2)$: $.42 + .08 + .50 = 1$
    $.36 + .12 + .52 = 1$
    $.35 + .10 + .55 = 1$

    For $\mathbf{P}(3)$: $.366 + .100 + .534 = 1$
    $.380 + .096 + .524 = 1$
    $.385 + .090 + .525 = 1$

FIGURE C8.6

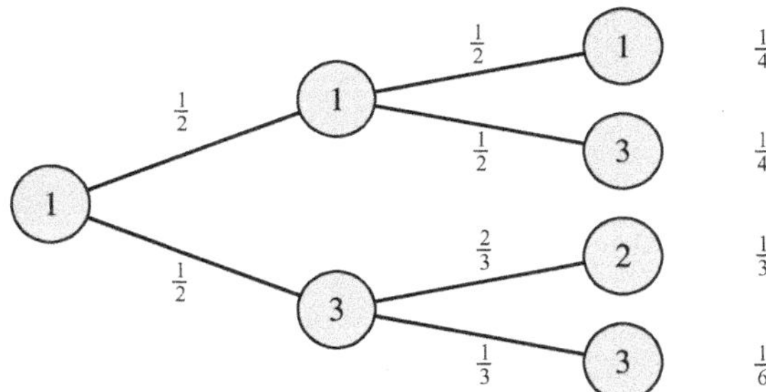

15. (*a*) .72 (*b*) .56

17. $\mathbf{P}(2) = \begin{bmatrix} .24 & .57 & .19 \\ .14 & .73 & .13 \\ .18 & .63 & .19 \end{bmatrix}$, $p_{33}(3) = .154$

19. .18, central

21. (*a*)

$$\mathbf{P}(2) = \begin{array}{c} \\ I \\ SB \\ SE \end{array} \begin{array}{c} \begin{array}{ccc} I & SB & SE \end{array} \\ \begin{bmatrix} .82 & .10 & .08 \\ .18 & .675 & .145 \\ .18 & .425 & .395 \end{bmatrix} \end{array}$$

(*b*) .10

23. Self-employed (*SE*), .395

25. Audi

27. State 4

29. (*a*) $\mathbf{P}(2) = \begin{bmatrix} .40 & .48 & .12 & 0 \\ .32 & .40 & .08 & .2 \\ 0 & 0 & .5 & .5 \\ 0 & 0 & .25 & .75 \end{bmatrix}$

$\mathbf{P}(4) = \begin{bmatrix} .3136 & .3840 & .1464 & .156 \\ .2560 & .3136 & .1604 & .270 \\ 0 & 0 & .375 & .625 \\ 0 & 0 & .3125 & .6875 \end{bmatrix}$

$\mathbf{P}(8) = \begin{bmatrix} .1966 & .2408 & .2112 & .3514 \\ .1606 & .1966 & .2323 & .4105 \\ 0 & 0 & .3359 & .6641 \\ 0 & 0 & .3320 & .6680 \end{bmatrix}$

(*b*) No

(*c*) No, from state 3 it is possible to reach only states 3 and 4.

31. $a = .1$, $p_{22}(3) = .825$

33. State 1

35. $k = 5$

Section 8.3

1. (*a*) Yes (*b*) no (*c*) no (*d*) yes

3. $[\frac{1}{4} \quad \frac{1}{4} \quad \frac{2}{4}]$

5. (*a*) $[\frac{2}{3} \quad \frac{1}{3}]$ (*b*) $\frac{188}{300}$ (*c*) $\frac{469}{750}$

7. (*a*) If the meadow is state 1, then the state vector is $[\frac{3}{4} \quad \frac{1}{4}]$ (*b*) $\frac{55}{108}$

9. $[\frac{5}{8} \quad \frac{3}{8}]$

11. $[\frac{4}{7} \quad \frac{3}{7}]$

13. Regular, stable vector is $[\frac{1}{4} \quad \frac{3}{4}]$.

15. Not regular

17. Regular, stable vector is $[\frac{5}{23} \quad \frac{4}{23} \quad \frac{10}{23} \quad \frac{4}{23}]$.

19. She makes 80 percent of her free throws.

21. The student attends class on Friday afternoons with probability $\frac{7}{13}$.

23. (*a*) $\mathbf{P}(4) = \begin{bmatrix} .3411 & .3207 & .2786 & .0595 \\ .2138 & .4180 & .2138 & .1543 \\ .2786 & .3207 & .3411 & .0595 \\ .1190 & .4630 & .1190 & .2990 \end{bmatrix}$

$\mathbf{P}(8) = \begin{bmatrix} .2697 & .3604 & .2658 & .1042 \\ .2403 & .3834 & .2403 & .1361 \\ .2658 & .3604 & .2697 & .1042 \\ .2083 & .4083 & .2083 & .1750 \end{bmatrix}$

For P_1

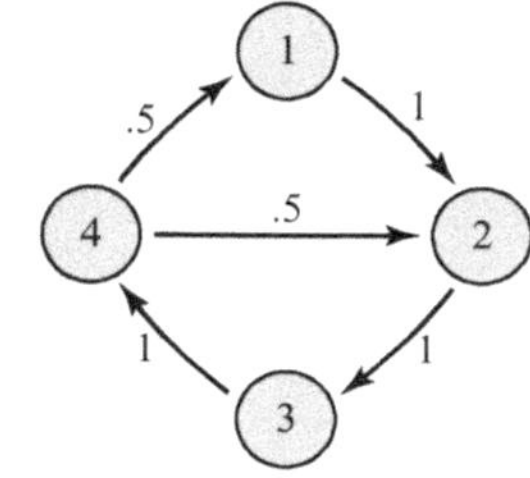

For P_2

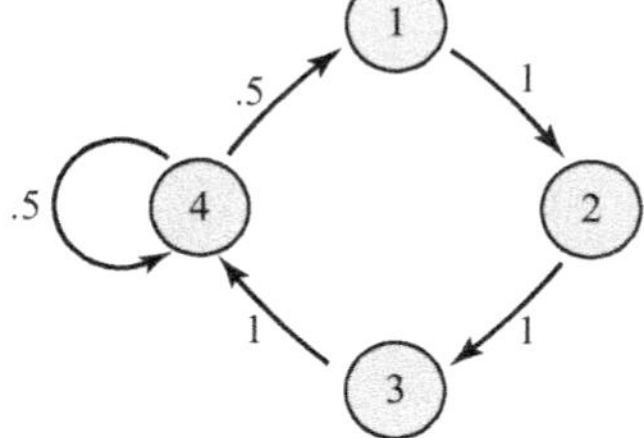

FIGURE C8.7

(*b*) .2221 in $\mathbf{P}^4$, .0614 in $\mathbf{P}^8$
(*c*) $\left[\frac{1}{4} \quad \frac{3}{8} \quad \frac{1}{4} \quad \frac{1}{8}\right]$
(*d*) State 2, food

25. (*a*) (Figure C8.7)
(*b*) $k = 10$ for P_1; $k = 6$ for P_2

27. The eighth power of the matrix **P** has a zero in the (1, 1) entry for any values of x, y, and z.

29. $\begin{bmatrix} \frac{b}{1+b-a} & \frac{1-a}{1+b-a} \end{bmatrix} \begin{bmatrix} a & 1-a \\ b & 1-b \end{bmatrix} = \begin{bmatrix} \frac{b}{1+b-a} & \frac{1-a}{1+b-a} \end{bmatrix}$

31. Stable vector is $\begin{bmatrix} \frac{b}{1+b} & \frac{1}{1+b} \end{bmatrix}$.

33. .5

35. (a) $\mathbf{W} = \left[\frac{1}{12} \quad \frac{5}{12} \quad \frac{6}{12}\right]$ (b) $k = 4$

Section 8.4

1. (*a*) Yes (*b*), (*c*) From state 1, one transition; state 2 is absorbing; from state 3, two transitions.

3. (*a*) Yes (*b*), (*c*) State 1 is absorbing; from state 2, one transition; state 3 is absorbing; from state 4, two transitions

5. (*a*) No (*b*) impossible to reach an absorbing state from either state 3 or state 4

7.
$$\begin{array}{c} \\ 3 \\ 1 \\ 2 \\ 4 \end{array} \begin{array}{c} \begin{array}{cccc} 3 & 1 & 2 & 4 \end{array} \\ \begin{bmatrix} 1 & 0 & 0 & 0 \\ \frac{1}{6} & \frac{2}{3} & \frac{1}{6} & 0 \\ \frac{1}{9} & \frac{1}{9} & \frac{2}{3} & \frac{1}{9} \\ 0 & 0 & \frac{1}{3} & \frac{2}{3} \end{bmatrix} \end{array}$$

9.
$$\begin{array}{c} \\ 2 \\ 1 \\ 3 \\ 4 \\ 5 \end{array}\begin{array}{c} \begin{array}{ccccc} 2 & 1 & 3 & 4 & 5 \end{array} \\ \begin{bmatrix} 1 & 0 & 0 & 0 & 0 \\ 0 & \frac{1}{3} & \frac{1}{3} & 0 & \frac{1}{3} \\ 0 & \frac{1}{2} & \frac{1}{2} & 0 & 0 \\ \frac{2}{10} & \frac{1}{10} & \frac{3}{10} & \frac{4}{10} & 0 \\ 0 & 0 & 0 & 1 & 0 \end{bmatrix} \end{array}$$

11.
$$\begin{array}{c} \\ 2 \\ 1 \\ 3 \end{array}\begin{array}{c} \begin{array}{ccc} 2 & 1 & 3 \end{array} \\ \begin{bmatrix} 1 & 0 & 0 \\ \frac{1}{2} & 0 & \frac{1}{2} \\ \frac{1}{3} & \frac{1}{3} & \frac{1}{3} \end{bmatrix} \end{array} \qquad \mathbf{N} = \begin{bmatrix} \frac{4}{3} & 1 \\ \frac{2}{3} & 2 \end{bmatrix}$$

13.
$$\begin{array}{c} \\ 2 \\ 4 \\ 1 \\ 3 \end{array}\begin{array}{c} \begin{array}{cccc} 2 & 4 & 1 & 3 \end{array} \\ \begin{bmatrix} 1 & 0 & 0 & 0 \\ 0 & 1 & 0 & 0 \\ \frac{1}{2} & \frac{1}{2} & 0 & 0 \\ 0 & \frac{1}{4} & \frac{1}{4} & \frac{1}{2} \end{bmatrix} \end{array} \qquad \mathbf{N} = \begin{bmatrix} 1 & 0 \\ \frac{1}{2} & 2 \end{bmatrix}$$

15.
$$\begin{array}{c} \\ 4 \\ 2 \\ 3 \\ 1 \end{array}\begin{array}{c} \begin{array}{cccc} 4 & 2 & 3 & 1 \end{array} \\ \begin{bmatrix} 1 & 0 & 0 & 0 \\ 0 & 0 & 0 & 1 \\ 0 & 1 & 0 & 0 \\ \frac{1}{4} & 0 & \frac{1}{4} & \frac{1}{2} \end{bmatrix} \end{array} \qquad \mathbf{N} = \begin{bmatrix} 2 & 1 & 4 \\ 2 & 2 & 4 \\ 1 & 1 & 4 \end{bmatrix}$$

17. $2 + \dfrac{5}{3} = \dfrac{11}{3}$

19. 27

21. 8 years

23. 3.2

25. (*a*) 1 (*b*) $\frac{2}{3}$

27. The matrix **P** is in canonical form with $\mathbf{Q} = [1 - a]$. Therefore, $\mathbf{I} - \mathbf{Q} = [1] - [1 - a] = [a]$ and $\mathbf{N} = \left[\dfrac{1}{a}\right]$.

29. (a) 1 (b) 3

31. (a) 6 (b) 12

Section 8.5

1. .1195, .2884
3. [.2703 .2606 .1020 .3671], about 37 percent of the time
5. [.3571 .2296 .0898 .3234], about 32 percent of the time
7. The stable vector is [.4545 .3030 .0808 .1616].
9. With states defined as in this section, the transition matrix is

$$\mathbf{P} = \begin{array}{c} \\ G \\ B \\ YF \\ MF \end{array}\begin{array}{c} \begin{array}{cccc} G & B & YF & MF \end{array} \\ \begin{bmatrix} .745 & .255 & 0 & 0 \\ .150 & .680 & .170 & 0 \\ .150 & 0 & .425 & .425 \\ .100 & 0 & 0 & .900 \end{bmatrix} \end{array}$$

and the stable vector is [.3296 .2627 .0777 .3301].

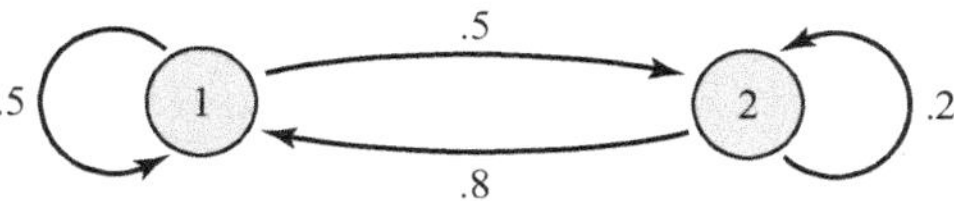

FIGURE C8.8

Review Exercises

1. (*a*) (Figure C8.8) (*b*) (.2)(.2) + (.8)(.5) = .44

3. (*a*) $\begin{bmatrix} .2 & .4 & .4 \\ 0 & 1 & 0 \\ 0 & .8 & .2 \end{bmatrix}$ (*b*) (.2)(.4) + (.4)(1) + (.4)(.8) = .80

5. (*a*) $\mathbf{P}(2) = \begin{bmatrix} 0 & .4 & .6 \\ 0 & 0 & 1 \\ .4 & .24 & .36 \end{bmatrix}$ (*b*) [.280 .288 .432]

7. .1

9. (*a*) Regular (*b*) $[\frac{6}{26} \quad \frac{10}{26} \quad \frac{10}{26}]$

11. (*a*) Regular (*b*) $[\frac{1}{9} \quad \frac{2}{9} \quad \frac{2}{9} \quad \frac{4}{9}]$ (*c*) State 4

13. (*a*) [.5 .5 0] (*b*) 25.25 percent blackgum, 32 percent red maple, and 42.75 percent beech
(*c*) 3.85 percent blackgum, 11.54 percent red maple, and 84.61 percent beech

15. $\frac{13}{5}$

17. 1.2

19. (*a*) $\frac{45}{17}$ (*b*) $\frac{20}{17}$

21. 2.5 weeks

23. 5

25. 13.5 (including the initial observation)

27. (*a*) $\mathbf{N} = \begin{bmatrix} \frac{5}{3} & \frac{2}{3} \\ \frac{5}{3} & \frac{8}{3} \end{bmatrix}$ (*b*) $\frac{13}{3}$

29. **P**(4) has all positive entries.

31. (*a*) States: 1, low volume; 2, average volume; 3, high volume.

Transition matrix is $\begin{vmatrix} .4 & .4 & .2 \\ .2 & .4 & .4 \\ 0 & .5 & .5 \end{vmatrix}$

(*b*) $\begin{bmatrix} \frac{5}{34} & \frac{15}{34} & \frac{14}{34} \end{bmatrix}$

33. (*a*) States: 1, current light is green; 2, current light is red

Transition matrix is $\begin{vmatrix} .6 & .4 \\ .3 & .7 \end{vmatrix}$

(*b*) .435

35. (*a*) States: 1, a blue ball is drawn from box I
2, a red ball is drawn from box I
3, a blue ball is drawn from box II
4, a red ball is drawn from box II

With this definition of states, the transition matrix is: $\begin{vmatrix} .75 & .25 & 0 & 0 \\ 0 & 0 & .4 & .6 \\ 0 & 0 & .4 & .6 \\ .75 & .25 & 0 & 0 \end{vmatrix}$

(*b*) .3065

Index